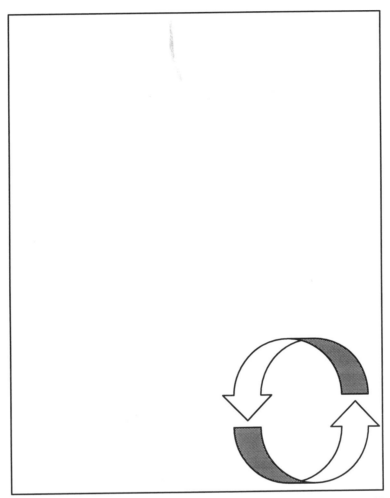

VOLUME III

P. E. (Civil) License Review Manual

CONCRETE DESIGN
Section 4
P. R. Chakrabarti, Ph.D., S.E.

CONCRETE MATERIALS AND MIX DESIGN
Section 5
Geoffrey D. Hichborn, Sr., B. S., P. E.

STEEL DESIGN
Section 6
Alexander Fattaleh, M.S., S.E.

P. E. (CIVIL) LICENSE REVIEW MANUAL
VOLUME III
Fourth Edition

ISBN 0−942115-39-2

Copyright © 1984, 1987, 1990, 1994 by C. V. Chelapati

Published by:

Professional Engineering Development Publications, Inc.
5912 Bolsa Avenue, Suite 108
Huntington Beach, CA 92649
Telephone (724) 898-3658, Fax (714) 898-4635

This manual is written for those preparing for the P.E. (Civil) Examination. Data presented in this manual is representative and is not intended to be exhaustive, precise, or useful for every application. By using this manual the user assumes all responsibility for its use. The author, publisher, distributors, and other interested entities do not assume or accept any responsibility or liability, including liability for negligence, for errors or oversight, or for the use of this manual in preparing engineering plans or designs.

CONTINUING CONTRIBUTORS

James E. Amrhein, M.S., S.E., Executive Director, Masonry Institute of America, Los Angeles, California (Volume IV, Section 7, Masonry Design)

C. V. Chelapati, Ph.D., P.E., Professor of Civil Engineering and Director, Continuing Engineering Education and Director, CAADS/AEC Training Research Laboratory, California State University, Long Beach, California (Volume I, Section 1, Structural Analysis and Volume II, Section 3, Seismic Principles)

Violet Jakab Chu, M.S.C.E., P.E., Associate Civil Engineer, Sacramento County Public Works, Sacramento, California (Volume V, Section 10, Hydraulics)

Alexander Fattaleh, M.S., S.E., Senior Vice President, American Bridge Company, Western Region, Long Beach, California (Volume III, Section 6, Steel Design)

Geoffrey Hichborn, Sr., B.S., P.E., Principal, Hichborn Consulting Group, Orange, California (Volume III, Section 5, Concrete Materials and Mix Design)

Fred L. Hinker, M.S., P.E., Consultant, Pasadena, California (Volume V, Section 13, Environmental Engineering II)

Marshall Lew, Ph.D., G.E., Vice President and Corporate Consultant, Law/Crandall, Inc., Los Angeles, California (Volume I, Section 2, Geotechnical Engineering)

Michael E. Mulvihill, Ph.D., P.E., Professor of Civil Engineering, Loyola Marymount University, Los Angeles, California (Volume V, Section 11, Hydrology)

W. Bruce Murray, M.S., P.E., Consulting Engineer, Irvine, California (Volume V, Section 12, Environmental Engineering I)

Carol J. Schumaker, M.S., P.E., Consulting Engineer, Yorba Linda, California (Volume IV, Section 9, Highway Traffic and Geometry Design)

John G. Shipp, M.S., S.E., Associate and Manager, Design Services, EQE Engineering, Inc., Irvine, California (Volume IV, Section 8, Timber Design)

THIRD EDITION CONTRIBUTORS

Chenchayya T. (C.T.) Bathala, Ph.D., P.E., Project Manager, Parsons Brinckerhoff, Orange, California (Volume V, Section 10, Hydraulics)

P. R. Chakrabarti, Ph.D., P.E., S.E., Professor of Civil Engineering, California State University, Fullerton, Califormia (Volume III, Section 4, Concrete Design)

Peter A. Cowan, Ph.D., Chairman and Professor of Civil Engineering, California State University, Long Beach, Califormia (Volume V, Section 10, Engineering Economics)

FOURTH EDITION CONTRIBUTORS

P. R. Chakrabarti, Ph.D., P.E., S.E., Chairman and Professor of Civil Engineering, California State University, Fullerton, Califormia (Volume III, Section 4, Concrete Design)

Yusef Jalali, Ph.D., P.E., Senior Engineer, Los Angeles County Sanitation District, Compton, California (Volume V, Section 13, Environmental Engineering II, Wastewater and Solid Waste)

Iraj Nasseri, Ph.D., P.E., Chief Hydrologist, Los Angeles County Department of Public Works, Hydraulic and Water Conservation, Alhambra, California (Volume 5, Section 11, Hydrology)

VOLUME INDEX

MASTER TABLE OF CONTENTS

Volume I

Volume II

Volume III

SECTION 5
CONCRETE MATERIALS AND MIX DESIGN

SECTION 6
STEEL DESIGN

Volume IV

Volume V

Volume VI

SECTION 14
ENGINEERING SURVEYING

VOLUME III

P. E. (Civil) License Review Manual

CONCRETE DESIGN
Section 4

P. R. Chakrabarti, Ph.D., S.E.
Chairman and Professor of Civil Engineering
California State University, Fullerton
Fullerton, California

CONTRIBUTORS

Contributing Author for First and Second Editions

James S. Lai, M.S., S.E.
Vice President
Johnson & Nielsen Associates
Los Angeles, California

Third and Fourth Editions Revised by

P. R. Chakrabarti, Ph.D., S.E.
Chairman and Professor of Civil Engineering
California State University, Fullerton
Fullerton, California

ACKNOWLEDGEMENTS

The manual is under continuous development since the beginning of P. E. (Civil) License Review classes at CSULB. Several people have contributed to this section of the manual. In particular, I would like thank Drs. W. H. Ying P.E. and the late J.K.S. Rao at CSULB and to Dr. R. M. Barker, P.E., of VPI who have taught this seminar and developed the materials during the earlier years.

Mr. James S. Lai, M.S., S.E., Vice President, Johnson and Nielsen Associates, Los Angeles has contributed materials for the first and second editions of this section. Dr. P. R. Chakrabarti, S.E., has revised the manual for its third and fourth editions using the 1989 ACI Code and the 1989/92 ACI Code.

These notes make extensive use of ACI 318-89 Code and Commentary and the PCA Notes on ACI 318-89. Many additions are made in the fourth edition and revisions are made according to the ACI 318-89/92 Code.

TABLE OF CONTENTS

CHAPTER 6
DEVELOPMENT AND SPLICES OF REINFORCEMENT

CHAPTER 7
SLABS

CHAPTER 8
WALLS

CHAPTER 10
FOOTINGS

APPENDIX

NOTES

INDEX

LIST OF FIGURES

LIST OF TABLES

ALPHABETICAL LIST OF SOLVED PROBLEMS

NOMENCLATURE

DEFINITIONS

Definitions and notations are crucial to an understanding of the strength design method, they are summarized as follows:

Service load

    Load specified by general building code (without load factors)

Factored load

    Load multiplied by appropriate load factors, used to proportion members by the strength design method

Required strength

    Strength of a member or cross section required to resist factored loads or related internal moments and forces in such combinations as are stipulated

Nominal strength

    Strength of a member or cross section calculated in accordance with provisions and assumptions of the strength design method before application of any strength reduction factors

Design strength

    Nominal strength multiplied by a strength reduction factor

NOTATIONS

Required Strength:

    M_u = factored moment at section

    P_u = factored axial load at given eccentricity

    V_u = factored shear force at section

    T_u = factored torsional moment

or

Nominal Strength:

M_n = nominal moment strength at section

M_b = nominal moment strength at balanced strain conditions

P_n = nominal axial load strength at given eccentricity

P_o = nominal axial load strength at zero eccentricity

P_b = nominal axial load strength at balanced strain conditions

V_n = nominal shear strength

V_c = nominal shear strength provided by concrete

V_s = nominal shear strength provided by shear reinforcement

T_n = nominal torsional moment strength

T_c = nominal torsional moment strength provided by concrete

T_s = nominal torsional moment strength provided by torsion reinforcement

Design Strength:

ϕ = strength reduction factor

ϕM_n = design moment strength at section

ϕP_n = design axial load strength at given eccentricity

ϕV_n = design shear strength = $\phi (V_c + V_s)$

ϕT_n = design torsional moment strength = $\phi (T_c + T_s)$

REFERENCES

1. *Notes on ACI 318-83 (ACI 318-89 is similar) Building Code Requirements for Reinforced Concrete with Design Applications,* Portland Cement Association, Skokie, Illinois.

2. *Building Code Requirements for Reinforced Concrete,* ACI 318-89 and ACI 318-89 (Revised 1992), American Concrete Institute, Detroit, Michigan.

3. *Commentary on Building Code Requirements for Reinforced Concrete,* ACI 318-89, American Concrete Institute, Detroit, Michigan.

4. *Design Handbook, In Accordance with the Strength Method of ACI 318-77,* Volume 1, ACI Publication SP-17(81), American Concrete Institute, Detroit, Michigan.

   This publication is replaced by:

   ACI Publication SP-17A(84) in accordance with ACI-83 Code

5. *Design Handbook, In Accordance with the Strength Design Method of ACI 318-77,* Volume 2, Columns, ACI Publication SP-17A(78), American Concrete Institute, Detroit, Michigan.

   This publication is replaced by:

   ACI Publication SP-17A(85) in accordance with ACI-83 Code

6. *Reinforced Concrete Design,* 4th ed., C. K. Wang and C. G. Salmon, Harper and Row, New York, 1984.

7. *Reinforced Concrete, A Fundamental Approach,* by E. G. Nawy, Prentice-Hall, 1985.

8. *Uniform Building Code*, International Conference of Building Officials, 1991, 5560 South Workman Mill Road, Whittier, CA 90601

1

INTRODUCTION

1.1 INTRODUCTION TO CONCRETE DESIGN

The notes presented here are a short review of the fundamentals of Reinforced Concrete Design with several example problems. It is important that each candidate be familiar with the current *ACI Code and Commentary* and also have a copy of the PCA notes on the ACI Codes. For an extensive review, many textbooks are available.

The notes are based on the ACI 318-89 Code and ACI 318-89 (Revision 1992) Code. Attention must be paid to the difference between the 1983 and 1989 codes.

Several figures and design aids were extracted with permission from the PCA notes on ACI 318-83 and 89 (Reference 1), and this publication can be obtained directly by writing to:

> Portland Cement Association,
> 5420 Old Orchard Road,
> Skokie, IL 60077-4321

The *ACI Code and Commentary* and the design handbooks (References 2 through 5) can be obtained directly by writing to:

> American Concrete Institute,
> P. O. Box 19150,
> Detroit, MI 48219

> Uniform Building Code 1991
> Chapters 23 and 26

Engineers preparing for the examinations are advised to see the latest publication of the above books or other standard text books.

2

BASIC STRENGTH DESIGN
OF CONCRETE

2.1 GENERAL PRINCIPLES FOR STRENGTH DESIGN

The strength design method requires that the computed nominal strengths reduced by specified strength reduction factors, i.e., design strengths, equal or exceed the service load effects (internal forces and moments) increased by specified load factors, i.e., required strengths.

2.2 BASIC STRENGTH REQUIREMENTS

The basic criterion for strength design may be expressed as follows:

> Required Strength $\leq$ Design Strength

or

> [Load factor][Service Load Effects]
> $\leq$
> [Strength Reduction Factor][Nominal Strength]

$P_u \leq \phi P_n$

$M_u \leq \phi M_n$

$V_u \leq \phi V_n$ shear

$T_u \leq \phi T_n$ (torsion)

Example:

$$M_u \quad = 1.4\,M_d \; + \; 1.7\,M_\ell$$

$$\phi\,M_n \; = \; \phi\left[A_s\,f_y\!\left(d - \frac{a}{2}\right)\right]$$

Where 1.4 and 1.7 are load factors given in Table 2.1, and ϕ is strength. Reduction factor is given in Table 2.2.

2.3   REASONS FOR LOAD AND STRENGTH REDUCTION FACTORS

A. Strength of materials less than assumed because of

   1. Variability in materials strengths

   2. Member size varies

   3. Simplified design assumptions

   4. Use of discrete bar sizes

B. Overloads may occur

   1. Magnitudes of loads vary from those assumed

   2. Uncertainties in assumed load effect

   3. Other secondary effects, e.g., creep, shrinkage, temperature change, settle-ment of supports, water and ice accumulation at roof, improper connections and lateral load transfer arrangements, etc.

C. Consequence of failure may be severe

   1. Pre-warning/load paths

   2. Potential loss of life

   3. Costs to society — time, money or life

   4. Importance of element

   5. Cost to replace

2.4   BASIC STRENGTH DESIGN RELATIONSHIP

Strength design of members for flexure and axial loads shall be based on the following assumptions and on satisfaction of applicable conditions of equilibrium and compatibility of strains:

Assumption (1) Sec. 10.2.2:

"Strain in reinforcement and concrete shall be assumed directly proportional to the distance from the neutral axis."

Nomenclature and assumptions on simple bending are shown in Figure 2.1.

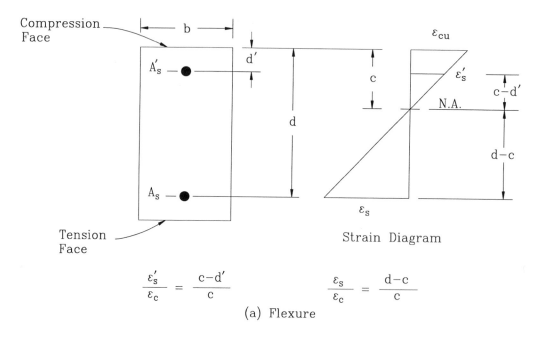

$$\frac{\varepsilon'_s}{\varepsilon_c} = \frac{c-d'}{c} \qquad\qquad \frac{\varepsilon_s}{\varepsilon_c} = \frac{d-c}{c}$$

(a) Flexure

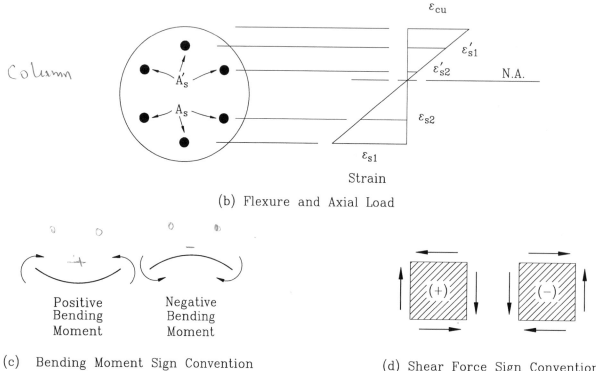

(b) Flexure and Axial Load

(c)   Bending Moment Sign Convention

(d) Shear Force Sign Convention

Figure 2.1 Assumed Strain Variation

Assumption (2) Sec. 10.2.3:

"Maximum usable strain at extreme concrete compression fiber shall be assumed equal to $\varepsilon_{cu} = 0.003$."

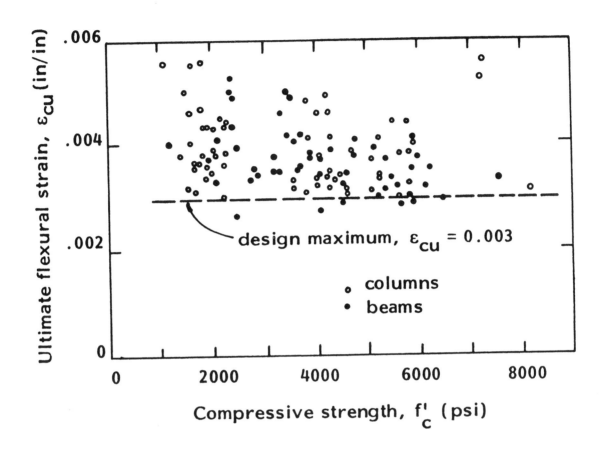

Figure 2.2 Ultimate Strain ε_{cu} from Tests of Reinforced Members

Assumption (3) Sec. 10.2.4:

"Stress in reinforcement below the yield strength f_y shall be taken as E_s times the steel strain ε_s ($f_s = E_s \varepsilon_s$). For strains greater than f_y, stress in reinforcement shall be considered independent of strain and equal to f_y."

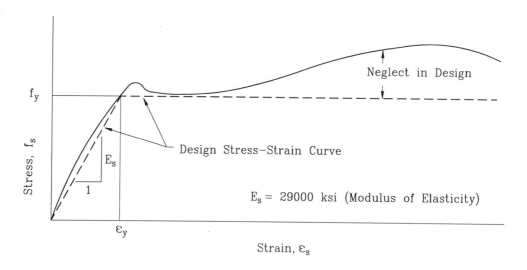

Figure 2.3 Stress-Strain Relationship for Reinforcement

The quality of reinforcing steel is identified by ASTM grading:

- ASTM A615, Grade 40, f_y = 40,000 psi
- ASTM A615, Grade 60, f_y = 60,000 psi
- ASTM A706, Grade 60, f_y = 60,000 psi, etc.

has carbon — for welding (earthqk areas)

For design work, $f_s = \varepsilon_s E_s \leq f_y$.

Assumption (4) Sec. 10.2.5:

"Tensile strength of concrete shall be neglected in flexure calculations of reinforced concrete."

The stress-strain behavior for concrete is non-linear at stress level above 0.5 f_c' approximately, the modulus of elasticity for concrete is given by:

$$E_c = (w_c)^{1.5} \times 33\sqrt{f_c'}$$ *compressive stress*

$$w_c = \text{concrete density} \ (weight)$$

For regular weight concrete:

$$w_c = 145 \ \text{lbs/ft}^3$$ *— conc. ī no reinforcement (should use 150 #/ft³ for design)*

$$E_c = 57,000\sqrt{f_c'}$$

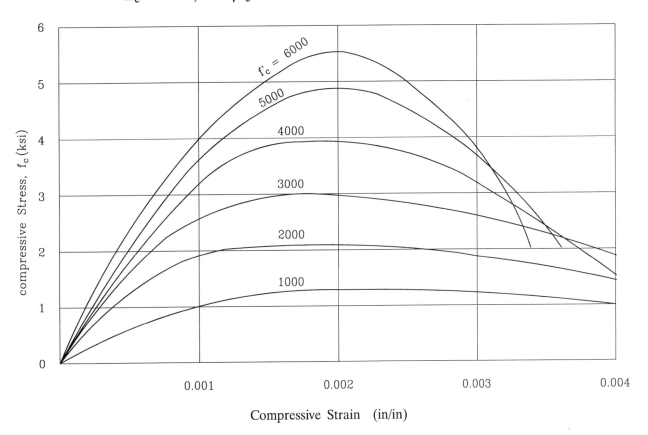

Figure 2.4 Typical Stress-Strain Curves for Concrete

Assumption (5) Sec. 10.2.6:

> "Relationship between concrete compressive stress distribution and concrete strain may be assumed to be rectangular, trapezoidal, parabolic, or any other shape that results in prediction of strength in substantial agreement with results of comprehensive tests."

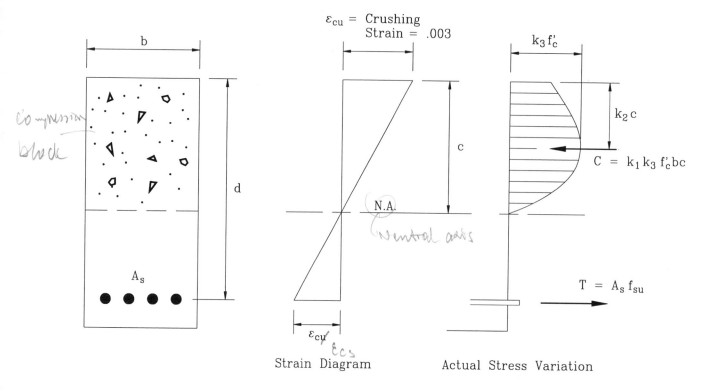

Figure 2.5 Stress-Strain Conditions at Nominal Strength in Flexure

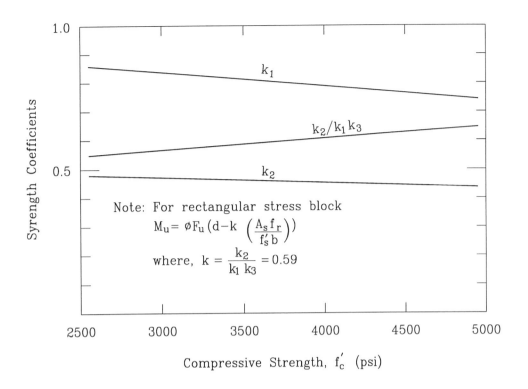

Figure 2.6 Stress-Block Parameters

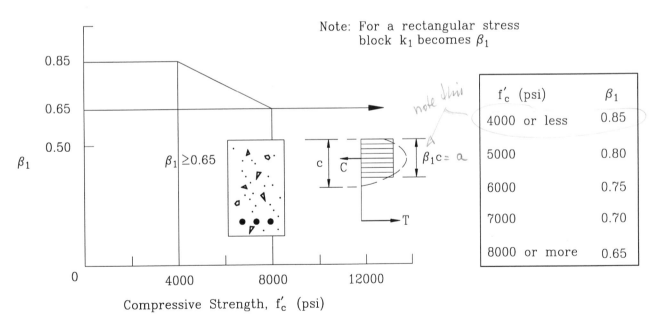

Figure 2.7 Strength Factor β_1 for Rectangular Stress Block

✕ Recommend to be used

Assumption (6) Sec. 10.2.7:

"Requirements of Assumption (5) may be considered satisfied by an equivalent rectangular concrete stress distribution defined as follows: A concrete stress of 0.85 f'_c shall be assumed uniformly distributed over an equivalent compression zone bounded by edges of the cross section and a straight line located parallel to the neutral axis at a distance a = $\beta_1 c$ from the fiber of maximum compressive strain. Distance c from fiber of maximum strain to the neutral axis shall be measured in a direction perpendicular to that axis. Factor β_1 shall be taken as 0.85 for strengths f'_c up to 4000 psi and shall be reduced continuously at a rate of 0.05 for each 1000 psi of strength in excess of 4000 psi, but β_1 shall not be taken less than 0.65."

In other words, for f'_c = 5000, 6000, 7000, 8000 psi, β_1 shall be 0.80, 0.75, 0.70 and 0.65 respectively.

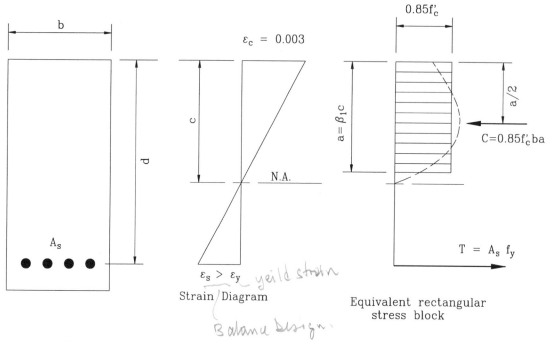

Figure 2.8 Equivalent Rectangular Concrete Stress Distribution

Using the equivalent rectangular stress distribution, and assuming that the reinforcement yields prior to crushing of the concrete ($\varepsilon_s > \varepsilon_y$), the nominal moment strength Mn can be computed by equilibrium of forces and moments.

For force equilibrium:

$$C = T \qquad a = \frac{A_s f_y}{0.85 f'_c b}$$

$$0.85 f'_c ba = A_s f_y$$

Nominal moment (moment arm = d − a/2)

For moment equilibrium:

$$M_n = (C \text{ or } T)(d - a/2)$$

$$M_n = A_s f_y (d - a/2) \qquad \# \text{ for } T$$

Substituting *a* from force equilibrium,

$$M_n = A_s f_y \left(d - 0.59 \frac{A_s f_y}{f'_c b} \right)$$

Note:

The 0.59 value corresponds to $k_2/(k_1 k_3)$. Substituting $A_s = \varrho b d$ and expressed in non-dimensional form, equation (2-1) may be written as:

$$\frac{M_n}{bd^2 f'_c} = \varrho \frac{f_y}{f'_c} \left(1 - 0.59 \varrho \frac{f_y}{f'_c} \right)$$

$$M_n = \omega (1 - 0.59\omega) bd^2 f'_c \qquad \text{where } \omega = \varrho \frac{f_y}{f'_c}$$

2.5   REQUIRED STRENGTH

The required strength is expressed in terms of factored loads or their related internal moments and forces. Factored loads are the loads specified in model building codes, multiplied by appropriate load factors. The Code prescribes load factors for specific combinations of loads. A list of these combinations are given in Table 2.1.

2.6   DESIGN STRENGTH

The design strength provided by a member is equal to the calculated nominal strength multiplied by a strength reduction factor ϕ. The ϕ factor prescribed by the code for different types of action are listed in Table 2.2.

2.7   DESIGN PROCEDURE

reduction factor   *tension (steel)*
compression (conc)

Obtain required strength using factored load and span (i.e., M_{UR}). Obtain design strength using the strength reduction factor (ϕ), stress block (β_1) and material strength (i.e., $M_u = \phi M_n$). The basic equation, $\phi M_n = \phi T_u (d - a/2) = \phi C_u (d - a/2)$ can be expressed in about a dozen formats. Different types of charts, nomograms, and tables are being used in different manuals and books. As a result, various parameters are introduced to express these equations. Some of these parameters are non-dimensional parameters. Because of this diversity, many expressions are often very confusing to the students.

A student must be able to do some quick check calculations by hand (particularly those students who are not familiar with the different design tools mentioned before). A short summary of various expressions for M_u and the method for quick check hand calculations are given below.

The load factors and combinations are given in Table 2.1 and the strength reduction factors are given in Table 2.2.

2.8   SHORT SUMMARY OF MOMENT EQUATIONS

$M_u \leq \phi M_n$

- $\phi M_n = \phi T_u \left(d - \frac{a}{2}\right)$ where, $T_u = A_s f_y$

    or $C_u = 0.85 f'_c ba$

    $= \phi C_u \left(d - \frac{a}{2}\right)$ $a = \dfrac{A_s f_y}{0.85 f'_c b}$

    $\phi = 0.9$

- $\phi M_n = \phi A_s f_y \left(d - \frac{a}{2}\right)$

    $\phi M_n = \phi A_s f_y (jd)$ where, $j = \left(1 - \dfrac{a}{2d}\right)$

- $\phi M_n = \phi A_s f_y \left(d - 0.59 \dfrac{A_s f_y}{f'_c b}\right)$ — useful

    $\phi M_n = \phi A_s f_y d \left(1 - 0.59 \dfrac{A_s f_y}{f'_c bd}\right)$

    $\phi M_n = \phi A_s f_y d \left(1 - 0.59 \varrho \dfrac{f_y}{f'_c}\right)$ where, $\varrho = \dfrac{A_s}{bd}$

    $\phi M_n = \phi \dfrac{A_s}{bd} \times f_y \times bd^2 \left(1 - 0.59 \varrho \dfrac{f_y}{f'_c}\right)$

- $\phi M_n = \phi \varrho f_y bd^2 \left(1 - 0.59 \varrho \dfrac{f_y}{f'_c}\right)$

    $\phi M_n = \phi \dfrac{\varrho f_y}{f'_c} \times f'_c bd^2 \left(1 - 0.59 \varrho \dfrac{f_y}{f'_c}\right)$

- $\phi M_n = \phi \omega f'_c bd^2 (1 - 0.59 \omega)$ where, $\omega = \dfrac{\varrho f_y}{f'_c}$

- $\phi M_n = K_n bd^2$ where, $K_n = \phi f'_c \omega (1 - 0.59\omega)$

    use design tables
    to find out Kn

    $\phi M_n = \phi A_s f_y (jd)$ psi

- $\phi M_n = A_s(a_n)d$ where, $a_n = \phi f_y j \rightarrow \dfrac{\phi f_y j}{12}$

steel

Note

- $\varrho_{min} = \dfrac{200}{f_y}$

balance pt

- $\varrho_b = \dfrac{0.85\ \beta_1\ f'_c}{f_y}\ \dfrac{87,000}{87,000 + f_y}$

- $\varrho_{max} = 0.75\ \varrho_b$ (75% of bal pt). [Real world 0.4 ϱ_b & 0.5 ϱ_b)

If $1.33\ \varrho < \varrho_{min}$, use $1.33\ \varrho$, where, $\varrho = \dfrac{A_s}{bd}$ = required steel   esp. for earthqk county

steel area (min)

$\left[A_{s\,min} = \dfrac{200\ bwd}{f_y} \right]$ ie $\dfrac{A_s}{bw} = \dfrac{200}{f_y}$

Useful for T-beam & majority of cases

For Quick Check:

Assume $jd = 0.75\ d$. Use j between 0.7 to 0.8

$$A_{s1} = \dfrac{M_{UR}}{f_y\ (0.75\ d)} \quad \begin{array}{l} \leq\ 0.75\ \varrho_b \times bd \\ \geq\ \varrho_{min} \times bd\ \text{or}\ \geq\ 1.33\ A_{s1}\ bd \end{array}$$

$$a = \dfrac{A_{s1}\ f_y}{0.85\ f'_c\ b} = \text{Depth of Stress Block}$$

$$M_{u1} = \phi \times A_{s1} \times f_y \times \left(d - \dfrac{a}{2} \right)$$

If $M_R << M_{u1}$, try $A_{s2} = \dfrac{M_R}{M_{u1}} \times A_{s1}$

where, M_{UR} is ultimate moment required

M_{u1} is ultimate moment capacity

Table 2.1
Required Strength for Combinations of Loadings

9.2.1 — Dead and Live Load

$$U = 1.4D + 1.7L \qquad (9\text{-}1)$$

9.2.2 — Dead, Live and Wind Load

$$U = 1.4D + 1.7L$$

or

$$U = 0.75(1.4D + 1.7L + 1.7W)$$

$$= 1.05D + 1.275L + 1.275W \qquad (9\text{-}2)$$

or

$$U = 0.9D + 1.3W \qquad (9\text{-}3)$$

9.2.3 — Dead, Live, and Earthquake Load

$$U = 1.4D + 1.7L$$

or

$$U = 0.75(1.4D + 1.7L + 1.87E)$$

$$= 1.05D + 1.275L + 1.402E$$

Note: $U = 1.4(D + L + E) \ldots$ UBC91

or

$$U = 0.9D + 1.43E$$

Note: $U = 0.9D + 1.4L \ldots$ UBC91

9.2.4 — Dead and Live Load plus Lateral Earth and Groundwater Pressure

$$U = 1.4D + 1.7L$$

or

$$U = 1.4D + 1.7L + 1.7H \qquad (9\text{-}4)$$

or

(D opposing H)

$$U = 0.9D + 1.7L + 1.7H$$

or

(L opposing H)

$$U = 1.4D + 1.7H$$

or

(D & L opposing H)

$$U = 0.9D + 1.7H$$

Table 2.1 (Continued)
Required Strength for Combinations of Loadings

9.2.5 – <u>Dead & Live Load Plus Liquid Pressure</u>*

$$U = 1.4D + 1.7L$$

or

$$U = 1.4D + 1.7L + 1.4F$$

or

(D reducing F)

$$U = 0.9D + 1.7L + 1.4F$$

or

(L reducing F)

$$U = 1.4D + 1.4F$$

or

(D & L reducing F)

$$U = 0.9D + 1.4F$$

---

*Weight and pressures of liquids with well–defined densities and controllable maximum heights

9.2.6 – <u>Impact</u>

In all equations substitute (L + Impact) for (L) when impact must be considered.

9.2.7 – <u>Dead & Live Load Plus Differential Settlement, Creep, Shrinkage,</u>

<u>or Temperature Change</u>

$$U = 1.4D + 1.7L$$

or

$$U = 0.75 (1.4D + 1.4T + 1.7L \qquad (9\text{-}5)$$

$$= 1.05D + 1.05T + 1.275L$$

or

$$U = 1.4D + 1.4T \qquad (9\text{-}6)$$

See ACI Code 318-89, Section 9.3.

Table 2.2 Strength Reduction Factor — Resistive side (steel)

Action	ϕ
Flexure, without axial load	0.90
Axial tension, and flexure with axial tension	0.90
Axial Compression, and flexure with axial compression:	
Members with spiral reinforcement conforming to Section 10.9.3	0.75*
Other reinforced members	0.70*
Shear and torsion	0.85
Bearing on concrete	0.70**
Flexure in plain concrete	0.65

*May be increased linearly to 0.90 as ϕP_n decreases
from $0.10 f'_c A_g$ or ϕP_b, whichever is smaller, zero.
** Does not apply to post-tensioning anchorage bearing plates.
See Section 18.13.*

For design in Seismic Zones 3 and 4, the reader is referred to the UBC 1991 Code, Section 2625 (A) and (B).

3

DESIGN FOR FLEXURE

3.1 BALANCED BEAM DESIGN

When a beam is designed to produce simultaneously (ACI Sec. 10.3.2),

$$\varepsilon_c \text{ (ultimate strain in concrete)} = 0.003 \qquad \textit{least amt of conc}$$

$$\text{and} \quad \varepsilon_s \text{ (yield strain in steel)} = \frac{f_y}{E_s} \qquad \textit{m u 'steel}$$

it is called a *balanced design beam*. Figure 3.1 shows such a beam made of a rectangular section. Next to the sketch of this section, both the strain and stress diagrams of the beam are given.

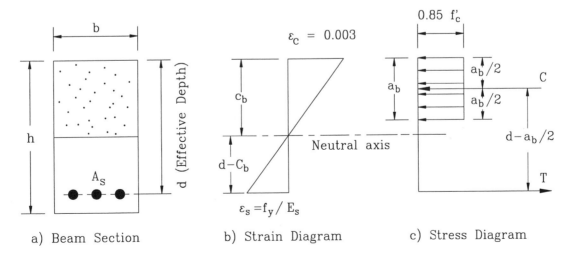

a) Beam Section   b) Strain Diagram   c) Stress Diagram

Figure 3.1 Balanced Beam

As it can be shown, the neutral axis of a balanced beam may be found at a location

$$c_b = \frac{0.003}{0.003 + f_y/E_s} d = \frac{87,000}{87,000 + f_y} d$$

measured from the top of beam. Sec. 10.2.7 of the ACI 318-89 Code gives the relation:

$$a_b = \beta_1 c_b \tag{3.2}$$

where

$$E_s = 29 \times 10^6 \text{ psi and}$$

$$\beta_1 = \begin{cases} 0.85 & \text{for } f'_c \le 4000 \text{ psi} \quad (3.3) \\ 0.85 - \left(\dfrac{f'_c - 4000}{1000}\right) 0.05 & \text{for } f'_c > 4000 \text{ psi} \\ 0.65 \text{ minimum} \quad \text{(Figure 2.7)} \end{cases}$$

and a_b represents the depth for equivalent rectangular stress block of the concrete in compression.

Let steel ratio ϱ be defined as

$$\varrho = A_s / \text{(effective concrete area)} \tag{3.4a}$$

for T-beams, L-beams, beams in a hole, etc.

or

$$\varrho = A_s/(bd) \qquad \text{For rectangular beam} \tag{3.4b}$$

This ratio has a fixed value for a balanced beam as follows:

Tension side: $T = f_y A_s = f_y \varrho_b b d$

Compression side: $C = 0.85 f'_c b \beta_1 d \left(\dfrac{87,000}{87,000 + f_y}\right)$

For equilibrium $T = C$

$$f_y \varrho_b b d = 0.85 f'_c b \beta_1 d \left(\frac{87,000}{87,000 + f_y}\right)$$

Bal. Steel ratio, $$\varrho_b = 0.85 \beta_1 \left(\frac{f'_c}{f_y}\right)\left(\frac{87,000}{87,000 + f_y}\right) \tag{3.5}$$

Table 3.1 shows ϱ_b and 0.75 ϱ_b for the most common values of f'_c and f_y.

Table 3.1 Values of ϱ_b and 0.75 ϱ_b

ϱ_b | 0.75 ϱ_b	$f'_c = 3000$	$f'_c = 4000$	$f'_c = 5000$
$f_y = 40{,}000$	0.0371 | 0.0278	0.0495 | 0.0371	0.0582 | 0.0437
$f_y = 50{,}000$	0.0275 | 0.0206	0.0367 | 0.0275	0.0432 | 0.0324
$f_y = 60{,}000$	0.0214 | 0.0160	0.0285 | 0.0214	0.0335 | 0.0251

    a.   Stresses are all in psi.

    b. ϱ_b left of vertical line.

    c.   0.75 ϱ_b right of vertical line.

3.2 UNDER-REINFORCED BEAM DESIGN

The ACI 318-89 Code, Section 10.3.3 sets an upper limit for the amount of tensile reinforcement to be used as a warning in approaching the maximum capacity.

$$\text{Max } \varrho \leq 0.75 \, \varrho_b \tag{3.6}$$

This assures that a beam and any lightly loaded columns retain certain ductility. However, this reduction is not necessary for compression reinforcement.

3.3 RECTANGULAR BEAMS WITH TENSION REINFORCEMENT ONLY ($\phi = 0.9$)

Terms and equations given for rectangular beams in. bending (Figure 3.2), used for either design or analysis, are listed below:

$$\varrho = \frac{A_s}{bd} \qquad \text{Tension steel ratio} \tag{3.7a}$$

$$\omega = \frac{\varrho \, f_y}{f'_c} \qquad \text{Reinforcing index} \tag{3.7b}$$

$$a = \frac{A_s \, f_y}{0.85 \, f'_c \, b} = \frac{\varrho \, f_y \, d}{0.85 \, f'_c} = \frac{\omega \, d}{0.85} \qquad \begin{array}{l}\text{Depth of}\\ \text{Compression}\\ \text{Stress Block}\end{array} \tag{3.7c}$$

$$M_u = \phi M_n = \phi f'_c \omega (1 - 0.59 \, \omega) \, bd^2 = K_n bd^2 \tag{3.7d}$$

or

$$M_u = \phi M_n = \phi A_s f_y (1 - 0.59 \, \omega) \, d = K_n bd^2 \tag{3.7e}$$

The depth of neutral axis, if desired, may be found from the following relation:

$$c = \frac{a}{\beta_1} \tag{3.7f}$$

in which β_1 can be obtained from Equation (3.3).

Tables given by Flexure 1.1 to Flexure 1.4 of the Design Handbook, ACI Sp-17 (85) can be used directly in design and analysis of rectangular beams. The above equations are also given in Section 2.8.

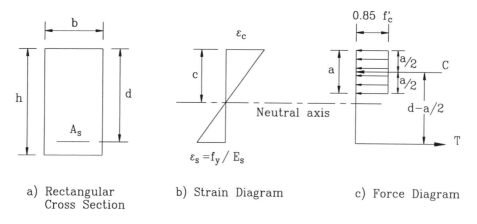

a) Rectangular   b) Strain Diagram   c) Force Diagram
Cross Section

Figure 3.2 Rectangular Beam in Bending

3.4   T-BEAM DESIGN ($\phi = 0.9$)

In T-Beam construction, the flange and web shall be built integrally or otherwise effectively bonded together. To form a T-beam, the ACI 318-89 Code, Section 8.10 provides the details for determining the effective flange width of the beam. Other requirements for T-beam construction can be found in the Code, Sections 8.10.2, 8.10.3 and 8.10.4.

3.4.1   EFFECTIVE T-BEAM FLANGE

Width of slab effective as a T-beam flange shall not exceed ¼ the span length of the beam, and the effective overhanging flange width on each side of the web shall not exceed:

A.   8 times the slab thickness, nor

B.   ½ the clear distance to the next web (s/2).

i.e., $b_e = $ $\ell/4$ or $(16 \times t + b_w)$ or $(s + b_w)$ whichever is smallest.

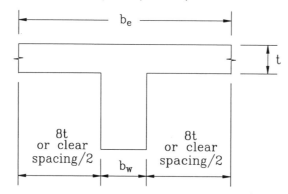

Figure 3.3 Effective Flange Width for T-Beam

3.4.2 EFFECTIVE L-BEAM FLANGE

For beams with a slab on one side only, the effective overhanging flange width shall not exceed:

A. 1/12 the span length of the beam,

B. 6 times the slab thickness, nor

C. 1/2 the clear distance to the next web (s/2).

i.e., $b_e = (\ell/12 + b_w)$ or $(6 \times t + b_w)$ or $(s/2 + b_w)$ whichever is smallest.

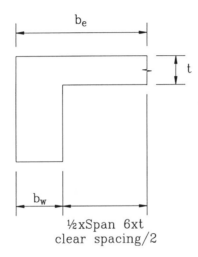

Figure 3.4 Effective Flange Width for L-Beam

3.4.3 DESIGN PROCEDURE

A general procedure outlining the solution for a T-beam is given in the following:

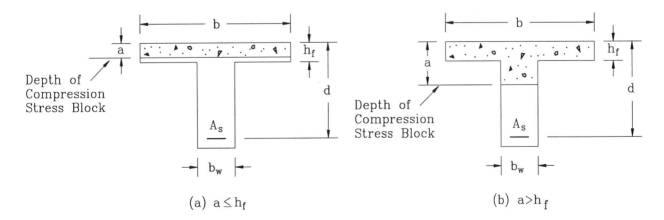

Figure 3.5 T-Beam

A. Assume $a \leq h_f$ [Figure 3.5]

By force equilibrium, C = T:

$$a = \frac{A_s f_y}{0.85 f'_c b} \tag{3-8}$$

If the calculated value of "a" is less than or equal to h_f, the beam may be treated the same way as a rectangular beam. If not, follow next Step (B):

B. $a > h_f$ [Figure 3.5]

From force equilibrium, C = T

$$a = \frac{A_s f_y - 0.85 f'_c (b - b_w) h_f}{0.85 f'_c b_w} \tag{3-9}$$

From this equation, the value of "a" and the value of M_u may be calculated.

3.5   DOUBLY REINFORCED BEAMS

Beams with both tension and compression reinforcement are called doubly reinforced beams. When a beam is limited by its size, it often requires additional steel to resist part of compression. Assume A'_s to be the compression steel area. From Figure 3.6, we have:

$$T_1 = C_1, \qquad A_{s_1} f_y = 0.85 f'_c (ab) \tag{3-10a}$$

or

$$a = \frac{A_{s_1} f_y}{0.85 f'_c b} \tag{3-10b}$$

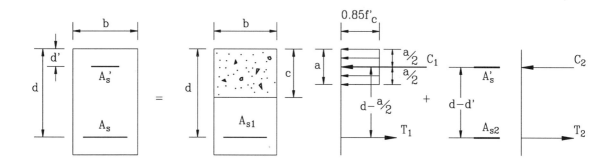

(a) Doubly   (b) With Tension   (c) Force   (d) Tension &   (e) Force
    Reinforced   Reinforcement   Diagram   Compression   Diagram
                        Only   of (b)   Steel   of (d)

Figure 3.6 Doubly Reinforced Beams

$$T_2 = C_2 \tag{3-10c}$$

$$A_{s_2}\, f_y = A'_s\, (f'_s - 0.85 f'_c)$$

or $$A_{s_2} = \frac{A'_s\, (f'_s - 0.85 f'_c)}{f_y} \tag{3-10d}$$

$$A_s = A_{s_1} + A_{s_2} \tag{3-10e}$$

$$M_{u_1} = \phi\, A_{s_1}\, f_y \left(d - \frac{a}{2}\right) \tag{3-11a}$$

$$M_{u_2} = \phi\, A_{s_2}\, f_y \left(d - d'\right) \tag{3-11b}$$

$$\phi = 0.9$$

$$M_u = M_{u_1} + M_{u_2} \tag{3-11c}$$

The term f'_s in. Equations 3-10c and 3-10d is denoted as compressive stress in steel. If this compression steel yields, we set $f'_s = f_y$.

If it does not yield, set:

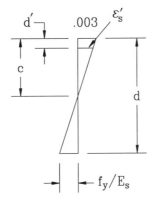

Figure 3.7 Strain in Compression Steel

$$f'_s = \varepsilon'_s\, E_s = 0.003 \left(\frac{c - d'}{c}\right) \times 29{,}000 \ (\text{ksi}) < f_y \tag{3-12}$$

with f'_s expressed in a unit of ksi.

The procedure that may be used in analyzing a doubly reinforced beam may now be summarized as follows:

A. Assume $A_{s_1} = A_s - A'_s$.

B. Substitute the value of A_{s_1} into Equation (3-10b) to obtain

$$a = \frac{A_{s_1}\, f_y}{0.85\, f'_c\, b}$$

C. Calculate:

$$c = \frac{a}{\beta_1}$$

$$\varepsilon'_s = 0.003\left(\frac{c - d'}{c}\right)$$

$$\text{Set } f'_s = \begin{cases} \varepsilon'_s E_s, & \text{if } \varepsilon'_s E_s < f_y \\ f_y, & \text{if } \varepsilon_s E_s > f_y \end{cases}$$

D. Calculate from Equation (3-10d) the value of

$$A_{s_2} = \frac{A'_s (f'_s - 0.85f'_c)}{f_y}$$

E. Substitute the value of A_{s_2} obtained from (D) into Equation (3-10e) to find new A_{s_1}

$$A_{s_1} = A_s - A_{s_2}$$

F. Calculate another new value of "a" by substituting the A_{s_1} value obtained from (E) into Equation (3-10b)

$$a = \frac{A_{s_1} f_y}{0.85 f'_c b}$$

G. Compare the calculated "a" value obtained from (F) with that from (B). If these two values do not differ too largely from each other, follow next step (H). If not, use new "a" value obtained from (F), and repeat steps (C) through (F).

H. Use the latest A_{s_1} and A_{s_2} obtained from steps (D) and (E), and the value of "a" obtained from step (F) to calculate M_{u_1} and M_{u_2} from Equations (3-11a) and (3-11b). Total M_u can now be obtained from Equation (3-11c).

3.6 CONTINUOUS BEAMS

In practice the vast majority of concrete members are either continuous or cantilevered or restrained. Hence, both positive and negative moments must be considered. Although members are generally prismatic, the designer must consider the beam section as T-section or as rectangular section, depending on positive moment or negative moment zone respectively. Additional considerations regarding redirection of design moments or placement of special steel in Seismic Zones 3 or 4 shall be considered separately.

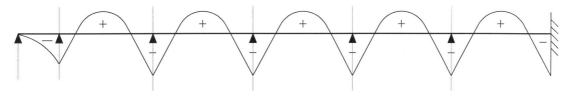

Moment Diagram of a Continuous Beam

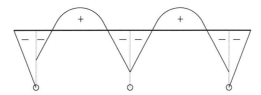

Moment Diagram of a Frame

Figure 3.8 Moment Diagrams of a Continuous Beam and a Frame

In actual design, cracked or uncracked sections are used for moment distribution. In one continuous beam, part of the span can be a T-beam, part of the span can be a rectangular beam with tension steel at the top, or part of the beam can be doubly reinforced beam.

3.7   OTHER CODE DESIGN REQUIREMENTS

3.7.1   MINIMUM REINFORCEMENT OF FLEXURAL MEMBERS SEC. 10.5.1.

At any section of a flexural member (except slabs of uniform thickness) where positive reinforcement is required by analysis, the ratio ϱ supplied shall not be less than that given by:

$$\varrho_{min} = \frac{200}{f_y} \qquad \text{ACI Equation (10-3)}$$

unless the area of reinforcement provided at every section, positive or negative, is at least one-third greater than that required by analysis. In T-beams and joists where the stem is in tension, the ratio ϱ shall be computed for this purpose using the width of the stem (b_w).

3.7.2 DETAILS OF REINFORCEMENT

Selected Code requirements from ACI 318, Chapter 7, are listed below:

7.6 Spacing limits for reinforcement:

7.6.1 Clear distance between parallel bars in a layer shall not be less than d_b nor 1 in. See also Section 3.3.3.

7.6.2 Where parallel reinforcement is placed in two or more layers, bars in the upper layers shall be placed directly above bars in the bottom layer with clear distance between layers not less than 1 in.

7.6.3 In spirally reinforced or tied reinforced compression members, clear distance between longitudinal bars shall not be less than $1.5d_b$ nor 1-1/2 in. See also Section 3.3.3.

7.6.4 Clear distance limitation between bars shall apply also to the clear distance between a contact lap splice and adjacent splices or bars.

7.6.5 In walls and slabs other than concrete joist construction, primary flexural reinforcement shall not be spaced farther apart than 3 times the wall or slab thickness, nor 18 in.

7.6.6 Bundled bars:

7.6.6.1 Groups of parallel reinforcing bars bundled in contact to act as a unit shall be limited to 4 in any one bundle.

7.6.6.2 Bundled bars shall be enclosed within stirrups or ties.

7.6.6.3 Bars larger than #11 shall not be bundled in beams.

7.6.6.4 Individual bars within a bundle terminated within the span of flexural members shall terminate at different with at least $40d_b$ stagger.

7.6.6.5 Where spacing limitations and minimum concrete cover are based on bar diameter d_b, a unit of bundled bars shall be treated as a single bar of a diameter derived from the equivalent total area.

7.7 Concrete protection for reinforcement

7.7.1 Cast-in-place concrete (non-prestressed).

The following minimum concrete cover (Sec. 7.7) shall be provided for reinforcement:

Minimum
Cover
in inches

A. Concrete cast against and permanently exposed to earth 3

B. Concrete exposed to earth or weather:

#6 through #18 bars 2

#5 bar, W31 or D31 wire, and smaller 1-1/2

C. Concrete not exposed to weather or in contact with ground:

Slabs, walls, joists:

#14 and #18 bars 1-1/2

#11 bar and smaller 3/4

Beams, columns:

Primary reinforcement, ties, stirrups, spirals 1-1/2

Shells, folded plate members:

#6 bar and larger 3/4

#5 bar, W31 or D31 wire, and smaller 1/2

7.12   Shrinkage and temperature reinforcement (Sec. 7.12):

7.12.1 Reinforcement for shrinkage and temperature stresses normal to flexural reinforcement shall be provided in structural floor and roof slabs where the flexural reinforcement extends in one direction only.

7.12.2 Area of shrinkage and temperature reinforcement shall provide at least the following ratios of reinforcement area to gross concrete area, but not less than 0.0014:

Slabs where Grade 40 or 50 deformed bars are used 0.0020

Slabs where Grade 60 deformed bars or welded wire fabric (smoothor deformed) are used 0.0018

Slabs where reinforcement with yield strength exceeding 60,000 psi measured at a yield strain of 0.35% is used . . $\dfrac{0.0018 \times 60,000}{f_y}$

7.12.3 Shrinkage and temperature reinforcement shall not be spaced farther apart than 5 times the slab thickness, nor 18 in.

3.8   P. E. PROBLEMS

3.8.1   P. E. PROBLEM 1 — BEAM WITH CONCENTRATED LOADS

Design a concrete beam, 24 ft span, simple supports, to carry its own dead weight plus a 16 kip load at each 1/3 point. Consider bending only.

* $f'_c = 5000$ psi, $f_y = 40,000$ psi

*   Limit beam width to 10 in. Show steel placement and use ACI 1989/1992 Code.

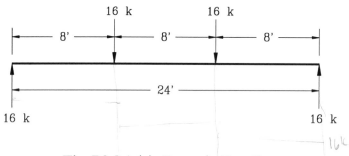

Fig. P3.8.1 (a) Beam in Bending

Solution

*   Use ACI 1989/1992 Code.

* $f'_c = 5000$ psi

* $f_y = 40,000$ psi

*   (Note: $\beta_1 = 0.8$ for $f'_c = 5000$ psi)

Consider the given loads include 8 kip dead load and 8 kip live load, and consider beam size 10 in. $\times$ 30 in. (For preliminary beam depth, see Table 4.3.)

$$\text{Beam weight} = \frac{10 \times 30}{144} \times 150 = 312.5 \text{ lb/ft}$$

$$w_u = 1.4 \times 312.5 \qquad\qquad = 0.438 \text{ kip/ft}$$

$$P_u = 1.4 \times 8.0 + 1.7 \times 8.0 \qquad = 24.8 \text{ kip}$$

$$M_u = \frac{w_u l^2}{8} + P_u \frac{L}{3}$$

$$= \frac{0.437 \times 24^2}{8} + 24.8 \times \frac{24}{3}$$

$$= 229.9 \text{ ft-kip}$$

$$\text{Eff. d} = 30.0 - 1.5 - 0.375 - \frac{1.0}{2} = 27.6 \text{ in.}$$

$$b = 10 \text{ in}$$

$$F = \frac{bd^2}{12000} = \frac{10 \times (27.6)^2}{12000} = 0.635$$

$$K_n = \frac{M_u}{F} = \frac{229.9}{0.635} = 362$$

(Ref: *Ultimate Strength Design Handbook* Tables ACI SP-17, Flexure 1.3)

For $f'_c = 5000$, $f_y = 40,000$ $K_n = 362$

$$a_u = 2.84$$

$$A_s = \frac{M_u}{a_u \ d} = \frac{229.9}{2.84 \times 27.6} = 2.93 \text{ in.}^2$$

Check $\varrho_{min} / \varrho_{max}$

Quick Check

$$M_{ur} = 229.9 \text{ ft-kip} \qquad jd = 0.75 \times 30 \text{ in. (Assume)}$$

$$f_y = 40,000 \text{ psi}$$

$$A_{s_1} = \frac{229.9 \times 12,000}{40,000 \times (0.75 \times 30)} = 3.06 \text{ in.}^2 \sim 3.0 \text{ in.}^2$$

A_{s_1} is very close to A_s. Find $\phi \ M_n$ as shown below. It is clear how quickly the result is obtained.

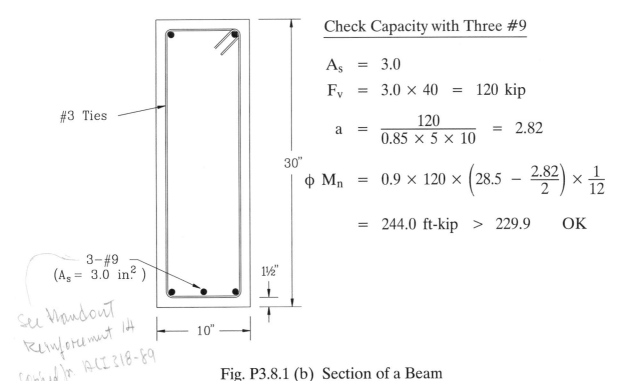

Check Capacity with Three #9

$$A_s = 3.0$$
$$F_v = 3.0 \times 40 = 120 \text{ kip}$$
$$a = \frac{120}{0.85 \times 5 \times 10} = 2.82$$
$$\phi \ M_n = 0.9 \times 120 \times \left(28.5 - \frac{2.82}{2}\right) \times \frac{1}{12}$$
$$= 244.0 \text{ ft-kip} > 229.9 \quad \text{OK}$$

#3 Ties

30"

3-#9
($A_s = 3.0$ in.^{2})

1½"

10"

Fig. P3.8.1 (b) Section of a Beam

3.8.2   P. E. PROBLEM 2 — DOUBLY REINFORCED BEAM

A doubly reinforced 12 in. × 20 in. concrete section is shown in the following figure and reinforced with 1 in.^{2} in compression at the top and 5 in.^{2} in tension at the bottom. The strength of the concrete is $f'_c = 4000$ psi at 28 days.

The reinforcing steel is hard grade with yield point $f_y = 50,000$ psi.

Determine the ultimate bending moment that the section will carry. Use ACI 318-89/92 Code.

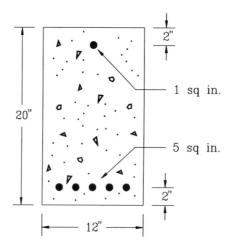

Fig. P3.8.2 (a) Doubly Reinforced Beam

Solution

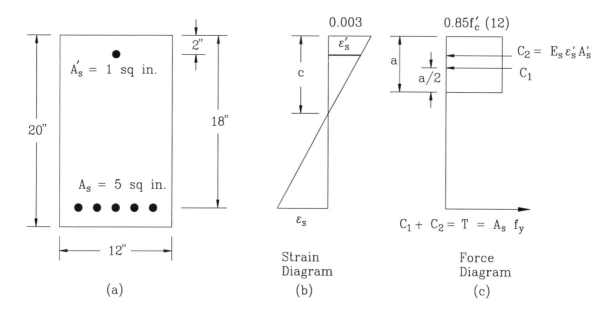

Fig. P3.8.2 (b) Analysis of Doubly Reinforced Beam

Note:

For $f'_c = 40,000$ psi and $f_y = 50,000$ psi,

$\varrho_b = 0.0367$

$0.75\, \varrho_b = 0.0275$

$\varrho = \dfrac{5}{12 \times 18} = 0.023 < 0.0275 < 0.0367$

Therefore, bottom steel is yielding and the beam is under-reinforced.

Assume compression steel yields:

$$C_1 + C_2 = T$$

$$0.85\,(f'_c)\,ab + A'_s\,(f_y - 0.85\,f'_c) = A_s f_y$$

$$0.85\,(4)\,(12)\,a + 1\,(50 - 0.85 \times 4) = 5(50)$$

Therefore, $a = 5.0$ in.; $C_c = \dfrac{a}{\beta_1} = \dfrac{5.0}{0.85} = 5.88$ in.

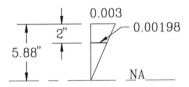

Fig. P3.8.2 (c)

Check if compression steel yields:

$$\varepsilon'_s = 0.003 \left(\frac{5.88 - 2}{5.88}\right) = 0.00198$$

$$\varepsilon_y = \frac{f_y}{E_s} = \frac{50}{29,000} = 0.00172 < \varepsilon'_s = 0.00198$$

Therefore, compression steel yielded as assumed.

$$M_n = C_1 \text{ (lever arm)} + C_2 \text{ (lever arm)}$$

$$= 0.85 \times 4 \times 12 \times 5 \times \left(18 - \frac{5}{2}\right) + 1 \times (50 - 0.85 \times 4) \times (18 - 2)$$

$$= 3908 \text{ in-kip} = 325.6 \text{ ft-kip}$$

$$M_u = \phi\, M_n = 0.9 \times 325.6 = 293.1 \text{ ft-kip}$$

3.8.3 P. E. PROBLEM 3 — BEAM SUPPORTING SLABS

The floor supports a live load of 200 psf. Due to architectural reasons, the beam size cannot be changed. Design the reinforcement for a maximum negative beam moment of $\dfrac{-w\ell_n^2}{11}$.

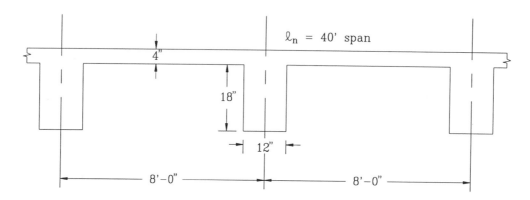

Fig. P3.8.3 (a) Slab Beam

Solution

(Use 1989/1992 ACI Code)

This is a problem of a shallow beam with compression steel at the support of a continuous span.

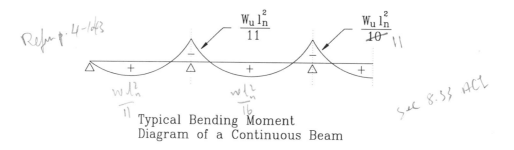

Typical Bending Moment
Diagram of a Continuous Beam

Fig. P3.8.3 (b)

Tributary Loads to Beam:

$$w_D = 50 \times 8 + 150 \times 1.5 \times 1.0 \qquad = 625 \text{ lb/ft}$$

$$w_L = 200 \times 8 \qquad = 1600 \text{ lb/ft}$$

$$w_u = 1.4\,D + 1.7\,L \qquad\qquad\qquad\qquad \text{Sec. 9.2.1}$$

$$\quad = 1.4 \times 0.625 + 1.7 \times 1.60 \qquad = 3.60 \text{ kip/ft}$$

$$l_n = 40 \text{ ft}$$

$$-M_u = \frac{1}{11}w_u\,l_n^2 = \frac{1}{11} \times 3.60 \times 40^2 = 524 \text{ ft-kip}$$

A. Determine the capacity of the section without compression steel:

Assume f'_c = 5000 psi and f_y = 60,000 psi

Balance ratio ϱ_b $= \dfrac{0.85\ \beta_1 f'_c}{f_y}\left(\dfrac{87,000}{87,000\ +\ f_y}\right)$ Eq. (8-1)

$= \dfrac{0.85 \times 0.80 \times 5.0}{60}\left(\dfrac{87}{87\ +\ 60}\right)$ Sec. 10.2.7(c)

$= 0.0335$

ϱ_{max} $= 0.75 \times \varrho_b$ $= 0.0252$ Sec. 10.3.3

A_{s1} $= 0.0252 \times 12 \times 18$ $= 5.44$ in.^{2}

Eff. d $= 22.0 - 1.5 - 2.0$ $= 18.5$ in.   Use 18.00 in.

(2 in. to clear cover, 2 in. to c.g. of comp. steel)

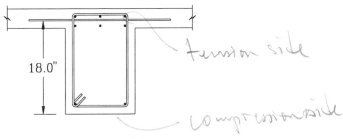

18.0"

Fig. P3.8.3 (c)

a $= \dfrac{A_s f_y}{0.85\ f_c'b}$ $= \dfrac{5.44 \times 60}{0.85 \times 5.0 \times 12}$ $= 6.40$ in.

$\phi\ M_n$ $= \phi\left[A_s f_y\left(d - \dfrac{a}{2}\right)\right]$

$= 0.90\left[5.44 \times 60\left(18.0 - \dfrac{6.40}{2}\right)\right] \times \dfrac{1}{12}$

$= 362$ ft-kip

Since required $M_u > \phi\ M_n$, compression steel at the bottom is required.

B.   Determine the area of compression steel:

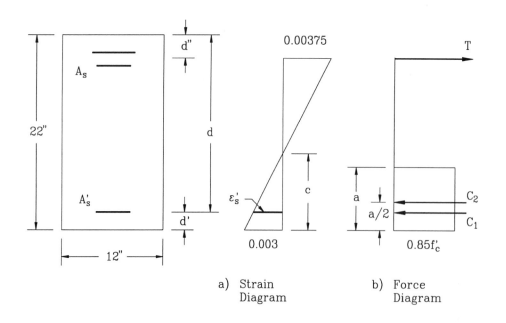

Fig. P3.8.3 (d) Analysis of Beam Section

$$c = \frac{a}{\beta_1} = \frac{6.40}{0.80} = 8.00 \text{ in.}$$

$$\frac{f_y}{E_s} = \frac{60,000}{29 \times 10^6} = 0.002069$$

$$\varepsilon'_s = \frac{c - d'}{c} \times 0.0030 = \frac{8.0 - 2.7}{8.0} \times 0.0030$$

$$= 0.00200 < 0.002069$$

∴ Compression steel does not yield.

$$f_s = \frac{0.00200}{0.002069} \times 60,000 = 58,000 \text{ ksi}$$

$$A'_s = \frac{M_u - K_u F}{(d - d') f_s} = \frac{(524 - 362) \times 12}{(18.0 - 2.7) \times 58.0} = 2.20 \text{ in.}^2$$

Use two #10 — 2.54 in.^{2} > 2.20 in.^{2} — OK

$$A_{s2} = A'_s \left(\frac{f'_s - 0.85 f'_c}{f_y} \right)$$

$$= 2.20 \left(\frac{58.0 - 0.85 \times 5.0}{60.0} \right) = 1.97 \text{ in.}^2$$

C. Determine the area of tension steel:

$$A_s = A_{s_1} + A_{s_2} = 5.44 + 1.97 = 7.41 \text{ in.}^2 \text{ — Use five \#11 — 7.62 in.}^2$$

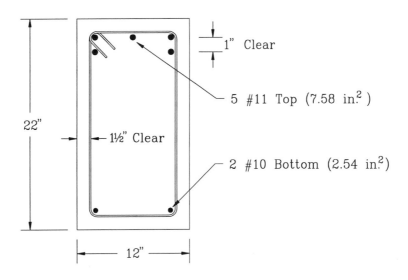

1" Clear

5 #11 Top (7.58 in.²)

22"

1½" Clear

2 #10 Bottom (2.54 in.²)

12"

Fig. P3.8.3 (e) Beam Detail

D. Using ACI Handbook, similar answers can be obtained.

$M_u = 524$ ft-kip $= \phi M_n$ $f'_c = 5.0$ ksi

$b = 12.0$ in. $f_y = 60$ ksi

$d = 18.0$ in. $\dfrac{d'}{d} = 0.15$

Note: The expressions for K_n, ω, a_n, M_u, etc. are given in Chapter 2. Tabulated values may be obtained from any handbook.

1. To find A_s, proceed initially as if section had no compression steel. From Flexure 1.3 for $f'_c = 5$ and $f_y = 60$, read:

$K_n = 1111$ $a_n = 3.70$ $\dfrac{c}{d} = 0.443$

for maximum value of ϱ which is 0.0250.

2. Calculate $F = \dfrac{bd^2}{12,000} = \dfrac{12 \times 18^2}{12,000} = 0.324$

3. Calculate $K_nF = 1111 \times 0.324 = 360$ ft-kip

Therefore, compression steel is required.

$$M'_u = M_u - K_nF = 524 - 360 = 164 \text{ ft-kip}$$

4. From Flexure 3.3 for $\frac{c}{d} = 0.443$ and $\frac{d'}{d} = 0.15$

Read: $a_n'' = 3.39$

From Flexure 2.2 for $d'/d = 0.15$ with $f'_c = 5$ and $f_y = 60$, read:

$a'_n = 3.83$

Since $a_n'' < a'_n,\ f'_s < f_y;$ Use $a'_n = 3.39$

5. $A'_s = \dfrac{M'_n}{a_n'' d} = \dfrac{164}{3.39 \times 18.0} = 2.69$ in.^{2}

6. $A_{s1} = \dfrac{K_n F}{a_n d} = \dfrac{360}{3.70 \times 18.0} = 5.41$ in.^{2}

$A_{s2} = \dfrac{\phi M_n - K_n F}{a'_n d} = \dfrac{164}{3.83 \times 18.0} = 2.38$ in.^{2}

$A_s = A_{s1} + A_{s2} = 5.41 + 2.38 = 7.79$ in.^{2}

Note: where A'_s does not yield,

find ε'_s and $f_s = \dfrac{\varepsilon'_s}{\varepsilon_y} f_y,$

and solve the problem.

Check $\rho - \rho' \dfrac{f_s}{f_y} \le 0.75\, \rho_b.$

However, if $\varepsilon'_s > \varepsilon_y$, use $f_s = f_y$.

7. Check $(\rho - \rho')$

$\rho = \dfrac{A_s}{bd} = \dfrac{7.79}{12 \times 18.0} = 0.0361$

$\rho' = \dfrac{A'_s}{bd} = \dfrac{2.69}{12 \times 18.0} = 0.0125$

$\rho - \rho' = 0.0361 - 0.0125$

$= 0.0236 < 0.75\, \rho_b = 0.0252$

ACI Section 10.3.3 is satisfied.

Note: Compression steel must be anchored by ties or stirrups as provided in ACI Section 7.11.1.

3.8.4   P. E. PROBLEM 4 — END-SUPPORTED CONCRETE BEAM

A concrete beam 12 in. wide spanning 20 ft is simply supported at the ends. The beam carries a uniform service live load of 1.5 kip/ft and a uniform service dead load of 2.3 kip/ft in addition to its self weight.

Criteria

- Concrete f'_c = 3,000 psi
- Reinforcement f_y = 36,000 psi
- Code: ACI 318-89/92   Strength Design
- No compression steel is allowed. Steel ratio not to exceed $0.5\varrho_b$.

Required

A. Determine the minimum beam depth which will satisfy the criteria.

B. Design the area of reinforcement.

C. Draw a sketch of the beam cross section.

Note: Do not design the shear reinforcement.

Solution

A. Consider beam size as 12 in. $\times$ 27 in.

   The solution of the preliminary beam depth depends on the designer. Generally, for a 20 ft beam, assume 20 in. depth. For further guidance, see Table 4.3.

$$\text{Beam weight} \ = \ \frac{12\ (27)}{144} \times \frac{150}{1,000} \ = \ 0.34 \ \text{kip/ft}$$

Factored load   (Sec. 9.2)

$$w_u \ = \ \left(w_D \times 1.4\right) + \left(w_L \times 1.7\right)$$

$$1.4 \ w_D \ = \ 1.4 \times (2.30 + 0.34) \ = \ 3.70 \ \text{kip/ft}$$

$$1.7 \ w_L \ = \ 1.7 \times 1.50 \qquad\qquad = \ 2.55 \ \text{kip/ft}$$

$$w_u \ = \ 1.4 \ w_D + 1.7 \ w_L \qquad = \ 6.25$$

$$M_u \ = \ \frac{w_u \ \ell^2}{8} \ = \ \frac{6.25\ (20^2)}{8} \ = \ 313 \ \text{ft-kip}$$

Using Equation 3.5:

$$\varrho_b \ = \ 0.85 \ \beta \left(\frac{f'_c}{f_y}\right) \left(\frac{87,000}{87,000 + f_y}\right)$$

$$= \ 0.85 \ (0.85) \left(\frac{3.0}{36.0}\right) \left(\frac{87.0}{87 + 36}\right) \ = \ 0.0426$$

$$0.5\varrho_b \ = \ 0.5 \times 0.0426 \ = \ 0.0213 \ \text{— maximum allowed in this problem}$$

Because of the heavy loads, consider two layers of reinforcing steel with c.g. of steel at 4.0 in. Eff. d = 27.0 − 4.0 = 23.0 in. Max. A_s = 0.0213 × 12 × 23.0 = 5.88 in.^{2}

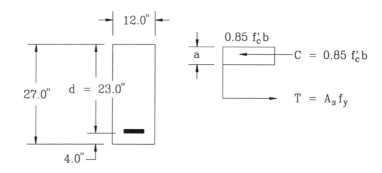

Fig. P3.8.4 (a)

$$T = A_s f_y = 5.88 \times 36.0 = 212 \text{ kip}$$

$$C = T = 0.85 \ (3.0) \ (12) \ a$$

$$a = \frac{212}{0.85 \ (3.0) \ (12)} = 6.93 \text{ in.}$$

$$M_n = T \ (d - a/2)$$

$$= 212 \times \left(23.0 - \frac{6.93}{2}\right) \times \frac{1}{12} = 345 \text{ ft-kip}$$

$$\frac{M_u}{\phi} = \frac{313}{0.9} = 347 \text{ ft-kip} \cong M_n \qquad \text{Close enough}$$

Note: With M_u, f'_c, f_y given, assume ϱ and b, and find approximate d. Use "*Quick Check.*" It will be faster to solve such problems.

Use: 12 in. × 27 in. beam.

B. Tensile Reinforcement

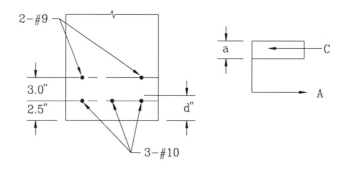

Fig. P3.8.4 (b)

$$A_s = 3 \times 1.27 + 2 \times 1.00 = 3.81 + 2.00 = 5.81 \text{ in.}^2$$

Locate c.g. of steel

$$d'' = \frac{3.81 \times 2.5 + 2.00 \times 5.5}{5.81} = 3.53 \text{ in.}$$

$$d = 27.0 - 3.53 = 23.47 \text{ in.} \qquad \text{(New d)}$$

$$T = 5.81 \times 36 = 209 \text{ kip}$$

$$a = \frac{209}{0.85 \ (3.0) \ (12)} = 6.83 \text{ in.}$$

$$M_n = 209 \left(23.47 - \frac{6.83}{2}\right) \left(\frac{1}{12}\right) = 349 \text{ ft-kip}$$

$$\frac{M_u}{\phi} = 347 \text{ ft-kip} < M_n \qquad\qquad \text{OK}$$

Note: Avoid placement of reinforcement as shown in Figure P3.8.4 (b). It is time consuming. However, when the placement of reinforcement is given, use the method shown above.

Use: Two #9 and three #10 at bottom.

C. Sketch of Beam Cross Section:

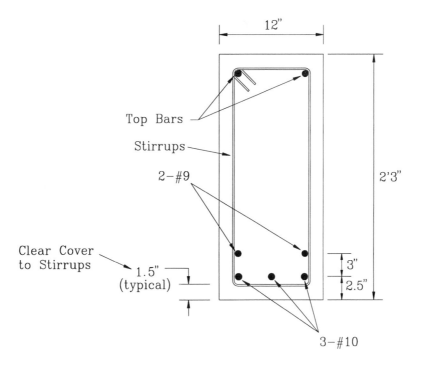

Fig. P3.8.4 (c) Beam Section

3.8.5   P. E. PROBLEM 5 — BEAM WITH A HOLE

What uniform load can the beam with a cross section shown in Figure 3.8.5 (a) support in addition to its own weight for a 24-ft simple span?

Concrete assumed to weigh 150 lb/ft3.

Use ACI 318-1989/1992 Code

- f'_c = 3000 psi
- f_y = 40,000 psi
- U = 1.4D + 1.7L

Do by USD Method or Alternate Design Method (WSD)

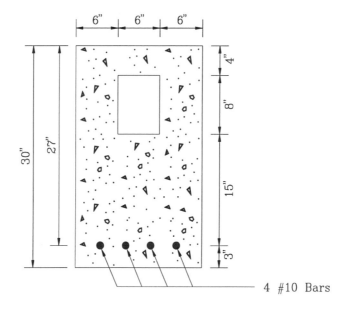

Fig. P3.8.5 (a)

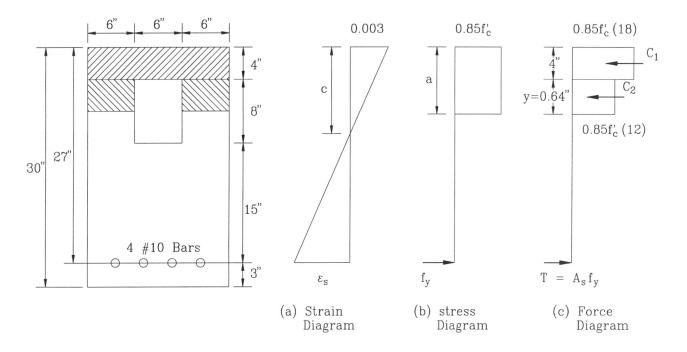

Fig. P3.8.5 (b) USD Stress-Strain Diagram

Solution

A. Ultimate Strength Design Method

Assume compression block is above the hole. Treat the beam as a rectangular beam.

Compression depth:

$$a = \frac{T}{0.85 \ f'_c \ b} = \frac{4 \times 1.27 \times 40}{0.85 \times 3 \times 18} = 4.43 \text{ in.}$$

a = 4.43 in. > 4 in.

(Compression block is partially in the hole area.)

Equilibrium:

$$T = C_1 + C_2$$

where

$$T = A_s f_y = 4 \times 1.27 \times 40 \qquad = 203.2 \text{ kip}$$
$$C_1 = 0.85 \times 3000 \times 18 \times 4 = 183.6 \text{ kip}$$
$$C_2 = 203.2 - 183.6 \qquad\qquad = 19.6 \text{ kip}$$

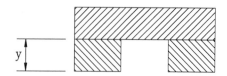

Fig. P3.8.5 (c) Compression Block

$$y = \frac{C_2}{0.85 \, f'_c \, (12)} = \frac{19.6}{30.6} = 0.64 \text{ in.}$$

$$M_n = C_1 \, (27 - 2) + C_2 \left[27 - \left(4 + \frac{0.64}{2} \right) \right]$$

$$= 183.6 \, (25) + 19.6 \, (22.68) = 5034.53 \text{ in.-kip}$$

$$M_u = \phi M_n = 0.9 \, (5034.53)$$

$$= 4531 \text{ in.-kip} = 377.6 \text{ ft-kip} \qquad \text{Sec. 9.3.2 (a)}$$

$$W_u = \frac{8M_u}{L^2} = \frac{8 \, (377.6)}{(24)^2} = 5.24 \text{ kip/ft}$$

$$W_u = 1.4W_D + 1.7W_L$$

Where

$$W_D = \left[(18 \times 30) - (6 \times 8) \right] \frac{150}{144} = 512.5 \text{ lb/ft}$$

$$1.4 \times 512.5 + 1.7 \, W_L = 5240$$

$$W_L = \frac{5240 - 1.4(512.5)}{1.7}$$

$$= 2660 \text{ lb/ft} = 2.66 \text{ kip/ft (Service Load)}$$

Check yielding of reinforcement:

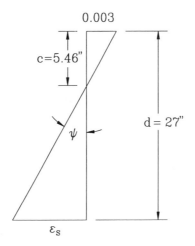

Fig. P3.8.5 (d) Strain Diagram

$$C = \frac{a}{\beta_1} = \frac{0.64 + 4}{0.85} = 5.46 \text{ in.}$$

$$\text{Curvature } \psi = \frac{0.003}{5.46} = 0.00055 \text{ radian}$$

$$\varepsilon_s = (27 - 5.46)\, 0.00055 = 0.0118 \text{ in./in.}$$

$$\varepsilon_y = \frac{f_y}{E_s} = \frac{40}{29,000} = 0.00138 \text{ in./in.}$$

$\varepsilon_s > \varepsilon_y$: <u>Tension</u> Failure

B. Alternate Design Method (or Working Stress Design Method)

ACI 318-89, Appendix A

Maximum Permissible:

$f_c \leq 0.45\, f'_c$ Sec. A.3.1(a)

$f_s \leq 0.5\, f_y$ (not to exceed 24 ksi)   Sec. A.3.2(b)

Locate the Neutral Axis Using Transformed Area:

$$n = \frac{E_s}{E_c} = 9 \ \left(\text{for } f'_c = 3,000 \text{ psi}\right) \qquad \text{Sec. A.5.4}$$

$n\, A_s = 9 \times 4 \times 1.27 = 45.72 \text{ in.}^2$

Take the first moment about N.A. [See Figure P3.8.5 (f)]

$$4 \times 6 \times (x - 2) + 2 \times 6x \times \left(\frac{x}{2}\right) = 45.72 \ (27 - x)$$

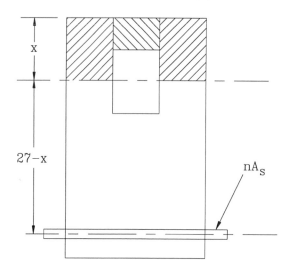

Fig. P3.8.5 (e)

$$24x - 48 + 6x^2 - 1234.44 + 45.72x = 0$$
$$6x^2 + 69.72x - 1282.44 = 0$$

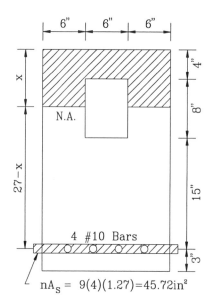

Fig. P3.8.5 (f)

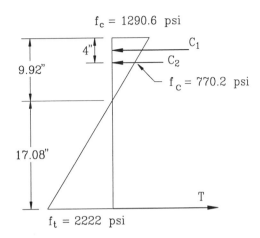

$$f_c = 1290.6 \text{ psi}$$

Fig. P3.8.5 (g)

$$x^2 + 11.62x - 213.74 = 0$$

$$x = \frac{-11.62 \pm \sqrt{(11.62)^2 + 4\,(213.74)}}{2}$$

4 in. < x = 9.92 in. < 12 in. OK

Allowable $f_c = 0.45f'_c = 0.45\,(3000) = 1350$ psi (Compression stress in concrete at top fiber)

Calculated $f_t = 1,350 \left(\dfrac{17.08}{9.92}\right) = 2,324.4$ psi (corresponding tensile stress in concrete at bottom fiber) > allowable $f_t = 2222$ psi.

Therefore, section is governed by tension.

Using strain-stress compatibility equation:

Allowable $f_s = 0.5\,f_y = 20,000$ psi

Allowable $f_t = \dfrac{0.5f_y}{n} = \dfrac{0.5(40,000)}{9} = 2,222$ psi

Actual $f_c = 2,222\left(\dfrac{9.92}{17.08}\right) = 1,290.6$ psi

$$C_1 = \left(\frac{1290.6 + 770.2}{2}\right) \times 4 \times 6 = 24,730 \text{ lb} = 24.73 \text{ kip}$$

Assume that C_1 is acting 2 in. below the top fiber.

$$C_2 = \tfrac{1}{2} \times 1,290.6 \times 9.92 \times 12 = 76,817 \text{ lb} = 76.8 \text{ kip}$$

$$T = 2222\,(45.72) = 101,590 \text{ lb} = 101.6 \text{ kip}$$

Allowable $M_W = C_1$ (lever arm) + C_2 (lever arm)

$$= 24.73 \times (27 - 2) + 76.8 \times \left(27 - \frac{9.92}{3}\right)$$

$$= 2,438 \text{ in-kip} = 203.2 \text{ ft-kip}$$

$$W_T = \frac{8M_W}{(24)^2} = 2.82 \text{ kip/ft}$$

$$W_T = W_D + W_L$$

$$W_L = W_T - W_D = 2.82 - 0.5125 = 2.31 \text{ kip/ft}$$

Compare to 2.66 kip/ft by USD.

3.8.6 P. E. PROBLEM 6 — BEAM WITH STEMS

The following requirements relate to the reinforced concrete beam section shown below:

Given

- $f'_c = 3000$ psi
- $f_s = 20,000$ psi
- $f_c = 1350$ psi
- $f_y = 50,000$ psi
- $n = 9$

Required

A. Determine the maximum allowable resisting moment, M_w, using the Working Stress Design Method (now called the Alternate Design Method by the ACI Code).

B. Determine the maximum permissible moment capacity of the section using the (Ultimate) Strength Method and the 1989/1992 ACI Code.

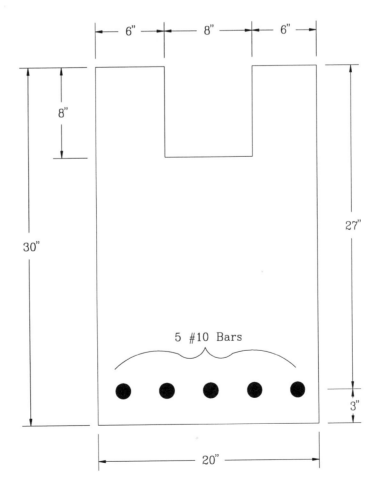

Fig. P3.8.6 (a) Reinforced Hollow Beam

Solution

A. Working Stress Design (WSD) for pure flexure:

f'_c = 3000 psi f_s = 20,000 psi   n = 9

f_c = 1350 psi f_y = 50,000

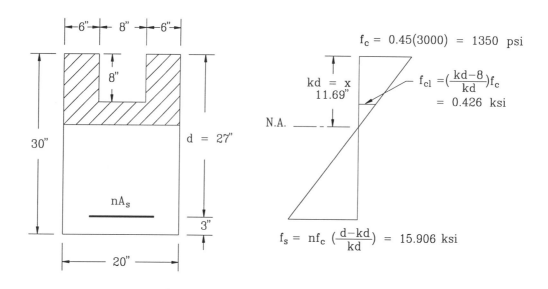

Fig. P3.8.6 (b) Stress Diagram (WSD)

Moment Capacity by Working Stress Method:

Assume transformed cracked section and elastic analysis

x = distance from top of beam to N.A. Try $x \leq 8$ in.

The neutral axis for elastic analysis is obtained by equating moment of areas of compression and tension zones about neutral axis

$$n A_s = 9 \times 5 \times 1.27 = 57.15$$

$$2 (6) \left(\frac{x}{2}\right) (x) = 57.15 (27 - x) \text{ or } 6x^2 + 57.15x - 1543 = 0$$

$$x = 11.97 > 8 \text{ in., so try } x > 8 \text{ in.}$$

$$(2) (6) \left(\frac{x}{2}\right) (x) + \frac{8 (x - 8)^2}{2} = 57.15 (27 - x)$$

$$6x^2 + 4 (x - 8)^2 = 1543 - 57.15x$$

or

$$10x^2 - 6.85x - 1287.0 = 0$$

$$x = 11.692 \text{ in.} > 8 \text{ in. OK}$$

Strain linearly proportional to distance from N.A.

$$\frac{\varepsilon_c}{x} = \frac{\varepsilon_s}{d-x} \text{ or } \frac{f_c/E_c}{x} = \frac{f_s/E_s}{d-x}$$

$$\frac{f_s}{E_s} = \frac{d-x}{x}\frac{f_c}{E_c} \text{ or } f_s = \frac{E_s}{E_c}\frac{d-x}{x}f_c$$

$$f_s = n\left(\frac{d-x}{x}\right)f_c = \frac{9\,(27-11.69)\,1,350}{11.69}$$

$$= 15,906 \text{ psi} < 20,000 \text{ psi} \quad \text{OK}$$

Thus, when the top concrete fiber reaches the maximum value of 1,350 psi, the steel stress is less than the maximum permissible stress of 20,000 psi. Thus, this section is over-reinforced as per Working Stress Design Theory. However, the beam is under-reinforced as per USD with a *tensile* steel reaching yield stress, because the percentage of steel ϱ < balanced percentage of steel ϱ_b.

Moment of compressive force about tensile force:

		Force	Arm	Moment
$2C_1 = \dfrac{2 \times 6 \times 11.692 \times 1,350}{2}$		= 94.7 kip	23.10 in.	2188 in.-kip
$C_2 = \dfrac{8 \times 3.692 \times 0.426}{2}$		= 6.3 kip	17.77 in.	112 in.-kip
	$\sum C$	= 101.7 kip	$\sum M$	= 2300 in.-kip

T = 15.906 × 6.35 = 101.0 kip = C

Resisting bending moment (working stress) = ΣM = 2300 in.-kip or 192 ft-kip

B. Moment Capacity by Ultimate Strength Method for Pure Flexure:

Assume $a > 8$ in. $\varepsilon_y = \dfrac{50,000}{29,000,000} = 0.0017241$

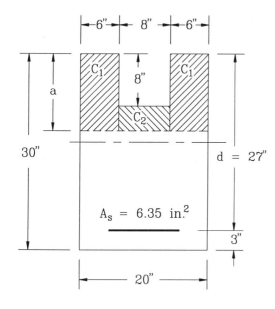
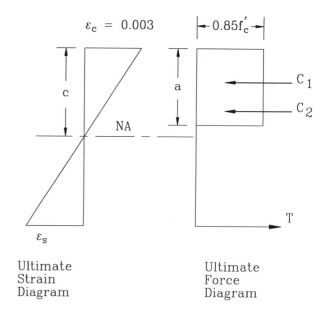

Fig. P3.8.6 (c)

Five #10, $A_s = 6.35$ in.2

$$\varrho_b = 0.85 \times 0.85 \times \left(\dfrac{3}{50}\right) \times \dfrac{87}{87 + 50} = 0.0275$$

$$\varrho = \dfrac{A_s}{bd} = \dfrac{6.35}{12 \times 27.0} = 0.0196 < 0.75\,\varrho_b = 0.0206$$

Reinforcement at the bottom will yield (i.e., $f_y = 50$ ksi). *Note* that b is only 12 in. (i.e., width of the top compression fiber only).

$T = A_s f_y = 6.35 \times 50 = 317.5$ kip

$C = 0.85\,f'_c \times$(Compression Area)

$C_1 = 2 \times [0.85\,(3)\,(6)\,a]$

$C_2 = 0.85\,(3)\,(8)\,(a - 8)$

$T = C_1 + C_2$

$317.5 = 2\,(0.85)\,(3)\,(6)\,a + 0.85\,(3)\,(8)\,(a - 8)$

$\qquad = 30.6\,(a) + 20.4\,(a) - 163.2$

$\quad a = 9.43$ in. > 8.0

$c = \dfrac{a}{\beta_1} = \dfrac{9.43}{0.85} = 11.09$ in.

Check if tensile steel yields:

$$\varepsilon_s = 0.003 \left(\frac{27 - 11.09}{11.09}\right) = 0.0043 \cong 2.5\, \varepsilon_y$$

Moment of Compressive Force about Tensile Force:

	Force	Arm	Moment
$C_1 = (2)(6)(0.85 \times 11.089)(0.85 \times 3.0)$ =	288.4 kip	27.29 in.	6428 in.-kip
$C_2 = 8(0.85 \times 11.089 - 8)(0.85 \times 3.0)$ =	29.1 kip	18.28 in.	532 in.-kip
$\sum C$ =	317.5 kip	$\sum M$ =	6960 in.-kip

$M_n = \Sigma M = 6960$ in.-kip or 580 ft-kip

Ultimate Moment Capacity = $0.9 \times 580 = 522$ ft-kip

This moment capacity corresponds to an overload from the full design loads used in WSD.

Assume 50% DL, 50% LL

Overload factor for a building element = $1.4 \times 0.5 + 1.7 \times 0.5 = 1.55$.

By USD, $M_w = \dfrac{522}{1.55} = 336.8$ ft-kip as compared with 192 ft-kip by WSD.

Comment:

Note that Ultimate Strength Design Method gives a better assessment of moment capacity.

3.8.7   P. E. PROBLEM 7 — CHANNEL-BEAM IN BENDING

Illustrated below is the cross section of a reinforced concrete channel. For a 15-ft simple span, determine the allowable uniform load per foot which this section can support in addition to its own weight. Assume a light-weight-aggregate concrete weighing 100 lb/ft^3. Use USD method and consider moments only. (Sufficient wire mesh is provided in the slab.) $f'_c = 3000$ psi, $f_y = 40,000$ psi.

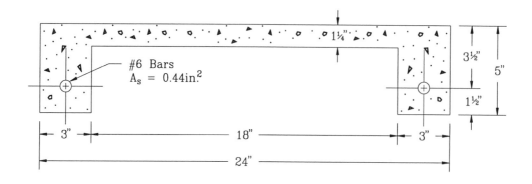

Fig. P3.8.7 (a) Channel-Beam

Solution

By ultimate strength design; use 1989/1992 ACI Code.

Effective flange overhang for L-shaped beam (see ACI Section 8.10.3):

    A. 6 times the slab thickness = 6 (1.25) = 7.50 in.

    B. $\frac{1}{12} \times$ beam span length = $\frac{1}{12}$ (15) (12) = 15 in.

    C. 1/2 × clear distance between two adjacent beams = 1/2 (18 in.) = 9 in.

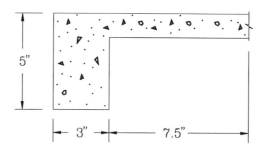

Fig. P3.8.7 (b)

Take least value 7.5 in. for beam section overhang. Therefore, we can consider this slab as an *effective T-beam* with the flange equal to (7.5 × 2) + 6 = 21 in. Assume that the stress block is in the flange and that steel yields at ultimate.

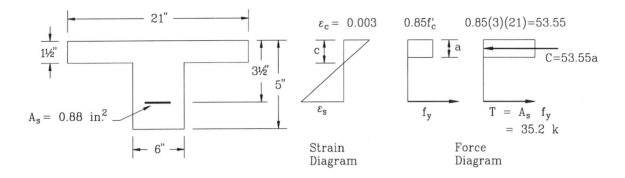

Fig. P3.8.7 (c) Analysis of a T-Beam

Equilibrium: C = T

Assume compression stress block is in flange.

$C = 0.85f'_c\,ba = 0.85\,(3)\,(21)\,a = 53.55a$ Sec. 10.2.7 (a)

$T = A_sf_y = 0.88\,(40) = 35.2$ kip

$53.55a = 35.2$

$\quad a = 0.66$ in. < thickness of flange = 1-1/2 in. OK

Ultimate Moment Capacity of the Beam:

$$M_n \;=\; T\!\left(d - \tfrac{a}{2}\right) \;=\; 35.2 \times \left(3.5 - \frac{0.66}{2}\right) \;=\; 111.6 \text{ in.-kip}$$

$$\qquad\quad =\; 9.3 \text{ ft-kip}$$

Maximum positive moment in the beam: $\dfrac{W_u\,L^2}{8} \;=\; M_u$

$$w_u \;=\; \frac{8M_u}{L^2} \;=\; \frac{8(8.37)}{(15)^2} \;=\; 0.298 \text{ kip/ft} \;=\; 298 \text{ lb/ft}$$

$$U \;=\; 1.4 \text{ DL} + 1.7 \text{ LL} \quad\text{or}\quad w_u \;=\; 1.4\,w_D + 1.7\,w_L$$

where

$$w_D \;=\; [(5 \times 6) + (18 \times 1.25)]\frac{100}{144} \;=\; 36.4 \text{ lb/ft}$$

Thus,

$$w_u \;=\; 1.4\,(36.4) + 1.7\,w_L \;=\; 298 \text{ lb/ft}$$

$$w_L \;=\; \frac{1}{1.7}\,(298 - 50.96) \;=\; 145.4 \text{ lb/ft}$$

Service load capacity of the beam is 145.4 lb/ft (i.e., 72.7 psf).

Check yielding of reinforcements:

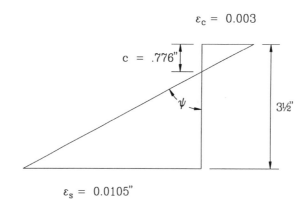

$$\varepsilon_c = 0.003$$

$$c = .776"$$

$$3\frac{1}{2}"$$

$$\psi$$

$$\varepsilon_s = 0.0105"$$

Fig. P3.8.7 (d) Strain Diagram

$$C = \frac{a}{\beta_1} = \frac{0.66}{0.85} = 0.776 \text{ in}$$

$$\text{Curvature } \psi = \frac{0.003}{0.776} = 0.00386 \text{ radian}$$

$$\varepsilon_s = (3.5 - 0.776)\, 0.00386$$

$$\varepsilon_s = 0.0105 \text{ in.} >> \varepsilon_y = \frac{f_y}{\varepsilon_s} = 0.00138 \text{ in.}$$

$$\varepsilon_s = 7.3\, \varepsilon_y \underline{\text{ Tension}} \text{ Failure}$$

Failure mode is *secondary compression failure* in which the concrete crushes in compression with steel yielding to about 7.3 times yield strain.

3.8.8   P. E. PROBLEM 8 — T-BEAM

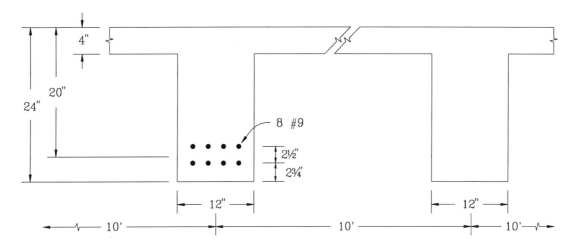

Fig. P3.8.8 (a) T-Beam

Given:

- T-beam simply supported, span = 30 ft 0 in.
- $f'_c = 3,000$ psi
- $f_y = 60,000$ psi

Required

A.   Calculate maximum and minimum areas of steel allowable.

B.   Given eight #9 bars shown, find ultimate moment capacity of T-beam. Find M_u and mode of failure.

C.   If the beam above is loaded only with dead load from the weight of the beam and slab, find the maximum super-imposed live load which can be carried by the beam.

Solution

A_s provided $= 8 \times 1.0 = 8$ in.^{2} Sec. 8.10.3

Effective flange width of T-beam b_f.

1. $\dfrac{L}{4} \;=\; \dfrac{30 \text{ ft}}{4} \;=\; 7.5 \text{ ft} \;=\; 90 \text{ in.}$

2. $b_w + 16t_f = 12 + 16\,(4) = 76$ in. Controls

3.   Center-to-Center of beams $= 10$ ft $= 120$ in.

$b_f \;= 76$ in.

$d \;\; = 20$ in.

A.   Calculate Maximum Allowable Steel for USD:

ACI 318-89/92 $A_s \;\leq\; \dfrac{3}{4}\,(A_s)_b$ Sec. 10.3.3

To provide more ductility for DMRF/SMRF in seismic areas SEAOC recommends:

$$A_s \le \frac{1}{2}(A_s)_b$$

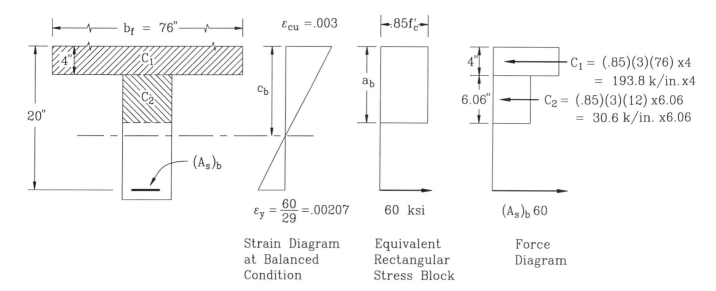

Fig. P3.8.8 (b)

First we need to find $(A_s)_b$ at Ultimate condition

Let a_b be the depth of stress block at balanced condition

$$c_b = \frac{0.003}{0.003 + 0.00207} \times 20 = 11.84 \text{ in.} >> t_f = 4 \text{ in.}$$

$$a_b = \beta_1 C_b = (0.85)(11.84) = 10.06 \text{ in.} >> t_f = 4 \text{ in.}$$

$$C_b = C_1 + C_2 = 193.8(4) + 30.6(6.06) = 960.64 \text{ kip}$$

$$T_b = 60 A_{sb}$$

For Equilibrium, $C_b = T_b$

$$60 A_{sb} = 960.64$$

$$A_{sb} = 16.01 \text{ in.}^2$$

(A_s) max by ACI code $= \frac{3}{4}(A_s)_b = 12.0 \text{ in.}^2$

(A_s) max by SEAOC — DMRF $= \frac{1}{2}(A_s)_b = 8.0 \text{ in.}^2$

$A_s = 8 \text{ in.}^2$ is good from ductility point of view (SEAOC).

Calculate Minimum Longitudinal Steel:

$$(A_s)_{min} = \frac{200 \, b_w \, d}{f_y} = \frac{200 \times 12 \times 20}{60,000} \qquad \text{ACI Sec. 10.5.1}$$

$$= \underline{0.8} \text{ in.}^2$$

Given: $A_s = 8 \text{ in.}^2$ is OK.

B. Ultimate Moment Capacity with given steel:

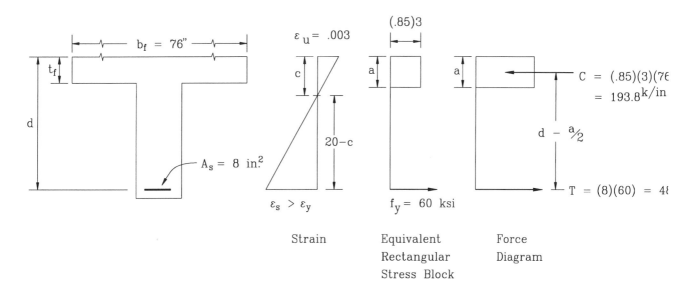

Fig. P3.8.8 (c) Strain, Stress and Force Diagram

Assume tensile steel yields.

Also assume

$a < t_f = 4$ in.

$C = T$ and $T = A_s f_y$

$0.85 \times 3 \times 76 \times a = 8.0 \times 60$

$a = 2.48$ in. < 4 in. OK.

$b = 76$ in. $d = 20$ in. $h = 24$ in. $A_s = 8 in^2$

Check if tensile steel yields:

$$c = \frac{a}{\beta_1} = \frac{2.48}{0.85} = 2.92 \text{ in.}$$

$$\varepsilon_s = 0.003 \left(\frac{20 - 2.92}{2.92}\right) \quad \text{from similar triangles of strain diagram}$$

$$= 0.0176 = 8.5 \, \varepsilon_y \quad \text{where } \varepsilon_y = 0.00207$$

Therefore, tensile steel yields.

Note: It is already shown that $A_s < (A_s)_b$. Proof for yielding of steel is not necessary. Also $A_s < 0.75 (A_s)_b$ satisfies ACI criteria.

The present failure mode will be secondary compression flexural failure, which is commonly noted as tension failure by yielding of steel and subsequent crushing of concrete.

Nominal Ultimate Moment

$$M_n = T\left(d - \frac{a}{2}\right) \quad = 480\left(20 - \frac{2.48}{2}\right)$$

$$= 9004.8 \text{ in-kip} \quad = 750.4 \text{ ft-kip}$$

Design Ultimate Flexural Moment, $M_u = \phi M_n$

$$= 0.9\,(750.4) = 675. \text{ ft-kip}$$

C. Superimposed Load Capacity of the Given Beam:

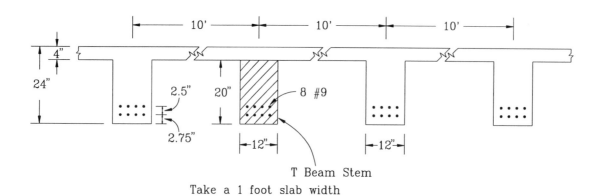

Fig. P3.8.8 (d) Load Superimposed on Beam

Given:

*   span = 30 ft f'_c = 3000 psi F_y = 60,000 psi
*   spacing of T-beams = 10 ft
*   w = 150 lb/ft^3 for RC construction using normal weight concrete
* M_u = 675.4 ft-kip (Interior Beams)

DL of slab/ft of T−beam $= \dfrac{4 \text{ in}}{12} \times 10 \text{ ft} \times 1 \times 150$

$$= 500 \text{ lb/ft of slab width}$$

DL of T−beam Stem $= \dfrac{12 \text{ in}}{12} \times \dfrac{20}{12} \times 1 \times 150 = 250 \text{ lb/ft}$

Total DL/ft slab width $= 0.500 + 0.25 = 0.75 \text{ kip/ft}$

(Strictly speaking add DL of flooring, partitions, etc.)

$$\text{Load } (w_{beam})_u = \frac{8M}{L^2} = 8\left(\frac{675.4 \text{ ft-kip}}{(30)^2}\right) = 6.00 \text{ kip/ft}$$

$$= 1.4(DL)_{beam} + 1.7(LL)_{beam}$$

$$(w_{LL})_{beam} = \frac{w_{beam} - 1.4(DL)}{1.7} = \frac{6 - 1.4(0.75)}{1.7}$$

$$\text{Live Load on beam} = 2.91 \text{ kip/ft}$$

If W_L is Live Load on slab/ft^2,

Tributary area for 1 ft of interior beam

$$10 \times 1 \times W_L = 2.91 \text{ kip/ft}$$

$$W_L = \frac{2.91 \text{ kip/ft}}{10 \text{ ft}} = 0.291 \text{ kip/ft}^2$$

Live Load (Superimposed) Capacity is 291 lb/ft^2

Note:

For the complete investigation of service load capacity, the following items should also be investigated:

1. Shear capacity and the corresponding service load.

2. Long term deflection criteria and the corresponding service load.

For the final design, the lowest load capacity shall be used.

4

SERVICEABILITY AND DEFLECTION

4.1 CRACK CONTROL FOR REINFORCED CONCRETE MEMBERS IN BUILDINGS

The significant variables controlling crack width are steel stress, thickness of concrete cover and the area of concrete surrounding each bar in zone of maximum tension. To reduce the size of cracks and to have many fine, hairline cracks rather than a few wide cracks, the ACI Building Code has provisions to control the cracking. These cracks are at full design load, which may not occur frequently in service. As a matter of fact, it rarely occurs and that is why flexural cracking due to normal loads is rare. However, cracking due to temperature and shrinkage is possible.

The width of the crack is given in ACI Code Commentary as,

$$w = 0.076 \ \beta \ f_s \ \sqrt[3]{d_c A} = 0.076 \ \beta \ z$$

(Multiply $w \times 0.001$ to obtain crack width in in.)

z is a factor which is a function of crack width, where

f_s = service load stress in steel, ksi; or an approximate value of $0.60f_y$, as permitted by the code;

d_c = thickness of concrete cover measured from the extreme tension fiber to the center of the bars closest thereto, inches;

A = A_e/m = effective concrete tensile area per bar;

A_e = $(2d_s)b_w$, twice the distance from the extreme tension fiber to the centroid of the tensile steel, multiplied by the web width of the beam;

m = number of bars

= total area of the tensile steel divided by area of largest bar size.

β = ratio of the depth of the tension fiber to the depth of the c.g. of tension steel both measured from NA = d_2/d_1 (use d_2/d_1 = 1.2 for beam and 1.35 for slab).

The following formula may be directly applied in cases where f_y exceeds 40 ksi.

A. Beam and one-way slabs: ACI Eq. (10-4)

Interior exposure: $z = f_s \sqrt[3]{d_c A} \leq 175$ kip/in.

Exterior exposure: $z = f_s \sqrt[3]{d_c A} \leq 145$ kip/in.

The above limitations for z do not apply for two-way slabs, nor do they apply for structures subject to very aggressive environments; nor for water-tight structures where z is limited to 45 kip/in.

B. Floor slabs: Based on commentary   ACI Sec. 10.6.4

Interior exposure: $z = f_s \sqrt[3]{d_c A} \leq 155$ kip/in.

Exterior exposure: $z = f_s \sqrt[3]{d_c A} \leq 130$ kip/in.

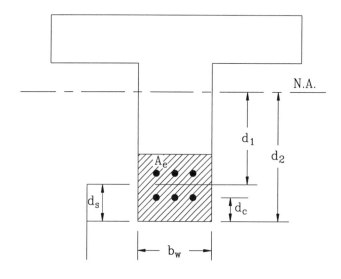

Figure 4.1 Section of a T-Beam

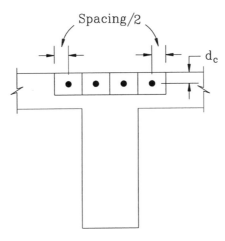

Figure 4.2 Section of T-Beam with $(-)$ Steel

The formula for z is based on empirical data and the limits for z may be derived in accordance with the limits of crack widths specified in the ACI Code Sec. 10.6.3 and 10.6.4, when the design yield stress f_y for tension reinforcement *exceeds* 40,000 psi. The crack widths are limited to 0.016 and 0.013 in. for interior and exterior exposures, respectively.

Refer to the following tables from the *ACI Design Handbook* which would help determine crack widths for given reinforcements detailing or check if it is okay for crack control. Alternately, if A_s is determined, it shows what combination of steel bars could be used to take care of crack control for interior and exterior exposure.

Table 4.1 Maximum Bar Spacing in Beams*

Bar Size	Outside Exposure z = 145			Inside Exposure z = 175		
	Cover (in.)			Cover (in.)		
	1-1/2	2	3	1-1/2	2	3
# 4	10.7	6.5	3.1	18.8	11.3	5.4
# 5	9.9	6.1	3.0	17.5	10.7	5.2
# 6	9.3	5.8	2.9	16.3	10.2	5.0
# 7	8.7	5.5	2.8	15.3	9.7	4.9
# 8	8.2	5.2	2.7	14.4	9.2	4.7
# 9	7.7	5.0	2.6	13.5	8.7	4.5
#10	7.2	4.7	2.5	12.6	8.3	4.3
#11	6.7	4.5	2.4**	11.8	7.8	4.2

*   *Values in inches, $f_s = 0.6 f_y = 36$ ksi, single layer of reinforcement [ACI 318-83 and ACI 318-89]*

**   *Spacing less than permitted by Section 7.6.1*

Table 4.2 Maximum Bar Spacing in One-Way Slabs*

(Grade 60 Reinforcement)

Bar Size	Outside Exposure z = 129				Inside Exposure z = 156			
	Cover (in.)				Cover (in.)			
	3/4	1	1-1/2	2	3/4	1	1-1/2	2
# 4	—	14.7	7.5	4.5	—	—	13.3	8.0
# 5	—	13.4	7.0	4.3	—	—	12.4	7.6
# 6	—	12.2	6.5	4.1	—	—	11.6	7.2
# 7	16.3	11.1	6.1	3.9	—	—	10.8	6.8
# 8	14.7	10.2	5.8	3.7	—	—	10.2	6.5
# 9	13.3	9.4	5.4	3.5	—	16.6	9.6	6.2
#10	12.0	8.6	5.0	3.3	—	15.2	8.9	5.9
#11	10.9	7.9	4.7	3.1	—	14.0	8.4	5.6

*   *Values in inches, $f_s = 0.6 f_y = 36$ ksi, single layer of reinforcement. Spacing should not exceed 3 times slab thickness nor more than 18 in. (Section 7.6.5). No value indicates calculated spacing greater than 18 in.*

4.2 EFFECTIVE MOMENT OF INERTIA FOR CALCULATING DEFLECTIONS

In a concrete beam, the effective cross section varies because of variations due to different degrees of cracking and uncracking due to loads. In regions of low moment, no cracks exist and the effective moment of inertia should logically be based on the gross transformed area of the section. When sections have high moment, cracking is extensive. Where a crack exists, the effective moment of inertia is more properly based on the transformed cracked section. To account for the variation of the moment of inertia along the beam axis, Section (9.5.2.3) of the ACI Code requires in the elastic deflection equations the use of an effective moment of inertia, I_e, which approximates the average effective moment of inertia.

$$I_e = \left[\frac{M_{cr}}{M_a}\right]^3 I_g + \left[1 - \left[\frac{M_{cr}}{M_a}\right]^3\right] I_{cr} \leq I_g \qquad \text{ACI Eq. (9-7)}$$

where $\quad M_{cr} = \dfrac{f_r I_g}{y_t}$ $\qquad\qquad\qquad\qquad$ ACI Eq. (9-8)

f_r = the modulus of rupture = $7.5\sqrt{f'_c}$

y_t = the distance from the centroid of the gross section to the extreme fiber in tension

M_{cr} = the cracking moment

M_a = the maximum moment (due to service load) in the member at the stage for which deflection is being computed.

I_g = the moment of inertia of the gross section neglecting the area of tension steel.

I_{cr} = moment of inertia of the transformed cracked cross section. By Straight Line Theory (WSD)

Note:

$$k = -\varrho n + \sqrt{2\varrho n + (\varrho n)^2}$$

$$c = kd$$

$$I_{cr} = \frac{bc^3}{3} + nA_s (d - c)^2$$

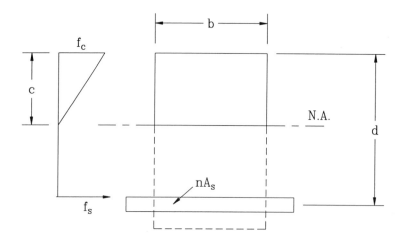

Figure 4.3 W.S.D. Cracked Section

The equation above should be used when:

$$1 \; \leq \; \frac{M_a}{M_{cr}} \; < \; 3$$

If $M_a/M_{cr} > 3$, the cracking is extensive and I_e can be taken $= I_{cr}$ with no significant error.

If $M_a/M_{cr} < 1$, no cracking is likely and I_e can be taken $= I_g$.

Deflection shall always be calculated for short-term and long-term service loading only. Short-term deflection equations can be found in any standard textbook on theory of structures.

4.3   LONG-TERM DEFLECTIONS

With time, deflections increase due to creep and shrinkage of concrete. By cambering forms an amount equal to the expected deflection, the appearance of sag can be eliminated. The long-term deflections can be reduced by the addition of compression steel. Based on experimental studies of beams, the additional long-term deflections can be evaluated by multiplying the immediate elastic deflections by a factor λ.

$$\lambda = \frac{\xi}{1 + 50\varrho'}$$

where ϱ' is the value at midspan for simple and continuous spans, and at support for cantilevers. The time-dependent factor ξ for sustained loads varies with time. For sustained loads ξ is 2.0, 1.40, 1.20 and 1.00, when the load duration is 5 years, 1.4 years, 1.2 years and 1.0 years respectively (Ref. ACI Sec. 9.5.2.5).

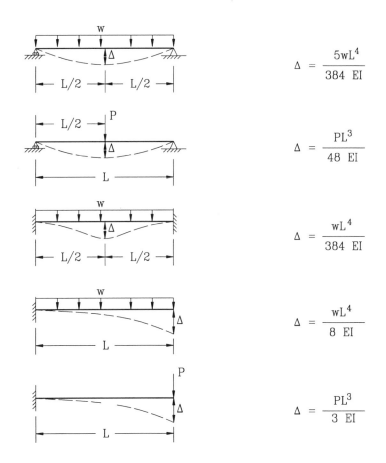

Figure 4.4   Deflection Factors

Modulus of Elasticity for Concrete   Sec. 8.5.1

For values of w_c between 90 and 155 lb/ft^3, $E_c = w_c^{1.5}\, 33\sqrt{f'_c}$ in (psi).

For normal weight concrete, E_c may be taken as $57,000\sqrt{f'_c}$.

Table 4.3 Minimum Thickness of Beams or One-Way Slabs
Unless Deflections Are Computed

Member	Minimum Thickness, h							
	Simply Supported		One End Continuous		Both Ends Continuous		Cantilever	
Solid One-Way Slabs	$\ell/23$	$\ell/25$	$\ell/27$	$\ell/30$	$\ell/32$	$\ell/35$	$\ell/11.5$	$\ell/12.5$
	$\ell/18$	$\ell/20$	$\ell/22$	$\ell/24$	$\ell/25.5$	$\ell/28$	$\ell/9$	$\ell/10$
Beams or Ribbed One-Way Slabs	$\ell/18$	$\ell/20$	$\ell/21$	$\ell/23$	$\ell/23.5$	$\ell/26$	$\ell/9$	$\ell/10$
	$\ell/14.5$	$\ell/16$	$\ell/17$	$\ell/18.5$	$\ell/19$	$\ell/21$	$\ell/7.5$	$\ell/8$

Key to Table:	Concrete Wt. (pcf)	$\rightarrow$	110 to 120	120 to 150
	$f_y = 40,000$ psi	$\rightarrow$	$\ell/23$	$\ell/25$
	$f_y = 60,000$ psi	$\rightarrow$	$\ell/18$	$\ell/20$

Span length, L, and thickness, h, must be in the same units.

Non-prestressed reinforced concrete:

Valid only for members not supporting or attached to partitions or other construction likely to be damaged by large deflections.

Note: For other than 60,000 psi, multiply the values given for

$f_y = 60,000$ psi by $(0.4 + f_y/100,000)$

Ref.: Notes on ACI 318-88 by PCA and later editions

Ref: ACI 318-89 for current specifications.

Maximum Allowable Deflection:

$$\Delta_{DD+LL} = \frac{L}{240}, \quad \Delta_{LL} = \frac{L}{360}$$

4.4   P. E. PROBLEMS

4.4.1   P. E. PROBLEM 1 — FLEXURAL DESIGN AND CRACK CONTROL

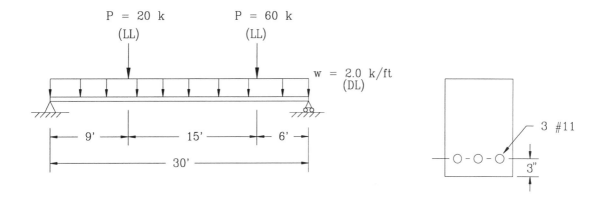

Fig. P4.4.1 (a) Simplified Beam

Required

Design for flexure only using ACI Code, USD, ϱ_{max}, $f'_c = 4$ ksi, and $f_y = 60$ ksi.

Use #11 bars and check the ACI Crack Control Provisions, assuming beam has exterior exposure.

Solution

A.   USD

The use of maximum steel percentages may not generate the ducility required in seismic areas. The depth of beam is usually smaller than that would be used for WSD. Smaller depth can cause deflection problems. The range of steel ratios to be used in the design is between:

$$\varrho \cong 0.375 \, \varrho_b$$

$$\varrho = 0.18 \, \frac{f'_c}{f_y}$$

Both equations provide practically the same value of ϱ for $f_y = 50,000$ psi or less.

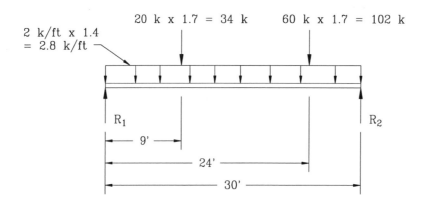

Fig. P4.4.1 (b) Loading Diagram

Factored Load, Shear and Moment Diagrams:

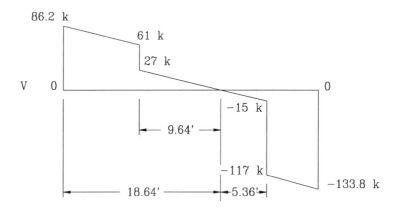

Fig. P4.4.1 (c) Shear Diagram

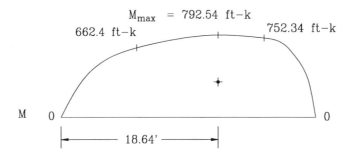

Fig. P4.4.1 (d) Moment Diagram

$$\sum M @ R_1 = 0 = 34 \times 9 + 24 \times 102 + (2.8 \times 30) \times \frac{30}{2} - R_2 \times 30$$

$$R_2 = \frac{4,014}{30} = 133.8 \text{ kip}$$

$$R_1 = 2.8 \times 30 + 34 + 102 - 133.8 = 86.2 \text{ kip}$$

Factored Design Moment:

$$M_{max} = 792.54 \text{ ft-kip}$$

We can design using formula or Design Handbook, Flexure 1.2:

$$\beta_1 = 0.85 \text{ for } f'_c = 4 \text{ ksi}$$

B. Balanced Condition

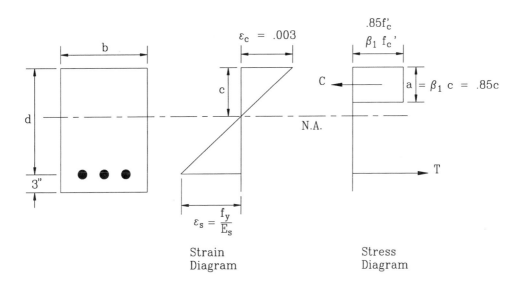

Fig. P4.4.1 (e) Strain, Stress Diagram

For balanced condition, the yield strains in both concrete and reinforcing steel must reach at the same time as shown in Fig. P4.4.1 (e)

$$c = d \frac{0.003}{0.003 + f_y/E_s} = d \frac{0.003}{0.003 + f_y/(29 \times 10^6)}$$

For equilibrium:

$$T = \varrho_b \text{ b d } f_y = C = b \beta_1 c \ 0.85 \ f'_c$$

$$= 0.85 \ f'_c \text{ b } \beta_1 \text{ d} \left(\frac{87,000}{87,000 + f_y}\right)$$

$$\varrho_b = \frac{\beta_1 \ 0.85 \ f'_c}{f_y} \times \frac{87,000}{87,000 + f_y}$$

$$\varrho_{max} = 0.75 \, \varrho_b$$

$$= \frac{0.75 \times 0.85 \times 0.85 \times 4}{60} \times \frac{87,000}{87,000 + 60,000}$$

$$= 0.0213 \cong 0.021$$

From equilibrium:

$$T = C$$

$$A_s \, f_y = 0.85 \, f'_c \, a \, b$$

$$a = \frac{A_s \, f_y}{0.85 \, f'_c \, b}$$

but $A_s = \varrho_{max} \, b \, d$

$$= 0.021 \times b \, d$$

Substituting:

$$a = \frac{0.021 \times d \times 60}{0.85 \times 4}$$

$$= 0.37d$$

$$\frac{M}{\phi} = A_s \, f_y \left(d - \frac{a}{2} \right)$$

Note: Try to keep the maximum value of "a" within d/3. If the value of "a" is more than 0.4d, chances are the steel will not yield.

Solve for d:

$$\frac{792.54 \times 12}{0.90} = 0.021 \times bd \left(d - \frac{0.37d}{2} \right) \times 60$$

This equation is in terms of b, d. Choose b/a ratio or b from practical formwork consideration.

Using b = 14 in

$$\frac{792.54 \times 12}{60 \times 0.90 \times 0.021 \times 14} = d^2 \left(1 - \frac{0.37}{2} \right)$$

$$d = 27.11 \qquad \text{say, } 27.0 \text{ in.}$$

$$A_s = \varrho_{max} \, bd$$

$$= 0.021 \times 14 \times 27$$

$$= 7.94 \text{ in.}^2 \quad \text{Use five \#11} \quad A_s = 7.80 \text{ in}^2$$

C. Alternately using the ACI Design Handbook, 318-89, Flexure 1.2:

For $f'_c = 4$ ksi   and $f_y = 60$ ksi

$$\varrho = \varrho_{max} = 0.0213$$

$$\omega = \varrho \frac{f_y}{f'_c} = 0.320$$

$$K_n = 935 \quad \text{and} \quad a_n = 3.65$$

$$F = \frac{bd^2}{12,000} = \frac{M_n}{K_n}$$

$$= \frac{792.5}{935} = 0.848$$

Try $b = 14.0$ in.

$$d = \left(\frac{0.848 \times 12,000}{14.0}\right)^{\frac{1}{2}} = 27.0 \text{ in.}$$

$$A_s = \frac{M_u}{a_n d} = \frac{792.5}{3.65 \times 27.75} = 7.84 \text{ in.}^2$$

Use 14-in. $\times$ 32-in. Beam with five #11 Bars ($A_s = 7.80$ in^2)

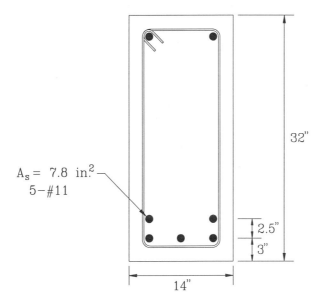

$A_s = 7.8$ in.^{2}
5−#11

32"

2.5"

3"

14"

Fig. P4.4.1 (f) Beam Detail

D. Check ACI 318-89, Crack Provisions (Sec. 10.6):

Check distribution of flexural reinforcement for beam using Eq. (10.4). Use exterior exposure z = 145 kip/in. and $f_y = 60$ ksi.

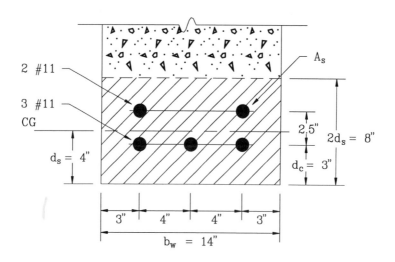

Fig. P4.4.1 (g) Beam Section

1. Locate centroid of reinforcement

$$d_s = \frac{3(1.56) \times 3.0 + 2(1.56) \times 5.5}{5(1.56)} = 4.0 \text{ in.}$$

2. Effective tension area of concrete

$$A_e = b_w (2 \times d_{c.g.}) = 14.0 \times 2(4.0) = 112 \text{ in.}^2$$

3. Equivalent number of #11 bars – Total area of reinforcement divided by the area of largest diameter bar.

$$m = \frac{3(1.56) + 2(1.56)}{1.56} = 5$$

4. $A = \dfrac{A_e}{m} = \dfrac{112}{5} = 22.4 \text{ in.}^2/\text{bar}$

5. $Z = f_s \sqrt[3]{d_c \, A}$

$$= 0.6 \times 60 \sqrt[3]{3.0 \times 22.4}$$

$$= 146 \text{ kip/in.} \cong 145$$

Say OK

The arrangement of reinforcement is adequate for exterior exposure using the ACI 318-89 approach.

Note:

Since the depth is found by using the maximum (0.75 A_b) steel percentage, this value is much less than the depths that we get using *reasonable* (economical) steel percentage. Shallow depth with high percentage of steel may cause deflection problems; also the ductility, thus obtained, may not be sufficient for high seismic areas.

4.4.2   P. E. PROBLEM 2 — SHORT AND LONG TERM DEFLECTiONS

A rectangular R.C. beam is simply supported and loaded with dead load of 1 kip/ft and live load of 2 kip/ft out of which 30% (LL) is assumed to be sustained. Furthermore, the following information is given:

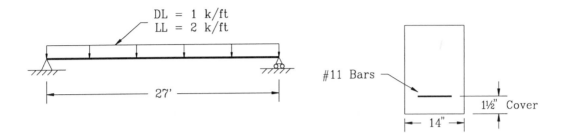

Fig. P4.4.2 (a) Crack Control on Beam

Given:

* $f'_c = 4$ ksi, $f_y = 60$ ksi

*   Clear cover $= 1\frac{1}{2}$ in.

*   Use rectangular stress block.

Find:

1.   Design section for ϱ_{max}.

2.   Check for #11 bars and find the required number of bars (use USD $\varrho = 0.75\, \varrho_b$).

3.   Check crack width internal exposure per ACI 318-89/92 Building Code.

4.   Instantaneous and long term deflection, if 30% of LL is sustained.

Comment:

For $\varrho = \varrho_{max}$, the section would be smaller than what is normally used for economically reasonable amount of steel and may have problems of excessive deflections besides having limited ductility and warning before failure. (Structural Engineers Association of California recommends $\varrho \leq 0.5\, \varrho_b \leq 0.025$ for seismic design.)

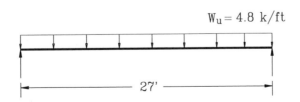

Fig. P4.4.2 (b)

DL = 1 kip/ft   (includes beam weight)

LL = 2 kip/ft

$$w_u = 1.4\,D + 1.7\,L = 1.4 \times 1 + 1.7 \times 2 = 4.8 \text{ kip/ft}$$

$$M_u = \frac{w_u\,L^2}{8} = \frac{4.8 \times 27^2}{8} = 437.4 \text{ ft-kip}$$

$$\rho_{max} = 0.75\,\rho_b$$

$$= 0.75 \times (0.85)\,(0.85)\,\frac{f'_c}{f_y} \times \left(\frac{87,000}{87,000 + 60,000}\right) \quad \text{ACI Eq. (8-1)}$$

$$= 0.321\,\frac{f'_c}{f_y} = 0.0214$$

$$M_u = \phi\,\rho\,f_y\,bd^2 \left(1 + 0.59\rho\,\frac{f'_c}{f_y}\right)$$

$$= 0.9 \times 0.321\,f'_c\,bd^2\,(1 - 0.59 \times 0.321) = 0.234\,f'_c\,bd^2$$

$$bd^2 = \frac{M_u}{0.234\,f'_c} = \frac{437.4 \text{ ft-kip} \times 12}{0.234 \times 4} = 5,607.69 \text{ in.}^3$$

$$d = \sqrt{\frac{5,607.69}{14}} = 20 \text{ in.} \qquad \text{Since, } b = 14 \text{ in.}$$

$$A_s = \rho\,b\,d = 0.0214 \times 14 \times 20 = 6.0 \text{ in.}^2$$

Use four #11 $A_s = 6.24 \text{ in.}^2$

Adjust d:

$$d = \frac{A_s}{\rho\,b} = \frac{6.24 \text{ in.}^2}{0.0214 \times 14} = 20.83 \text{ in. (minimum)}$$

Total depth of beam

$$\underset{\text{Clear}\atop\text{Cover}}{20.83 \text{ in.} + 0.375 + 1.5} + \frac{1.41}{2} = 23.4$$

#3 bar   #11 bar

If these beams are mass produced for precast concrete, h = 23.5 in. would be OK.

However, generally integer values are used for depth.

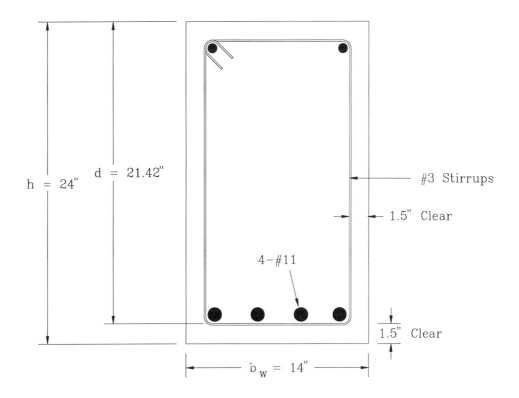

Fig. P4.4.2 (c) Concrete Beam Detail

Check to see if the beam web is wide enough for the above arrangement of the bars. The diameter of #11 bar = 1.4 in. Hence, the clear distance between bars = 1.41 in.

Minimum cover = 1.5 in.

Assume #3 stirrups $d_b = 0.375$

Minimum beam web required $= 2(1.5 + 0.375) + (4 + 3)(1.41)$

$$= 13.62 < 14 \text{ in. OK}$$

Use: 14 in. x 24 in. section with 4 − #11 bars.

Check for satisfactory crack width:

ACI Code permits using $f_s = 0.6\, f_y = 0.6 \times 60$

$$z = f_s \sqrt[3]{d_c\, A}$$

$$d_c = 1.5 \text{ in.} + 0.375 + 0.705 = 2.58 \text{ in.}$$

$$A = \frac{2.58 \times 2 \times 14}{4} = 18.06 \text{ in.}^2/\text{bar}$$

$$f_s = 0.6\, f_y = 36 \text{ ksi}$$

$$z = 36 \sqrt[3]{2.58 \times 18.06} = 129.5 < 145 < 175 \quad \text{OK}$$

Check deflection assuming d = 21.42 in., h = 24.0

$$E_c = 57,000 \sqrt{4,000} = 3.6 \times 10^6 \text{ psi}$$

$$E_s = 29 \times 10^6 \text{ psi}$$

$$n = \frac{29 \times 10^6}{3.6 \times 10^6} = 8$$

$$\varrho = \frac{A_s}{bd} = \frac{6.24}{14 \times 21.42} = 0.0208$$

$$f_r = 7.5 \sqrt{4,000} = 475 \text{ psi}$$

$$I_g = \frac{bh^3}{12} = \frac{14 \times (24.0)^3}{12} = 16,128$$

$$k = \sqrt{2\varrho n + (\varrho n)^2} - \varrho n$$
$$= \sqrt{2 (0.0208) (8) + (0.0208 \times 8)^2} - 0.0208 \times 8$$
$$= 0.434$$

$$kd = 0.434 (21.42) = 9.30 \text{ in.}$$

$$I_{cr} = \frac{b(kd)^3}{3} + nA_s (d - kd)^2$$
$$= \frac{14 \times (9.30)^3}{3} + 8 \times 6.24 (21.42 - 9.30)^2$$
$$= 11,086 \text{ in.}^4$$

$$M_{cr} = \frac{f_r I_g}{y_t} = \frac{475 \times 16,128}{\frac{24}{2} \times 1000} = 638.4 \text{ in.-kip}$$

$$M_{a(D+L)} = \frac{wL^2}{8} = \frac{3 \times 27^2}{8} \times 12 = 3,280.5 \text{ in.-kip}$$

Note: M_a is for service load only.

$$I_e = \left(\frac{M_{cr}}{M_a}\right)^3 I_g + \left[1 - \left(\frac{M_{cr}}{M_a}\right)^3\right] I_{cr}$$

$$= \left(\frac{638.4}{3,280.5}\right)^3 \times 16,128 + \left[1 - \left(\frac{638.4}{3,280.5}\right)^3\right](11,086)$$

$$= 11,123 \text{ in.}^4$$

Calculate immediate deflection:

$$\Delta = \frac{5wL^4}{384 \ EI} = \frac{5w \ (L \times 12)^4}{384 \ EI \times 12} = \frac{22.5wL^4}{EI}$$

$$\Delta_D = \frac{22.5 \ w_d \ L^4}{E_c \ I_e} = \frac{22.5 \times 1.0 \times 27^4}{3,600 \times 11,123} = 0.30 \ \text{in.}$$

$$\Delta_L = 0.30 \times \frac{2.0}{1.0} = 0.60 \ \text{in.}$$

Allowable immediate deflection due to live load:

$$\Delta = \frac{L}{360} = \frac{27 \times 12}{360} = 0.90 \ \text{in.} > 0.60 \ \text{in.}$$

Beam satisfies Table 9.5(b) for immediate live load deflection. Calculate long-term deflection, considering no compression steel,

$$\lambda = \frac{2.0}{1 + 50\varrho'} \qquad \qquad \text{ACI Eq. 9-10}$$

Because $\varrho' = 0, \lambda = 2.0$ as shown above

and consider 30% live load contribute to long term deflection.

$$w_{(D+0.3L)} = 1.0 + 0.3 \times 2.0 = 1.6 \ \text{kip/ft}$$

$$\Delta_{(D+0.3L)} = 0.30 \times \left(\frac{1.6}{1.0}\right) = 0.48 \ \text{in.}$$

$$\Delta_{LT} = \lambda \left(\Delta_{(d+0.3L)}\right) = 2.0 \times 0.48 = 0.96 \ \text{in.}$$

Additional live load deflection $\Delta_{0.7L} = 0.7 \times 0.60 = 0.42$ in.

$$\Delta_T = \Delta_{0.7L} + \Delta_{LT} = 0.42 + 0.96 = 1.38 \ \text{in.}$$

Assuming non-structural elements are not likely to be damaged by large deflection, the allowable deflection is given by:

$$\Delta = \frac{L}{240} = \frac{27 \times 12}{240} = 1.35 \ \text{in.} \cong \Delta T, \quad \text{say OK}$$

5

SHEAR

5.1 CODE DESIGN REQUIREMENTS (ACI 318-89/92, SEC. 11.1)

Required Shear Strength $\leq$ Design Shear Strength

$$V_u \leq \phi V_n \; = \; \phi(V_c + V_s)$$ ACI Eq. (11-1)

conc   steel

Where

V_u	=	Factored Shear Force
V_n	=	Nominal Shear Strength
	=	$V_c + V_s$ ACI Eq. (11-2)
ϕ	=	0.85

Refer to Figure 5.1 for location of critical shear forces at typical support conditions.

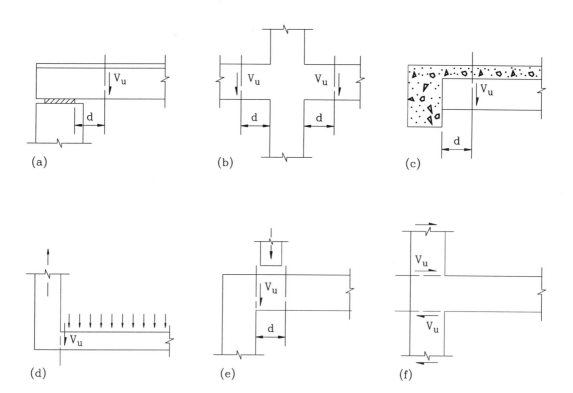

Figure 5.1 Typical Support Conditions for Locating Factored Shear Force, V_u

5.2   SHEAR STRENGTH PROVIDED BY CONCRETE FOR NON-PRESTRESSED MEMBERS

Simplified Method: $V_c = 2\sqrt{f'_c}\; b_w\, d$ ACI Eq. (11-3)

Detailed Method: $V_c = \left(1.9\sqrt{f'_c} + 2{,}500\varrho_w \dfrac{V_u\, d}{M_u}\right)b_w\, d$ ACI Eq. (11-6)

$\dfrac{V_u\, d}{M_u}$ not to exceed unity, $\varrho_w = \dfrac{A_s}{b_w d}$

Modification factors for concrete shear strength:

A. Concrete joists

Allow 10% increase in V_c Sec. 8.11.8

B. Lightweight concrete when f_{ct} is specified:

Use smaller of $\dfrac{f_{ct}}{6.7}$ for $\sqrt{f'_c}$ Sec. 11.2.1.1

C. Lightweight concrete when f_{ct} is not specified:

Use $0.75\,(2\sqrt{f'_c})$ for all lightweight concrete

or $0.85\,(2\sqrt{f'_c})$ for sand lightweight concrete   Sec. 11.2.1.2

5.3   SHEAR STRENGTH PROVIDED BY SHEAR REINFORCEMENT

For shear reinforcement perpendicular to the axis of member:

$$V_s = \frac{A_v f_y d}{s}$$ ACI Eq. (11-17)

For inclined stirrups used as shear reinforcement:

$$V_s = A_v f_y (\sin\alpha + \cos\alpha)\frac{d}{s}$$ ACI Eq. (11-18)

s = spacing of rebar

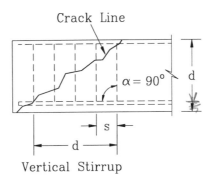

Vertical Stirrup

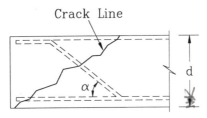

Inclined Stirrup

Figure 5.2 Beam Stirrups

Minimum shear reinforcement:

$$A_v = 50 \frac{b_w s}{f_y}$$ ACI Eq. (11-14)

Design yield strength not to exceed:

$$f_y = 60 \text{ ksi}$$ Sec. 11.5.2

Maximum shear strength:

$$V_s \text{ not to exceed} 8\sqrt{f'_c} \; b_w d$$ Sec. 11.5.6.8

5.4 MINIMUM SHEAR REINFORCEMENT SHALL BE PROVIDED WHEREVER

$$V_u > \frac{V_c}{2}$$

except

- slabs and footings
- joists
- small beams shallower than 10 in depth, 2½ times flange thickness, or $b_w/2$

5.5 SPACING LIMITS FOR SHEAR REINFORCEMENT PERPENDICULAR TO AXIS OF MEMBER

Maximums $= \dfrac{d}{2} \leq 24$ in.   if $V_s \leq 4\sqrt{f'_c}\, b_w\, d$ Sec. 11.5.4.1

Maximums $= \dfrac{d}{4} \leq 12$ in.   if $V_s \geq 4\sqrt{f'_c}\, b_w\, d$ Sec. 11.5.4.3

5.6 TORSIONAL MOMENT STRENGTH

Required Torsional Strength < Design Torsional Moment Strength

$$T_u \leq \phi T_n \qquad\qquad \text{ACI Eq. (11-20)}$$

where

T_u = Factored torsional moment

T_n = Nominal torsional moment strength

$\quad = T_c + T_s \qquad\qquad \text{ACI Eq. (11-21)}$

$\phi = 0.85$

Refer to Figure 5-2 for evaluation of $\Sigma x^2 y$ for typical member cross sections.

5.7 TORSIONAL MOMENT STRENGTH PROVIDED BY CONCRETE

$$T_c = \frac{0.8\sqrt{f'_c}\,\sum x^2 y}{\left[1 + \left(\frac{0.4 V_u}{C_t T_u}\right)^2\right]^{\frac{1}{2}}} \qquad\qquad \text{ACI Eq. (11-22)}$$

where $\quad C_t = \dfrac{b_w\, d}{\sum x^2 y}$

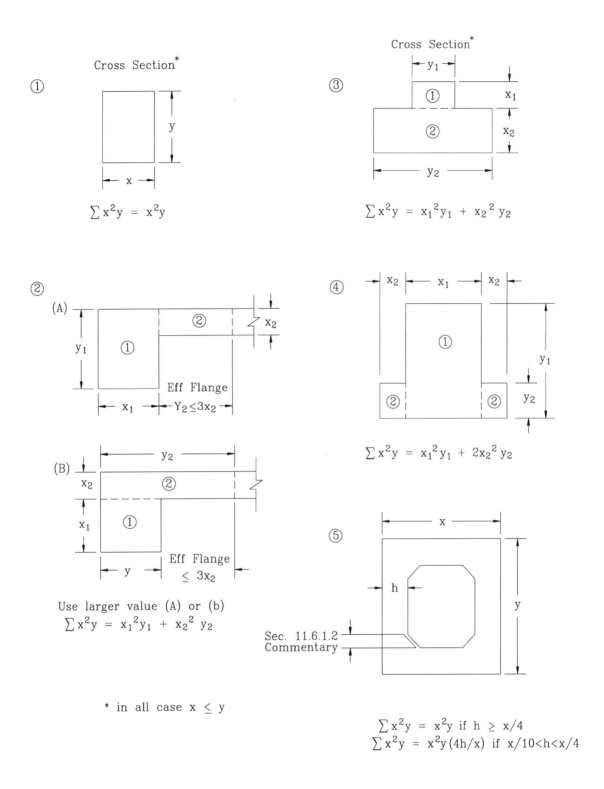

Figure 5.3 Evaluation of $\Sigma(x^2y)$

5.8   TORSIONAL MOMENT STRENGTH PROVIDED BY TORSION REINFORCEMENT

$$T_s = \frac{A_t \, \alpha_t \, x_1 \, y_1 \, f_y}{s}$$ ACI Eq. (11-23)

where

A_t = area of one leg of closed stirrup

$$\alpha_t = 0.66 + 0.33 \left(\frac{y_1}{x_1}\right) \le 1.50$$

and

α_t is called aspect ratio.

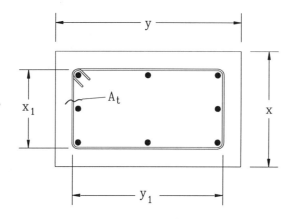

Figure 5.4 Torsional Stirrups

From ACI Sec. 11.6.8.1:

$$\text{Spacing} \quad s \le \frac{(x_1 + y_1)}{4}, \quad \text{or 12 in.}$$

5.9   LONGITUDINAL BARS

Longitudinal bars, A_ℓ, distributed evenly around the perimeter of the closed stirrups. A_ℓ shall be computed by Eq. (11-24) or Eq. (11-25) of ACI Code.

Table 5.1 Decision Table for Combined Shear and Torsion

Interaction Zone Fig. 14-1	Design Conditions	Code Reference	Required Reinforcement
(1)	1. $T_u < \varphi(0.5\sqrt{f_c'}\,\Sigma x^2 y)$ Torsion may be neglected 2. $V_u < \varphi V_c/2$	11.6.1 11.5.5.1	None
(2)	1. $T_u < \varphi(0.5\sqrt{f_c'}\,\Sigma x^2 y)$ Torsion may be neglected 2. $\varphi V_c > V_u > \varphi V_c/2$	11.6.1 11.5.5.3	Minimum Shear Only $A_v = \dfrac{50\,b_w s}{f_y}$ (11-14)
(3)	1. $T_u < \varphi(0.5\sqrt{f_c'}\,\Sigma x^2 y)$ Torsion may be neglected 2. $V_u > \varphi V_c$	11.6.1 11.5.6.1	Calculate shear only $A_v = \dfrac{(V_u - \varphi V_c)s}{\varphi f_y d}$ (11-17)
(4)	1. $T_u > \varphi(0.5\sqrt{f_c'}\,\Sigma x^2 y)$ 2. $V_u < \varphi V_c/2$	11.6.1 11.5.5.1	Minimum torsion only $2A_t = \dfrac{50\,b_w s}{f_y}$ (11-16) $A_\ell = $ Eq. (11-24) or (11-25)
(5)	1. $T_u > \varphi(0.5\sqrt{f_c'}\,\Sigma x^2 y)$ 2. $\varphi V_c > V_u > \varphi V_c/2$	11.6.1 11.5.5.5	Minimum combined shear and torsion $A_v + 2A_t = \dfrac{50\,b_w s}{f_y}$ (11-16) $A_\ell = $ Eq. (11-24) or (11-25)
(6) or (7)	1. $T_u > \varphi T_c$ 2. Torsional moment required for equilibrium 3. Design for T_u	11.6.9.1 11.6.2	Calculate combined shear and torsion $A_t = \dfrac{(T_u - \varphi T_c)s}{\varphi f_y \alpha_t x_1 y_1}$ (11-23) $A_\ell = $ Eq. (11-24) or (11-25)
(6)	1. $T_u > \varphi T_c$ 2. Uncracked section analysis for torsional moment T_u 3. Design for T_u or over design for cracking torque $T_u = \varphi(4\sqrt{f_c'}\,\Sigma x^2 y/3)$	11.6.9.1	Calculate combined shear and torsion $A_t = \dfrac{(T_u - \varphi T_c)s}{\varphi f_y \alpha_t x_1 y_1}$ (11-23) $A_\ell = $ Eq. (11-24) or (11-25)
(7)	1. $T_u > \varphi T_c$ 2. Redistribution of torsional moment after cracking 3. Design for cracking torque $T_u = \varphi(4\sqrt{f_c'}\,\Sigma x^2 y/3)$	11.6.9.1 11.6.3	Calculate combined shear and torsion $A_t = \dfrac{(T_u - \varphi T_c)s}{\varphi f_y \alpha_t x_1 y_1}$ (11-23) $A_\ell = $ Eq. (11-24) or (11-25)
(8)	1. $T_u > \varphi 5 T_c$	11.6.9.4	Increase member section

5.10 P. E. PROBLEMS

5.10.1 P. E. PROBLEM 1 — SHEAR DESIGN OF BEAM

Typical 14-in × 40-in concrete beams spanning 40 ft are spaced at 10 ft on center. Uniform vertical loads supported are:

Dead Load = 125 lb/ft^2

Live Load = 150 lb/ft^2

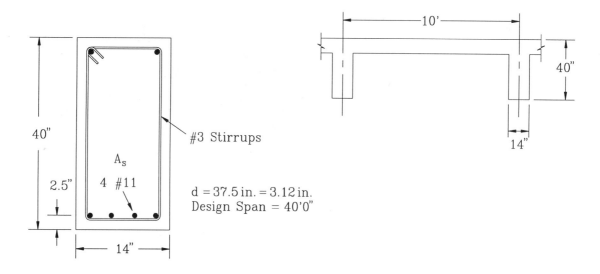

#3 Stirrups

A_s

4 #11

$d = 37.5$ in. $= 3.12$ in.
Design Span = 40'0"

Fig. P5.10.1 (a)

Criteria:

      Code: ACI 318

      Concrete: f'_c = 4000 psi

      Reinforcing: f_y = 40000 psi for stirrups

      Reinforcing: f_y = 60000 psi for main steel

Required:

A. Find maximum shear at critical distance from support.

B. Find shear capacity, V_c, based on concrete only.

C. Design stirrups.

Solution

A. Maximum shear at critical distance from support:

Factored load for 10-ft tributary:

$w_u = (1.4 \times 125 + 1.7 \times 150) \quad \times 10 = 4.30 \text{ k/ft}$

At support, $\qquad V_u = 4.30 \times 40 \quad \times 1/2 \qquad = 86.0 \text{ kip}$

At d = 3.12 ft, $\quad V_u = 86.0 - 4.30 \times 3.12 \qquad = 72.6 \text{ kip}$

Shear is critical at d, distance from support.

B. Shear capacity, V_c, based on concrete only:

$$V_c \;=\; 2\sqrt{f'_c}\,b_w d \qquad\qquad \text{ACI Eq. (11-3)}$$

$$=\; 2\sqrt{4,000} \times 14 \times 37.5$$

$$=\; 66.4 \text{ kip}$$

$$\phi V_c \;=\; 0.85 \times 66.4$$

$$=\; 56.4 \text{ kip}$$

C. Design of stirrups:

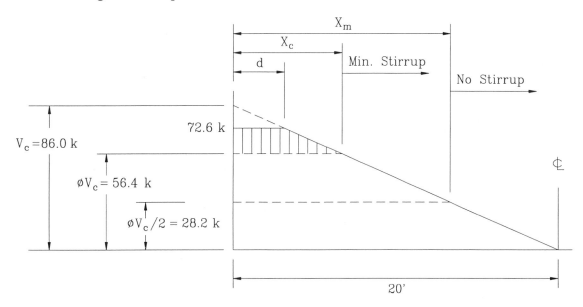

Fig. P5.10.1 (b) Shear Diagram

1. Determine x_c from support beyond which concrete can carry total shear:

$$x_c \;=\; \frac{V_u - \phi V_c}{V_u} \times 20.0 \;=\; \frac{86.0 - 56.4}{86.0} \times 20.0$$

$$=\; 6.88 \text{ ft}$$

2. Determine x_m from support over which minimum shear reinforcement must be provided (up to $V_u = 1/2 \, \phi \, V_c$):

$$x_m = \frac{V_u - \frac{1}{2}\phi V_c}{V_u} \times 20.0 = \frac{86.0 - 28.2}{86.0} \times 20.0$$

$$= 13.44 \text{ ft}$$

3. Determine required spacing of U, stirrups:

Required:

$$\phi V_s = V_u - \phi V_c \qquad\qquad \text{ACI Eq. (11-2)}$$

$$= 72.6 - 56.4$$

$$= 16.2 \text{ kip}$$

$$V_s = \frac{A_v \, f_y \, d}{s} \qquad\qquad \text{ACI Eq. (11-17)}$$

$$A_v = 2 \times 0.11 = 0.22 \text{ in}^2$$

Fig. P5.10.1 (c)

$$s = \frac{\phi \, A_v \, f_y \, d}{V_u - \phi V_c}$$

$$= \frac{0.85 \times 0.22 \times 40 \times 37.5}{16.2}$$

$$= 17.3 \text{ in.}$$

Maximum spacing $= \dfrac{d}{2} = \dfrac{37.5}{2} = 18.7 \text{ in.}$ \qquad ACI Sec. 11.5.4.1

Minimum $A_v = \dfrac{50 \, b_w \, s}{f_y}$

$$= \frac{50 \times 14 \times 12}{40,000} \qquad\qquad \text{ACI Eq. (11-4)}$$

$$= 0.21 \text{ in.}^2/\text{ft}$$

\#3 stirrups @ 12 in o.c. $= 0.22 \text{ in.}^2/\text{ft}$

No. of stirrups @ 12 in o.c. $= \dfrac{13.4}{1.0} = 13$

Use #3 stirrups: one @ 3 in., thirteen @ 12 in. and balance @ 18 in. from support.

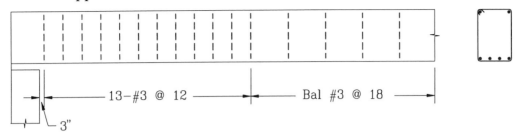

Fig. P5.10.1 (d)

4. Alternate solution for shear strength using formula:

$$V_c = \left(1.9\sqrt{f'_c} + 2,500\, \varrho_w \frac{V_u\, d}{M_u}\right) b_w\, d \qquad \text{ACI Eq. (11-6)}$$

$$d = 3.12 \text{ ft}$$

Moment at a distance, d, from the support is given as:

$$M_u = 86.0 \times 3.12 - 4.30 \times 3.12^2 \times \frac{1}{2}$$

$$= 247.4 \text{ ft-kip}$$

$$\varrho_w = \frac{A_s}{b_w\, d} = \frac{6.24}{14 \times 37.5} = 0.0119$$

$$V_c = \left(1.9\sqrt{4,000} + 2,500 \times 0.0119 \times \frac{72.6 \times 37.5}{247.4 \times 12}\right) \frac{14 \times 37.5}{1,000}$$

$$= (120.2 + 27.3) \frac{14.0 \times 37.5}{1,000}$$

$$= 77.4 \text{ kip} > 66.4 \text{ k obtained by previous equation}$$

$$V_s = \frac{A_v\, f_y\, d}{s} = \frac{0.22 \times 40 \times 37.5}{12} = 27.5 \text{ kip}$$

where

A_v = area of two legs of one # ⌐‾⌐ stirrup.

$$\phi V_n = 0.85\,(V_c + V_s) = 0.85\,(77.4 + 27.5)$$

$$= 89.2 \text{ kip}$$

Based on Eq. (11-3),

$$\phi V_n = 0.85\,(66.4 + 27.5) = 79.8 \text{ kip}$$

which is approximately 11% lower than the detailed shear equation.

5.10.2 P. E. PROBLEM 2 — SHEAR REINFORCEMENT OF BEAM

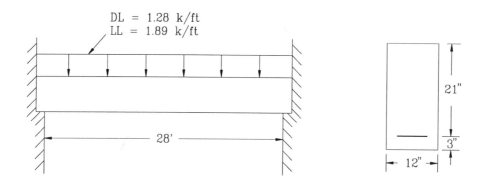

Fig. P5.10.2 (a) Beam for Shear Reinforcement

A 12-in. × 24-in. concrete beam spanning 28 ft-0 in. supports a uniform vertical service load of:

Dead Load   = 1.28 k/ft
Live Load   = 1.89 k/ft

Criteria:

• ACI Code 318-89/92

• Concrete: f'_c = 3,000 psi

• Reinforcing: f_y = 60,000 psi

Required:

A. Calculate shear reinforcement required.

B. Show limits of shear reinforcement.

C. Show spacing of # 3 stirrups.

Solution

1. Factor uniform load:

$$w_u = 1.4\,(1.28) + 1.7\,(1.89) = 5.00 \text{ kip/ft}$$

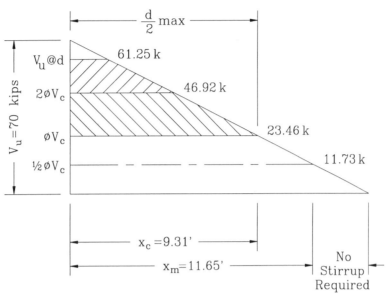

Fig. P5.10.2 (b) Shear Diagram

At support,

$$V_u = 5.00 \times 14 = 70.00 \text{ kip}$$

At d = 1.75 ft,

$$V_u = 70.00 - 5.00 \times 1.75 = 61.25 \text{ kip}$$

2. Shear strength of concrete:

$$V_c = 2\sqrt{f'_c}\ b_w\ d \qquad\qquad \text{ACI Eq. (11-3)}$$

$$= 2\sqrt{3,000} \times 12 \times 21.0 = 27.60 \text{ kip}$$

$$\phi V_c = 0.85 \times 27.60 = 23.46 \text{ kip} < V_u$$

3. Determine x_c from support beyond which concrete can carry total shear:

$$x_c = \frac{V_u - \phi V_c}{V_u} \times 14.0 = \frac{70.0 - 23.46}{70.0} \times 14.0 = 9.31 \text{ ft}$$

4. Determine x_m from support over which minimum shear reinforcement must be provided:

$$x_m = \frac{V_u - \frac{1}{2}\phi V_c}{V_u} \times 14.0 = \frac{70.0 - 11.73}{70.0} \times 14.0 = 11.65 \text{ ft}$$

5. Determine shear strength based on shear reinforcement:

Since V_u @ d = 61.25 kip,

$$V_{s_{required}} = (V @ d - \phi V_c)\frac{1}{\phi} = 44.5 \text{ k} < 4\sqrt{f'_c} \, b_w d = 2V_c$$

Maximum stirrup spacing,

$$\frac{d}{2} = 10.5 \text{ in.}$$

$V_u = 70 \text{ k}$

V_u @ d = 61.25 k

$\phi V_c = 23.5 \text{ k}$

Therefore,

$\phi V_s = 61.25 - 23.5 = 37.75 \text{ k}$

Spacing,

$$s = \frac{A_v f_y d}{\phi V_s} = \frac{0.22 \times 60 \times 21}{37.75} = 7.34 \text{ in.} \sim 7\frac{1}{2}$$

6. Since shear force varies linearly, stirrup spacing is inversely proportional to ratio of shear force.

$s_{max} = 10\frac{1}{2}$ in.

$A_v = 0.22$ in.^{2}

Corresponding,

$$\phi V_s = \frac{0.22 \times 60 \times 21}{10.5} = 26.40 \text{ kip}$$

$$V_u = 23.5 + 26.4 = 49.9\text{k} \sim 50 \text{ kip}$$

Distance from the support,

$$\frac{70 - 50}{70} \times 14 = 4 \text{ ft-0 in.}$$

From support to 4 ft-0 in., s = $7\frac{1}{2}$ in. c to c

Beyond 4 ft-0 in. to 11.65 ft, s = $10\frac{1}{2}$ in. c to c.

7. Check minimum shear reinforcement:

$$A_v = \frac{50\ b_w\ s}{f_y} = \frac{50 \times 12 \times 15}{60,000} = 0.15 < 0.22$$

8. Summary of shear reinforcement

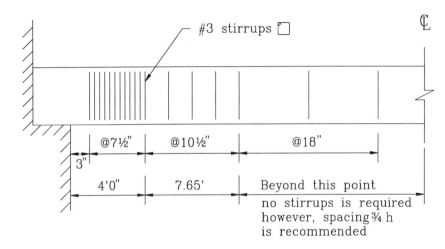

Fig. P5.10.2 (c) Stirrups Detail

6

DEVELOPMENT AND SPLICES OF REINFORCEMENT

Chapter 12 of the ACI Building Code 318-83 deals with development and splices of reinforcement. The emphasis in bond and anchorage calculations is on average values at ultimate rather than maximum values at a section because of the complexity of calculating experimentally observed values.

Many changes that are made in Chapter 12 of ACI 1983 Code are listed here. However, the changes in Chapter 12 of 1989 Code are significant. A summary of Chapter 12 is listed at the end of this chapter. Students are advised to read this chapter of the 1989 Code and the 1989 Code (Revision 1992). The 1992 revision of Chapter 12 (ACI-318-89) is not that significant.

Note from Editor:

Solutions to problems from several past examinations are given here. The codes continue to change. Sometimes, these changes are relevant due to technical findings but sometimes they are made purely to save some material costs, at the expense of complicating the code, so that concrete as a material can stay competitive with other construction materials like steel or masonry. It is not possible nor necessary to change the entire volume of review material every time the code changes. In addition, examination problems from past years may not have the information needed to solve problems using the new code. However, significant changes to solutions using new code are shown.

The solutions using older codes provides a historical perspective and readers may find these very useful in their practice while checking older buildings.

6.1   BASIC DEVELOPMENT LENGTH FOR TENSION REINFORCEMENT

The term *development length* may be defined as the length of embedment needed in concrete to develop the yield stress in the reinforcement. Formulas for the basic development length of tension reinforcement as stated in *ACI 318-83*, Sec. 12.2 are:

A. For #11 or small bars,

$$L_{db} \geq \begin{cases} 0.04 \dfrac{A_b\, f_y}{\sqrt{f'_c}} \\ 0.0004 d_b\, f_y \quad \leftarrow \text{ not in ACI 1989/92 Code} \\ 12 \text{ in.} \end{cases} \tag{6.1}$$

B. For #14 bars,

$$L_{db} = \begin{cases} \dfrac{0.085\, f_y}{\sqrt{f'_c}} \\ 12 \text{ in. } * \end{cases}$$

C. For #18 bars,

$$L_{db} = \begin{cases} \dfrac{0.11\, f_y}{\sqrt{f'_c}} \quad \leftarrow 0.125 \text{ in ACI 1989/92 Code} \\ 12 \text{ in. } * \end{cases}$$

*Except in computation of lap splices and development of web reinforcement in which:

d_b = nominal bar diameter (in.)

f'_c = ultimate strength in concrete (psi)

f_y = yield stress in steel (psi)

A_b = area of the bar (in^2)

The above basic development lengths need to be modified to take care of lesser bond strength, for example, in top bars due to compaction and increased water content.

Refer to Table 6.1 for tabulation of the basic development length for deformed bars in tension.

Table 6.1 "Basic" Development Length for Deformed Bars in Tension (inches)**

Bar Size	$f_y = 40,000$ psi Values of f'_c			$f_y = 60,000$ psi Values of f'_c		
	3000	4000	5000	3000	4000	5000
# 3	6.0*	6.0*	6.0*	9.0*	9.0*	9.0*
# 4	8.0*	8.0*	8.0*	12.0	12.0	12.0
# 5	10.0*	10.0*	10.0*	15.0	15.0	15.0
# 6	12.9	12.0	12.0	19.3	18.0	18.0
# 7	17.5	15.2	14.0	26.3	22.7	21.0
# 8	23.1	20.1	17.9	34.6	29.9	26.8
# 9	29.2	25.3	22.6	43.8	37.9	33.9
#10	37.1	32.1	28.7	55.7	48.1	43.1
#11	45.6	39.5	35.3	68.4	59.1	52.9
#14	62.1	53.8	48.1	93.1	80.6	72.1
#18	80.3	69.6	62.2	120.5	104.4	93.3

*Development length, L_d, must not be less than 12 in. (including modification factors)

**[ACI 318-83]

Table 6.2 "Basic" Development Length for Deformed Bars in Tension (inches)***

Bar Size	f'_c (Normal Weight Concrete), psi					
	3000	4000	5000	6000	8000	10,000
# 3	12.3	10.7	9.5	8.7	7.5	6.8
# 4	16.4	14.2	12.7	11.6	10.1	9.0
# 5	20.5	17.8	15.9	14.5	12.6	11.3
# 6	24.6	21.3	19.1	17.4	15.1	13.5
# 7	28.8	24.9	22.3	20.3	17.6	15.8
# 8	34.6	30.0	26.8	24.5	21.2	19.0
# 9	43.8	37.9	33.9	31.0	26.8	24.0
#10	55.6	48.2	43.1	39.3	34.1	30.5
#11	68.4	59.2	52.9	48.3	41.9	37.4
#14	93.1	80.6	72.1	65.8	57.0	51.0
#18	136.9	118.6	106.1	96.8	83.9	75.0

*** [ACI 318-89/92]

6.2   MODIFICATION FACTORS FOR BASIC DEVELOPMENT LENGTH FOR TENSION

Reinforcement:

As stated in Sec. 12.2.3 of *ACI 318-83 Code*, the basic development length may be multiplied by the applicable factor or factors to reflect either favorable or unfavorable conditions. These factors or modification factors are summarized in Table 6.3 below.

Table 6.3 Modification Factors for Basic Development Length
(Ref: ACI 318-83, Sections 12.2.3 and 12.2.4)

Condition	Multiplier*
1. Top bars; horizontal bars with more than 12 in. of concrete cast beneath them	1.4
2. Bars with f_y greater than 60,000 psi	$2 - \dfrac{60,000}{f_y}$
3. Lightweight concrete: (a) "All-lightweight" concrete "Sand-lightweight" concrete (linear interpolation may be used when partial sand replacement is used) or	1.33 1.18
(b) When average splitting tensile strength f_{cs} is specified, and concrete is proportioned according to ACI-4.2	$\dfrac{6.7\sqrt{f'_c}}{f_{cs}} \geq 1.0$
4. Wide lateral spacing of bars; at least 6 in. on center and at least 3 in from the side face of member	0.8
5. Excess reinforcement is used for flexural member	$\dfrac{\text{Required } A_s}{\text{Provided } A_s} \leq 1.0$
6. Bars enclosed within a spiral not less than 1/4 in diameter and not more than 4 in pitch	0.75

*See Section 6.10 for ACI 318-89 Code (Revision 1992) Multipliers.

It should be noted that the development length obtained by multiplying the basic development length of Eq. (6.1) by modification factors given in Table 6.2 shall not be less than 12 in. (Sec. 12.2.5).

6.3 DEVELOPMENT LENGTH FOR COMPRESSION REINFORCEMENT*

Given in Sec. 12.3, ACI 318-83 and 318-89/92 is the development length L_d for bars in compression:

$$L_{db} = \begin{cases} \dfrac{0.02\ f_y\ d_b}{\sqrt{f'_c}} \\ 0.0003\ f_y\ d_b \\ 8\ \text{in} \end{cases} \qquad \text{ACI Eq. (6.2)}$$

When the reinforcement area provided is greater than that required, or when the reinforcement is enclosed by spirals not less than 1/4-in. in diameter and not more than 4 in. pitch, the development length given in Eq. (6.2) may be reduced by the following factors:

$$\frac{\text{Required A}_s}{\text{Provided A}_s} \leq 1.0 \qquad\qquad \text{ACI Eq. (6.3a)}$$

With spirals, $0.75\ L_{db}$ $\qquad\qquad$ ACI Eq. (6.3b)

*No change in ACI 1989 Code.

Note: Lap splices for compression (minimum) = $0.0005\ f_y\ d_b$ for $f_y \leq 60{,}000$ psi.

6.4   MINIMUM EMBEDMENT LENGTH L_{dh}

Listed in Table 6.4 is equivalent embedment length, L_{dh} in inches, by standard hooks as per ACI 318-83 Code and ACI 318-89/92 Code.

Table 6.4 Standard Hooks — Equivalent Embedment Length
(See Section 12.4)

Bar Size	(a) General Use • Side Cover ≥ 2-1/2 in. • End Cover (90° hooks) ≥ 2 in.			(b) Special Confinement • Side Cover ≥ 2-1/2 in. • End Cover (90° hooks) ≥ 2 in. • Ties or Stirrups Spaced ≥ $3d_b$		
	$f'_c = 3000$	$f'_c = 4000$	$f'_c = 5000$	$f'_c = 3000$	$f'_c = 4000$	$f'_c = 5000$
# 3	6	6	6	6	6	6
# 4	8	7	6*	7	6	6*
# 5	10	9	8	8	7	6*
# 6	12	10	9	10	8	8
# 7	14	12	11	11	10	9
# 8	16	14	12	13	11	10
# 9	18	15	14	14	12	11*
#10	20	17	16	16	14	13*
#11	22	19	17	18	15	14*
#14	38	33	29	—	—	—
#18	50	43	39	—	—	—

* For 180 hooks normal to exposed surfaces, minimum embedment to provide 2 in. (recommended) cover to tail of hook:

Bar Size	#3	4	5	6	7	8	9	10	11	14	18
Embedment Length (in.)	6	7	7	8	9	10	12	13	15	19	25

6.5   BAR BENDS AND CUTOFFS

Stated in ACI 318-83, Sec. 12.11.3 (ACI 1989/92, Sec. 12.10.3)

> "Reinforcement shall extend beyond the point at which it is no longer required to resist flexure for a distance equal to the effective depth of the member or 12 bar diameters, whichever is greater, except at supports of simple spans and at free end of the cantilevers."

This permits bars to be cut off or bent when they are no longer needed, after extended a distance d or 12 bar diameters, whichever is greater.

Sec. 12.12.1 — Positive moment reinforcement (ACI 1989/92, Sec. 12.11.1)

"At least one-third the positive moment reinforcement in simple members and one-fourth the positive moment reinforcement in continuous members shall extend along the same face of the member into the support, and in beams at least 6 in."

Sec. 12.13.3 — Negative moment reinforcement (ACI 1989/92, Sec. 12.12.3)

"At least one-third the total reinforcement provided for negative moment at the support shall have an embedment length beyond the point of inflection not less than the effective depth of the member, 12d, or one-sixteenth of the clear span, whichever is greater."

Refer to Figures 6.1 through 6.5 for samples of flexural reinforcement cut off and anchorage of bars.

6.6 TENSION LAP SPLICES

When bar length required in structures exceed the length available, splices become necessary.

ACI 318-83 Code:

Sec. 12.15.2.1 (ACI 1989/92, Sec. 12.14.2.1)

"Lap splices shall not be used for bars larger than #11 except as provided in Section 15.8.6

Sec. 12.15.2.3 (ACI 1989/92, Sec. 12.14.2.3)

"Bars spliced by non-contract lap splices in flexural members shall not be spaced traversely farther apart than one-fifth the required length of lap splice length, nor 6 in."

Sec. 12.16.1 (ACI 1989/92, Sec. 12.15.1)

Has defined tension lap splices in three classes, A, B, and C. A summary of the requirements for these three classes appears in Table 6.5.

Minimum length of lap for tension lap splices shall be as required for Class A, B, or C splice, but not less than 12 in, where:

Class A splice ....$1.0 L_d$

Class B splice ....$1.3 L_d$

Class C splice ....$1.7 L_d$ (Not in ACI 1989/92)

Where L_d is the tensile development length for the specified yield strength f_y in accordance with Section 12.2.

Sec. 12.16.2

Lap splices of deformed bars and deformed wire in tension shall conform to Table 6.5.

Table 6.5 Tension Lap Splices
(Reference: ACI 318-83 Code, American Concrete Institute)

$\dfrac{A_s \text{ provided}}{A_s \text{ required}}$	Maximum percent of A_s spliced within required lap length		
	50	75	100
Equal to or greter than 2	Class A	Class A	Class B
Less than 2	Class B	Class C	Class C

6.7 COMPRESSION LAP SPLICES

ACI 318-83 Code:

Sec. 12.17.1 (ACI 1989/92, Sec. 12.16.1)

A. For $f'_c \geq 3000$ psi, $f_y \leq 60{,}000$ psi

$$\text{Lap} \geq \begin{cases} L_d & \text{(development length in comp.)} \\ 0.0005\ f_y\ d_b \\ 12\ \text{in} \end{cases} \quad \text{ACI Eq. (6.4a)}$$

B. For $f'_c \geq 3000$ psi, $f_y > 60{,}000$ psi

$$\text{Lap} \geq \begin{cases} L_d & \text{(development length in comp.)} \\ (0.0009\ f_y - 24)\ d_b \\ 12\ \text{in} \end{cases} \quad \text{ACI Eq. (6.4b)}$$

C. For $f'_c < 3000$ psi

$$\text{Lap} = \tfrac{4}{3}\text{Lap} \quad \text{(Eq. 6.4a or 6.4b)} \quad \text{ACI Eq. (6.4c)}$$

Sec. 12.17.2 — In tied compression members,

$$\text{Required Lap} > \begin{cases} 0.83 \times \text{Lap} & \text{(Eq. 6.2)} \\ 12\ \text{in} \end{cases} \quad \text{ACI Eq. (6.5a)}$$

Minimum area of ties $= 0.0015\ h\ s$,
where h = minimum dimension of compression member and s = spacing of tie.

Sec. 12.17.3 — In spiral compression members,

$$\text{Required Lap} > \begin{cases} 0.75 \times \text{Lap} & \text{(Eq. 6.2)} \\ 12\ \text{in} \end{cases} \quad \text{ACI Eq. (6.5b)}$$

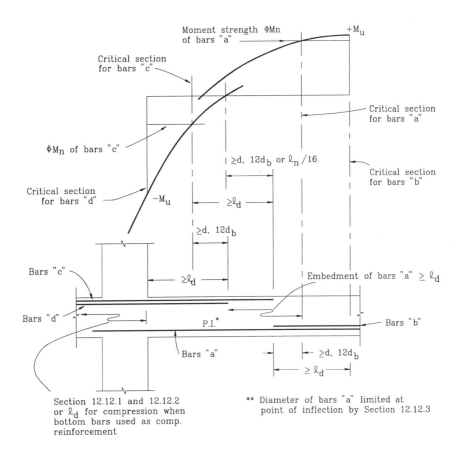

Figure 6.1 Development of Flexural Reinforcement in a Typical Continuous Beam
(ACI 318-83)

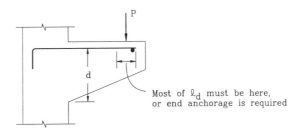

Figure 6.2 Special Member Largely Dependent on End Anchorage
(ACI 318-83)

Sec. 12.12 Development of Positive Moment Reinforcement

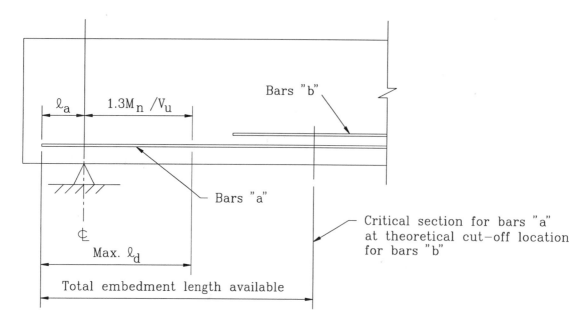

Figure 6.3 Development Length Requirements at Simple Support
(ACI 318-83)

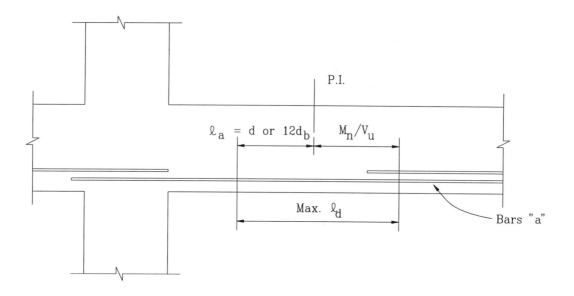

Figure 6.4 Concept for Determining Maximum Size Bar "a" at Point of Inflection
(ACI 318-83)

Sec. 12.13   Development of Negative Moment Reinforcement

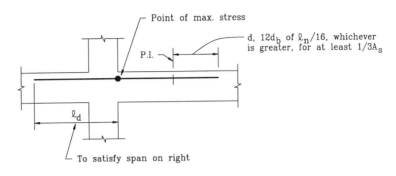

Figure 6.5 Anchorage into Adjacent Beam
(ACI 318-83)

(Usually such anchorage becomes part of adjacent beam reinforcement.)

6.8   EXAMPLE PROBLEM

6.8.1   EXAMPLE PROBLEM 1 — DEVELOPMENT LENGTHS IN A CANTILEVER BEAM

Determine the minimum development length required for four #6 bars placed in the tension zone of a 10 in. × 20 in. cantilever beam with effective depth of 18 in. The beam is made of lightweight concrete. The longitudinal steel area required to resist the bending moment is 1.6 in.^{2} f_y = 40 ksi, f'_c = 4 ksi.

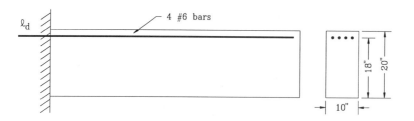

Fig. P6.8.1 (a) Cantilever Beam

* A_s (required) = 1.6 in.^{2}
* A_s provided = 4 (0.44) = 1.76 in.^{2}
* A_b = Area of each bar = 0.44 in.^{2}

$$d_b = \frac{6}{8} = 0.75 \text{ in.}$$

$\begin{bmatrix} \text{Notice the different} \\ \text{equations used in} \\ \text{ACI 1989/92 Code} \end{bmatrix}$

$$L_{db} = 0.04 \, A_b \frac{f_y}{\sqrt{f'_c}}$$
$$= 0.04 \times 0.44 \times \frac{40,000}{\sqrt{4,000}} = 11.13 \text{ in.}$$

$\begin{bmatrix} \text{only this equation} \\ \text{is not changed in} \\ \text{ACI 31-1989/92 Code} \end{bmatrix}$

L_{db} (11.13 in.) shall be multiplied by applicable factors in 12.2.3.1 to 12.2.3.5

$$L_{db} = 0.0004 \, d_b \, f_y = 0.0004 \times 0.75 \times 40,000 = 12.0 \text{ in.}$$

L_d must be greater than 12 in. $\boxed{L_d \geq 12 \text{ in.}}$

Therefore, basic development length = 12 in.

$$L_{db \text{ min}} = 0.03 \times d_b \times \frac{f_y}{\sqrt{f'_c}} \qquad \text{(ACI Code 1989/92)}$$
$$= 0.03 \times 0.75 \times \frac{40,000}{\sqrt{4,000}} = 14.23$$
$$L_{db} = 14 - 1/4 \text{ in. controls}$$

Modification factors for the present conditions are:

A. Top bar L_d $=$ 12×1.4 $=$ 16.8 in.

$$L_d = 14\frac{1}{4} \times 1.3 = 18.5 \text{ in.} \qquad \text{(ACI Code 1989/92)}$$

B. Reinforcement provided being more than calculated requirement

$$16.8 \left(\frac{1.6}{1.76}\right) = 15.27 \text{ in.}$$

$$L_d = 18.5 \times \frac{1.6}{1.76} = 16.8 \text{ in.} \qquad \text{(ACI Code 1989/92)}$$

C. Lightweight concrete 1.18 to 1.33 times 15.18 in.

Using 1.18 (15.18 in.) $=$ 17.91 in.

$L_d = 16.8 \times 1.3$ $=$ 21.9 in.   (ACI Code 1989/92)

Use L_d minimum of 18 in.   (ACI Code 1983)

Use L_d minimum of 22 in.   (ACI Code 1989/92)

6.9   P. E. PROBLEM

6.9.1   P. E. PROBLEM 1 — CANTILEVER BEAM DESIGN

If the service dead load = 400 lb/ft (including beam weight), live load = 1000 lb/ft, f'_c = 3000 psi, f_y = 40,000 psi and seven #3 stirrups are provided at 12 in. spacing from the face of support, does the beam meet the latest available ACI requirements for bending and shear?

Explain and Justify.

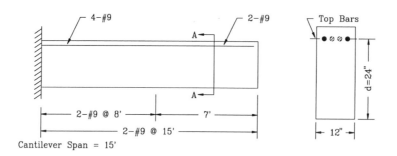

Fig. P6.9.1 (a) Cantilever Beam

Solution

(Use ACI Code 318-89/92)

1. Factored uniform load:

$$w_u = 1.4\,(0.40) + 1.7\,(1.00) = 2.26 \text{ k/ft}$$

At support, $V_u = 2.26 \times 15 \text{ ft} = 33.90 \text{ k}$

At d = 2.0 ft, $V_u = 33.9 - 2.26 \times 2 = 29.4 \text{ k}$

At support, $M_u = 2.26 \times 15^2 \times \dfrac{1}{2} = 254 \text{ ft-k}$

The ultimate shear and moment diagrams are both plotted in Fig. P6.9.1 (b).

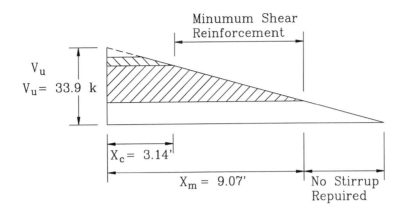

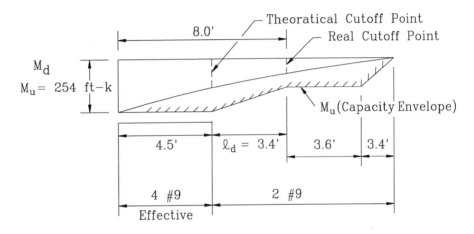

Fig. P6.9.1 (b) Shear and Moment Diagram

2. Shear strength of concrete:

$$V_c = 2\sqrt{f'_c}\ b_w\ d \qquad\qquad \text{Eq.} \quad (11\text{-}3)$$

$$= 2\sqrt{3{,}000} \times 12 \times 24 = 31.5 \text{ kip}$$

$$\phi V_c = 0.85 \times 31.5 = 26.8 \text{ kip} < V_u \quad \text{Need stirrups}$$

3. Determine X_c from support beyond which concrete can carry total shear:

$$X_c = \frac{V_u - \phi V_c}{V_u} \times 15.0 = \frac{33.9 - 26.8}{33.9} \times 15.0 = 3.14 \text{ ft}$$

4. Determine x_m from support over which minimum shear reinforcement must be provided:

$$X_m = \frac{V_u - \frac{1}{2}\phi V_c}{V_u} \times 15.0 = 9.07 \text{ ft}$$

Beyond 9.07 ft from the support, no stirrup is theoretically required.

5. Determine shear strength based on shear reinforcement:

$$V_s = \frac{A_v\ f_v\ d}{s} \qquad\qquad \text{Eq. (11-17)}$$

$$= \frac{0.22 \times 40,000 \times 24}{12} = 17.6 \text{ kip} < 4\sqrt{f'_c}\ b_w d$$

$$A_v = 2 \times 0.11 = 0.22 \text{ in.}^2$$

Fig. P6.9.1 (c)

Maximum stirrup spacing = d/2 = 12 in.

$$V_n = V_c + V_s = 31.5 + 17.6 = 49.1 \text{ kip}$$

$$\phi V_n = 0.85 \times 49.1 = 41.7 \text{ kip} > V_u = 29.4 \text{ kip} \qquad \text{OK}$$

6. Check minimum shear reinforcement:

$$A_v = \frac{50\ b_w\ s}{f_y} = \frac{50 \times 12 \times 12}{40,000} \qquad\qquad \text{Eq. (11-14)}$$

$$= 0.18 \text{ in.}^2 < 0.22$$

7. Considering the first stirrup spaced at 3-in. from support,

$$\text{number of stirrups at 12 in. o.c.} = 1 + \frac{9.07}{1.0} = 10.07$$

The 7 stirrups provided are not adequate to satisfy the minimum area of shear reinforcement, use ten #3 stirrups at 12 in. c to c. Beyond 9.07 ft provide stirrups of 18 in. c to c.

Developmental Lengths

1. Basic development length for No. 9 bars:

$$L_d = \frac{0.04\ A_b\ f_y}{\sqrt{f'_c}} \qquad\qquad \text{ACI Sec. 12.2.2}$$

$$= \frac{0.04 \times 1.0 \times 40,000}{\sqrt{3,000}}$$

$$= 29.2 \text{ in.}$$

[Only this equation is not changed in ACI 318−89]

or

$$L_d = 0.0004 \times d_b \, f_y$$
$$= 0.0004 \times \frac{9}{8} \times 40,000$$
$$= 18.0 \text{ in.}$$

or

$$L_d = 12 \text{ in.}$$

but using ACI 318-89:

$$L_{d\,min} = 0.03 \times d_b \times \frac{f_y}{\sqrt{f'_c}} = 0.03 \times \frac{9}{8} \times \frac{40,000}{\sqrt{3,000}} = 24.6 \text{ in.}$$

2. Development length for top bars:

$$L_d = 1.4 \times 29.2 = 40.9 \text{ in.} \sim 3.5 \text{ ft} \qquad\qquad \text{Sec. 12.2.3}$$
$$L_d = 1.3 \times 29.2 = 38 \text{ in.} \qquad\qquad\qquad \text{(ACI 318-89/92)}$$

3. Check top steel cutoff:

Required moment at $8 - 3.5 = 4.5$ ft from support

$$M_u = 2.26 \times \frac{(10.5)^2}{2} = 124.6 \text{ ft-kip}$$

Allowable (with two #9) $M_u \cong A_s \, (a_n \, d)$
$$= 2.0 \, (2.77 \times 24.0)$$
$$= 133 \text{ ft-kip} > 124.6 \text{ OK}$$

Quick Check:

Two #9: $A_s = 2 \text{ in.}^2$ $\qquad$ $F_u = 2 \times 40 = 80 \text{ k}$

$$a = \frac{80}{0.85 \times 3 \times 12} = 1.96 \text{ in.}$$

$$M_u = 0.9 \times 80 \times \left(24 - \frac{1.96}{2}\right) \frac{1}{12}$$

$$= 138 \text{ ft-k} > 124.6 \qquad \text{OK}$$

Since the top steels furnished are fully developed at the cut-off point minus the development length, the section as reinforced is adequate.

6.10   DISCUSSION OF CHAPTER 12 ACI CODE 318-89 (REVISED 1992)

Significant changes are made in Chapter 12 of ACI-318-89 code, with respect to 1983 codes. Major items are listed briefly. However, students are advised to review Chapter 12 thoroughly.

- Basic Development Length, ℓ_{db}
- Development Length, ℓ_d
- Determine ℓ_{db} for different cases (e.g., tension, compression, lap, etc.)

Apply various multiplying factors (e.g., top bar, epoxy coating, etc.) to ℓ_{db} for the determination of ℓ_d.

Limit $\sqrt{f'_c} = 100$ maximum.

Note: f'_c and f_y in psi.

The following sections describe the provisions of Chapter 12. The section numbers relate to ACI Code section numbers.

12.2   DEVELOPMENT OF DEFORMED BARS AND WIRES IN TENSION

1. Determine basic development length ℓ_{db} Section 12.2.2

   #11 or smaller or deformed wire $\qquad \ell_{db} = 0.04\ A_b \dfrac{f_y}{\sqrt{f'_c}}$

   #14 bar $\qquad \ell_{db} = 0.085 \dfrac{f_y}{\sqrt{f'_c}}$

   #18 bar $\qquad \ell_{db} = 0.125 \dfrac{f_y}{\sqrt{f'_c}}$

2. Modify development length using the following multipliers:

   Section 12.2.3.1   *multiplier*= 1.00 provided conditions stated in (a), (b), (c), (d) are satisfied,

   (a) Bars in beams and columns with
   1. Minimum cover given in 7.7.1
   2. Transverse reinforcements satisfying tie requirements of 7.10.5 or stirrup requirement of 11.5.4, 11.5.5.3, and
   3. Clear spacing > 3 d_b Clear cover > 2 d_b

(b) Minimum cover Section (7.7.1)

Enclosed transverse reinforcement $\quad A_{tr} \geq \dfrac{d_b \, s \, N}{40}$ (12-1)

[where N is the number of bars being spliced or developed at a critical section.]

(c) Bars at inner layer of slab sand walls, clear spacing $\geq 3 \, d_b$

(d) Any bar, cover $\geq 2 \, d_b$, clear spacing $\geq 3 \, d_b$

(e) Section 12.2.3.2 $\quad$ *multiplier* $= 2.00$

Where, cover $\leq \, d_b$, clear spacing $< \, 2 \, d_b$

(f) Section 12.2.3.3 $\quad$ *multipliers* $= 1.4$

When not included 12.2.3.1, 12.2.3.2

3. Modify development length using the following multipliers:

Section 12.2.3.4 $\quad$ *multiplier* $= 0.80$

For #11 bars or smaller, with clear spacing $\geq 5 \, d_b$ and clear cover $\geq 2.5 \, d_b$

Section 12.2.3.5 $\quad$ *multiplier* $= 0.75$

For spiral reinforcement of #2 @ 4 in. maximum or ties @ 4 in. maximum

4. *Or* use *minimum* length given in

Section 12.2.3.6 $\quad\quad \ell_d = 0.03 d_b \dfrac{f_y}{\sqrt{f_c'}}$

(See Figure 12.2.3, Figure 12.2.3.1, 12.2.3.4 of ACI Code Commentary)

5. Modify for top bars (12 in. or more concrete below) as given in

Section 12.2.4.1 $\quad$ *multiplier* $= 1.30$

6. Section 12.2.4.2 Lightweight concrete (Lt.wt. Con.) $\quad \left[\begin{array}{l} \textit{multiplier} \;=\; 1.3 \\ \textit{multiplier} \;=\; 6.7\dfrac{\sqrt{f_c'}}{f_{ct}} \\ \qquad\quad \geq \; 1.00 \end{array} \right.$

7. Modify for Epoxy Coated bar as given in

Section 12.2.4.3 $\quad$ *multiplier* $= 1.5$

For clear cover $\leq \, 3 \, d_b$, clear spacing $\leq \, 6 \, d_b$

For all other conditions $\quad$ *multiplier* $= 1.2$

Product of item 5 and item 6 $\leq$ item 7

8. Modify for excess reinforcement as given in

Section 12.2.5 $multiplier = \dfrac{\text{As required}}{\text{As provided}}$

Example

$\ell_d = \ell_{db} \times 1.4 \ @ \ (2) \times 1.3 \ @ \ (5) \times 1.5 \ @ \ (7) \geq (4)$

$\ell_d = \ell_{db} \times 1.00 \ @ \ (2) \times 0.75 \ @ \ (3) \times \dfrac{\text{As required}}{\text{As provided}} \ @ \ (8) \geq (4)$

12.3   DEVELOPMENT OF DEFORMED BARS IN COMPRESSION

12.3.1. ℓ_d min $=$ 8 in.

12.3.2   Basic development length ℓ_{db}

$\ell_d = multiplier \ (1) \times multiplier \ (2) \times \text{etc.} \times .....\ell_{db}$

12.3.3 $\ell_{db} = 0.02 \times d_b \times \dfrac{f_y}{\sqrt{f_{c,}}} \geq 0.0003 \ d_b \ f_y$

12.3.3   Multiplying factors are,

   12.3.3.1 Excess reinforcement $multiplier = \dfrac{\text{As required}}{\text{As provided}}$

   12.3.3.2 Spirals and Ties $multiplier = 0.75$

12.4   DEVELOPMENT OF BUNDLED BAR

12.4.1   Increase development length by
          20% for 2 bar bundle, i.e., $multiplier = 1.2$
          33% for 3 to 4 bar bundle, i.e., $multiplier = 1.3$

12.5   DEVELOPMENT OF STANDARD HOOKS IN TENSION

12.5.1   Development length ℓ_{dh} [See Table 6.4]

          $\ell_{dh} \geq 8 \ d_b$

12.5.2   Basic development length for hook bar $\ell_{hb} = \dfrac{1200 \ d_b}{\sqrt{f'_c}}$

          $\ell_{dh} = multiplier \times \ell_{hb}$

12.5.3 The multipliers are,

12.5.3.1   For different f_y $multiplier = \dfrac{f_y}{60000}$

12.5.3.2   For #11 or smaller bar and concrete cover not less than 2½ in.

$$multiplier = 0.70$$

12.5.3.3   For #11 or smaller bar inside ties or
stirrups spaced $\le 3\ d_b$ $multiplier = 0.8$

12.5.3.4   Excess reinforcement $multiplier = \dfrac{\text{As required}}{\text{As provided}}$

12.5.3.5   Light weight concrete $multiplier = 1.3$

12.5.3.6   Hooked bars with epoxy coating $multiplier = 1.2$

Note that the total ℓ_{dh} is cumulative.

$$\ell_{dh} = \ell_{hb} \times 0.7 \times 0.8 \times 1.3$$

$$\ell_{dh} = \ell_{hb} \times 0.7 \times 0.8 \ \text{ and so on}$$

12.5.4   For discontinuous ends with cover less than 2 1/2 inch enclose hooks within ties and stirrups

(See Figure 12.5.1, Figure 12.5.4 of ACI Code Commentary)

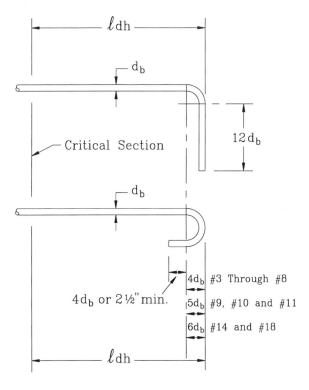

Fig. 12.5.1 Hooked-bar Details for Development of Standard Hooks

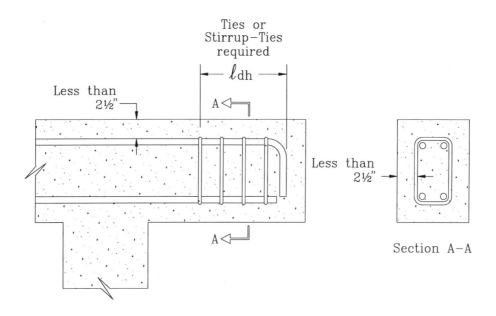

Fig. 12.5.4 Concrete Cover per 12.5.4

12.6   MECHANICAL ANCHORAGE

Mechanical anchorage is permitted if it can develop (with additional embedment length if required) the strength of reinforcement.

12.7   DEVELOPMENT OF WELDED DEFORMED WIRE FABRIC IN TENSION

12.7.1 ℓ_d = multiplier × ℓ_{db}. Measured from critical section with first cross wire at 2 in. from critical section. Apply modification factors of Section 12.2. ℓ_d = 8.0 in. minimum.

12.7.2 ℓ_{db} = 0.03 × d_b $(f_y - 20000)/\sqrt{f'_c}$

   or $0.20 \dfrac{A_w}{S_w} \dfrac{f_y}{\sqrt{f'_c}}$ whichever is largest.

12.8   DEVELOPMENT OF WELDED PLAIN WIRE FABRIC IN TENSION

ℓ_d = multiplier × ℓ_{db}
$\geq$ 6 in.

Measured from critical section. With two cross wires first cross wire is 2 inches from critical section. Modify per Section 12.2.

$$\ell_{db} = 0.27 \frac{A_w}{S_w} \frac{f_y}{\sqrt{f'_c}}$$

(See Figure 12.7, Figure 12.8 of ACI Code Commentary)

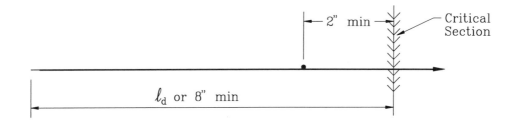

Fig. 12.7 Development of Welded Deformed Wire Fabric

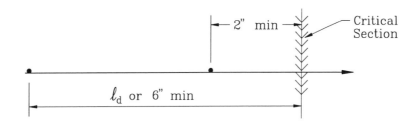

Fig. 12.8 Development of Welded Prestressing Strand

12.9   DEVELOPMENT OF PRESTRESSING STRAND

(See ACI Code)

12.10   DEVELOPMENT OF FLEXURAL REINFORCEMENT (GENERAL)

- Critical section is the section with maximum stress.
- Extend flexural reinforcement beyond the critical section
- The distance = beam depth d or = 12 d_b whichever is larger.
- Provide sufficient embedment length.
- Confine flexural reinforcement within additional stirrup when terminated within tension zone.
- Check shear at cutoff point.
- Provide adequate anchorage for non-prismatic members (see Code Commentary and Figures 12.10.2 and 12.10.6).

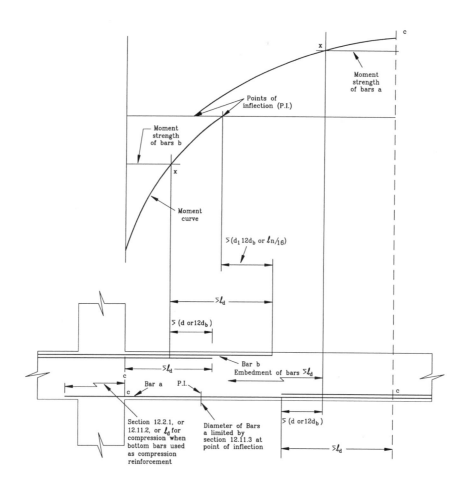

Fig. 12.10.2 Development of Flexural Reinforcement
in a Typical Continuous Beam

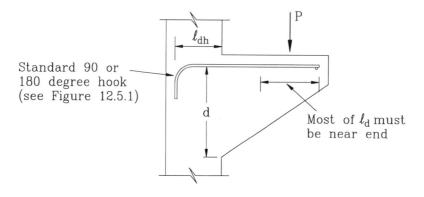

Fig 12.10.6 Special Member Largely Dependent on Reinforcement

12.11 DEVELOPMENT OF POSITIVE MOMENT REINFORCEMENT

12.11.1 Extend reinforcements minimum 6 inches into the support.

    a)   Minimum 1/3 of all positive reinforcement for simple members

    b)   Minimum 1/4 of all positive reinforcement for continuous members

12.11.2 For lateral load resting frames the positive reinforcement must be anchored to develop the full strength of the bar (f_y).

12.11.3 $\ell_d = \dfrac{M_n}{V_u} + \ell_a$

where

    M_n = Nominal Moment Strength $[A_s f_y (d - a/2)]$

    V_u = Factored Shear Force

    ℓ_a = Depth of Beam or 12 d_b, whichever is larger (see Figure 12.11.3 of ACI Code Commentary).

Choose bar diameter such that the above equation is satisfied.

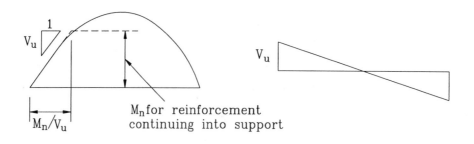

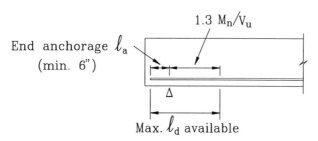

Note: The 1.3 factor is usable only if the reaction
confines the ends of the reinforcement.

(a) Maximum size of bar at simple support

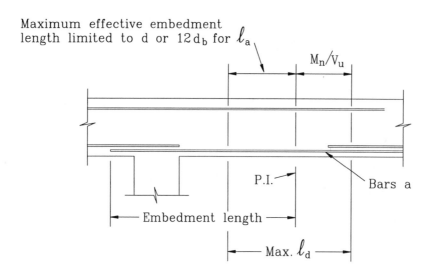

(b) Maximum size of Bar "a" at point of inflection

Fig. 12.11.3 Concept for Determining Maximum Bar Size per 12.11.3

12.12   DEVELOPMENT OF NEGATIVE MOMENT REINFORCEMENT

- All negative reinforcement shall be anchored by embedment length, hook or mechanical anchorage.

- For embedment length, see Sections 12.1 and 12.10.

- At least one-third of the reinforcement must extend beyond the inflection point by a distance equal to the depth of the beam or $12 \, d_b$ (see Figure 12.12 of ACI Code Commentary).

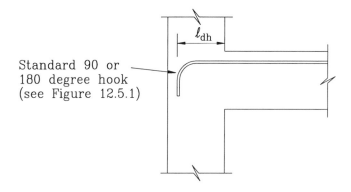

(a) Anchorage into exterior column

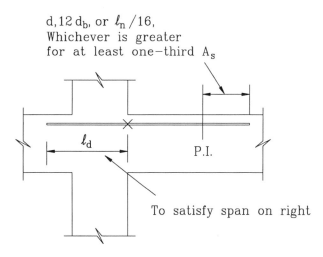

(b) Anchorage into adjacent beam

Fig. 12.12 Development of Negative Moment Reinforcement

12.13   DEVELOPMENT OF WEB REINFORCEMENT

12.13.1 Extend web reinforcement close to the tension and compression surface.

12.13.2 Anchor single leg, simple U or multiple U as follows:

With Standard hook around the longitudinal reinforcement.

For #5 bars and D31 wire, and smaller, #6, #7, and #8 with $f_y = 40,000$ psi or less, standard hook around the longitudinal bar plus embedment between mid height of the member to the outside end of hook equal to or greater than the following recommended values,

For #6, #7, and #8 with f_y greater than 40,000 psi or less (see code 12.13.2.2)

For welded plain wire fabric U stirrup (see Code)

For welded plain wire fabric single leg (see Code)

12.13.3 Each bend of stirrup shall have full development length beyond mid depth of beam.

12.13.4 Longitudinal bent bars shall have full development length beyond mid depth of beam.

12.13.5 If a pair of U-Stirrups form a closed unit, spliced length must be 1.3 l_d.
In members at least 18 in. deep, if $A_b f_y$ not more than 9000 lb per leg shall be considered adequate if the stirrups extend full depth.

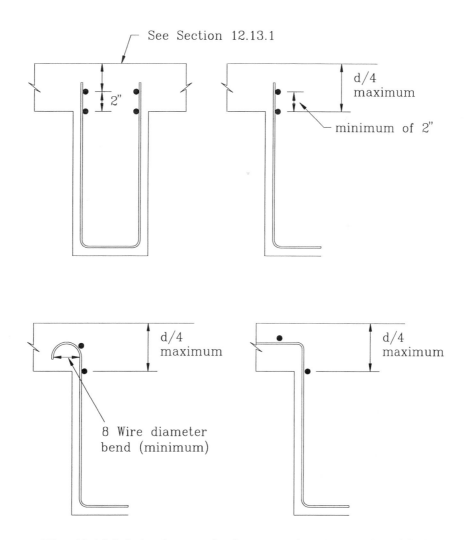

Fig. 12.13.2.3 Anchorage in Compression Zone of Welded
Smooth Wire Fabric U-Stirrups

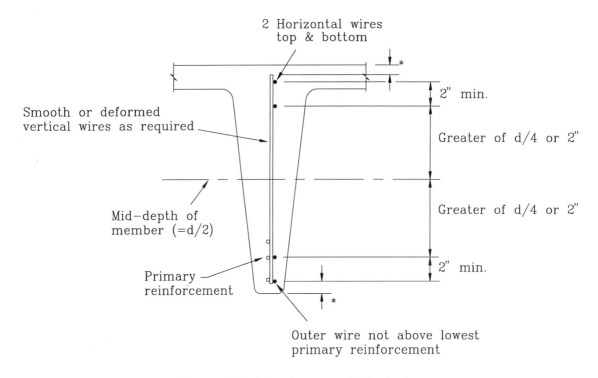

Fig. 12.13.2.5 Anchorage of Single Leg
Welded Wire Fabric Shear Reinforcement

12.14 SPLICES OF REINFORCEMENT

12.14.2 Lap splices for #11 or smaller bars only

Lap splices for bundled bars must be modified.

Maximum distance for non-contact lap splices is 6 inches.

12.14.3 Welding of splices shall be done as per AWSD 1.4

Welding must develop 125% yield strength (f_y) of the bar.

Mechanical connection must develop 125% yield strength (f_y) of the bar.

12.15 SPLICES OF DEFORMED BARS AND DEFORMED WIRE IN TENSION

12.15.1 Minimum tension lap 12 in.

or if required, Class A or Class B, whichever is greater.

Class A Splice 1.0 ℓ_d , Class B Splice 1.3 ℓ_d

12.15.2 Use Class B splice unless

a)   Area of reinforcement is twice that required.

b)   Only one-half or less bars are spliced

For welded and mechanical splices, see Code (see Figure 12.15.1 of ACI Code)

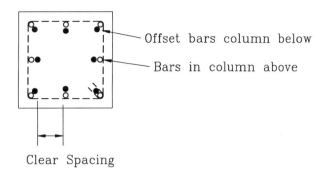

Clear Spacing

(a) Offset Column Bars

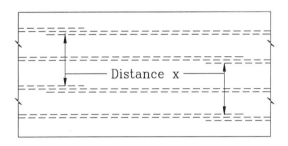

(b) Staggered Splices

Fig. 12.15.1 Clear Spacing of Spliced Bars

12.16   SPLICES OF DEFORMED BARS IN COMPRESSION

12.16.1-3   Length of Compression Lap Splice,

$0.0005\, f_y\, d_b$ for $f_y \leq 60000$ psi

$0.0009\, (f_y - 24)\, d_b$ for $f_y > 60000$ psi

Minimum length 12 in.

Increase length by $\frac{1}{3}$ if $f'_c < 3000$ psi

Development length of larger bar controls the lap length. Bar size #14 and #18 may be lapped with smaller bars.

12.16.4   For end bearing splice, see Code.

12.17   SPECIAL SPLICE REQUIREMENTS FOR COLUMNS

12.17.2.2

- Class A splicing if tensile stress is less than 0.5 f_y.
- Class A splicing if half of the bars or less are spliced and staggered by ℓ_d.
- Otherwise Class B splicing
- If splices confined by sufficient ties *multiplying factor* = 0.83
- Minimum splice length 12 inches
- If splices confined by spirals, *multiplying factor* = 0.75

12.17.3 Welded or mechanical splices in columns (see Sections 12.14.3.3 and 12.14.3.4)

12.17.4 End bearing splice in compression is permissible (see Code).

12.18   SPLICES OF WELDED DEFORMED WIRE FABRIC IN TENSION

Minimum length of lap of deformed wire fabric, 1.3 ℓ_d or 8 inches, whichever is larger
Distance between cross ties minimum 2 inches. (See Figure 12.18 of ACI Code)

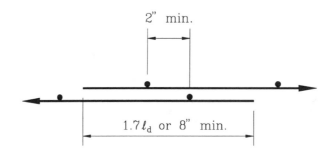

(a) Section 12.18.1

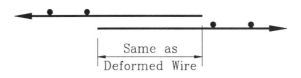

(b) Section 12.18.2

Fig. 12.18 Lap Splices of Deformed Fabric

12.19 SPLICES OF WELDED PLAIN WIRE FABRIC IN TENSION

Minimum length of lap between outermost cross ties 1.5 ℓ_d or 6 in. whichever is larger.

If the area of steel is twice that required min. lap length is 2 in.

(See Figure 12.19, ACI Code)

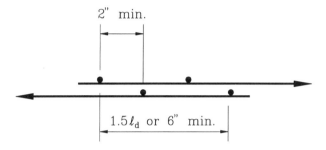

2" min.

$1.5\ell_d$ or 6" min.

(a) Section 12.19.1

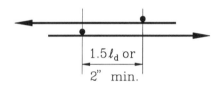

$1.5\ell_d$ or

2" min.

(b) Section 12.19.2

Fig. 12.19 Lap Splices of Smooth Fabric

6.11   DESIGN AIDS — ACI 318-89 CODE (REVISION 1992)

(*Reference*: Notes on ACI 318-89 by PCA)

SUMMARY

Development length l_d for deformed bars and deformed wire in tension must be computed as the product of the basic development length l_{db} of Section 12.2.2 and the applicable modification factors of Sections 12.2.3 through 12.2.5, but l_d must not be less than 12 in.:

$$l_d = l_{db} \times \text{(applicable modification factors)} \geq 12 \text{ in.}$$

The following step-by-step procedure illustrates proper application of the various modification factors to determine development length l_d.

Calculations	Code Reference
(1) Determine basic development length l_{db}	12.2.2
(2) Multiply l_{db} by applicable factor for bar spacing, cover, and enclosing transverse reinforcement	12.2.3.1-12.2.3.3
(3) Multiply by factor for wide bar spacing if applicable.	12.2.3.4
(4) Multiply by factor for closely spaced spirals or ties, if applicable	12.2.3.5
(5) Check minimum development length	12.2.3.6
(6) Multiply by factor if top reinforcement	12.2.4.1
(7) Multiply by factor if lightweight concrete	12.2.4.2
(8) Multiply by factor if epoxy-coated reinforcement after checking that the product of multipliers for top bar and epoxy coating does not exceed 1.7	12.2.4.3
(9) Multiply by ratio if excess reinforcement	12.2.4.4
(10) Check minimum development length ≥ 12 in.	12.2.1

Table 4-1—Summary of Modification Factors for Development Length in Tension

Item	Parameters	Value of Modification Factor	Corresponding Code Section
1	Bar spacing, cover, and enclosing transverse reinforcement	1.0, 2.0, or 1.4	12.2.3.1 to 12.2.3.3
2	Bar spacing	0.8	12.2.3.4
3	Enclosing transverse reinforcement	0.75	12.2.3.5
4	Top bar effect*	1.3	12.2.4.1
5	Lightweight aggregate concrete	1.3 or $6.7 \sqrt{f_c'}/f_{ct} \not< 1$	12.2.4.2
6	Epoxy coated bars*	1.5 or 1.2	12.2.4.3
7	Excess reinforcement	A_s required / A_s provided	12.2.5

*The product of items 4 (top bar effect) and 6 (epoxy coated bars) need not exceed 1.7.

Table 4-2—"Basic" Tension Development Length l_{db} (inches) for Grade 60 Bars*

Bar Size	f_c' (Normal Weight Concrete), psi					
	3000	4000	5000	6000	8000	10,000
#3	4.8	4.2	3.7	3.4	3.0	2.6
#4	8.8	7.6	6.8	6.2	5.4	4.8
#5	13.6	11.8	10.5	9.6	8.3	7.4
#6	19.3	16.7	14.9	13.6	11.8	10.6
#7	26.3	22.8	20.4	18.6	16.1	14.4
#8	34.6	30.0	26.8	24.5	21.2	19.0
#9	43.8	37.9	33.9	31.0	26.8	24.0
#10	55.6	48.2	43.1	39.3	34.1	30.5
#11	68.4	59.2	52.9	48.3	41.9	37.4
#14	93.1	80.6	72.1	65.8	57.0	51.0
#18	136.9	118.6	106.1	96.8	83.9	75.0

*Development length, l_d (including all applicable modification factors), must not be less than 12 in.

Table 4-3—Transverse Reinforcement $A_{tr}/s = Nd_b/40$

Bar Size	Number of Bars Being Developed					
	N = 2		N = 3		N = 4	
	A_{tr}/s (in.^{2}/in.)	Stirrups or ties	A_{tr}/s (in.^{2}/in.)	Stirrups or ties	A_{tr}/s (in.^{2}/in.)	Stirrups or ties
#5	0.031	#4@13	0.047	#4@8.5	0.063	#4@6
#6	0.038	#4@10.5	0.056	#4@7	0.075	#4@5
#7	0.044	#4@9	0.066	#4@6	0.088	#5@7
#8	0.050	#4@8	0.075	#4@5	0.100	#5@6
#9	0.056	#4@7	0.085	#5@7	0.113	#5@5.5
#10	0.064	#4@6	0.095	#5@6.5	0.127	#5@5
#11	0.071	#4@5.5	0.106	#5@6	0.141	#5@4.5

Table 4-4—Minimum Basic Development Length $\ell_{db} = 0.03d_b f_y/\sqrt{f'_c}$ (inches) for Grade 60 Bars

Bar Size	f'_c (Normal Weight Concrete), psi					
	3000	4000	5000	6000	8000	10,000
#3	12.3	10.7	9.5	8.7	7.5	6.8
#4	16.4	14.2	12.7	11.6	10.1	9.0
#5	20.5	17.8	15.9	14.5	12.6	11.3
#6	24.6	21.3	19.1	17.4	15.1	13.5
#7	28.8	24.9	22.3	20.3	17.6	15.8
#8	32.9	28.5	25.5	23.3	20.1	18.0
#9	37.1	32.1	28.7	26.2	22.7	20.3
#10	41.7	36.1	32.3	29.5	25.6	22.9
#11	46.3	40.1	35.9	32.8	28.4	25.4
#14	55.6	48.2	48.2	39.3	34.1	30.5
#18	74.2	64.2	57.5	52.4	45.4	40.6

(a) Clear Spacing $\geq 6d_b$ and
Cover $\geq 3d_b.\ldots l_d = 1.2\,l_{db}*$

Table 4-5—Multiples of Bar Diameter d_b for Bar Spacing and Cover Check (Sections 12.2.3 and 12.2.4)

Bar	d_b	$2d_b$	$2.5d_b$	$3d_b$	$5d_b$	$6d_b$
#3	0.375	0.75	0.94	1.13	1.89	2.25
#4	0.500	1.00	1.25	1.50	2.50	3.00
#5	0.625	1.25	1.56	1.88	3.13	3.75
#6	0.750	1.50	1.88	2.25	3.75	4.50
#7	0.875	1.75	2.19	2.63	4.38	5.25
#8	1.000	2.00	2.50	3.00	5.00	6.00
#9	1.128	2.25	2.81	3.38	5.63	6.75
#10	1.270	2.54	3.18	3.81	6.35	7.62
#11	1.410	2.82	3.53	4.23	7.06	8.46
#14	1.693	3.39	—	5.08	—	10.16
#18	2.257	4.51	—	6.77	—	13.54

(b) Clear Spacing $< 6d_b$ or
Cover $< 3d_b.\ldots l_d = 1.5\,l_{db}*^+$

Table 4-6—Minimum Beam Width (inches)

Bar Size	Number of Bars in Single Layer					
	3		4		5	
	'83 Code*	'89 Code**	'83 Code	'89 Code	'83 Code	'89 Code
#5	8.5	10.3	10.1	12.8	11.8	15.3
#6	8.8	11.3	10.5	14.3	12.3	17.3
#7	9.0	12.3	10.9	15.8	12.8	19.3
#8	9.3	13.3	11.3	17.3	13.3	21.3
#9	9.8	14.3	12.0	18.8	14.3	23.3
#10	10.3	15.4	12.9	20.5	15.4	25.6
#11	10.9	16.5	13.7	22.2	16.5	27.8

*To satisfy larger of one-bar diameter (d_b) or 1 in. clear spacing
**To satisfy three-bar diameters ($3d_b$) clear spacing

Table 4-7—"Basic" Compression Development Length l_{db} (inches) for Grade 60 Bars

Bar Size	f_c' (Normal Weight Concrete), psi		
	3000	4000	≥ 4444*
#3	8.2	7.1**	6.8**
#4	11.0	9.5	9.0
#5	13.7	11.9	11.3
#6	16.4	14.2	13.5
#7	19.2	16.6	15.8
#8	21.9	19.0	18.0
#9	24.7	21.4	20.3
#10	27.8	24.1	22.9
#11	30.9	26.8	25.4
#14	37.1	32.1	30.5
#18	49.4	42.8	40.6

*For $f_c' \geq 4444$ psi, minimum basic development length $0.0003d_b f_y$ governs; for Grade 60, $l_d = 18d_b$.

**Development length l_d (including applicable modification factors) must not be less than 8 in.

Table 4-8—Basic Development Length l_{hb} of Standard Hooks for Grade 60 Bars

Bar Size	f_c' (Normal Weight Concrete), psi					
	3000	4000	5000	6000	8000	10,000
#3	8.2	7.1	6.4	5.8	5.0	4.5
#4	11.0	9.5	8.5	7.7	6.7	6.0
#5	13.7	11.9	10.6	9.7	8.4	7.5
#6	16.4	14.2	12.7	11.6	10.1	9.0
#7	19.2	16.6	14.8	13.6	11.7	10.5
#8	21.9	19.0	17.0	15.5	13.4	12.0
#9	24.7	21.4	19.1	17.5	15.1	13.5
#10	27.8	24.1	21.6	19.7	17.0	15.2
#11	30.9	26.8	23.9	21.8	18.9	16.9
#14	37.1	32.1	28.7	26.2	22.7	20.3
#18	49.4	42.8	38.3	35.0	30.3	27.1

$$l_{hb} = 1200\, d_b / \sqrt{f_c'}$$

Embedment Length ℓ (in.) for Grade 60 Bars

Bar Size	Concrete Compressive Strength, f'_c psi					
	3000	4000	5000	6000	8000	10,000
#6	11.5	10.0	8.9	8.1	7.0	6.3
#7	13.4	11.6	10.4	9.5	8.2	7.4
#8	15.3	13.3	11.9	10.8	9.4	8.4

Minimum depth of member (in.) to accommodate #6, #7, and #8 in Grade 60

Min. Cover and Exposure	Bar Size	3000	4000	5000	6000	8000	10,000
1½ in. Interior Exposure	#6	26	23	21	20	17	16
	#7	30	27	24	22	20	18
	#8	34	30	27	25	22	20
2 in. Exterior Exposure	#6	27	24	22	21	18	17
	#7	31	28	25	23	21	19
	#8	35	31	28	26	23	21

7

SLABS

7.1 ONE-WAY SLABS

One-way slabs are reinforced to resist flexural stresses in only one direction. One-way slabs in bending may be designed as beams. The width of the slabs is traditionally taken as one foot (or 12 in.). Typical moment coefficients and reinforcement arrangements of a continuous one-way slab are shown in Figure 7.1.

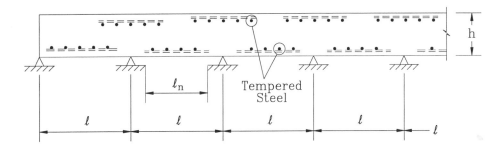

Typical Rebar Placement for One-way Slab

(a)

Temperature Steel: 0.0018 bh for f_y = 60 ksi or more; and 0.002 bh for f_y = 40 ksi

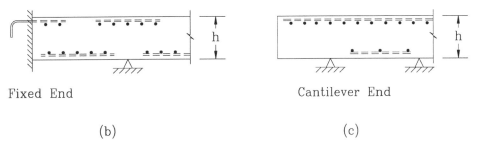

Fixed End

Cantilever End

(b)   (c)

Figure 7.1 One-Way Slab

7.2   TWO-WAY SLABS

These slab systems are reinforced for flexure in more than one direction and built with or without beams between supports. These slabs are usually subdivided into column strips and middle strips. Generally beams are avoided to save forming cost.

The common types of two-way slabs are:

- A.   Two-way flat plates — recommend for shorter spans
- B.   Two-way flat slabs — recommend for larger spans and heavy shear around columns
- C.   Two-way waffle slabs — recommend for large spans and very heavy loads

Refer to ACI 318-89/92, Section 13.6 for Direct Design Method. Note that the absolute sum of positive and negative factored moments in each direction shall not be less than:

$$M_o = \frac{w_u \, L_2 \, (L_n)^2}{8} \qquad\qquad \text{ACI Eq. (13-3)}$$

Distribution of longitudinal and transverse moments and the distribution of reinforcements are shown in Figure 7.2.

Use Equivalent Frame Method (ACI 318-89/92, Section 13.7) where Direct Design Method is not applicable.

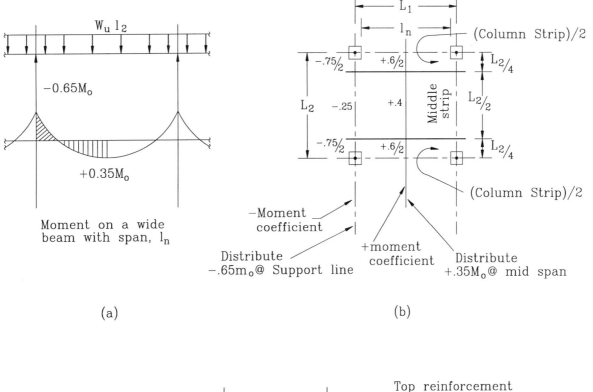

(a)

(b)

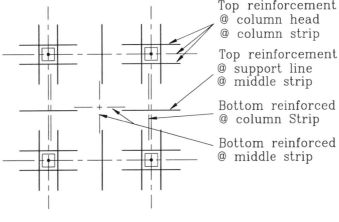

Reinforcement placement
at a typical bay

(c)

Direct Design Method
Typical Interior Bay of a Flat Plate

Figure 7.2 Two-Way Slab

7.3   TWO-WAY SLAB SHEAR STRENGTH

$$V_u \; < \; \phi \, V_n \; = \; \phi \, V_c \; + \; V_s \qquad\qquad \text{ACI Eq. (11-1)}$$

$$V_c \; = \; \left(2 \; + \; \frac{4}{\beta_c}\right) \sqrt{f'_c} \; b_o \, d \qquad\qquad \text{ACI Eq. (11-36)}$$

$$V_c \; = \; \left(\frac{\alpha_s \, d}{b_o} \; + \; 12\right) \sqrt{f'_c} \; b_o \, d$$

$$< \; 4 \sqrt{f'_c} \; b_o \, d$$

Shear force around a typical interior column is given by:

$$V_{UR} \; = \; w_u \left[L_1 \times L_2 - (c_1 + d) \times (c_2 + d)\right]$$

$$\phi V_c \; \geq \; V_{UR}$$

where

β_c = Ratio of long side to short side

b_o = Perimeter of critical section for slab shear

c_1 and c_2 are the sides of the column

d = depth of the slab − concrete cover

α_s = 40, 30, 20 for interior, edge, corner column respectively.

7.4   APPROXIMATE METHOD FOR CONTINUOUS BEAMS

Approximate method for continuous beams and one-way slab may be used in accordance with ACI Section 8.3.3, which has been reproduced below.

> 8.3.3 – In lieu of a more accurate method of frame analysis, the following approximate moments and shears may be used in design of continuous beams and one-way slabs (slabs reinforced to resist flexural stresses in only one direction), provided:
>
> (a) There are two or more spans,
>
> (b) Spans are approximately equal, with the larger of two adjacent spans not greater than the shorter by more than 20 percent,
>
> (c) Loads are uniformly distributed, and
>
> (d) Unit live load does not exceed 3 times unit dead load.
>
> (e) Members are prismatic

Positive moment

End spans
Discontinuous end
unrestrained . . . . $w_u \ell_n^2 / 11$
Discontinuous end integral
with support . . . . $w_u \ell_n^2 / 14$

Interior spans . . . . $w_u \ell_n^2 / 16$

Negative moment at exterior face
of first interior support

Two spans. . . . . $w_u \ell_n^2 / 9$

More than two spans . . . . $w_u \ell_n^2 / 10$

Negative moment at other faces
of interior supports . . . . $w_u \ell_n^2 / 11$

Negative moment at face of all
supports for:

Slabs with spans not
exceeding 10 ft; and
Beams where ratio of
sum of column stiff-
nesses to beam stiff-
ness exceeds eight at
each end of the span . . . . $w_u \ell_n^2 / 12$

Negative moment at interior face
of exterior support for members built integrally with
supports

Where support is a spandrel
beam . . . . $w_u \ell_n^2 / 24$

Where support is a column . . . . . . $w_u \ell_n^2 / 16$

Shear in end members at face of
first interior support . . . . $1.15 \, w_u \ell_n / 2$

Shear at face of all other
supports . . . . $w_u \ell_n / 2$

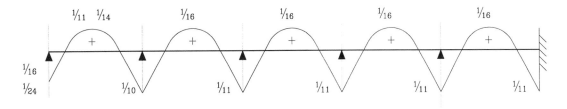

Figure 7.3 Approximate Moments and Shears in Slabs

7.5   EXAMPLE PROBLEMS

7.5.1   EXAMPLE PROBLEM 1 — ONE-WAY CONTINUOUS SLAB

Determine required reinforcement for a one-way slab continuous over two or more equal spans. Clear span, $L_n = 18$ ft. Assume slab is 6 in. thick.

Use $f'_c = 4000$ psi and $f_y = 60,000$ psi

Service loads: $w_D = 75$ psf (Dead Load)

$w_L = 50$ psf (Live Load)

Solution

1. Compute required moment strengths using the approximate moment analysis permitted by Section 8.3.3. Design for an end span.

$$w_u = 1.4 \times 75 + 1.7 \times 50 = 190 \text{ psf}$$

Note: See Table 4.3:

$$\frac{18 \times 12}{28} = 7.7 \text{ in. } > 6 \text{ in. (Assumed slab thickness)}$$

Diffusion check will be necessary.

$$+ M_u = \frac{w_u L_n^2}{14} = \frac{0.190 \times (18)^2}{14} = 4.40 \text{ ft-kip/ft}$$

$$- M_u = \frac{w_u L_n^2}{10} = \frac{0.190 \times (18)^2}{10} = 6.16 \text{ ft-kip/ft}$$

2. Assume 6-in. thick slab.

Note: Any standard manual, handbook, or textbook may be used to obtain ϱ from K_a. Be consistent with units.

$$d = 6.0 - 0.75 - 0.50 = 4.75 \text{ in.}$$

$$F = \frac{bd^2}{12,000} = \frac{12 \times 4.75^2}{12,000} = 0.0226$$

$$+ K_u = \frac{4.40}{0.0226} = 195$$

$$- K_u = \frac{6.16}{0.0226} = 272$$

$$+ A_s = \frac{4.40}{4.35 \times 4.75} = 0.21 \text{ in.}^2/\text{ft} \qquad \text{Flex. 1.2, ACI SP-17}$$

$$- A_s = \frac{6.16}{4.29 \times 4.75} = 0.30 \text{ in.}^2/\text{ft}$$

Quick Check:

By using the following steps, the reinforcements can be obtained very quickly:

$$A_{s\,(min.)} = 0.0018 \times 6 \times 12 = 0.13 \text{ in.}^2$$

Try:

$$A_s = \frac{4.40 \times 12}{(0.80 \times 4.75) \times 60} = 0.23 \text{ in.}^2$$

$$0.23 \times 60 = 13.9 \text{ k}$$

$$a = \frac{13.9}{0.85 \times 4 \times 12} = 0.34 \text{ in.}$$

$$M_u = 0.9 \times 13.9 \times \left(4.75 \times \frac{0.34}{2}\right)\frac{1}{12} = 4.78 \text{ ft-k} > 4.40 \text{ ft-k} \quad \text{OK}$$

Use #4 at 12 in. spacing.

Similarly, try:

$$A_s = \frac{6.16 \times 12}{(0.80 \times 4.75) \times 60} = 0.32 \text{ in.}^2$$

$$M_u = 6.56 \text{ ft-k} > 6.16 \text{ ft-k} \quad \text{OK}$$

Use #5 at 12 in. spacing.

3. Min. $A_s = \dfrac{200}{f_y}bd = 0.00333 \times 12 \times 4.75 = 0.19 \text{ in.}^2/\text{ft.}$

Temperature Steel $A_s = 0.0018$ bt is usually used as minimum steel. (Total thickness of slab is used.)

Temperature Steel $A_s = 0.0018 \times 6 \times 12 = 0.13 \text{ in.}^2/\text{ft}$

Use: 6-in. concrete slab

at bottom	#5 @ 16 in. o.c. ($A_s = 0.21 \text{ in.}^2/\text{ft}$)
	or #4 @ 12 in. o.c. ($A_s = 0.20 \text{ in.}^2/\text{ft}$)
at top	#6 @ 16 in. o.c. ($A_s = 0.33 \text{ in.}^2/\text{ft}$)
	or #5 at 12 in. o.c. ($A_s = 0.31 \text{ in.}^2/\text{ft}$)
temperature steel	#4 @ 18 in. o.c. ($A_s = 0.133 \text{ in.}^2/\text{ft}$)

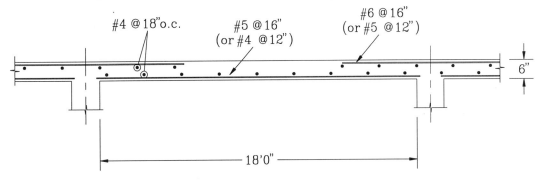

Fig. P7.5.1 (a)

4. Deflection Check

$$\Delta_{middle} = \frac{wL^4}{384EI}$$

where

$$E = 57{,}000\sqrt{4000} = 3.6 \times 10^6 \text{ psi}$$

$$I = 12 \times 6^3/12 = 216 \text{ in.}^4$$

$$w = 50 + 75 = 125 \text{ psf} = 10.42 \text{ lb/in.}$$

$$L = 18 \text{ ft-0 in.} = 216 \text{ in.}$$

$$\Delta_{middle} = 0.076 \text{ in.} < 0.9 \text{ in.} \quad \text{OK}$$

$$\frac{L}{240} = \frac{18 \times 12}{240} = 0.9 \text{ in.} > \Delta_{(DD+LL)} \quad \text{OK}$$

$$\frac{L}{360} = 0.6 \text{ in.} > \Delta_{(LL)} \quad \text{OK}$$

5. Check moment capacity with #6 @ 12 and #5 @ 18:

#6 @ 12:

$$A_s = 0.44$$

$$F_v = 0.44 \times 60 = 26.4 \text{ k}$$

$$a = \frac{26.4}{0.85 \times 4 \times 12} = 0.65 \text{ in.}$$

$$\phi M_n = 0.9 \times 26.4 \times \left(4.74 - \frac{0.65}{2}\right) \times \frac{1}{12} = 8.74 \text{ ft-k} > 6.16 \text{ ft-k}$$

#6 @ 12 is too much steel. Use #5 @ 12 in.

#5 @ 18:

$$A_s = 0.2$$

$$F_v = 0.2 \times 60 = 12''$$

$$a = \frac{12}{0.85 \times 4 \times 12} = 0.294$$

$$\phi M_n = 0.9 \times 12 \times \left(4.75 - \frac{0.294}{2}\right) \times \frac{1}{12}$$

$$= 4.14 \text{ ft-k/ft} < 4.4$$

Try #5 @ 16:

$$\phi M_n = \frac{18}{16} \times 4.14 = 4.65 > 4.4 \quad \text{OK}$$

or use #4 @ 12 in.

7.5.2   EXAMPLE PROBLEM 2 — TWO-WAY SLAB

A typical interior bay of a two-way flat plate is 20 ft-0 in. $\times$ 15 ft-0 in.

Required

A. Check shear capability of the slab.

B. Using Direct Design Method, distribute the moments in the long direction and calculate the reinforcements in the column strip only.

Given

- Column 18 in. $\times$ 18 in.
- Slab 7½ in. thick
- Partition — 20 psf
- LL — 40 psf
- f'_c = 4000 psi
- f_y = 60,000 psi
- Ignore column fixity.

Solution

Loads:

$$DL = (94 + 20) \times 1.4 = 160$$
$$LL = 40 \times 1.7 = \underline{68}$$
$$228 \text{ psf}$$

$$h = 7\tfrac{1}{2} \text{ in.}$$
$$d_{(av)} = 7\tfrac{1}{2} - \tfrac{3}{4} - \tfrac{1}{2} = 6\tfrac{1}{4} \text{ in.}$$

A. Shear Capability of the Slab

Check slab shear at a distance, d/2

$$b_0 = 4 \times (18 + 6.25) = 4 \times 24.25 = 97 \text{ in.}$$
$$V_u = 0.228 \left\{ 20 \times 15 - 2.02^2 \right\}$$
$$= 67.5 \text{ k}$$

From Section 7.3:

$$\phi \, V_c = \phi \left(\frac{\alpha_s \, d}{b_o} + 2 \right) \sqrt{f'_c} \, b_o \, d$$
$$= 0.85 \times \left(\frac{40 \times 6.25}{97} + 2 \right) \sqrt{4000} \times 97 \times 6.25$$
$$= 149 \text{ k}$$

$$\phi V_c \leq 0.85 \times 4 \sqrt{f'_c} \, b_o \, d$$

$$= 0.85 \times 4 \sqrt{400} \; 97 \times 6.25$$

$$= 130.5 \text{ k}$$

$$\phi V_c = 130.5 > V_u = 67.5 \qquad\qquad \text{OK}$$

B. Assume that the slab meets all the Direct Design Method criteria.

$$M_0 = w_u \times \ell_2 \times \frac{\ell_n^2}{8} = 0.228 \times 15 \times \frac{18.5^2}{8} = 185 \text{ ft-k}$$

Typical interior span moment distribution along 20 ft-0 in. span:

$$\begin{aligned}
M\,(-)\,@ \text{ support line} &= 0.65 \times 185 &= 120.25 \text{ ft-k} \\
M\,(+)\,@ \text{ middle span} &= 0.35 \times 185 &= 64.75 \text{ ft-k}
\end{aligned}$$

Therefore:

$$\begin{aligned}
M\,(-)\,@ \text{ column strip} &= 0.75 \times 120.25 &= 90 \text{ ft-k} \\
M\,(-)\,@ \text{ middle strip} &= 0.25 \times 120.25 &= 30.25 \text{ ft-k} \\
M\,(+)\,@ \text{ column strip} &= 0.60 \times 64.75 &= 38.85 \approx 39 \text{ ft-k} \\
M\,(+)\,@ \text{ middle strip} &= 0.40 \times 64.75 &= 25.90 \approx 26 \text{ ft-k}
\end{aligned}$$

Reinforcement at column strip at column top:

Width of column strip = 7 ft-6 in. = 90 in.

$$A_{s_1} = \frac{90 \times 12}{(0.75 \times 6.25) \times 60} = 3.84 \text{ in.}^2$$

$$F_u = 3.84 \times 60 = 230 \text{ k}$$

$$a = \frac{230}{0.85 \times 4 \times 90} = 0.75 \text{ in.}$$

$$M_{u_1} = 0.9 \times 230 \times \left(6.25 - \frac{0.75}{2} \right) \frac{1}{12}$$

$$= 101 \text{ ft-k} > 90 \text{ ft-k}$$

Use $A_s = \dfrac{90}{101} \times 3.84 \sim 3.5 \text{ in.}^2$

Temperature steel: $0.0018 \times 90 \times 7.5 = 1.21 < 3.5$ OK

Use twelve #5 $\times$ 11 ft-0 in. @ column head at top (3.6 in.^{2}).

Reinforcement at column strip at middle span:

$$A_{s1} = \frac{39 \times 12}{(0.75 \times 6.25) \times 60} = 1.664 > 1.21$$

$$F_u = 1.664 \times 60 = 100 \text{ k}$$

$$a = \frac{100}{0.85 \times 4 \times 90} = 0.33 \text{ in.}$$

$$M_{u1} = 0.9 \times 100 \times \left(6.25 - \frac{0.33}{2}\right) \frac{1}{12}$$

$$= 45.6 \text{ ft-k} > 39 \text{ ft-k} \quad \text{OK}$$

Use six #5 × 11 ft-0 in. @ column strip at middle span (1.80 in.^{2}).

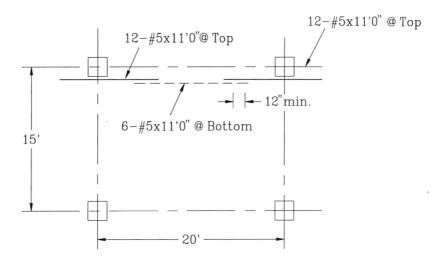

Fig. P7.5.2 (a)

8

WALLS

8.1 TYPES OF WALL

8.1.1 SUPPORTED WALLS

Walls braced top and bottom against lateral translation. Wall may be designed as an axial member for combined flexure and axial load.

8.1.2 CANTILEVERED WALLS

Walls braced at one end against lateral translation and major rotation and free to move at the other end.

8.1.3 RETAINING WALLS

Walls used to retain earth. Retaining walls are primarily designed as cantilever, flexural members subjected to transverse earth or water pressure. Along the length of the wall, minimum temperature steel must be provided.

8.1.4 SHEAR WALLS

Where walls are expected to carry vertical and in-plane lateral loads, additional horizontal reinforcements may be required. Where lateral load is large, the vertical edges of the walls are thickened and additional vertical reinforcing bars are placed within ties and spirals. For further details, readers are suggested to see the Uniform Building Code, Chapter 26, and ACI Code Chapter 11.

8.2 EMPIRICAL DESIGN METHOD

Applicable to walls of solid rectangular cross section with resultant of all factored loads located within the middle-third of the overall thickness of the wall. The design *axial load strength* is calculated as:

$$\phi\, P_{nw} = 0.55\, \phi\, f'_c\, A_g \left[1 - \left(\frac{kL_c}{32h}\right)^2 \right] \qquad \text{ACI Eq. (14-1)}$$

where

f'_c = concrete strength (psi)

ϕ = 0.70

h = thickness of the wall (in.)

A_g = $12 \times h$ (in.^{2}) for 1 ft-0 in. length of wall

k = effective length factor   ACI Sec. 14.5.2.

L_c = vertical distance between the supports (in.)

For walls braced top and bottom against lateral translation and

A. restrained against rotation at one or both ends   k = 0.8
   (Fixed at least at one end)

B. unrestrained against rotation at both ends   k = 1.0
   (Simply supported)

For walls not braced against lateral translation   k = 2.0   (Cantilever)

The empirical method given above does not include eccentric loading, large end moments or out−of−plane transverse loading. A wall must be designed as a beam−column where such loads exist. Designer is recommended to see UBC 1991 Section 2614(i).

8.3   MINIMUM REINFORCEMENT

The minimum ratio of reinforcement area to gross concrete area (ACI Sec. 14.3) shall be:

A.   For deformed bars not larger than #5 with $f_y > 60$ ksi:

Vertical reinforcement	0.0012
Horizontal reinforcement	0.0020

B.   For other deformed bars:

Vertical reinforcement	0.0015
Horizontal reinforcement	0.0025
Vertical welded wire fabric (W31, D31)	0.0012
Horizontal welded wire fabric (W31, D31)	0.0020

C.   For walls more than 10 in. thick, two layers of reinforcements must be placed.

D.   Spacing of any reinforcement shall not exceed 18 in.

E.   Minimum two #5 must be placed around the door and window openings. These bars must extend 24 in. beyond the corner.

8.4   EXAMPLE PROBLEM

8.4.1   EXAMPLE PROBLEM 1 — RETAINING WALL

Calculate the reinforcement required at the critical points of the stem, heel and toe of the retaining wall shown in Figure P8.4.1 (a).

Given

- f'_c = 4000 psi
- f_y = 60,000 psi
- w_{soil} = 125 lb/ft^3
- $w_{concrete}$ = 150 lb/in-ft

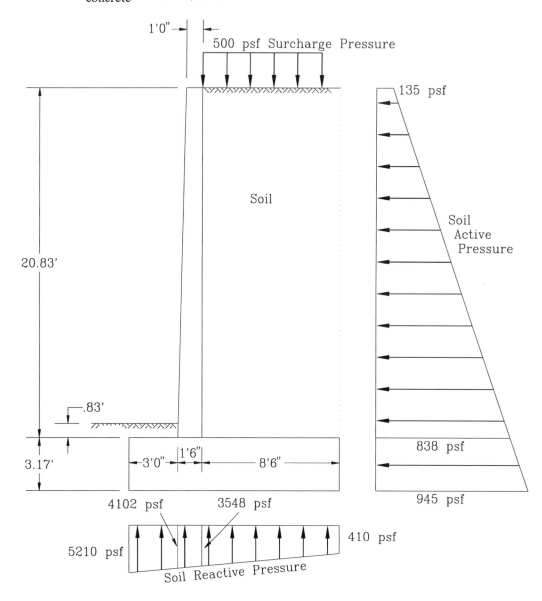

Fig. P8.4.1 (a)

Solution

Stem Design

$$\text{Moment} = (0.135 \times 20.83) \times \frac{20.83}{2} + (0.838 - 0.135)(20.83)\left(\frac{20.83}{3}\right)$$

$$= 29.3 + 50.8 = 80.1 \text{ ft-k}$$

$$M_{ur} = 1.7 \times 80.1 = 136.17 \text{ ft-k}$$

$$d = 18 \text{ in.} - 3 \text{ in.} = 15 \text{ in.}$$

$$A_{s1} = \frac{136.17 \times 12}{(0.75 \times 15) \times 60} = 2.42 \text{ in.}^2/\text{ft of wall}$$

Try #9 bars at 5 in. c/c: $A_s = 2.4 \text{ in.}^2$ $F_u = 2.4 \times 60 = 144 \text{ k}$

$$a = \frac{144}{0.85 \times 4 \times 12} = 3.53 \text{ in.}$$

$$M_{u_1} = 0.9 \times 144 \times \left(15 - \frac{3.53}{2}\right)\frac{1}{12}$$

$$= 143 \text{ ft-k/ft of wall} > 136.17 \text{ ft-k}   \text{OK}$$

Provide #9 at 5 in. vertical bars at bottom of stem

Reduction of steel at the upper part of the stem shall be done in actual design.

Temperature steel

$$0.0018 \times \frac{12 + 18}{2} \times 12 = 0.324 \text{ in.}^2/\text{ft}$$

Provide #4 at 12 in. c/c horizontal bars at each face.

Toe Design

Neglect soil weight.

Concrete $= 3.17 \times 0.15 = 0.47 \text{ k/ft}$

$$M = \left(4.102 \times 3 \times \frac{3}{2} + \frac{1.108}{2} \times 3 \times 2\right) - \left(0.47 \times 3 \times \frac{3}{2}\right)$$

$$= (18.6 + 3.3) - (2.1)$$

$$= 21.9 - 2.1 = 19.8 \text{ ft-k}$$

$$M_{UR} = 1.7 \times 21.9 - 1.5 \times 2.1 = 34 \text{ ft} - \text{k/ft of toe}$$

$$A_{s_1} = \frac{34 \times 12}{(0.75 \times 34) \times 60} = 0.27 \text{ in.}^2/\text{ft}$$

$$d = 38 - 4 = 34 \text{ in.}$$

Try #5 at 12. $A_s = 0.3 \text{ in.}^2$ at bottom

The stem bars i.e., #9 at 5 in. c to c will be bent and placed at toe for anchorage. Hence no moment calculation is necessary.

$$\text{Minimum Steel is } \frac{200}{f_y} = 0.0033$$

$$0.0033 \times 34 \times 12 = 1.34 \text{ in.}^2/\text{ft} < 2.4 \text{ in.}^2/\text{ft} \qquad \text{OK}$$

Heel Design

Rather than the upward pressure, it is a downward load that controls the design:

$$
\begin{array}{llll}
0.5 \times 8.5 & = 4.25 \text{ k/ft} \times 1.7 & = & 7.23 \\
0.125 \times 8.5 \times 20.83 = & 22.13 \text{ k/ft} \times 1.4 & = & 30.98 \\
0.15 \times 8.5 \times 3.17 = & 4.04 \text{ k/ft} \times 1.4 & = & \underline{5.66} \\
& & & 43.87 \text{ k/ft}
\end{array}
$$

$$M_{ur} = 43.87 \times 4.25 = 187 \text{ ft-k/ft of heel}$$

Retaining Wall

$$A_{s_1} = \frac{187 \times 12}{(0.75 \times 34) \times 60} = 1.5 \text{ in.}^2$$

$$d = 38 - 4 = 34 \text{ in.}$$

Try #8 at 6 in.: $\quad A_s = 1.58 \text{ in.}^2 \quad F_u = 1.58 \times 60 = 94.8$

$$a = \frac{94.8}{0.85 \times 4 \times 12} = 2.32 \text{ in.}$$

$$M_{u_1} = 0.9 \times 94.8 \times \left(34 - \frac{2.32}{2}\right) \frac{1}{12}$$

$$= 233.5 \text{ ft-k/ft} > 187$$

Try $A_{s_2} = 1.58 \times \dfrac{187}{233.5} = 1.26$ in.^{2}

Try #8 at 8 in.: $A_s = 1.185$ $F_u = 72$

  $a = 1.74$

$M_{u_2} = 0.9 \times 72 \times \left(34 - \dfrac{1.74}{2}\right) \dfrac{1}{12} = 178$ ft-k/ft < 187 ft-k/ft

Use #8 at 7½ c.c.

Temperature steel: $0.0018 \times 38 \times 12 = 0.82$, i.e., #5 at 5 in. or #5 at 10 t/b

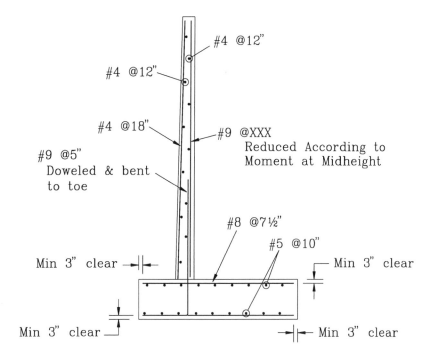

Fig. P8.4.1 (b) Retaining Wall Reinforcement

8.5   P. E. PROBLEM

8.5.1   P. E. PROBLEM 1 — TOXIC WATER STORAGE TANK

A water storage tank with slightly toxic additive is shown below. Tank will be lined. Cracks are undesirable. Assume backfill has no lateral load on the wall of the tank. Use ACI 318-89/92 Code.

Criteria:

Concrete f'_c = 3.0 ksi

Reinforcement f_y = 60 ksi

Required:

A. Design wall of the water tank out of reinforced concrete.

B. Neatly sketch reinforcement detail required at the critical areas.

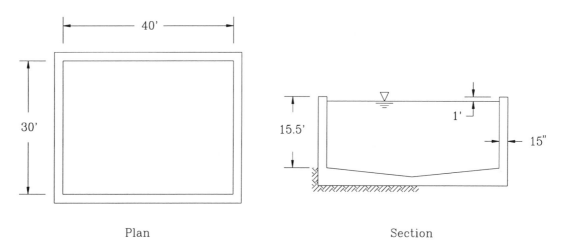

Plan   Section

Fig. P8.5.1 (a) Water Tank

Solution

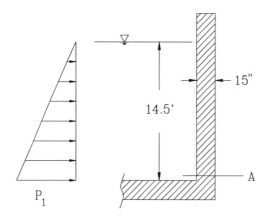

Fig. P8.5.1 (b)

A. Fluid pressure $\quad = \quad 62.5$ pcf

$$p_1 \; = \; 14.5 \times 62.5 \; = \; 906.3 \text{ psf}$$

$$M_A \; = \; \frac{906.3}{1,000} \times \frac{(14.5)^2}{6} \; = \; 31.8 \text{ ft-kip/ft} \quad \text{(Cantilever action only)}$$

Using ACI Sec. 9.2.5

$$U \; = \; 1.4D \; + \; 1.7L \; + \; 1.4F$$
$$M_u \; = \; 1.4 \times 31.8 \; = \; 44.5 \text{ ft-kip/ft}$$
$$d \; = \; 15.0 \; - \; 2.0 \; - \; 0.4 \; = \; 12.6 \text{ in.}$$

$$F \; = \; \frac{12 \times (12.6)^2}{12,000} \; = \; 0.158$$

$$K_n \; = \; \frac{44.5}{0.158} \; = \; 282$$

$$A_s \; = \; \frac{M_u}{a_n \, d} \; = \; \frac{44.5}{4.20 \times 12.6} \; = \; 0.84 \text{ in.}^2/\text{ft}$$

Flex. 1.1, ACI SP-17 (85)

$$\left[\begin{array}{l} \text{or using Structural} \\ \text{Handbook obtain } \varrho \\ A_s \; = \; \varrho \times b \times d \end{array}\right]$$

#6 @ 6 in. o.c. $\quad A_s \; = \; 0.88 \text{ in.}^2/\text{ft}$

Quick Check:

$$A_{s1} \; = \; \frac{44.5 \times 12}{0.8 \times 12.6 \times 60} \; = \; 0.88 \text{ in.}^2$$

$$a \; = \; \frac{0.88 \times 60}{0.85 \times 3 \times 12} \; = \; 1.72$$

$$M_u \; = \; 0.9 \times (0.88 \times 60) \left(12.6 - \frac{1.72}{2}\right) \frac{1}{12}$$
$$= \; 46.49 > 44.5 \quad \text{OK}$$

Use #6 at 6 in.

Check distribution of flexural reinforcement:

$$z \; = \; f_s \sqrt[3]{d_c \, A} \; \le \; 145$$

ACI Eq. (10-4)

$$= \; 0.6 \times 60 \; \sqrt[3]{\left[(2.0 \; + \; 0.4)\left(\frac{2 \times 2.4 \times 12}{2}\right)\right]}$$

$$= \; 147 \quad \text{(Close enough)}$$

Minimum A_s at exterior face (ACI Sec. 14.3):

Vertical A_s
$$= 0.0015 \text{ bt} \times 1/2$$
$$= 0.0015 \times 12 \times 15 \times 1/2 = 0.14 \text{ in.}^2/\text{ft}$$

Horizontal A_s
$$= 0.0025 \text{ bt} \times 1/2$$
$$= 0.0025 \times 12 \times 15 \times 1/2 = 0.225 \text{ in.}^2/\text{ft}$$

Use: 15 in. concrete wall with:

#6 @   6 in. o.c. vertical inside face,

#5 @ 18 in. o.c. vertical outside face, and

#4 @ 10 in. o.c. horizontal each face.

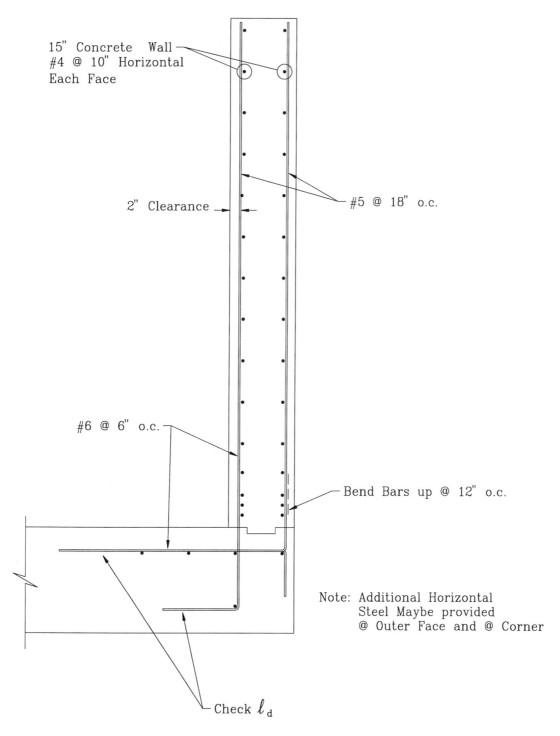

15" Concrete Wall
#4 @ 10" Horizontal
Each Face

#5 @ 18" o.c.

2" Clearance

#6 @ 6" o.c.

Bend Bars up @ 12" o.c.

Note: Additional Horizontal
Steel Maybe provided
@ Outer Face and @ Corner

Check ℓ_d

Fig. P8.5.1 (c) Water Tank Wall Section Showing Reinforcement Details

9

COLUMNS

9.1　TYPES OF COLUMNS

9.1.1　PLAIN CONCRETE PEDESTALS

Maximum height ≤ 3 times the least lateral dimension.

9.1.2　TIED COLUMNS

Tied columns have the bars braced or tied at intervals by closed ties ($\phi = 0.70$).

9.1.3　SPIRAL COLUMNS

Spiral Columns have the bars and core concrete wrapped with a closely spaced spiral of small diameter rod ($\phi = 0.75$).

9.1.4　COMPOSITE COLUMNS

Columns contain a structural steel shape surrounded by longitudinal bars with ties or spirals and encased in concrete.

9.2   INTERACTION OF AXIAL LOAD AND BENDING MOMENT IN A COLUMN

When combined axial compression and bending act on a section, there may be (a) compression over most or all of the section such that the compressive strain in the concrete reaches 0.003 before the tension steel yields, known as the compression failure zone, or (b) tension in a large portion of the section such that the strain in the tension steel is greater than the yield point strain when the compression strain in the concrete reaches 0.003, known as the tension failure zone. The intersect at these two zones is known as balanced failure zone.

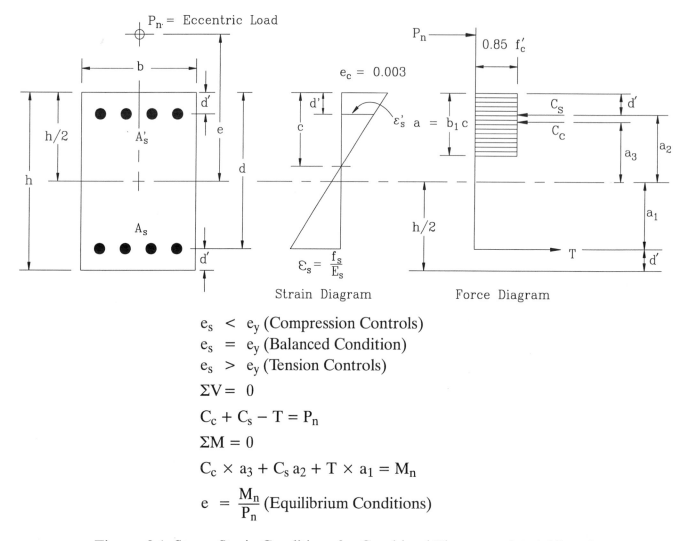

$e_s < e_y$ (Compression Controls)
$e_s = e_y$ (Balanced Condition)
$e_s > e_y$ (Tension Controls)

$\Sigma V = 0$

$C_c + C_s - T = P_n$

$\Sigma M = 0$

$C_c \times a_3 + C_s\, a_2 + T \times a_1 = M_n$

$e = \dfrac{M_n}{P_n}$ (Equilibrium Conditions)

Figure 9.1 Stress-Strain Conditions for Combined Flexure and Axial Load

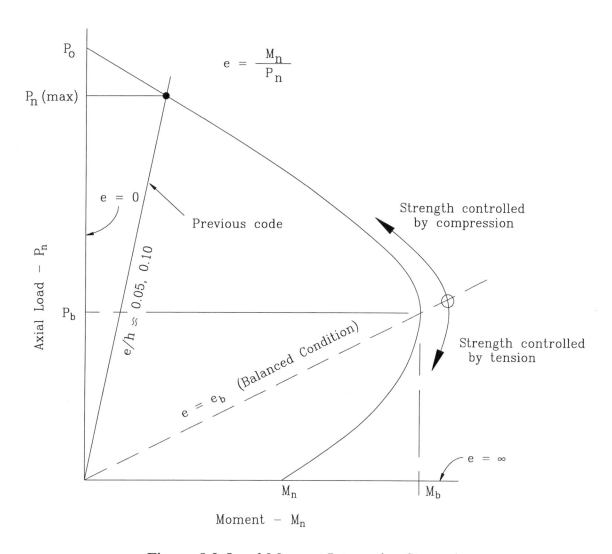

Figure 9.2 Load-Moment Interaction Strength

9.3   SHORT COLUMNS

Ultimate Load Capacity Controlled by Compression:

A straight line approximation may be obtained by joining P_o and P_b of the interaction diagram given in Figure 9.2 to give P_u in either of the following forms:

$$P'_u = \frac{P_o}{1 + \left[(P_o/P_b) - 1\right](e'/e_b)} \tag{9.1}$$

where

$$e' = \frac{M_u}{P'_u}, \qquad e = \frac{M_u}{P_u}, \qquad e_b = \frac{M_b}{P_b}$$

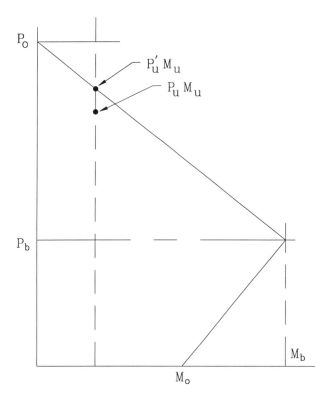

Figure 9.3 Interaction Diagram for Short Column

$$P'_u = P_o - (P_o - P_b)\left(\frac{M_u}{M_b}\right) \tag{9.2}$$

9.3.1 CODE DESIGN REQUIREMENTS

ACI 318-89 Code Section 9.3.2 (c) Axial Compression or Axial Compression combined with Bending.

A. Reinforced members with spiral reinforcement conforming to
   ACI Section 10.9.3 $\quad\quad\quad\quad$ $\phi = 0.75$

B. Other reinforced members $\quad$ $\phi = 0.70$

C. With $f_y \leq 60,000$ psi, the ϕ values given in A and B may be increased linearly to 0.9 as ϕP_n decreases from $(0.10 \, f'_c \, A_g)$ to zero for sections with symmetrical reinforcement and $(h - d' - d_s)/h$ not less than 0.70 (see Figure 9.5).

D. The ϕ values given in A and B may be increased linearly to 0.90 as ϕP_n decreases from $0.10 \, f'_c \, A_g$ or ϕP_b, whichever is smaller to zero for sections with small axial compression not satisfying paragraph C above.

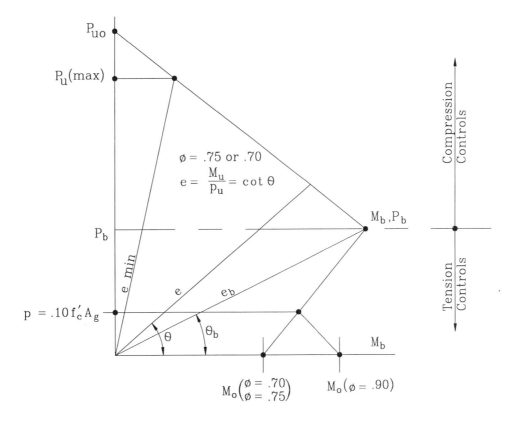

Figure 9.4 Idealized P-M Interaction Plot

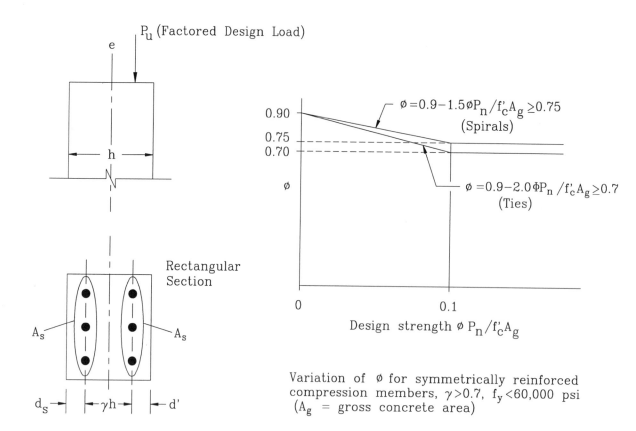

Variation of ϕ for symmetrically reinforced compression members, $\gamma > 0.7$, $f_y < 60,000$ psi (A_g = gross concrete area)

(b) Interpretation for ACI Section 9.3.2 (c)

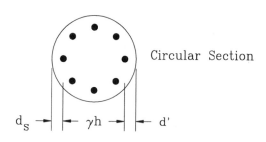

(a) Definition of γ value

Figure 9.5 Strength Reduction Factor for Columns

Prior to the 1977 ACI Code, all compression members were required to be designed for at least a minimum eccentricity of 0.05h for spirally reinforced or 0.10h for tied reinforced members. The specified minimum eccentricities were originally intended to serve as a means of reducing the axial design load strength of a section in pure compression to account for accidental eccentricities, not considered in the analysis that may exist in a compression member and to recognize that concrete strength is less than f'_c at sustained high loads.

Since the primary purpose of designing columns with minimum eccentricity was to limit the pure axial load capacity, the Section 10.3.5 of the 1983 ACI Code was revised by limiting the axial load strength of a section to 85% (spirals) and 80% (tied) of axial load strength at zero eccentricity (P_o). The effect of minimum eccentricity need not be separately considered any more.

Section 10.9 — Limits for reinforcement of compression members.

Section 10.9.1 — For non-composite compression members,

$$0.01 \leq \varrho_g \leq 0.08 \qquad\qquad (9.3)$$

where

$\varrho_g = A_s/A_g$

$A_s = $ longitudinal reinforcement

Section 10.9.2:

For tied columns: Minimum number of longitudinal bars = 4

For spiral columns: Minimum number of longitudinal bars = 6

9.4   DESIGN OF SPIRAL REINFORCEMENT

(ACI Section 10.9.3)

The ratio of spiral reinforcement ϱ_s shall not be less than the value given by:

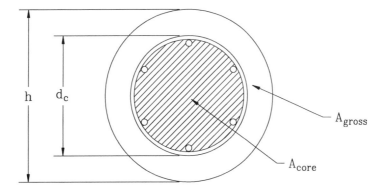

Figure 9.6 Spiral Reinforcement

$$\varrho_s = 0.45\left(\frac{A_g}{A_c} - 1\right)\frac{f'_c}{f_y} \qquad\qquad \text{ACI Eq. (10-5)}$$

where

$f_y \leq 60,000$ psi

$A_c = $ area of core of spirally reinforced column measured to the outside diameter of the spiral $= \pi(d_c)^2/4$

$A_g = $ gross concrete area $= \pi h^2/4$

$\varrho_s = $ ratio of volume of spiral reinforcement to volume of concrete core

The ratio of spiral reinforcement ϱ_s may first be determined by the ACI Eq. (10-5). Then, from the expression given below and an assumed size of spiral wire, the pitch of spirals, s, can be found.

$$ s = \frac{a_{sp} \, \pi \, (D_c - d_b)}{(\pi/4) \, D_c^2 \cdot \varrho_s} = \frac{a_{sp}(D_c - d_b)}{(\varrho_s/4) \, D_c^2} \tag{9.4} $$

a_{sp} = area of the spiral

d_b = diameter of the spiral wire

D_c = diameter of the core   (inside ties or spirals)

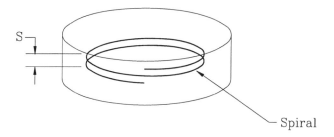

Figure 9.7 Pitch of Spiral Reinforcement

ACI 318-89/92, Section 7.10.4.3 requires that the *clear spacing* shall not be less than 1.0 in. but not more than 3 in. between spirals. Spirals shall have minimum 3/8 in. in diameter for cast-in-place construction.

9.5 DESIGN OF COLUMN TIES

(ACI 318-89, Section 7.10.5)

Ties must be at least:

A. #3 size for #10 or smaller longitudinal bars

B. #4 size for #11 or larger or all bundled bars

The spacing of the ties must not be greater than

A. $16d_b$ of the longitudinal bars

B. 48 tie diameters

C. least column dimension

Every corner bar and every alternate longitudinal bar must be braced by the tie. No bar shall be farther than *6 in clear* on either side from such a laterally supported bar (tie). See Figure 9.8.

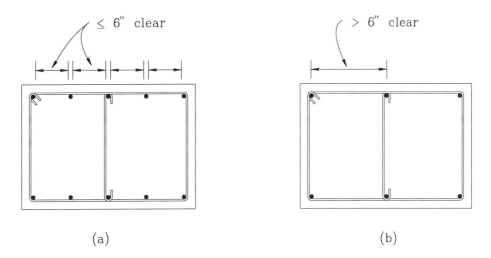

(a)   (b)

Figure 9.8 Tied Columns

9.6   CONCENTRICALLY LOADED SHORT COLUMNS

The ultimate compression load that a short column can take without bending is:

$$P_o = 0.85 f'_c (A_g - A_{st}) + f_y A_{st} \tag{9.5}$$

For spirally reinforced members,

$$\phi P_n \text{ (max)} = 0.85\, \phi P_o$$
$$= 0.85\, \phi[0.85 f'_c (A_g - A_{st}) + f_y A_{st}] \qquad \text{ACI Eq. (10-1)}$$

For tied reinforced members,

$$\phi P_n \text{ (max)} = 0.80\, \phi P_o$$
$$= 0.80\, \phi[0.85 f'_c (A_g - A_{st}) + f_y A_{st}] \qquad \text{ACI Eq. (10-2)}$$

where

$A_g =$ gross concrete area
$A_{st} =$ total reinforcement area

ϕ = 0.70 for tied column
   = 0.75 for spiral column

9.7   LIMITS FOR SHORT COLUMN CLASSIFICATION (ACI SEC 10.11.4)

The effect of slenderness may be neglected when, for unbraced frames:

$$\frac{kL_u}{r} \le 22 \qquad r = \begin{cases} 0.3h & \text{(rectangular column)} \\ 0.25h & \text{(circular column)} \end{cases} \tag{9.6}$$

or

$$\frac{kL_u}{h} \le 6.6 \qquad \text{(for rectangular column)} \tag{9.7a}$$

$$\frac{kL_u}{h} \le 5.5 \qquad \text{(for circular column)} \tag{9.7b}$$

and for braced frames:

$$\frac{kL_u}{r} \le 34 - 12\frac{M_1}{M_2} \tag{9.8}$$

where

$M_1 =$ Smaller end moment

where M_1 and M_2 are end moments. M_1/M_2 is positive when the column forms a single curvature and is negative otherwise.

9.8 SLENDER COLUMNS — MAGNIFIED MOMENT METHOD (ACI SEC 10.11.5)

ACI 318-83 and 89 Code adopts the moment magnifier concept for the effect of slenderness. The primary moment caused by transverse loads is magnified by the effect of axial forces or the secondary moment. The magnification factor is so termed to multiply the primary moment to give the magnified design moment.

Consider a column which is subjected to end moments M_1 and M_2, with $M_2 \geq M_1$. Magnified moment can then take the form:

$$M_c = \delta \, M \tag{9.9}$$

$$\delta = \frac{C_m}{1 - (P_u/\phi P_c)} \geq 1.0 \tag{9.10}$$

$$P_c = \frac{\pi^2 EI}{(k \, L_u)^2} \tag{9.11}$$

(Obtain k from alignment chart. See ACI Commentary, Chapter 10.)

in which C_m is an equivalent moment correction factor to take care of different shapes of moment diagrams and shifts in points of maximum moment. Under ACI 318-83 and 89, Section 10.11.5.3, the values of C_m are summarized as follows:

For braced frames:

A. with transverse loading, $C_m = 1.0$ $\qquad\qquad$ (9.12a)

B. with end moments only,

$$C_m = 0.6 + 0.4 \, \frac{M_1}{M_2} \geq 0.4 \tag{9.12b}$$

where M_1/M_2 is positive when the column is bent to form a single curvature and is negative otherwise. In ACI 318-89 Code magnification factor is presented with more modifications (Sec. 10.11.5).

If $M_1 = M_2$:

	Single Curvature	Double Curvature
$\dfrac{kL_u}{r}$	22	46
C_m	1.0	0.4

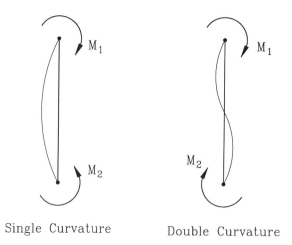

Figure 9.9 Single and Double Curvatures

$$M_c = \delta_b M_{2b} + \delta_s M_{2s} \qquad \text{ACI Eq. (10-6)}$$

where

$$\delta_b = \frac{C_m}{1 - \frac{P_u}{\phi P_c}} \geq 1.0 \qquad \text{ACI Eq. (10-7)}$$

$$\delta_s = \frac{1}{1 - \frac{\Sigma P_u}{\phi \Sigma P_c}} \geq 1.0 \qquad \text{ACI Eq. (10-8)}$$

δ_b = Moment magnification factor for frames braced against side sway

δ_s = moment magnification factor for frames not braced against side sway

The effects of unbalanced loads and lateral loads are reflected by δ_s for unbraced frames. All the columns in the frames are engaged to resist these loads. If the frames are braced $\delta_s = 1$

For unbraced frames:

All cases $C_m = 1.0$ \hfill (9.13)

In Eq. (9.10), P_c is the critical load and is defined by the Eq. (9.11). The effect of column length, L_u (unsupported length) and the support condition described by the parameter k have both been included. The term kL_u is often referred to as the effective column length. Values of k for both the braced and unbraced frames can be found from the diagrams given in the ACI SP.17A (85), Design Handbook. These diagrams shown as Column 2 on Page 49 of the Handbook are reproduced and given in the Appendix. In finding k values it requires to calculate the ψ values on top (ψ_A) and on bottom (ψ_B) of the column considered:

$$\psi = \frac{\sum EI/L_u \text{ columns in plane of bending}}{\sum EI/L_u \text{ beams in plane of bending}} \tag{9.14}$$

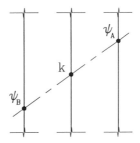

Figure 9.10 Alignment Chart

By entering the ψ_A and ψ_B values on the diagram, and joining ψ_A and ψ_B by a straight line, the k value reads at the intersection with the middle vertical scalar line. ACI 318-83 and 89, Section 10.11.5 has given expressions for the term EI in Eq. (9.11).

The effects of creep in concrete and nonlinearity of E value for concrete have both been included.

$$EI = \frac{(E_c I_g/5) + E_s I_{se}}{1 + \beta_d} \qquad \text{ACI Eq. } (10-10)$$

Or, conservatively,

$$EI = \frac{(E_c I_g/2.5)}{1 + \beta_d} \qquad \text{ACI Eq. } (10-11)$$

where,

$$E_c = w^{1.5} \, 33 \sqrt{f'_c}$$
$$\text{or } E_c = 57,000 \sqrt{f'_c} \quad \text{(for normal weight concrete)}$$

$$E_s = 29,000 \text{ ksi}$$

I_g = moment of inertia of gross concrete section about the centroid axis, neglect the steel

I_{se} = moment of inertia of steel about the centroidal axis of the member cross section

$1 + \beta_d$ = creep factor

β_d = ratio of maximum design dead load moment to maximum design total load moment, always positive

$$= \left| \frac{M_d}{M_u} \right| \quad \text{both these moments, } M_d \text{ and } M_u \text{ are factored.} \tag{9.17}$$

9.9   P. E. PROBLEMS

9.9.1   P. E. PROBLEM 1 — AXIALLY LOADED SHORT-TIED COLUMN

Design the section of a short-tied column axially loaded with a factored load $P_u = 1550$ kip. The design is subjected to only two limitations, namely:

A. Section must be rectangular with the lengths of the sides having a ratio of about two to one.

B. The size of the long side of the column section may not exceed 40 in.

Assume $f'_c = 6000$ psi; $\varrho_g = 0.02$; $f_y = 60$ ksi. Make a detailed sketch of the section showing all the necessary dimensions.

Solution

$$\frac{h}{b} = 2 \quad h = 40 \text{ in.}$$

$$f'_c = 6,000 \text{psi}, \quad f_y = 60,000 \text{ psi}, \quad \varrho_g = 0.02.$$

(ACI-89 Code, Section 10.3.5)

A.   Solve for A_g:

$$\phi \, P_n = 0.80 \, \phi \left[0.85 \, f'_c (A_g - A_{st}) + f_y \, A_{st} \right] \qquad \text{ACI Eq. (10.2)}$$

$$\text{where} \quad A_{st} = \varrho_g \, A_g = 0.02 \, A_g$$

$$\text{and} \quad P_u = \phi \, P_n$$

$$1,550 = 0.80 \, (0.70) \left[0.85 \, (6.0) \, (A_g - 0.02 \, A_g) + 60 \, (0.02 \, A_g) \right]$$

$$= 0.56 \left[4.998 \, A_g + 1.20 \, A_g \right]$$

$$= 3.471 \, A_g$$

$$A_g = \frac{1,550}{3.471} = 447 \text{ in.}^2$$

$$A_g = bh = b \, (2b)$$

$$b = \sqrt{\frac{447}{2}} = 14.9 \text{ in.}$$

$$b = 15 \text{ in.} \quad h = 30 \text{ in.}$$

$$A_{st} = \varrho_g \, b \, h = 0.02 \times 15 \times 30 = 9.0 \text{ in.}^2$$

$$A_g = 15 \times 30 = 450 \text{ in.}^2$$

$$P_u = \phi \, P_n$$

$$= 0.80 \, (0.70) \left[0.85 \, (60) \, (450 - 9.0) + 60 \, (9.0) \right]$$

$$= 1,562 \text{ kip} > 1,550 \text{ kip} \quad \text{OK}$$

Use 15 in. × 30 in. Column with four #10 and four #9.

B. Design for Ties:

(ACI-89, Code Section 7.10.5)

Use #3 ties for #10 or smaller longitudinal bars.

$$\text{spacing of ties } \leq \begin{cases} 16 \, d_b \text{ of longitudinal bars} = 16 \times 1.27 = 20.3 \text{ in.} \\ 48 \text{ tie diameter} = 48 \times 0.375 = 18 \text{ in.} \\ \text{least column dimension} = 15 \text{ in.} \end{cases}$$

Use 15-in. spacing for ties.

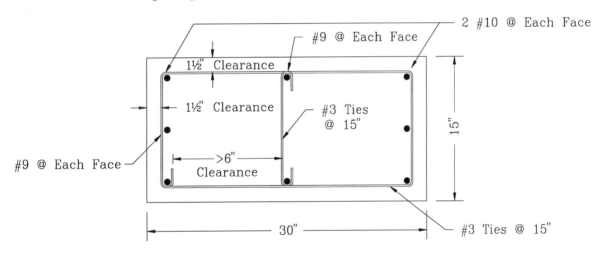

Fig. P9.9.1 (a) Tied-Column Detail

9.9.2   P. E. PROBLEM 2 — SHORT SPIRAL COLUMN WITH MOMENT

Check the strength adequacy of a short spiral column given the following factors:

- M = 600 in. kip
- P = 320 kip
- Reinforcement:
    - Eight #8 bars (symmetric)
    - Intermediate grade (f_y = 60,000 ksi)
    - 3/8-in. cold drawn spirals with 1.5-in. cover
- Column diameter = 24 in.
- f'_c = 3000 psi

Assume DL = LL and assume Load Factor of 1.55

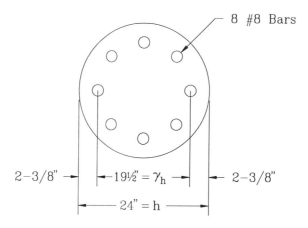

Fig. P9.9.2 (a) Spiral-Column Section

Solution

$$f'_c = 3 \text{ ksi}$$

$$f_y = 60 \text{ ksi}$$

$$\gamma = \frac{19.25}{24} = 0.8$$

$$\varrho_g = \frac{A_{st}}{A_g} = \frac{8 \times 0.79}{\pi \times 12^2} = 0.014$$

$$\text{Design } M_u = 1.55 \times M = 1.55 \times 600 \text{ in.-kip}$$

$$= 930 \text{ in.-kip} = 77.5 \text{ ft-kip}$$

Design P_u $=$ 1.55 P $=$ 1.55 × 320 kip $=$ 496 kip

$$e \;=\; \frac{M_u}{P_u} \;=\; \frac{77.5}{496} \;=\; 0.156 \text{ ft} \;=\; 1.875 \text{ in.}$$

$$>\; 1 \text{ in.}\quad \text{or}\quad 0.05 \text{ h}\quad (\text{ACI } 318-77 \text{ Code Requirement})$$

Design   e $=$ 1.875 in.

$$\frac{e}{h} \;=\; \frac{1.875}{24} \;=\; 0.078$$

For short column, $\delta \;=\; 1.0, \quad \delta\,\dfrac{e}{h} \;=\; 0.078$

where, $\delta \;=\;$ moment magnifier

From Column 2.5, Page 277 of Design Handbook:

A.   For $\gamma \;=\; 0.75:$ $\dfrac{\delta\,e}{h} \;=\; 0.05$ $\qquad \dfrac{P_u}{A_g} \;=\; 2.20$

$$\frac{\delta\,e}{h} \;=\; 0.10 \qquad \frac{P_u}{A_g} \;=\; 1.92$$

By interpolation, $\dfrac{\delta\,e}{h} \;=\; 0.078$

$$\frac{P_u}{A_g} \;=\; 2.20 \;-\; \left[\frac{0.078 \;-\; 0.05}{0.10 \;-\; 0.05} \,(2.20 \;-\; 1.92)\right]$$

$$=\; 2.04$$

Therefore, for given $\delta = 0.75$ and $\delta\dfrac{e}{h} \;=\; 0.078,$

$\dfrac{P_u}{A_g} \;=\; 2.04$ is obtained by interpolation.

B. For $\gamma = 0.90$: $\dfrac{\delta\, e}{h} = 0.05$ $\dfrac{P_u}{A_g} = 2.22$

$\dfrac{\delta\, e}{h} = 0.10$ $\dfrac{P_u}{A_g} = 1.96$

By interpolation, $\dfrac{\delta\, e}{h} = 0.078$

$$\dfrac{P_u}{A_g} = 2.22 - \left[\dfrac{0.078 - 0.05}{0.10 - 0.05}\, (2.22 - 1.96) \right]$$

$$= 2.074$$

C. For $\gamma = 0.80$: $\dfrac{P_u}{A_g} = 2.04 - \left[\dfrac{0.8 - 0.75}{0.9 - 0.75}\, (2.074 - 2.04) \right]$

$$= 2.051$$

Capacity of the column is:

$$P_u = 2.051\, A_g = 2.051 \times \pi \times (12)^2$$

$$= 928 \text{ kip} > 496 \text{ kip}$$

Thus, the design is adequate.

If the design tables are not available, P-M interaction curve has to be developed. Development of P-M interaction curve could be very time consuming for non-rectangular or unsymmetrical sections.

9.9.3 P. E. PROBLEM 3 — SHORT SPIRAL COLUMN WITH MOMENT (ACI 1989/92)

Solve P. E. Problem 2 with the following data.

$$M = 600 \text{ in.-kip} \qquad P = 320 \text{ kip}$$

Eight #8, 3/8-in cover drawn sprial 1 ½ cover

$$\begin{cases} f_y = 60 \text{ ksi} & \text{Column Diameter 24 in.} \\ f'_c = 4 \text{ ksi} & \text{(instead of 3 ksi)} \end{cases}$$

Use 1989/92 ACI Code. Assume load factor as 1.55.

Use ACI Design Handbook (1984). *Draw interaction diagram.*

In this problem,

$$f'_c = 4.0 \text{ ksi}, \quad f_\gamma = 60 \text{ ksi}, \quad \gamma = 0.8, \quad \varrho_g = 0.014 \text{ (eight #8 bars)}$$

Solution

$$\text{Design } M_u = 1.55 \times 600 = 930 \text{ in.-kip}$$

$$= 77.5 \text{ ft-kip} = \phi M_n$$

$$\frac{\phi M_n}{A_g \, h} = \frac{77.5}{\pi \times 12^2 \times 2} = 0.086 \text{ ksi}$$

$$\text{Design } P_u = 1.55 \times 320$$

$$= 496 \text{ kip} = \phi P_n$$

$$\frac{\phi P_n}{A_g} = \frac{496}{\pi \times 12^2} = 1.096 \text{ ksi}$$

$$e = \frac{M_u}{P_u} = 0.156 \text{ ft} = 1.875 \text{ in.}$$

Table P9.9.3 (a)

ϱ_g	(1) $\phi\dfrac{P_n}{A_g}$ $M_u = 0$	(2) $\phi\dfrac{P_n}{A_g}$ $\dfrac{\phi M_n}{A_g\, h}$ Max @ Code $\dfrac{P_u}{A_g}$		(3) $\phi\dfrac{P_n}{A_g}$ $\dfrac{\phi M_n}{A_g\, h}$ $f_s = 0$		(4) $\phi\dfrac{P_n}{A_g}$ $\dfrac{\phi M_n}{A_g\, h}$ $f_s = 0.5 f_y$	
$\gamma = 0.75$							
0.01		2.528	0.156	2.271	0.224	1.572	0.330
0.02		2.889	0.170	2.507	0.269	1.698	0.394
0.014		2.6724	0.1616	2.3654	0.242	1.622	0.3556
$\gamma = 0.90$							
0.01		2.528	0.162	2.453	0.185	1.745	0.333
0.02		2.889	0.181	2.699	0.238	1.892	0.411
0.014		2.6724	0.169	2.5514	0.2062	1.8038	0.3642
$\gamma = 0.8^*$							
0.014	3.5632	2.6724	0.164	2.4274	0.2301	1.6826	0.3594

* Interpolate between $\gamma = 0.75$ and $\gamma = 0.9$

Table P9.9.3 (b)

ϱ_g	(5) $\phi\dfrac{P_n}{A_g}$ $\dfrac{\phi M_n}{A_g h}$ $\dfrac{e}{h}$ $f_s = f_y$ Balanced Condition			(6) $\phi\dfrac{P_n}{A_g}$ $\dfrac{\phi M_n}{A_g h}$ $\phi = 0.9$		(7) $\phi\dfrac{M_n}{A_g}$ $P_u = 0$ $\phi = 0.9$
$\gamma = 0.75$						
0.01	1.082	0.348	0.322	0.400	0.277	0.2001
0.02	1.083	0.432	0.399	0.400	0.388	0.3645
0.014	1.0824	0.3816	0.3528	0.400	0.3214	0.2659
$\gamma = 0.90$						
0.01	1.242	0.376	0.303	0.400	0.289	0.2157
0.02	1.280	0.482	0.376	0.400	0.427	0.4052
0.014	1.266	0.4184	0.3322	0.400	0.3442	0.2915
$\gamma = 0.8$						
0.014	1.1436	0.3939	0.3459	0.400	0.3290	0.2700

Note: From ACI Eq. (10-1)

$$\phi P_n = 0.85\phi [0.85f'_c (A_g - A_{st}) + f_y A_{st}]$$

$$\rightarrow \phi \frac{P_n}{A_g} = 0.85\phi [0.85f'_c(1 - \varrho_g) + f_y\varrho_g] \quad @ \text{ Column 2}$$

and

$$\phi \frac{P_n}{A_g} = \phi [0.85f'_c(1 - \varrho_g) + f_y\varrho_g] \quad @ \text{ Column 1}$$

$\phi = 0.75$ for spiral column

$\phi = 0.70$ for tied column

Using the bottom most row of the table where, using $\gamma = 0.8$ and $\varrho_g = 0.014$, the interaction diagram is drawn [see Figure P9.9.3 (c)].

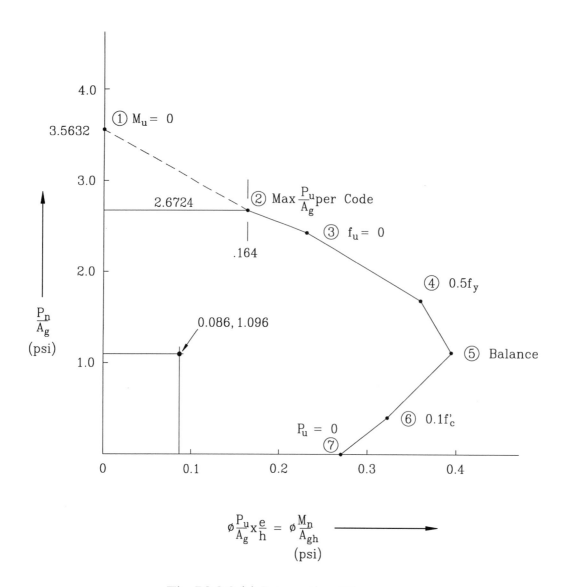

Fig. P9.9.3 (c) Interaction Diagram

9.9.4   P. E. PROBLEM 4 — ECCENTRICALLY LOADED SHORT-TIED COLUMN

The reinforced concrete rectangular-tied column shown is 14 in. × 20 in. in cross section and is reinforced with fourteen #11 bars as shown. It carries a direct load of 140 kip plus a shear from the framing beam of 20 kip and a moment from the beam as indicated of 126 ft-kip. The 126 ft-kip moment includes the effect of 20 kip shear. Its unsupported length is 12 ft-0 in., and it is not subjected to sidesway.

Using ACI Specifications, Ultimate Strength Design Methods, determine if this column is satisfactory in its design.

$$\text{Concrete:} \quad f'_c = 3,000 \text{ psi}$$

$$\text{Steel:} \quad f_y = 50,000 \text{ psi}$$

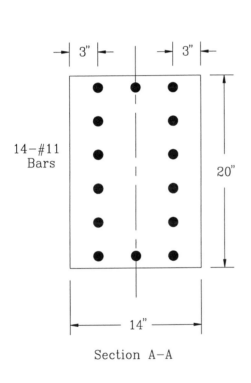

Section A-A

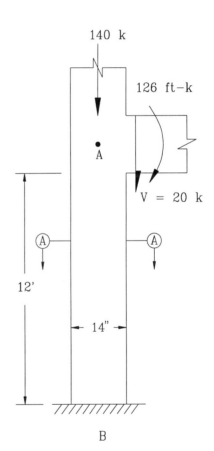

Fig. P9.9.4 (a) Tied Column

Solution

(Use ACI-89 Code, USD)

Assume load factor 1.7 (corresponding to live loads) for all loads and moments.

Design P_u $= 1.7 \times (140 + 20) = 272$ kip

Design M_u $= 1.7 \times 126 = 214.2$ ft-kip

Since the moment at the fixed end bottom is not given,

assume $\dfrac{M_1}{M_2} = -\dfrac{1}{2}$ (side-sway is prevented).

Also, the stiffness of the beam is not known.

We assume $\psi_A = 2.$ and, because of fixity at the end B, $\psi_B = 0$.

On Column 2, Page 49, "Braced Frames" of ACI Publication, SP-17A(78), Design Handbook, draw a straight line from the point $\psi_A = 2$ to that $\psi_B = 0$. Find k = 0.65.

Note: By using ACI Design Handbook SP-17(85) one may obtain similar result.

Thus,

$$\frac{k\,L_u}{r} = \frac{0.65 \times 12 \times 12}{0.3 \times 14}$$

$$= 22.3 < 34 - \frac{M_1}{M_2} = 34 - 12\left(-\frac{1}{2}\right) = 40$$

Hence, slenderness can be neglected, and the column may be treated as a short column. That is, $\delta = 1.0$

$$e = \frac{M_u}{P_u} = \frac{214.2}{272} = 0.78 \text{ ft} = 9.45 \text{ in.}$$

$$\frac{\delta\,e}{h} = \frac{1 \times 9.45}{14} = 0.68$$

$$\varrho_g = \frac{A_s}{A_g} = \frac{14 \times 1.56}{14 \times 20} = 0.078 < 0.08$$

$$\gamma = \frac{14 - 2 \times 3}{14} = 0.57$$

Note: No table is available for the case where $f'_c = 3$ ksi, $f_y = 50$ ksi.

A. For $f'_c = 3$ ksi, $f_y = 40$ ksi, $\varrho_g = 0.078$, Columns 2.1 [p. 268, ACI Publication SP-17A(78)], gives:

	P_u/A_g		
	From Tables		By Linear Interpolation
$(\delta\ e)/h$ γ	0.6	0.8	0.68
0.45	0.90	0.68	0.812
0.60	1.11	0.85	1.006
0.57	—	—	0.967

B. For $f'_c = 3$ ksi, $f_y = 60$ ksi, $\varrho_g = 0.078$, Columns 2.4 gives:

	P_u/A_g		
	From Tables		By Linear Interpolation
$(\delta\ e)/h$ γ	0.6	0.8	0.68
0.45	0.90	0.69	0.816
0.60	1.26	0.98	1.148
0.57	—	—	1.082

C. For $f'_c = 3$ ksi, $f_y = 50$ ksi, $\varrho_g = 0.078$, by linear interpolation,

$$\frac{\delta\ e}{h} = 0.68, \qquad \gamma = 0.57$$

$$\frac{P_u}{A_g} = 0.967 + \frac{1}{2}(1.082 - 0.967) = 1.025$$

Thus, $P_u = 1.025\ A_g = 1.025\ (14 \times 20) = 286.7$ kip > 272 kip

Therefore, the design is satisfactory.

Try interaction diagram similar to P. E. Problem 3.

9.9.5   P. E. PROBLEM 5 — ECCENTRICALLY LOADED SHORT-TIED COLUMN

Repeat the Problem 9.9.4 by using the straight line approximation. The maximum value of P_u (P'_u) for a given M_u can be obtained from the P-M interaction curve as given below:

$$P'_u = \frac{P_o}{1 + \left[(P_o/P_b) - 1 \right] (e/e_b)}$$

$$= P_o - (P_o - P_b) \times \frac{M_u}{M_b}$$

where

$$e' = \frac{M_u}{P'_u} \text{ and } e = \frac{M_u}{P_u}$$

Solution

From previous example, $e = 9.5$ in., design $P_u = 272$ kip, $M_u = 214.2$ ft-k

Consider the balance condition, $\varepsilon_c = 0.003$, $\varepsilon_s = f_y/E_s = \varepsilon_y$

$$\varepsilon_y = 50/29,000 = 0.00171$$

The corresponding strain diagram is shown below.

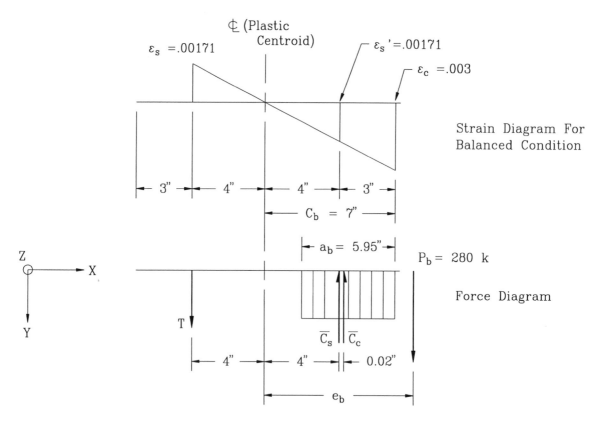

Fig. P9.9.5 (a) Strain and Force Diagram

In the same figure, it also shows the diagram for forces in equilibrium.

Solved by straight line approximation:

$$c_b = \frac{0.003}{0.003 + 0.00171} \times 11 = 7.0 \text{ in.}$$

$$a_b = \beta_1 c_b = 0.85 \times 7.0 = 5.95 \text{ in.}$$

$$\overline{T} = 6 \times 1.56 \times 50 = 468 \text{ kip}$$

$$\overline{C}_s = 6 \times 1.56 \times 50 = 468 \text{ kip}$$

$$\overline{C}_c = 0.85 \times 3 \times (20 \times 5.95 - 6 \times 1.56) = 280 \text{ kip}$$

$$\sum F_y = 0 : \quad \overline{T} + \overline{P}_b - \overline{C}_s - \overline{C}_c = 0$$

$$\overline{P}_b = \overline{C}_s + \overline{C}_c - \overline{T} = 468 + 280 - 468 = 280 \text{ kip}$$

$$P_b = \phi \overline{P}_b = 0.7 \times 280 = 196 \text{ kip}$$

Note: $\phi = 0.7$, since $0.1 f'_c A_g = 0.1 \times 3 \times 14 \times 20 = 84 \text{ k} < 196 \text{ k}$

Taking moments about the center line:

$$\sum M = 0:$$

$$4\overline{T} + 4\overline{C}_s + 4.02\overline{C}_c - \overline{M}_b = 0$$

$$\overline{M}_b = 4\overline{T} + 4\overline{C}_s + 4.02\overline{C}_c$$

$$= \frac{4 \times 468 + 4 \times 468 + 4.02 \times 280}{12}$$

$$= 405.8 \text{ ft-k}$$

$$e_b = \frac{\overline{M}_b}{\overline{P}_b} = 17.4 \text{ in.} \gg e = 9.5 \text{ in.}$$

$$M_b = \phi \overline{M}_b = 0.7 \times 406 = 284 \text{ ft-k}$$

$$\phi \overline{M}_b > M_u = 214.2 \text{ ft-k}$$

$$\phi \overline{P}_b < P_u = 272 \text{ kip}$$

Hence, compression controls.

$$\bar{P}_o = 0.85 \, f'_c \, (A_c - A_{st}) + A_{st} \, f_y$$

$$= 0.85 \times 3 \times (14 \times 20 - 14 \times 1.56) + 14 \times 1.56 \times 50$$

$$= 1,750 \text{ kip}$$

$$P_o = \phi \, \bar{P}_o = 0.7 \times 1,750 = 1,225 \text{ kip}$$

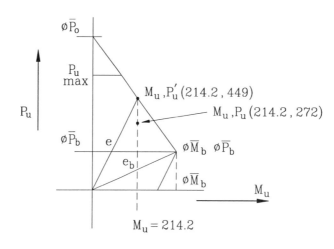

Fig. P9.9.5 (b)

Note: $P = 272$ k, $M_u = 214.2$ ft-k was given. Holding 214.2 ft-k as a given item, one may find $\bar{P}'_u$ by simple proportion. If $\bar{P}'_u > P_u$ then column is OK.

$$\bar{P}'_u = P_o - \left(P_o - P_b\right) \frac{M_u}{M_b}$$

$$= 1,225 - (1225 - 196) \times \frac{214.2}{284}$$

$$= 449 \text{ kip} > 272 \text{ kip}$$

Demand/Capacity ratio:

$$\frac{272}{449} = 0.60 < 1.0 \quad \text{OK}$$

Therefore, the design is satisfactory.

Using ACI 318-83, 89 Code, for a tied column:

$$P_{u\,max} = \phi \, P_{n\,max} = 0.80\phi \, [0.85f'_c \, (A_g - A_{st}) + f_y A_{st}]$$

$$\therefore \quad P_{u\,max} = 0.80 \times 1225 = 980 \text{ kip} \gg 449 \text{ kip}$$

$$\therefore \quad \bar{P}'_u = 449 \text{ kip} \quad \text{OK}$$

9.9.6   P. E. PROBLEM 6 — ECCENTRICALLY LOADED SHORT COLUMN

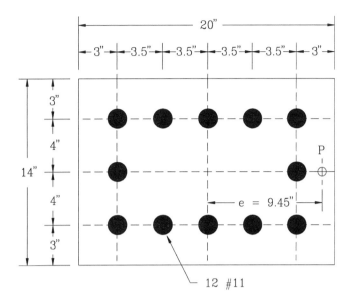

Fig. P9.9.6 (a)

Given Service Loads:

$\quad$ P $\;=\;$ 260 kip

$\quad$ M $\;=\;$ 126 ft-kip

and

$\quad$ f'_c $\;=\;$ 3.5 ksi

$\quad$ f_y $\;=\;$ 50 ksi

Load factor $=$ 1.7

$\quad$ A_s $\;=\;$ Twelve #11

Assume length effects negligible.

Required:

A.   Find maximum allowable axial load.

B.   Find P_b and M_b.

C.   Is column section adequate for the above service loads?

Solution

A. Maximum ultimate axial load at $M_u = 0$.

$$P_o = \phi \left[0.85 \, f'_c \, (A_g - A_{st}) + f_y \, A_{st} \right]$$

$$A_g = 14 \times 20 = 280 \text{ in.}^2$$

$$A_{st} = 12 \times 1.56 = 18.76 \text{ in.}^2$$

$$P_o = 0.70 \left[0.85 \times 3.5 \, (280 - 18.72) + 50 \times 18.72 \right]$$

$$= 0.70 \, [777 + 936]$$

$$= 1,199 \text{ kip}$$

For tied column, allowable ultimate capacity:

$$P_u = 0.80 \, P_o = 0.80 \times 1,199 = 959 \text{ kip}$$

B. At balanced strain condition:

$$\varepsilon_c = 0.0030$$

$$\varepsilon_s = \frac{f_y}{E_s} = \frac{50}{29000} = 0.001724$$

Fig. P9.9.6 (b) Strain and Stress Diagram

$$c = \left(\frac{\varepsilon_c}{\varepsilon_c + \varepsilon_s}\right)$$

$$= \left(\frac{0.0030}{0.0030 + 0.00172}\right) \times 17.0 = 10.80 \text{ in.}$$

$$a = \beta_1 c = 0.85 \times 10.80 = 9.18 \text{ in.}$$

Concrete Compression:

$$C_c = 0.85 \text{ f}'_c \text{ ba} = 0.85 \times 3.5 \times 14 \times 9.18 = 382 \text{ kip}$$

Compression in Steel:

$$C_s = \left(f_y - 0.85 \text{ f}'_c\right) A_{st}$$

$$C_{s1} = (50 - 0.85 \times 3.5) \times 3 \times 1.56 = 220 \text{ kip}$$

Note: $\varepsilon_s = 0.00220 > 0.00172$, $f_s = f_y$

$$C_{s2} = \left[\left(\frac{119}{172}\right) \times 50 - 3.0\right] \times 2 \times 1.56 = 99 \text{ kip}$$

$$C_{s3} = \left(\frac{22}{172}\right) \times 50 \times 2 \times 1.56 = 20 \text{ kip}$$

$$\sum C = C_c + C_{s1} + C_{s2} + C_{s3} = 721 \text{ kip}$$

Tension:

$$T_1 = 50 \times 3 \times 1.56 = 234 \text{ kip}$$

$$T_2 = \left(\frac{75}{172}\right) \times 50 \times 2 \times 1.56 = 68 \text{ kip}$$

$$\sum T = T_1 + T_2 = 302 \text{ kip}$$

Net Compression Capacity:

$$P_n = C - T = 721 - 302 = 419 \text{ kip}$$

$$P_b = \phi P_n = 0.70 \times 419 = 293 \text{ kip}$$

Moment Capacity about Center Line for Each Term:

$$M_n = 382 \times \left(10.0 - \frac{9.18}{2}\right) = 2,067 \text{ in.-kip}$$

$$220 \times 7.0 = 1,540$$

$$99 \times 3.5 = 346$$

$$20 \times 0 = 0$$

$$68 \times 3.5 = 238$$

$$234 \times 7 = 1638$$

$$\sum M = 5,829 \text{ in.-kip}$$

C. Check adequacy of column under given loads:

$$M_n = 5,829 \text{ in-kip} = 485 \text{ ft-kip}$$

$$e_b = \frac{5,829}{419} = 13.91 \text{ in.} = 1.159 \text{ ft}$$

$$M_b = 293 \times 1.159 = 340 \text{ ft-kip}$$

Design $P_u = 260 \times 1.7 = 442 \text{ kip} > 293 \text{ kip}$

Compression controls. No need to calculate M_o.

$$M_u = 126 \times 1.7 = 214 \text{ ft-kip}$$

At $M_u = 214$ ft-kip

$$P_u = P_o - (P_o - P_b)\left(\frac{M_u}{M_b}\right)$$

$$= 1,199 - (1,199 - 293)\frac{214}{340}$$

$$= 1,199 - 570$$

$$= 629 \text{ kip} > 442 \text{ kip}$$

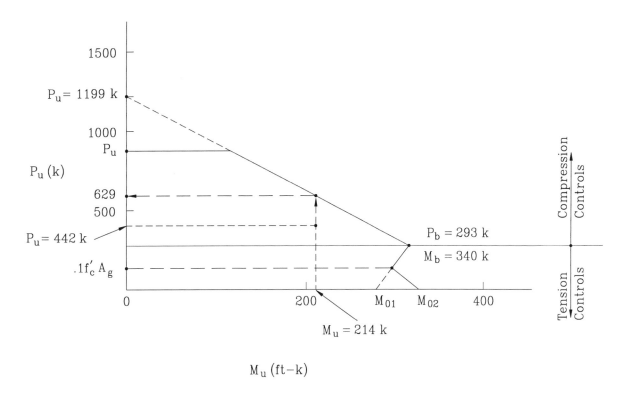

Fig. P9.9.6 (c) Load-Moment Interaction

In this particular problem, it is not necessary to draw the P-M interaction diagram below the "compression control" zone. However, if the complete P-M interaction diagram has to be drawn, the point, M_o, shall be determined by trial and error method.

9.9.7   P. E. PROBLEM 7 — COLUMN DESIGN IN A FRAME

A. A laterally supported frame is shown below in Figure P9.9.7 (a) and is loaded by:
  - DL and weight = 100 psf
  - LL = 50 psf
  - The frame is 20 ft-0 in. c/c

Determine the internal forces in Column AB.

(The solution for this part is given in the Volume 1, Section 1, Structural Analysis).

B. Determine the reinforcement at Section A-A and show bar locations on sketch.

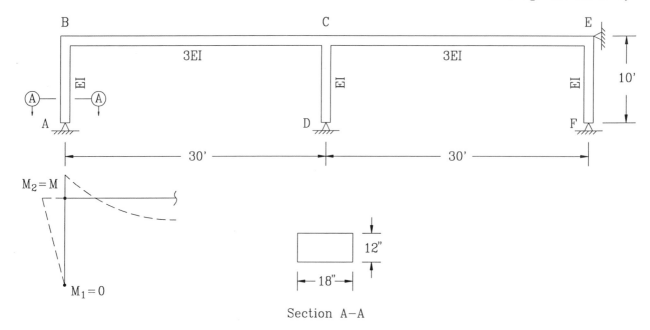

Fig. P9.9.7 (a)

Solution

From results of moment distribution and analysis the maximum unfactored axial load and moments in column AB are:

Axial load   P = 41.08 kip
Moment   M = 110.8 ft-kip

Consider:

Column size 12 in. × 18 in.

$$f'_c = 3500 \text{ psi}$$
$$f_y = 60,000 \text{ psi}$$

(1) Average load factor $= \dfrac{1.4 \times 100 + 1.7 \times 50}{100 + 50} = 1.50$

Factored Load

$$P_u = 41.08 \times 1.5 = 61.6 \text{ kip}$$

$$M_u = 110.8 \times 1.5 = 166.2 \text{ ft-kip}$$

$$e = \frac{166.2 \times 12}{61.6} = 32.4 \text{ in.}$$

Assume tension controls and try four #10:

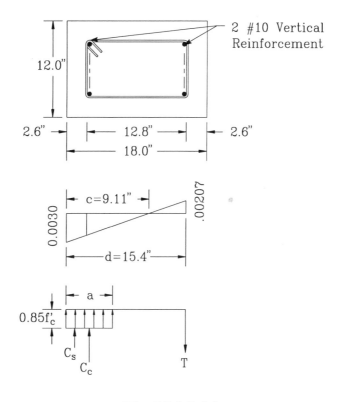

Fig. P9.9.7 (b)

(2) Find P_b, M_b

At balanced strain condition:

$$\varepsilon_c = 0.0030$$

$$\varepsilon_s = \frac{f_y}{E_s} = \frac{60}{29,000} = 0.00207$$

$$c = \left(\frac{\varepsilon_c}{\varepsilon_c + \varepsilon_s}\right) d = \left(\frac{0.0030}{0.0030 + 0.00207}\right) \times 15.40 = 9.11 \text{ in.}$$

$$a = \beta_1 c = 0.85 \times 9.11 = 7.74 \text{ in.}$$

Concrete compression:

$$C_c = 0.85 \, f'_c \, ba = 0.85 \times 3.5 \times 12.0 \times 7.74 = 276.3 \text{ kip}$$

Compression in steel:

$$\varepsilon_s = 0.0030 \times \frac{6.51}{9.11} = 0.00214 > 0.00207$$

$$C_c = \left(f_y - 0.85 \, f'_c\right) A_{st} = (60 - 0.85 \times 3.5) \times 2.54 = 144.8$$

$$\sum C = C_c + C_s = 276.3 + 144.8 = 421.1 \text{ kip}$$

Tension:

$$T = f_y \, A_{st} = 60.0 \times 2.54 = 152.4 \text{ kip}$$

Net compression capacity:

$$P_n = C - T = 421.1 - 152.4 = 268.7 \text{ kip}$$

$$P_b = \phi \, P_n = 0.7 \times 268.7 = 188.1 \text{ kip}$$

Moment capacity about centerline:

$$M_n = 276.3 \left(9.0 - \frac{9.11}{2}\right) + 144.8 + (9.0 - 2.6) + 152.4 \, (9.0 - 2.6)$$

$$= 1,228 + 927 + 975 \text{ in.-kip}$$

$$= 3,130 \text{ in.} - \text{kip} = 260.8 \text{ ft-kip}$$

$$M_b = \phi \, M_n = 0.7 \times 260.8 = 182.6 \text{ ft-kip}$$

(3) Moment capacity when $P_u = 0$:

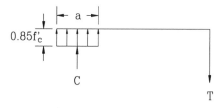

Fig. P9.9.7 (c)

The effect of compression steel is neglected in this diagram.

$$T = f_y A_s = 60 \times 2.54 = 152.4 \text{ kip}$$

$$a = \frac{T}{0.85 \ f'_c \ b} = \frac{152.4}{0.85 \times 3.5 \times 12.0} = 4.27 \text{ in.}$$

$$M_n = T\left(d - \frac{a}{2}\right) = 152.4\left(15.4 - \frac{4.27}{2}\right)$$

$$= 2,022 \text{ in.-kip} = 168.5 \text{ ft-kip}$$

$$\phi \ M_n = 0.90 \times 168.5 = 151.6 \text{ ft-kip}$$

(4)

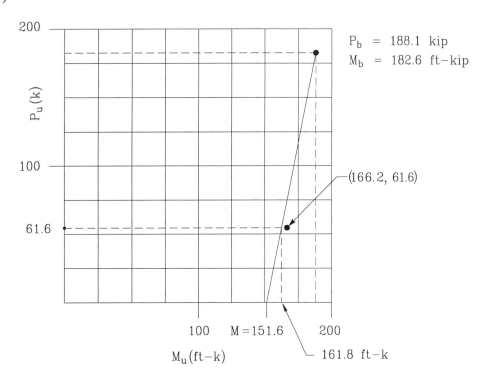

$$P_b = 188.1 \text{ kip}$$
$$M_b = 182.6 \text{ ft-kip}$$

Fig. P9.9.7 (d)

At $P_u = 61.6$ kip

Allow $M_u = 151.6 + \dfrac{61.6}{188.1} (182.6 - 151.6) = 161.8$ ft-kip

Required $M_u = 166.2$ ft-kip   Say close enough

10

FOOTINGS

10.1 TYPES OF FOOTINGS

1. Wall footings, used to support continuous walls of a building or a base for a retaining wall.

2. Single-column footings, also called isolated footing used to support the load of one single column.

3. Combined footings, generally used to support the load of two or more columns where the exterior column cannot extend beyond the property line or when the two columns are close together.

4. Cantilever Footings — The eccentric exterior-column footing is connected with the nearest interior-column footing by means of a concrete beam or strap poured monolithically with the two footings.

5. Raft or mat foundation, used when the soil is of poor quality or the loads are very large that 50% or more of the building plan is covered by footings.

6. Pile caps — reinforced concrete slabs used to transfer column loads to groups of piles.

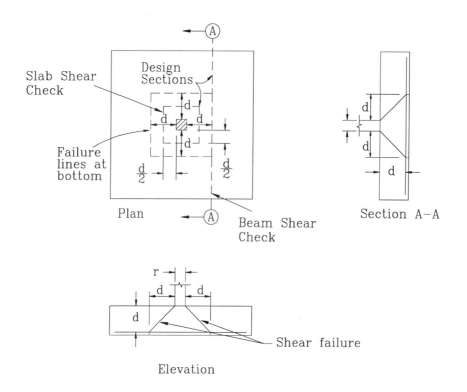

Figure 10.1 Column or Spread Footing

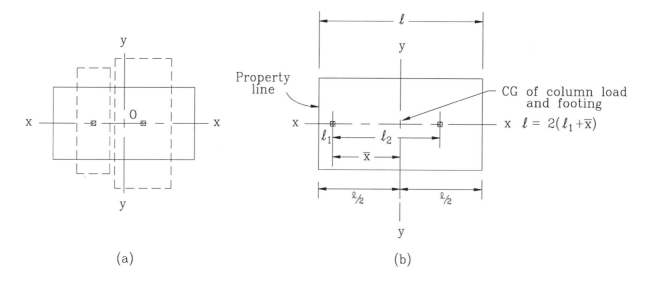

(a)   (b)

Figure 10.2 Combined Footing

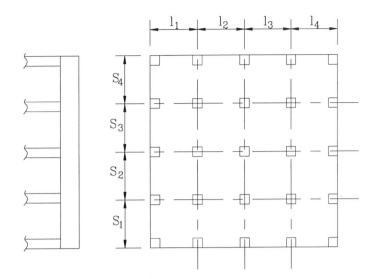

Generally designed as
an inverted flat slab

Figure 10.3 Mat Footing

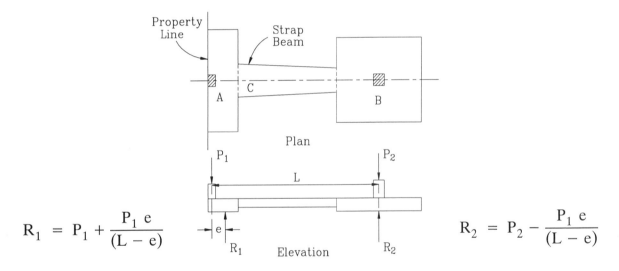

$$R_1 = P_1 + \frac{P_1\,e}{(L - e)}$$

$$R_2 = P_2 - \frac{P_1\,e}{(L - e)}$$

Figure 10.4 Cantilever Footing

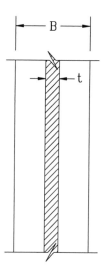

Figure 10.5 Wall Footing

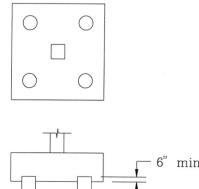

Figure 10.6 Pile Footing

10.2 DESIGN OF WALL FOOTINGS

Step 1:

Assume a thickness of the footing, t, the effective depth, d = t − 3.5 in. where 3.5 in. is clear cover.

Step 2:

Calculate effective bearing capacity q_e

$$q_e = q_a - \left(\frac{t}{12}\right) 150 - \left(\frac{D - t}{12}\right) \gamma$$

where

q_a = allowable bearing capacity of soil (psf)

t   = thickness assumed in Step 1 (in.)

D   = depth of bottom of the footing (in.)

γ = unit weight of soil (lb-ft^3)

Step 3:

Obtain width of footing $= \dfrac{DL + LL}{q_e}$

Step 4:

Obtain bearing pressure for design (q_u)

$$q_u = \frac{1.4(DL) + 1.7(LL)}{\text{width of footing from Step 3}}$$

Step 5:

Calculate depth required for shear at a distance d = t − 3.5 in.

$$V_u = \left(\frac{\text{width of footing}}{2} - \frac{\text{thickness of wall}}{2 \times 12} - \frac{d}{12}\right) q_u$$

$$d = \frac{V_u}{0.85 \times 2\sqrt{f'_c} \times b}$$

b   = 1 ft width of the wall   = 12 in.

If d from Step 5 ≤ d assumed in Step 1   OK

If greater, repeat Steps 1 through 5 with higher assumed d until the value calculated and the value assumed are close enough.

Step 6:

Take moments at face of wall:

$$\text{Cantilever length } L = \frac{\text{width of footing}}{2} - \frac{\text{wall thickness (in.)}}{12}$$

$$M_u = L q_u \frac{L}{2} = \frac{q_u L^2}{2} \text{ (ft-kip)}$$

$$\text{Get } F = \frac{b\, d^2}{12,000}, \text{ where b usually taken at 1 ft}$$

$$\text{From tables with } K_n = \frac{M_u}{F} \text{ known, get } a_n$$

$$A_s = \frac{M_u}{a_n d}$$

10.3   DESIGN OF SQUARE ISOLATED FOOTINGS

A. There are two situations to consider in footings:

1. One-way shear or flexure shear where

$$d = \frac{V_u}{\phi \, 2\sqrt{f'_c} \, b}$$ ACI Sec. 11.3.1.1

V_u = total shear

   = net soil pressure times the crosshatched area (Figure 10.7)

d = effective depth

f'_c = concrete cylinder strength (specified)

Net Soil Pressure = q_e = q_a − (weight of footing+soil above)/unit area as defined in Step 4 in the next section.

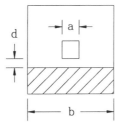

Figure 10.7 One-Way Shear in Rectangular Footing

2. Two-way shear or punching shear where

$$d = \frac{V_u}{\phi \, 4\sqrt{f'_c} \, b_o}$$ ACI Sec. 11.12.2.1

V_u = net soil pressure times the crosshatched area (Figure 10.8)

b_o = 4(a + d)

where

   a = size of the column

   d = effective depth of the footing

ACI 318-89 Code requires that the lowest value for V_c be used and that the following equations be checked: ACI Eq. (11-36), (11-37), (11-38).

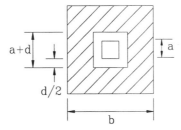

Figure 10.8 Two-Way Shear in Rectangular Footing

B. Maximum moment occurs at the face of reinforced concrete column. (ACI Sec. 15.4)

C. To estimate the initial thickness, many designers use 20% of the footing width or the column diameter plus 3.0-in. cover.

Steps for Design

1. Assume initial thickness, t ($d = t - 4.0$ in.)

2. Obtain q_e as described in wall footings.

3. Obtain area required $= \dfrac{DL + LL}{q_e} = A$

4. Obtain bearing pressure for design (q_u):

$$q_u = \frac{1.4\,(DL) + 1.7\,(LL)}{A}$$

5. Check d for one-way shear and two-way shear. If d in either case < d assumed in Step 1, assume higher value and go back to *Step 1*.

6. Calculate $M_u = \dfrac{(b - a)}{2} \times b \times q_u \times \dfrac{(b - a)}{4} = \dfrac{b\, q_u\, (b - a)^2}{8}$

Then obtain $F = \dfrac{bd^2}{12,000}$

7. Enter Table with $K_n = \dfrac{M_u}{F}$ to get a_n

8. $A_s = \dfrac{M_u}{a_n\, d} > \dfrac{200}{f_y}\, b_w\, d$

Or from Step 6:

7A. $A_{s_1} = \dfrac{200}{f_y} \times b \times d$ (This is minimum steel if flexure controls)

$F_u = A_{s1} \times f_y$

$a = \dfrac{F_u}{0.85 \times f'_c \times b}$

$M_u = 0.9 \times F_u \times \left(d - \dfrac{a}{2}\right)$

If $M_u > M_u\, R_{req}$ OK

8A. If not try $A_{s2} > A_1$

Quick Check:

Without using any table, calculations can be done using following steps:

Assume lever arm = 0.75 d

$$A_{s_1} = \frac{M_u}{0.75d \times f_y} \quad \text{go to Step 7A.}$$

If A_{s_1} obtained above is substantially less than $A_{s\ min}$,

use $A_{s_2} = A_{s_1} \times 1.33$.

If A_{s_1} is not adequate by first iteration, try

$$A_{s_2} = \frac{M_{UR}}{M_{u_1}} \times A_{s_1} \quad \text{go to Step 7A.}$$

10.4   LOAD TRANSFER FROM COLUMNS TO FOOTINGS (ACI SEC. 15.8)

At the base of the column the allowable bearing strength is:

$$\phi\ (0.85\ f'_c\ A_1) \hspace{4cm} \text{ACI Sec. 10.15}$$

where

$\phi\ =\ 0.7$

$A_1\ =\ $ column area

$d\ =\ $ effective depth

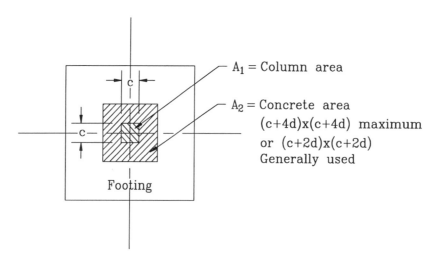

Figure 10.9 Plan View of Footing

$$\text{Allowable bearing on footings}\ =\ \phi\ (0.85)\ f'_c\ A_1\ \sqrt{\frac{A_2}{A_1}} \hspace{1cm} \text{ACI Sec. 10.15.1}$$

Where

$A_2\ =\ $ portion of footing geometrically similar and concentric with the columns.

$$\left(\text{ACI code limits}\ \sqrt{\frac{A_2}{A_1}}\ \text{to}\ <\ 2\right) \hspace{2cm} \text{ACI Sec. 10.15.1}$$

If the computed bearing stress is higher than the smaller of the two allowable values, it will be necessary to carry the excess with dowels or extend the column bars into the footing.

In case no dowels are needed, the code requires 4 bars or dowels of area no less than 0.005 times A_1 and the diameter of dowels may not exceed the diameter of column bars by more than 0.15 in. This is done to ensure sufficient bond between column and footing.

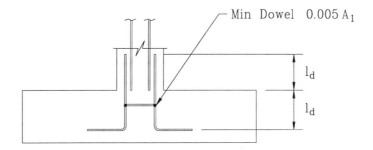

Figure 10.10 Footing Dowel Details

10.4.1 DESIGN FOR LOAD TRANSFER

Step 1:

Obtain factored load which is the bearing force at base of column

$$W = 1.4 \, DL + 1.7 \, LL$$

Step 2:

Calculate allowable bearing force at base of column, $P_1 = \phi(0.85)f_c'A_1$
Note: Use appropriate f_c' for column and footing.

Step 3:

Calculate allowable bearing force on footing, $P_2 = \phi \, (0.85) \, f'_c \, A_1 \, \sqrt{\dfrac{A_2}{A_1}}$

where $\sqrt{\dfrac{A_2}{A_1}} \leq 2$

If the force obtained in Step 2 or 3 is:

A. Greater than 1.4 DL + 1.7 LL, use minimum dowels, $A_s = 0.005 \, (A_1)$
(Remember to use a minimum of 4 dowels.)

B. Less than 1.4 DL + 1.7 LL, the larger value in Steps 2 and 3 controls.

Step 4:

Subtract 1.4 DL + 1.7 LL from the larger value of Steps 2 and 3 and get the excess
load that must be carried by dowels.

Step 5:

Get area of dowels:

$$A_s \;\; = \;\; \frac{\text{excess load}}{f_y} \;\; = \;\; \frac{W - \left(P_1 \text{ or } P_2\right)}{f_y}$$

Note that this value should not be < $0.005A_1$, where A_1 = column area.

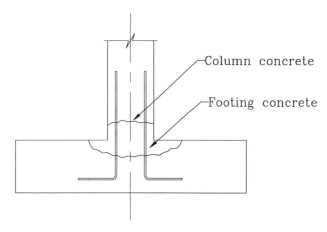

Figure 10.11 Column and Footing Details

10.5 DEVELOPMENT OF REINFORCEMENT IN FOOTINGS (ACI SEC. 15.6)

Development of lengths of dowels (i.e. reinforcement in compression), use the larger of:

a. $\quad L_d = \dfrac{0.02 \, f_y \, d_b}{\sqrt{f'_c}}$ $\qquad$ ACI Sec. 12.3.2

b. $\quad L_d = 0.0003 \, f_y \, d_b$

c. $\quad L_d = 8$ in.

where d_b = diameter of one of the bars used in *Step 5* of Section 10.4.1.

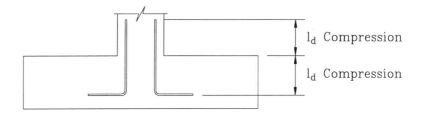

Figure 10.12 Development Lengths in Columns and Footings

In some cases f'_c used for footing is different from f'_c used for columns. Hence, when calculating the development lengths of dowels in:

a. columns — use f'_c used for columns

b. footings — use f'_c used for footings

Critical sections for development of reinforcement shall be assumed at the same locations as for maximum factored moment and at all other vertical plans where changes of section or reinforcement occur. $\qquad$ ACI Section 15.6.3

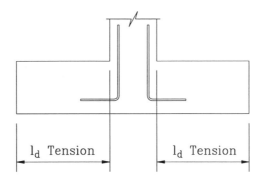

Figure 10.13 Development Lengths in Footings

10.6   P. E. PROBLEMS

10.6.1   P. E. PROBLEM 1 — SQUARE SPREAD FOOTING

Given:

Column f'_c = 5,000 psi

Footing f'_c = 3,000 psi

f_y = 60,000 psi

Allowable soil bearing pressure = 4,000 psf.

Weight of soil = 100 pcf

Design the footing for the footing size and depth, using Strength Method. Do not design steel in footing. Consider load transfer from the column to footing. Use ACI 318-89/92.

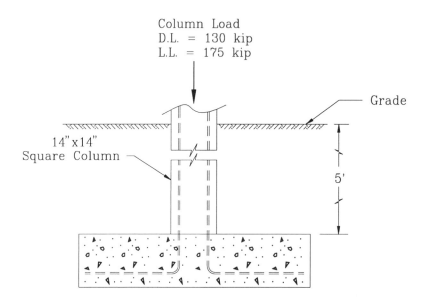

Fig. P10.6.1 (a) Spread Footing

Solution

Given:

Column f'_c	= 5,000 psi
Footing f'_c	= 3,000 psi
Allowable bearing	= 4,000 psf
Weight of soil	= 100 pcf
f_y	= 60,000 psi

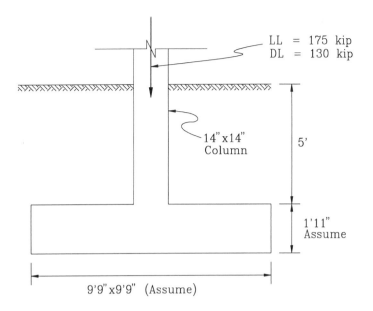

Fig. P10.6.1 (b) Footing Section

A. Try footing size   =   (9 ft-9 in.) × (9 ft-9 in.) × (1 ft-11 in.)

   (Where footing size is not given, add between 5% to 10% of the total service load.)

   Weight of footing = $9.75^2 \times \dfrac{23}{12} \times 0.15$ = 27.3

   Weight of soil   = $(9.75^2 - 1.17^2) \times 5 \times 0.10$ = 46.9

   DL   = 130.0

   LL   = 175.0

                                                    Total = 379.2 kip

   Gross soil pressure = $\dfrac{379.2}{9.75 \times 9.75}$ = 3.99 ksf < 4.0 ksf

   P_u = 1.4(DL) + 1.7(LL)

        = 1.4 × 130 + 1.7 × 175

        = 479.5 kip

   q_u = $\dfrac{479.5}{9.75 \times 9.75}$ = 5.04 ksf

B. Shear (Two-Way Action)   ACI Sec. 11.12.2

Shear strength of concrete:

$$V_c = \left(2 + \frac{4}{\beta_c}\right) \sqrt{f'_c}\ b_o\ d \ \leq\ 4\sqrt{f'_c}\ b_o\ d$$

$$b_o = 4\left(14 + 2 \times \frac{19}{2}\right) = 132 \text{ in.}$$

$$\beta_c = 1.0 \text{ for square column}$$

Assume #8 bars:

Average d $= 23 - (3 + 1) = 19$ in.

$V_c = 4 \times \sqrt{3,000} \times 132 \times 19 = 550.0$ kip

$V_s = 0$ No stirrups

$V_n = V_c + V_s = 550.0$ kip

Ultimate shear $= 5.04\left(9.75^2 - \left(\frac{33}{12}\right)^2\right)$

$V_u = 441.0$ kip $< \phi\ V_n = 0.85 \times 550.0$
$= 468$ kip

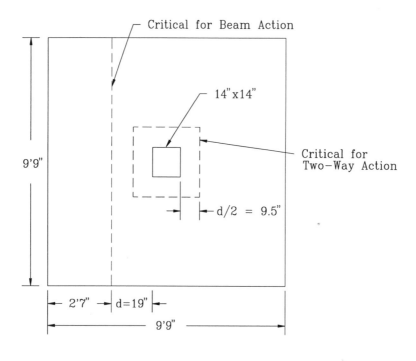

Fig. P10.6.1 (c) Footing Plan

C. Shear — Beam Action (One-Way Shear)

Shear strength of concrete:

$$V_n = 2\sqrt{f'_c}\ b_w\ d$$

$$= \frac{2\sqrt{3,000}}{1,000} \times 9.75 \times 12 \times 19$$

$$V_n = 243.5\ \text{kip}$$

$$V_u = 5.04 \times 2.583 \times 9.75$$

$$= 127.0\ \text{kip}\ <\ \phi\ V_n = 0.85 \times 243.5 = 207\ \text{kip}$$

D. Check column size:

Assume tied column

$$P_n = 0.85\ f'_c\ A_g = 0.85 \times 5.0 \times 14^2 = 833\ \text{kip}$$

Permissible ultimate bearing strength

$$= \phi\ P_n$$

$$= 0.7 \times 833$$

$$= 583\ \text{kip}\ >\ 479.5\ \text{kip} \qquad \text{OK}$$

Check bearing stress on concrete:

$$f_c = \frac{479,500}{14 \times 14} = 2,446\ \text{psi}\ <\ 0.85\ \phi\ f'_c\ \sqrt{\frac{A_2}{A_1}}$$

from ACI 10.15,

$$A_2 = (14 + 4 \times 19)^2, \quad A_1 = 14^2, \quad \sqrt{\frac{A_2}{A_1}} = 6.43\ >\ 2.0$$

Therefore, Use 2.0 max.

$$0.85 \times 0.7 \times 3,000 \times 2 = 3,570\ \text{psi}\ >\ 2,446\ \text{psi} \qquad \text{OK}$$

Minimum $A_s = 0.005\ A_g = 0.005 \times 14^2 = 0.98\ \text{in.}^2$

Therefore, use four #6, $A_s = 1.76\ \text{in.}^2$

Development length of dowel (compression)

$$= \frac{0.02\ d_b\ f_y}{\sqrt{f'_c}} \quad \text{but not less than } 0.0003\ d_b\ f_y$$

$$L_d \text{ in column} = 0.02 \times 0.75 \times \frac{60,000}{\sqrt{5,000}} = 12.7 \text{ in.}$$

$$\text{or} = 0.0003 \times 0.75 \times 60,000 = 13.5 \text{ in.} > 12.7 \text{ in.}$$

$$L_d \text{ in footing} = 0.02 \times 0.75 \times \frac{60,000}{\sqrt{3,000}} = 16.4 \text{ in.}$$

$$< 23 \text{ in} - (3 + 1) = 19 \text{ in.} \qquad \text{OK}$$

10.6.2 P. E. PROBLEM 2 — SQUARE SPREAD FOOTING

Design of square spread footing to resist a single column load of 500 kip due to dead load and 200 kip due to live load. The footing is to be located as shown in the diagram of Section A-A Fig. P10.6.2 (a). The weight of the soil fill on top of the footing is to be included as a load on the footing and not to be neglected. Use latest ACI specification available to you. Use ACI 318-89/92 Code.

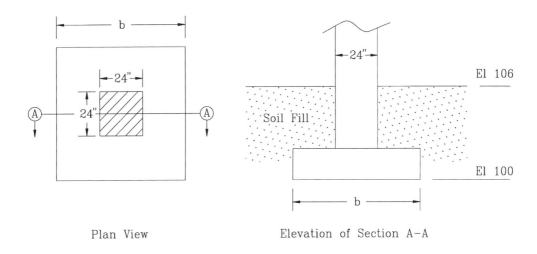

| Plan View | Elevation of Section A-A |

Fig. P10.6.2 (a) Square Footing

Solution

Assume:

$$\text{Maximum Bearing Capacity of Soil} = 5 \text{ ksf}$$
$$\text{Soil Weight} = 0.12 \text{ kip/ft}^3$$
$$f'_c = 4,000 \text{ psi}$$
$$f_y = 60,000 \text{ psi}$$

$$DL = 500 \text{ k} \qquad LL = 200 \text{ k}$$

The above loads are unfactored service loads.

A. Determination of plan size of the spread square footing.

Assume d = 26 in. for a total depth = 30 in. = 2.5 ft

$$q_e = 5,000 - \frac{30}{12}(150) - \frac{6(12) - 30}{12}(120)$$

$$= 5,000 - 375 - 420 = 4,205 \text{ psf} = 4.205 \text{ ksf}$$

$$A_{req} = \frac{500 + 200}{4.205} = 167 \text{ ft}^2 \quad (\text{Say } 13 \text{ ft} \times 13 \text{ ft})$$

B. Check shear capacity:

Bearing pressure for design factored loads:

$$q_u = \frac{1.4 \times 500 + 1.7 \times 200}{169} = 6.15 \text{ ksf}$$

1. Two-Way Shear:

$$b_o = 4 \times (24 + 26) = 200 \text{ in.}$$

$$V_u = \left[169 - 4.17^2\right] \times 6.15 = 933 \text{ kip}$$

$$\phi\, V_n = \phi\, 4\sqrt{f'_c}\, b_o\, d$$

$$= 0.85 \times \frac{4\sqrt{4,000}}{1000} \times 200 \times 26.0 = 1,118 \text{ kip} > V_u$$

2. Beam Shear:

$$b_w = 6.50 - 1.0 - 2.17 = 3.33 \text{ ft}$$

$$V_u = 6.15 \times 13 \times 3.33 = 266 \text{ kip}$$

$$\phi\, V_n = \phi\, 2\sqrt{f'_c}\, b_w\, d$$

$$= 0.85 \times \frac{2\sqrt{4,000}}{1000} \times 13 \times 12 \times 26.0 = 436 \text{ kip} > V_u$$

Use 13 ft $\times$ 13 ft square by 30-in. thick footing

C. Determine reinforcement for moment:

$$F = \frac{b_w\, d^2}{12,000} = \frac{13 \times 16 \times 26.0^2}{12,000} = 11.72$$

$$M_u = 6.15 \times 13.0 \times 5.50^2 \times \frac{1}{2} = 1,209 \text{ ft-kip}$$

$$K_n = \frac{M_u}{F} = \frac{1,209}{8.79} = 138$$

$$a_n = 4.13 \qquad \text{Flex. 2.2, ACI SP-17 (84)}$$

$$A_s = \frac{M_u}{a_n\, d} = \frac{1,209}{4.13 \times 26.0} = 11.26 \text{ in.}^2$$

$$\text{Minimum } A_s = \frac{200}{f_y}\, b_w\, d$$

$$= \frac{200}{60,000} \times 13 \times 12 \times 26.0 = 13.50 \text{ in.}^2$$

Use the above equation when design is controlled by flexure:

Use eleven #10 bars in two layers with 3-in. cover.

Quick Check:

$$\text{Try } A_{s_1} = \frac{1209 \times 12}{0.75 \times 26 \times 60} = 12.4 \text{ in.}^2$$

Try ten #10 = 12.70 in.^{2}

$$F_y = 12.7 \times 60 = 762 \text{ kip}$$

$$a = \frac{762}{0.85 \times 4 \times (13 \times 12)} = 1.44$$

$$M_u = 0.9 \times 762 \times \left(26 - \frac{1.44}{2}\right) \frac{1}{12}$$

$$= 1445 \text{ ft-k} > 1209 \text{ ft-kip}$$

$$\text{Try } A_{s_2} = 12.7 \times \frac{1209}{1445 \times 5} = 10.6$$

Say eleven #9s

$$A_{s\,min} = 0.0018 \times 12 \times 13 \times 30$$

$$= 8.42 \text{ in.}^2 < 11 \text{ in.}^2 \quad \text{OK}$$

D. Check moment capacity with eleven #10

$$A_s = 11 \times 1.27 = 13.97 \text{ in.}^2$$

$$F_u = 13.97 \times 60 = 838.2 \text{ k}$$

$$a = \frac{F_u}{0.85f_c'b} = \frac{838.2}{0.85 \times 4 \times (13 \times 12)} = 1.58 \text{ in.}$$

$$M_u = 0.9 \times 838.2 \times (26 - \frac{1.58}{2}) \times \frac{1}{12}$$

$$= 1585.0 \text{ k} > 1209 \text{ k} \quad \text{(Too conservative)}$$

Use eleven #9s   Check again.

E. Check development length (bond and anchorage):

According to ACI Code:

$$\text{Minimum Length} = 0.03 \times d_b \times \frac{f_y}{\sqrt{f'_c}}$$

$$= 0.03 \times 1 \times \frac{60,000}{\sqrt{4000}}$$

$$= 28.5 \text{ in.}$$

Development length required for #11 bars:

$$= \frac{0.04\, A_b\, f_y}{\sqrt{f'_c}} \qquad \text{ACI 12.2.2}$$

$$= \frac{0.04 \times 0.79 \times 60,000}{\sqrt{4,000}}$$

$$= 30 \text{ in.}$$

but not less than $0.0004\, d_b\, f_y = 0.0004 \times 1.0 \times 60,000 = 24$ in.

Development length provided $= 5.5 \times 12$ in. $- 3.0$ (cover)

$$= 63 \text{ in.} > 30 \text{ in.} \qquad \text{OK}$$

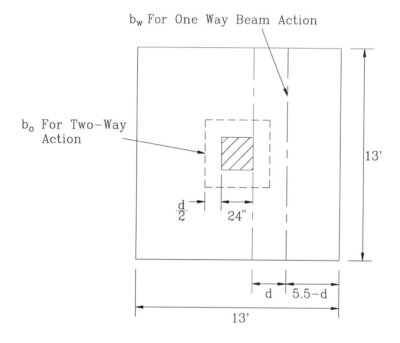

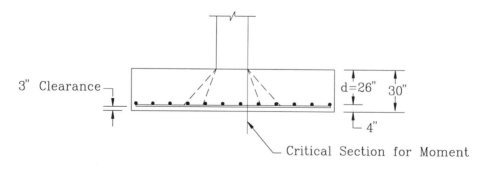

Fig. P10.6.2 (b) Square Footing Detail

10.6.3 P. E. PROBLEM 3 — DOWEL BARS IN FOOTINGS

In the previous problem of spread footing, check the dowel steel requirement for transfer of stress at base of column.

$$f'_c = 4,000 \text{ psi}$$

$$f_y = 60,000 \text{ psi}$$

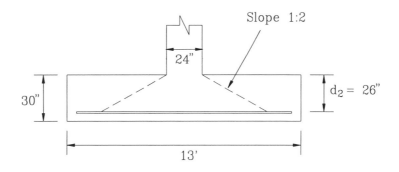

Fig. P10.6.3 (a) Footing Steel Requirement

Solution

Bearing force at base of column:

$$1.4 (500) + 1.7 (200) = 1040 \text{ kip}$$

A. Allowable bearing at base of column

$$0.7 \times 0.85 \times 4 \times (24 \times 24) = 1,371 \text{ kip} > 1,040 \text{ kip} \quad \text{OK}$$

Note, since $B' = 24 + 4 \times 26 = 128 \text{ in.} < B = 169 \text{ in.}$

$$\sqrt{\frac{\text{Area of } B' \times B'}{\text{Area of column}}} = \sqrt{\frac{A_2}{A_1}} = \sqrt{\frac{10.67 \times 10.67}{2 \times 2}} = 5.33 > 2$$

B. Allowable bearing force in footing, according to ACI 10.15 at stress of $2 (\phi) (0.85 \text{ } f'_c)$ is given by:

$$2 \times 0.7 \times 0.85 \times 4 \times (24 \times 24) = 2,742 \text{ kip} > 1,040 \text{ kip} \quad \text{OK}$$

Use minimum dowels (ACI Section 15.8.4.1):

Dowel steel area $= 0.5\%$ of column size 24 in. $\times$ 24 in.

$$= 0.005 \times (24 \times 24) = 2.88 \text{ in.}^2$$

Use four #8 ($A_s = 3.16 \text{ in.}^2$)

C. Development length in compression   ACI Sec. 12.3.2

$$L_d = \frac{0.02\ f_y\ d_b}{\sqrt{f'_c}} = \frac{0.02 \times 60,000 \times 1.0}{\sqrt{4,000}} = 18.97\ \text{in.}$$

$$L_d = 0.0003 \times 60,000 \times 1.00 = 18.0\ \text{in.}$$

$$L_d = 8\ \text{in. minimum}$$

Use 19-in. minimum development length in both column and footing.

If footing and column concrete are of different strength (f'_c), both cases must be checked.

10.6.4 P. E. PROBLEM 4 — RECTANGULAR FOOTING

Given an 18-in. square column load with a DL of 140 kip and an LL of 140 kip, design a footing with the long length approximately two times the short length. The base of the footing is 6 ft below grade. The soil base of the footing having a unit weight of 100 pcf. Find the footing size and depth. Use the ACI-89/92 Code. f'_c = 3000 psi, f_y = 40,000 psi and allowable soil bearing capacity = 4 ksf.

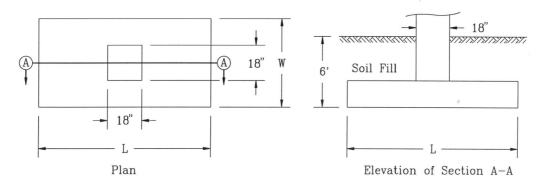

Fig. P10.6.4 (a) Rectangular Footing

Solution

Given:

- P_{DL} = 140 kip
- f'_c = 3000 psi
- P_{LL} = 140 kip
- f_y = 40,000 psi
- Soil weight = 0.10 k/ft^3
- Soil bearing capacity = 4 ksf

A. Determination of base area (plane size) of the footing:

Assume 22-in. footing,   d = 18 in.

Let W = width of the footing

$$q_e = 4,000 - \frac{22}{12}(150) - \frac{(6 \times 12 - 22)\,100}{12}$$

$$= 4,000 - 275 - 417 = 3,308 \text{ psf}$$

$$A_{req} = \frac{280}{3.308} = 84.6 \text{ ft}^2$$

$$= (\text{length})(\text{width}) = (2W)(W)$$

Try 6.5 ft × 13 ft   A = 84.5 ft^2

$$q_u = \frac{1.4(140) + 1.7(140)}{84.5} = 5.13 \text{ ksf}$$

B. Check for footing depth:
1. Depth for one-way shear:

$$b_w = 6.5 \times 12 = 78 \text{ in.}$$

$$\ell = 6.5 - \left(\frac{1.5}{2} + 1.5\right) = 4.25 \text{ ft}$$
$$V_u = 6.5 \times 4.25 \times 5.13 = 142 \text{ kip}$$

$$d = \frac{142,000}{0.85 \times 2\sqrt{3,000} \times 78} = 19.55$$

Say 20.0 in.

2. Depth for two-way shear (punching shear):

$$= 4 \times (c + d)$$
$$b_o = 4 \times 36 = 144 \text{ in.}$$

$$V_u = \left(84.5 - 3^2\right) 5.13 = 387 \text{ kip}$$

$$d = \frac{387,000}{0.85 \times 4\sqrt{3,000} \times 144} = 14.43 < 18 \text{ in.}$$

Use d = 20 in.

Use 6 ft-6 in. × 13 ft-0 in. × 24 in. thick footing

Note:

$$\phi V_n = \phi \left(2 + \frac{4}{\beta_c}\right) \sqrt{f'_c} \, b_o d \leq 4 \sqrt{f'_c} \, b_o d$$

where $\beta_c = \dfrac{L}{\beta}$

C. Determination of Reinforcement

Design of longitudinal steel:

$$d = 24.0 - 3.0 - 0.6 = 20.4 \text{ in.}$$

$$F = \frac{b_w \, d^2}{12,000} = \frac{78 \times 20.4^2}{12,000} = 2.70$$

$$M_u = 5.13 \times 6.5 \times \frac{5.75^2}{2} = 551 \text{ ft-kip}$$

$$K_n = \frac{M_u}{F} = \frac{551}{2.70} = 204$$

$$a_n = 2.86 \qquad \text{Flex. 2.1, ACI SP-17 (84)}$$

$$A_s = \frac{M_u}{a_n \, d} = \frac{551}{2.86 \times 20.4} = 9.44 \text{ in.}^2$$

Use ten #9 longitudinal direction ($A_s = 10.0$ in.^{2})

Check M_u try ten #9:

$$A_s = 10 \times 1 = 10 \text{ in.}^2$$

$$F_u = 10 \times 40 = 400 \text{ k}$$

$$a = \frac{400}{0.85 \times 3 \times (6.5 \times 12)} = 2.01$$

$$M_u = 0.9 \times 400 \times \left(20.4 - \frac{2.01}{2}\right) \times \frac{1}{12}$$

$$= 582 \text{ ft} - \text{k} > 551 \text{ ft} - \text{k required} \quad \text{OK}$$

Quick Check:

$$A_{s_1} = \frac{551 \times 12}{0.75 \times 20.4 \times 40} = 10.8 \text{ in.}^2$$

Try ten #9 — a = 2.01

$$M_u = 0.9 \times (10 \times 40) \times \left(20.4 - \frac{2.01}{2}\right)\frac{1}{12}$$

$$= 582 \text{ ft} - \text{k} > 551 \text{ ft} - \text{k required} \quad \text{OK}$$

Minimum steel:

$$\frac{200}{f_y} \times b \times d = 8 \text{ in.}^2 < 10 \text{ in.}^2 \quad \text{OK}$$

β = ratio of long side to short side of footing:

$$\frac{13}{6.5} = 2.0$$

$$\frac{\beta}{\beta + 1} = \frac{2}{2 = 1} = \frac{2}{3}$$

2/3 of steel along short direction must be placed within the band w:

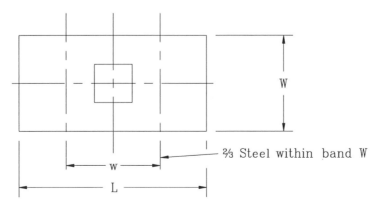

Fig. P10.6.4 (b)

Design of transverse steel:

$$d = 24.0 - 3.0 - 1.2 - 0.6 = 19.2 \text{ in.}$$

$$F = \frac{13.0 \times 12 \times 19.2^2}{12,000} = 4.79$$

$$M_u = 5.13 \times 13.0 \times 2.5^2 = 416.8$$

$$K_n = \frac{416.8}{4.79} = 87 < 172$$

$$\varrho_{min} = \frac{200}{f_y} = \frac{200}{40,000} = 0.0050$$

Use only when design is controlled by flexure:

$$A_s = 0.0050 \times 13.0 \times 12 \times 19.2 = 15.0 \text{ in.}^2$$

Use fifteen #9 transverse direction ($A_s = 15.0$ in.^{2})

$$\text{Reinforcing in band width} = \frac{2}{2+1} = \frac{2}{3}$$

Say 10 bars in band width (6 ft-6 in. $\times$ 6 ft-6 in.)

Check M_u with fifteen #9:

$$A_s = 15 \times 1 = 15 \text{ in.}^2$$

$$F_u = 15 \times 40 = 600$$

$$a = \frac{600}{0.85 \times 3 \times (13 \times 12)} = 1.51$$

$$M_u = 0.9 \times 600 \times \left(19.2 - \frac{1.51}{2}\right) \times \frac{1}{12}$$

$$= 830 \text{ k} \gg 416.8 \text{ k} \quad \text{OK}$$

Too conservative, use twenty #6.

Quick Check:

$$A_{s_1} = \frac{416.8 \times 12}{0.75 \times 19.2 \times 40} = 8.7 \text{ in.}^2$$

Minimum steel:

$$0.0018 \times 13 \times 12 \times 24 = 6.74 \text{ in.}^2 < 8.7 \quad \text{OK}$$

$$a = \frac{8.7 \times 40}{0.85 \times 3 \times (13 \times 12)} = 0.87 \text{ in.}$$

$$M_u = 0.9 \, (8.7 \times 40) \left(19.2 - \frac{0.87}{2}\right) \frac{1}{12}$$

$$= 490 \text{ ft-k} > 416.8 \qquad \text{OK}$$

Use twenty #6 $8.8 \text{ in.}^2 > 8.7$

Place   twelve #6 within band

       four #6 at each side

Total of twenty #6 $\times$ 6 ft-0 in.

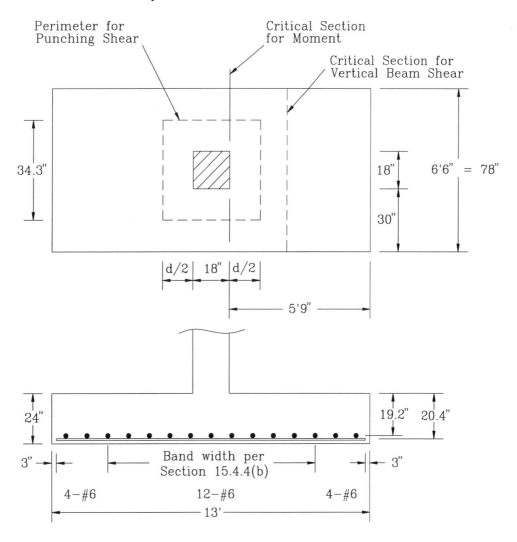

Fig. P10.6.4 (c)   Rectangular Footing Detail

10.6.5 P. E. PROBLEM 5 — SQUARE FOOTING — LOAD AND MOMENT

A rigid square concrete footing shown below supporting a square concrete column is subjected to combined vertical dead and live loads and a bending moment due to live load.

Criteria:

Materials and service loads.

Soil bearing pressure	q = 4.0 ksf	
Concrete	f'_c = 3.0 ksi	
Reinforcement	f_y = 40 ksi	
Dead Load	P = 65 kip;	M = 0
Live Load	P = 100kip;	M = 20 ft-kip

(Use ACI 318-89/92 Ultimate Strength Design.)

Required:

A. Determine soil pressure for given loading conditions based on the service loads.

B. Determine the footing thickness.

C. Determine the bending moment and design the main reinforcing in the footing.

D. Based on No. 7 rebars, check the development length.

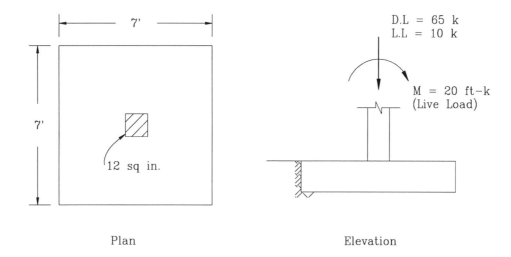

Plan   Elevation

Fig. P10.6.5 (a) Square Footing with Moment

Solution

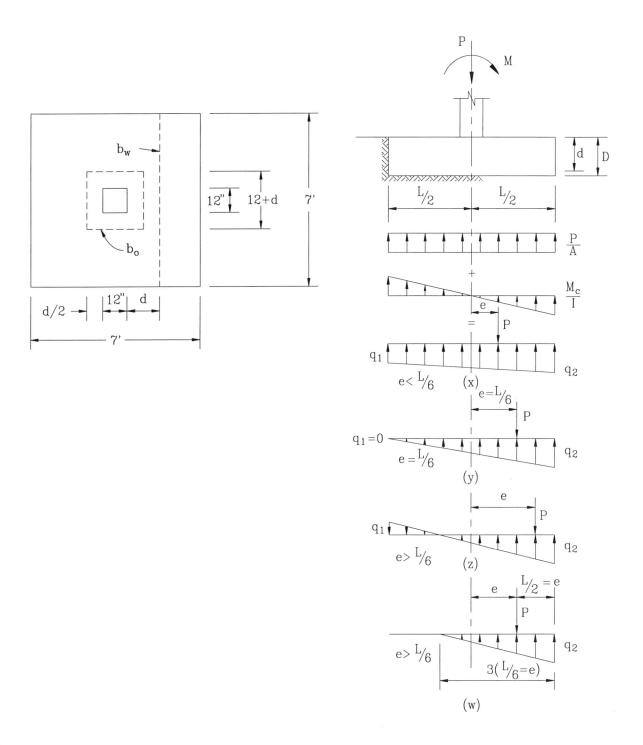

Fig. P10.6.5 (b) Shear and Moment Diagram

Combined stem diagrams can be (x) or (y) or (z). However, soil can not take tension. Therefore, the diagram (z) is not possible. The modified diagram of (z) must look like (w).

A.   Soil Bearing Pressure:

$$\left(\frac{P}{A}\right)_{DL} = \frac{65}{7 \times 7} = 1.326 \text{ ksf} \quad \times 1.4 = 1.856$$

LF q_u

$$\left(\frac{P}{A}\right)_{LL} = \frac{100}{7 \times 7} = 2.041 \quad \times 1.7 = 3.470$$

$$\left(\frac{Mc}{I}\right)_{LL} = \frac{20 \times 3.5}{\frac{1}{12} \times 7 \times 7^3} = \pm 0.350 \times 1.7 = 0.595$$

Combined Net Soil Pressure:

$$q_{a1} = 1.326 + 2.041 - 0.350 = 3.017 \text{ ksf} \qquad q_{u1} = 4.731$$

$$q_{a2} = 1.326 + 2.041 + 0.350 = 3.717 < q_a \qquad q_{u2} = 5.921$$

Assuming $D = 2 - 6$ in.

Allowable Net Soil Pressure:

$$q_a = 4.00 - 2.5 \times (0.150 - 0.110) = 3.90 \text{ ksf}$$

B.   Footing Thickness Design:

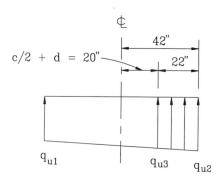

Fig. P10.6.5 (c)

$$q_{u1} = 1.856 + 3.470 - 0.595 = 4.731 \text{ ksf}$$

$$q_{u2} = 1.856 + 3.470 + 0.595 = 5.921 \text{ ksf}$$

Assume footing thickness:

$$D = 18 \text{ in.}$$

Effective depth:

$$d = 18.0 - 3.0 - 1.0 = 14.0 \text{ in.}$$

$$q_{u3} = 5.921 - \frac{22}{84}(5.921 - 4.731) = 5.609 \text{ ksf}$$

Shear strength based on beam action:

$$V_u \ \le \ \phi \ V_n \ = \ \phi \ 2 \sqrt{f'_c} \ b_w \ d$$

$$b_w \ = \ 7.0 \ ft \ = \ 84 \ in.$$

$$V_u \ = \ \frac{1}{2}(5.609 \ + \ 5.921) \times 7.0 \times \frac{22}{12} \ = \ 74.0 \ kip$$

$$\phi \ V_n \ = \ 0.85 \times \frac{2\sqrt{3,000}}{1,000} \times 84.0 \times 14.0 \ = \ 109.5 \ kip$$

$$74.0 \ kip \ < \ 109.5 \ kip$$

Shear strength based on two-way action:

$$V_u \ \le \ \phi \ V_n \ = \ \phi \left(2 \ + \ \frac{4}{\beta_c}\right) \sqrt{f'_c} \ b_o \ d$$

but not greater than $\phi \ 4\sqrt{f'_c} \ b_o \ d$

$$V_u \ = \ 1.4 \times 65 \ + \ 1.7 \times 100 \ = \ 261 \ kip$$

$$b_o \ = \ 4(c \ + \ d) \ = \ 4 \times (12 \ + \ 14) \ = \ 104 \ in.$$

$$\phi \ V_n \ = \ 0.85 \times \frac{4\sqrt{3,000}}{1,000} \times 104 \times 14.0 \ = \ 271 \ kip \ > \ V_u \ = \ 261 \ kip$$

Use D = 18 in.

C. Footing Reinforcement Design:

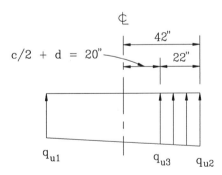

Fig. P10.6.5 (d)

Critical section for moment is at face of column.

$$q_{u4} \ = \ 5.921 \ - \ \frac{36}{84}(5.921 \ - \ 4.731) \ = \ 5.411 \ ksf$$

$$M_u \ = \ 5.921 \times \frac{3.0^2}{3} \times 7.0 \ + \ 5.411 \times \frac{3.0^2}{6} \times 7.0$$

$$= \ 124.3 \ + \ 56.8 \ = \ 181.1 \ ft\text{-}kip$$

$$b_w \;=\; 84.0 \text{ in., } d \;=\; 14.0 \text{ in}$$

$$F \;=\; \frac{b\, d^2}{12,000} \;=\; \frac{84 \times 14.0^2}{12,000} \;=\; 1.372$$

$$K_n \;=\; \frac{M_u}{F} \;=\; \frac{181.1}{1.372} \;=\; 132$$

For $f_y \;=\; 40$ ksi, $f'_c \;=\; 3.0$ ksi

$$a_n \;=\; 2.90 \quad \text{Flex. 2.1 ACI SP}-17\,(84)$$

$$A_s \;=\; \frac{181.1}{2.90 \times 14.0} \;=\; 4.46 \text{ in.}^2$$

Min $A_s \;=\; 0.005 \times 84 \times 14 \;=\; 5.88 \text{ in.}^2$

Say ten #7 $(A_s = 6.0 \text{ in.}^2)$

Quick Check:

$$A_s \;=\; \frac{181.1 \times 12}{(0.75 \times 14) \times 40} \;=\; 5.17 \text{ in.}^2$$

Close to $A_{s\,(min)} = 5.88 \text{ in.}^2$

Also $A_{s\,(min)} \;=\; 0.0018 \times 84 \times 18$

$$= 2.72 \text{ in.}^2 < 5.17 \text{ in.}^2 \quad \text{OK}$$

Try 5.17 in.^{2}. Use eight #7 — 4.8 in.^{2}

$$a \;=\; \frac{4.8 \times 40}{0.85 \times 3 \times 84} \;=\; 0.90$$

$$M_u \;=\; 0.9 \times 192 \times \left(14 - \frac{0.9}{2}\right) \frac{1}{12}$$

$$= 195 \text{ ft-k} > 181.1 \quad \text{OK}$$

D. Check Development Length of Reinforcement:

Basic development length for #7 bars

$$= \frac{0.04\, A_b\, f_y}{\sqrt{f'_c}} \;=\; 0.04 \times 0.60 \times \frac{40,000}{\sqrt{3,000}} \;=\; 17.5 \text{ in.}$$

But not less than $0.0004\, d_b\, f_y \;=\; 0.0004 \times \frac{7}{8} \times 40,000 \;=\; 14.0 \text{ in.}$

$$L_d \;=\; 17.5 \times 1.0 \times 0.8 \;=\; 14.0 \text{ in.} > 12.0 \text{ in.}$$

Development length for footing $=\; 33 \text{ in.} > 14 \text{ in.}$

10.6.6 P. E. PROBLEM 6 — SQUARE FOOTING WITH AXIAL LOAD AND MOMENT

For the square footing shown in Fig. P10.6.6 (a):

f'_c = 3000 psi

f'_y = 60 ksi

Allowable soil bearing pressure

q = 3000 psf

Dead load, P_{DL} = 50 kips

Live load, P_{LL} = 30 kips

Live load moment, M_{LL} = 50 ft-kips

Loads given are service loads.

Required:

A. Determine size of footing.

B. Verify minimum footing thickness.

C. Determine reinforcement size and spacing.

D. Draw a section of footing and show reinforcement in footing.

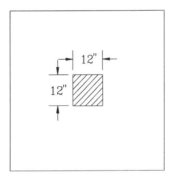

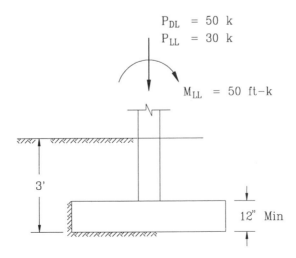

Fig. P10.6.6 (a)

Solution

A. Try 7 ft-0 in. square × 12 in. thick footing

P_{DL} = 50 kip

P_{LL} = 30 kip

Footing   = 7 × 7 × 0.15 = 7.35 kip

Total concentric load   =   50 + 30 + 7.35   =   87.35 kip

Eccentricity due to M_{LL},   e = (50)/(87.35) = 0.572 ft

Because resultant is within the kern area, soil pressure may be calculated as

$$P/A \pm M/S = q$$

where

A = 7 × 7   = 49 ft²

S = (1/6) × 7 × (7)²   = 57.17 ft³

Dead Load	(50000)/49	= 1020
Live Load	(30000)/49	= 612
Moment	±(50000)/57.17	= ±875
Footing	(7350)/49	= 150
Maximum pressure		= 2657 lb/ft²
Minimum pressure		= 907 lb/ft²

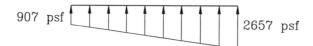

907 psf   2657 psf

Fig. P10.6.6 (b) Pressure Diagram

Calculated maximum pressure is less than allowable bearing pressure of 3000 psf.

B. For the design of the footing reinforcement, ignore weight of footing. The factored pressures are:

$$\text{Maximum } q = 1.4(1020) + 1.7(612 + 875) = 3956 \text{ lb/ft}^2$$

$$\text{Minimum } q = 1.4(1020) + 1.7(612 - 875) = 981 \text{ lb/ft}^2$$

$$\text{Factored } P_u = 1.4(50) + 1.7(30) = 121.0 \text{ kip}$$

$$\text{Effective } d = 12.0 - 3.0 - 0.75 = 8.25 \text{ in.}$$

$$b_o = 4(12.0 + 8.25) = 81.0 \text{ in.}$$

$$V_c = 4\sqrt{f'_c}\, b_o\, d$$

$$V_c = 4\frac{\sqrt{3,000}}{1000} \times 81.0 \times 8.25 = 146 \text{ kip}$$

$$V_s = 0$$

$$V_n = (V_c + V_s) = 146 \text{ kip}$$

$$V_u = 121.0 - \frac{3.956 + 0.981}{2}\left(\frac{20.25}{12}\right)^2 = 114.0 \text{ kip}$$

$$V_u/\phi = 114.0/0.85 = 134.1 \text{ kip} < V_n$$

Minimum footing thickness of 12 inches is adequate for slab shear.

Verify minimum footing thickness:

$$q_2 = 3.956 - (3/7)(3.956 - 0.981)$$

$$= 2.681 \text{ kip/ft}^2$$

@d $$q_3 = 3.956 - (2.313/7)(3.956 - 0.931) = 2.973 \text{ k/ft}^2$$

$$V_u = 3.956 \times 3/2 + 2.681 \times 3/2$$

$$= 5.934 + 4.022 = 9.956 \text{ kip}$$

@d $$V_u = (3.956 + 2.973)(2.313/2) = 8.01 \text{ kip}$$

$$V_c = 2\sqrt{f'_c}\, b\, d$$

$$V_c = \frac{2\sqrt{3000} \times 12 \times 8.25}{1000} = 10.84 \text{ kip/ft}$$

$$V_s = 0$$

$$V_n = 10.84 \text{ kip/ft}$$

$$V_u/\phi = 8.01/0.85 = 9.43 \text{ kip/ft} < V_n$$

Minimum footing thickness is adequate for beam shear.

When the soil pressure is uniform and the footing is a square footing, slab shear will control the design thickness. However, when the soil pressure diagram is not uniform both cases must be checked.

C. Footing reinforcement for flexure

Critical section at face of column

$$M_n = \frac{3.956 \times 3^2}{3} + \frac{2.681 \times 3^2}{6}$$

$$= 11.87 + 4.02 = 15.89 \text{ ft-kip per ft}$$

Try eleven #5.

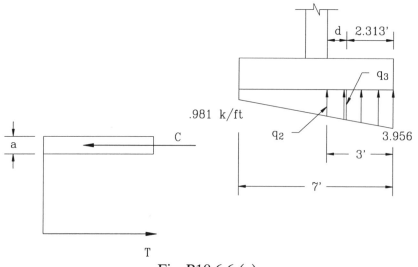

Fig. P10.6.6 (c)

b	= 84.0 in.	d	= 8.25 in.	
T	= 11 × 0.31 × 60		= 204.6 kip	
C	= 0.85(3.0)(84.0)a		= 214.2a	
C	= T			
a	= 204.6/ 214.2		= 0.955 in.	
M_n	= T(d − a/2)		= 204.6 (8.25 − 0.955/2) × 1/12	
			= 132.5 ft-kip	

$$M_u/\phi = (15.89 \times 7.0) / 0.90 = 123.6 \text{ ft-kip} < M_n$$

$$200 / f_y (bd) = (200/60000) \times 84 \times 8.25 = 2.31 \text{ in.}^2 < 3.41 \text{ in.}^2$$

Use: 7 ft-0 in. square × 12 in. thick footing with eleven #5 each way bottom.

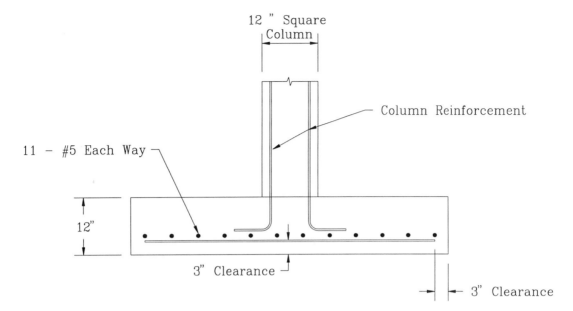

Fig. P10.6.6 (d)

10.6.7 P. E. PROBLEM 7 — SQUARE FOOTING WITH LOAD

A 12-in. $\times$ 12-in. square reinforced concrete column with four #10 vertical bars has been designed to carry a dead load of 150 kip and a live load of 135 kip.

Criteria:

Loads given are service loads.

Net allowable soil pressure q_a = 4,300 psf

Concrete for column f'_c = 4,500 psi

Concrete for footing f'_c = 3,000 psi

Reinforcement f_y = 60,000 psi

Code: ACI 318-83, 89 Strength Design

Check all the development lengths.

Required:

A. Determine the width and thickness of a square spread footing to support this column. Assume no shear reinforcing bars will be used and #6 bars will be used for the tensile reinforcement in the footing.

B. Determine the bending moment and design the tensile reinforcing in the footing.

C. Verify load transfer from the column to footing and check minimum dowel size and length.

D. Check development length of footing tensile reinforcement.

Solution

A. Determine footing size.

Factored load, P_u = 1.4 $\times$ 150 + 1.7 $\times$ 135 = 440 kip   ACI Eq. 9-1

Assume 24 in. footing thickness.

q_{net} = 4300 − 300 = 4000 psf

Required area based on net allowable soil pressure

$$= \frac{150 + 135}{4.0} = 71.25 \text{ ft}^2$$

Try 8 ft-6 in. square

$$A = 8.5 \times 8.5 = 72.25 \text{ ft}^2$$

$$q_u = \frac{440}{72.25} = 6.09 \text{ ksf}$$

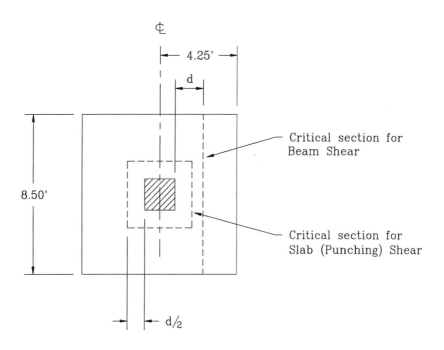

Fig. P10.6.7 (a)

Try D = 24 in.

Effective d = 24.0 − 3.0 − 0.75 = 20.25 in.

Shear strength based on beam action   ACI Sec. 11.11.1.1

$$V_n \leq \phi V_n = 2 f'_c b_w d \qquad\qquad \text{ACI Eq. 11-1 \& 11-3}$$

$$V_u = 6.09 \left(4.25 - 0.5 - \frac{20.25}{12}\right) \times 8.50 = 106.8 \text{ kip}$$

$$\phi V_n = 0.85 \times \left(2\frac{\sqrt{3,000}}{1,000}\right) \times 102.0 \times 20.25 = 192.3 \text{ kip}$$

106.8 kip < 192.3 kip

Shear strength based on two-way action:

$$V_u \leq \phi V_n = \phi (2 + 4/\beta_c) \sqrt{f'_c} b_o d = \phi 4 \sqrt{f'_c} b_o d \quad \text{ACI Eq. 11-36}$$

$b_o = 4 (12 + 2 \times 20.25/2) = 129.0 \text{ in.}$

$V_u = 440.0 - 6.09 \times (32.25/12)^2 = 396.00 \text{ kip}$

$\phi V_n = 0.85 \times (4\sqrt{3000}/1000) \times 129.0 \times 20.25 = 486.5 \text{ kip}$

400.0 kip < 486.5 kip

Use: 8 ft-6 in. square × 24 in. thick footing

B.   Footing reinforcement:

Moment is critical at face of column   ACI Sec. 15.4.2

$$M_u = 6.09 \times 8.5 \times \frac{(4.25 - 0.50)^2}{2} = 364 \text{ ft-kip}$$

$$d = 20.25 \text{ in.}$$

$$b = 102.0 \text{ in.}$$

$$F = \frac{bd^2}{12000} = \frac{102.0 \times (20.25)^2}{12000} = 3.49$$

$$K_n = \frac{364}{3.49} = 104$$

For $f_c' = 3.0$ ksi, $f_y = 60$ ksi and reference Flexure 2.1

$$a_n = 4.39$$

$$A_s = \frac{364}{4.39 \times 20.25} = 4.10 \text{ in.}^2$$

$$\text{Min. } A_s = \frac{200}{60,000} \times 102.0 \times 20.25 = 6.89 \text{ in.}^2 \quad \text{ACI Sec. 10.5.2}$$

or

$$\text{Min. } A_s = 1.33 \times 4.10 = 5.45 \text{ in.}^2$$

Use thirteen #6 $A_s = 13 \times 0.44 = 5.72$ in.$^2 > 5.45$ in.^{2} OK

Use thirteen #6 each way at bottom.

Quick Check

$$A_s = 0.0018 \times 24 \times 102 = 4.40 \text{ in.}^2$$

$$A_s = \frac{364 \times 12}{(0.75 \times 20.25) \times 60} = 4.80 \text{ in.}^2 > 4.40$$

Try 4.80, i.e., eleven #6 = 4.84 in.^{2}

$$a = \frac{4.84 \times 60}{0.825 \times 4.5 \times 102} = 0.77 \text{ in.}$$

Since $f'_c = 4500$ psi, $\beta = 0.825$

$$M_u = 0.9 \times (4.84 \times 60) \left(20.25 - \frac{0.77}{2}\right) \frac{1}{12}$$

$$= 432.6 \text{ ft-k} > 364 \text{ ft-k} \quad \text{OK}$$

Use eleven #6.

C. Load transfer column to footing: ACI Sec. 15.8

Bearing strength on column concrete: ACI Sec. 10.15

$$P_{nb} = 0.85\, f'_c\, A_g$$

$$\phi\, P_{nb} = 0.7(0.85 \times 4.5 \times 12 \times 12) \quad = 385 \text{ kip}$$

$$P_u = 1.4 \times 150 + 1.7 \times 135 \quad = 440 \text{ kip}$$

385 kip < 440 kip

The column load cannot be transferred by bearing on concrete alone. Transfer the excess load by reinforcement.

Bearing strength on footing concrete: ACI Sec. 15.8.1.1

$$A_1 = 12^2$$

$$A_2 = (12 + 4 \times 20.75) = 95^2$$

$$\sqrt{\frac{A_2}{A_1}} = \sqrt{\frac{95^2}{12^2}} = 7.91 > 2$$

ACI Sec. 10.15.1.1

Maximum strength, $\phi\, P_{nb} = \phi\, (0.85\, f'_c\, A_1) \sqrt{\dfrac{A_2}{A_1}}$

$$= 2 \times (0.7 \times 0.85 \times 3.0 \times 12 \times 12)$$

$$= 514 \text{ kip} > 440 \quad \text{OK}$$

Required dowel area   ACI Sec. 15.8.1.2

$$A_s = \frac{\left(P_u - \phi\, P_{nb}\right)}{\phi\, f_y}$$

$$= \frac{440 - 385}{0.7 \times 60} = 1.31 \text{ in.}^2$$

Min $A_s = 0.005 \times (12 \times 12) = 0.72 \text{ in.}^2$

Four #6 $A_s = 1.76 \text{ in.}^2$

Consider column reinforced with four #9 vertical bars:

$$\phi P_n = 0.8\,(0.7\,[0.85 \times 4.5 \times (144 - 4) + 60 \times 4.0]) \quad \text{ACI Eq. 10-2}$$

$$= 434 \text{ kip} \quad = \text{Say } 440 \text{ kip} \quad \text{OK}$$

Development length of #9 bar in compression: ACI Sec. 12.3.2

$$L_d = 0.02\, d_b\, \frac{f_y}{\sqrt{f'_y}}$$

$$= 0.02 \times 1.125 \times \frac{60,000}{\sqrt{4,500}} = 20.1 \text{ in.}$$

or

$$L_d = 0.0003 \ d_b \ f_y$$

$$= 0.0003 \times 1.125 \times 60,000 = 20.3 \text{ in.}$$

Minimum $L_d = 8$ in.

Lap length of #6 bars   ACI Sec. 12.16.1

$$L_d = 0.02 \times 0.75 \times \frac{60,000}{\sqrt{4,500}} = 13.4 \text{ in.}$$

or

$$L_d = 0.0005 \times 0.75 \times 60,000 = 22.5 \text{ in.} \quad \text{Say 24 in. @ columns}$$

Development length of #6 in compression into footing   ACI Sec. 15.8.2.4

$$L_d = 0.02 \times 0.75 \times 60,000 \times \frac{1}{\sqrt{3,000}} = 16.4 \text{ in.} \quad \text{ACI 12.3.2}$$

or

$$L_d = 0.0003 \times 0.75 \times 60,000 = 13.5 \text{ in.}$$

since

$$\frac{A_s \text{ Required}}{A_s \text{ Provided}} = \frac{1.31}{1.76} = 0.744 < 1.0 \quad \text{ACI Sec. 12.3.3.1}$$

Required $L_d = 16.4 \times 0.744 = 12.2$ in.   Say 14 in. @ footing

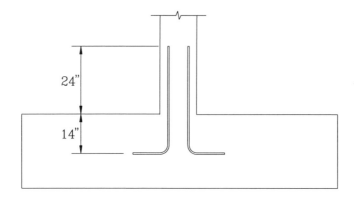

Fig. P10.6.7 (b)

Total dowel length $= 24 + 14 = 38$ in.

Provide four #6 Dowels $\times$ 3 ft-2 in. long with 24 in. into column.

D. Development length of footing tensile reinforcement   ACI Sec. 15.6

Critical section for development of footing reinforcement is
the same plane as that for moment or at face of column   ACI Sec. 15.6.3

For #6 bars:

$$L_d = \left[0.04 \ A_s \ \frac{f_y}{\sqrt{f_c'}}\right]0.8 \qquad\qquad \text{ACI Sec 12.2.3.4 1992}$$

$$= \left(0.04 \times 0.44 \times \frac{60,000}{\sqrt{3,000}}\right)0.8$$

$$= 15.4 \text{ in.} < (45 - 3) = 42.0 \text{ in.}$$

ACI 1989 (Sec 12.2.2):

$$L_d = 0.04 \ A_b \ \frac{f_y}{\sqrt{f_c'}}$$

$$L_d = 0.04 \times 0.44 \times \frac{60,000}{\sqrt{3,000}} = 19.3 \text{ in.}$$

Projection beyond face of column = $51.0 - 6.0 = 45.0$ in

Development length of tensile reinforcement is adequate.

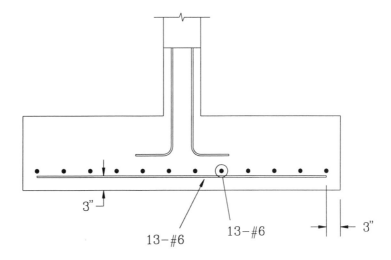

3"   3"

13–#6   13–#6

Fig. P10.6.7 (c)

10.7   COMBINED FOOTINGS

10.8   EXAMPLE PROBLEMS

10.8.1   EXAMPLE PROBLEM 1 — DESIGN OF A RECTANGULAR COMBINED FOOTING

(References: ACI Code and *Foundation Analysis and Design* by J.E. Bowles)

Given:

$$f'_c = 3000 \text{ psi}$$

$$f_y = 60 \text{ ksi}$$

$$q_a = 2.3 \text{ ksf}$$

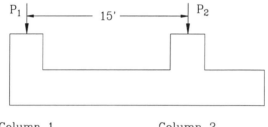

Column 1	Column 2
12"x12"	15"x15"
DL = 60 kips	DL = 110 kips
LL. = 60 kips	LL = 90 kips

Fig. P10.8.1 (a)

Solution

Assume 24-in. thick (300 psf) footing:

$$q_e = 2.3 \text{ ksf} - 0.3 = 2.00 \text{ ksf}$$

Step 1:

Convert loads to ultimate:

$$P_{u1} = 1.4(60) + 1.7(60) = 186 \text{ kip}$$

$$P_{u2} = 1.4(110) + 1.7(90) = 307 \text{ kip}$$

$$P_1 + P_2 = 60 + 60 + 110 + 90 = 320 \text{ kip}$$

$$\text{Ultimate ratio} = \frac{186 + 307}{320} = 1.54$$

$$q_e = q_a(1.54) = 2 \times 1.54 = 3.08 \text{ ksf}$$

This is necessary so that eccentricity is not introduced in finding L using working loads and then switching to *ultimate* values.

Step 2:

Find L and the width of footing B.

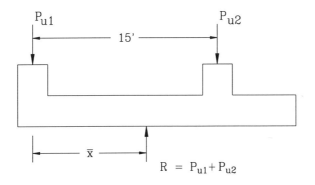

Fig. P10.8.1 (b)

Assume the reaction R is acting at a distance $\bar{x}$ from P_{u1}.

Taking moment about $P_{u1} = 0$, we get:

$$R\,(\bar{x}) - P_{u2}\,(15) = 0$$

$$(186 + 307)\,\bar{x} - 307\,(15) = 0$$

$$\bar{x} = 9.341 \text{ ft}$$

Note: Normally, $\bar{x}$ is calculated using service loads (i.e., 320 kip) and the size is calculated by using q_e (i.e., 2 ksf).

To take R fall at $\dfrac{L}{2}$, we have:

$$\bar{x} + \text{half width of left column} = \frac{L}{2}$$

$$9.341 + 0.5 = \frac{L}{2} \quad \rightarrow \quad L = 19.682 \text{ ft} \qquad \text{(Say 19.75 ft)}$$

Step 3:

Find B:

$$BLq_u = P_{u1} + P_{u2}$$

$$B = \frac{493}{19.68 \times 3.08} = 8.17 \text{ ft}$$

In practice, 20 ft × 8 ft footing is preferable.

Step 4:

Draw shear and bending moment diagram (see Fig. P10.8.1 (c)).

Equivalent uniform pressure per foot:

$$\frac{493}{19.68} = 25.05 \text{ kip/ft}$$

$$V_{1\text{-}1} = -186 \text{ kip} + 25.05 \times 1.0 = -160.95 \text{ kip}$$

$$V_{2\text{-}2} = -160.95 \text{ kip} + 25.05 \times 13.875 = +186.62 \text{ kip}$$

$$V_{3\text{-}3} = +186.62 \text{ kip} - 307 + 25.05 \times 1.25 = -89.1 \text{ kip}$$

$$M_{1\text{-}1} = -186 \times 0.5 + 25.05 \times 1.0 \times 0.5 = -80.5 \text{ ft-kip}$$

$$\text{Max. M} = -80.5 - 160.95 \left(\frac{6.425}{2}\right) = -597.5 \text{ ft-kip}$$

$$M_{2\text{-}2} = -597.5 + 186.62 \left(\frac{7.450}{2}\right) = +97.6 \text{ ft-kip}$$

$$M_{3\text{-}3} = 25.05 \times 3.555 \times \frac{3.555}{2} = +158.3 \text{ ft-kip}$$

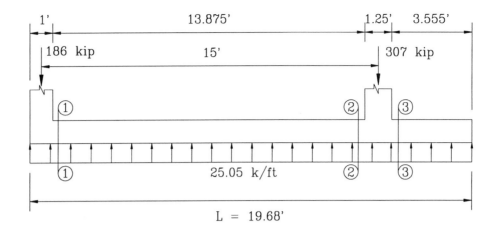

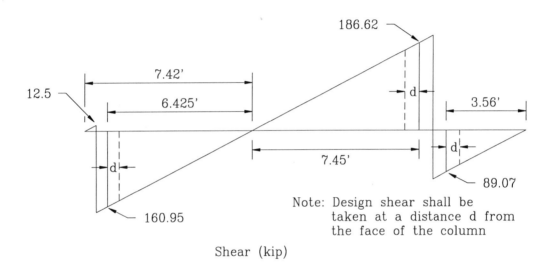

Shear (kip)

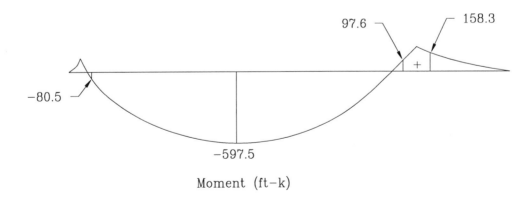

Moment (ft-k)

Fig. P10.8.1 (c) Shear & Moment Diagram for Combined Footing

Step 5:

Select depth based on analysis for both one-way shear and two-way shear.

A. One-way shear:

$$\text{Max V} = 186.6 \text{ kip at Column 2}$$

$$\text{B } v_c d = 186.6 - q_u d$$

$$v_c = \phi \, 2\sqrt{f'_c} = 0.85 \times 2 \times \sqrt{3{,}000}$$

$$= 93.11 \text{ psi} = 13.41 \text{ ksf}$$

$$8.17 \times 13.41 \times d = 186.6 - 25.05 \, d$$

$$d = 1.39 \text{ ft} = 16.7 \text{ in.}$$

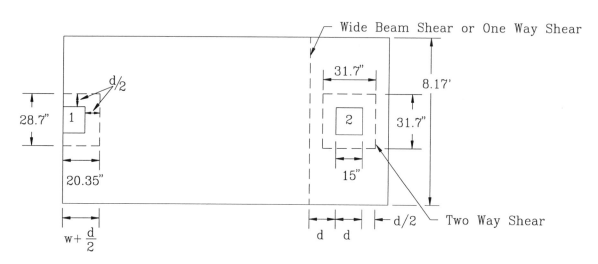

Fig. P10.8.1 (d) Footing Plan

B. Two-way shear:

1. At Column 1: Assume d = 16.7 in.

$$\text{Perimeter } b_o = 2\left(12 + \frac{d}{2}\right) + (12 + d)$$

$$= 2(20.35) + 28.7 = 69.4 \text{ in.}$$

$$\text{Allowable } V_u = V_c = \phi \, 4\sqrt{f'_c} \, b_o \, d$$

$$= 0.85 \times 4 \times \frac{\sqrt{3{,}000}}{1{,}000} \times 69.4 \times 16.7 = 216 \text{ kip}$$

$$\text{Net } V_u = 186 - 3.08 \frac{20.35 \times 28.7}{144}$$

$$= 173.5 \text{ kip} < 216 \text{ kip}$$

2. At Column 2:

$$\text{Perimeter } b_o = 4\left(15 + \frac{d}{2} \times 2\right)$$

$$= 4 \times 31.7 = 126.8 \text{ in.}$$

$$\text{Allowable } V_u = V_c$$

$$= 0.85 \times 4 \times \frac{\sqrt{3,000}}{1,000} \times 126.8 \times 16.7$$

$$= 394 \text{ kip}$$

$$\text{Net } V_u = 307 - 3.08 \frac{31.7 \times 31.7}{144}$$

$$= 285.5 \text{ kip} < 394 \text{ kip}$$

Note: d = 16.7 is determined by one-way shear, which controls the design.

Step 6:

Design of negative steel between Columns 1 and 2:

$$M_{UR} = \phi A_s f_y \left(d - \frac{a}{2}\right) = 597.5 \text{ ft-kip} \qquad \text{(from moment diagram)}$$

$$a = \frac{A_s f_y}{0.85 f_c' b} = \frac{A_s (60)}{0.85 \times 3 \times 12} = 1.96 A_s \qquad \text{(for 1-ft width)}$$

$$M_U = 0.9 A_s (60)\left(16.7 - \frac{1.96 A_s}{2}\right) \times \frac{8.17}{12} \text{ ft-kip}$$

Equate $M_{UR} = M_U$

$$A_s = 8.5 \text{ in.}^2$$

$$A_s = \frac{8.5}{8.17} = 1.037 \text{ in.}^2/\text{ft}$$

Check for ϱ minimum:

$$\varrho = \frac{1.037}{16.7 \times 12} = 0.0052 > \varrho_{min}$$

where

$$\varrho_{min} = \frac{200}{f_y} = 0.0033$$

Use twelve #8 longitudinal at top.

Quick Check:

$$A_s = \frac{597.5 \times 12}{(80 \times 16.7) \times 60} = 8.94 \text{ in.}^2$$

Try eleven #8s   8.68 in.^{2} steel

$$A_{min} = 0.0033 \times (8.17 \times 12 \times 16.7) = 5.4 \text{ in.}^2$$

$$a = \frac{8.68 \times 60}{0.85 \times 3 \times (8.17 \times 12)} = 2.08 \text{ in.}$$

$$M_u = 0.9 \times (8.68 \times 60) \left(16.7 - \frac{2.08}{2}\right) \times \frac{1}{12}$$

$$= 611 \text{ ft-k} > 597.5 \qquad \text{OK}$$

Use eleven #8 at top.

Step 7:

Since the load will be more concentrated near the columns, assume steel spreads only over width of column + 2 × 0.75d on each side.

Note: However, our original assumption was that the footing will act like a rigid footing and therefore the soil pressure was uniformly distributed.

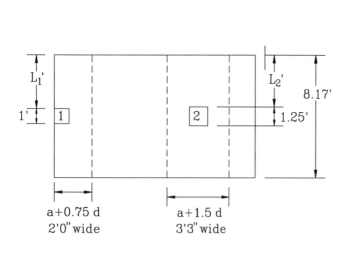

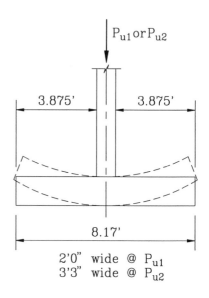

Fig. P10.8.1 (e)

At Column 1:

$$a + 0.75d = 12 + 0.75 \times 16.7 = 24.5 \text{ in.} = 2.0 \text{ ft}$$

$$q = \frac{186}{8.17 \times 2} = 11.38 \text{ ksf}$$

$$L_1' = \frac{8.17 \text{ ft} - 1 \text{ ft}}{2} = 3.585 \text{ ft}$$

$$M = \frac{11.38 \times (3.585)^2}{2} \times 12 = 877.5 \text{ in.-kip}$$

To get A_s, use the same procedure in *Step 6:*

$$A_s = 1.11 \text{ in.}^2/\text{ft}$$

Total $A_s = 1.11 \times (2 \text{ ft}) = 2.11 \text{ in.}^2$

Use four #7 at 6 in. within 2 ft-0 in. band.

At Column 2:

$$a + 1.5d = 15 + 1.5 \times 16.7 = 39 \text{ in.} = 3.25 \text{ ft}$$

$$q = \frac{307}{3.25 \times 8.17} = 11.56 \text{ ksf}$$

$$L_2' = \frac{8.17 \text{ ft} - 1.25 \text{ ft}}{2} = 3.46 \text{ ft}$$

$$M = \frac{11.56 \times (3.46)^2}{2} \times 12 = 830.35 \text{ in.-kip}$$

$$A_s^2 - 16.02 \ A_s = 15.69$$

$$A_s = 1.05 \text{ in.}^2/\text{ft}$$

Total $A_s = 1.05 \times (3.25 \text{ ft}) = 3.4 \text{ in.}^2$

Use six #7 at 6.5 in. within.

Provide minimum steel ($0.002 \times b \times t$) between the band. In this case:

$0.002 \times 12 \times 16.7 = 0.4$

i.e., #5 at 8 in. or #6 at 12 in. or #7 at 18 in. c to c.

Step 8:

Check dowel requirement.

At Column 1, the supporting area is not on all sides; therefore, the bearing stress is limited to:

$$f_c = 0.85 \; (0.7) \; f'_c = 1.785 \; \text{ksi}$$

$$P = 12 \text{ in.} \times 12 \text{ in.} \times 1.785 = 257 \text{ kip} > 186 \text{ kip} \qquad \text{OK}$$

Use minimum 4 dowels of area:

$$A_s = 0.005 \times 12 \times 12 = 0.72 \text{ in.}^2$$

Use four #6 for $4 \times 0.44 = 1.76$ in.^{2}

At Column 2:

$$\sqrt{\frac{A_2}{A_1}} > 2 \qquad \text{(Use 2)}$$

$$\text{Allowable } f = 0.85 \; (0.7) \; f'_c \; (2) = 3.57 \text{ ksi}$$

$$P = 15 \times 15 \times 3.57 = 803 > 307 \qquad \text{OK}$$

Use 4 dowels same size as Column 1.

Step 9:

Steel in cantilever portion is found to be 0.28 for moment and 0.67 in.^{2}/ft

($\varrho_{min} = 200/f_y$ for minimum requirement).

Use ten #7. $A_s = 6$ in.$^2 > 0.67 \times 8.17 = 5.47$ in.^{2}

10.9　P. E. PROBLEMS

10.9.1　P. E. PROBLEM 1 — COMBINED FOOTING

An equipment weighing 48 kip is supported on four 12 in. $\times$ 12 in. concrete pedestals over two footings.

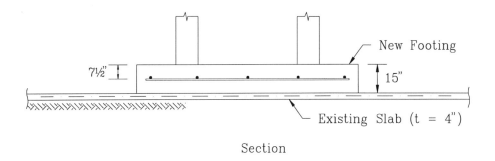

Section

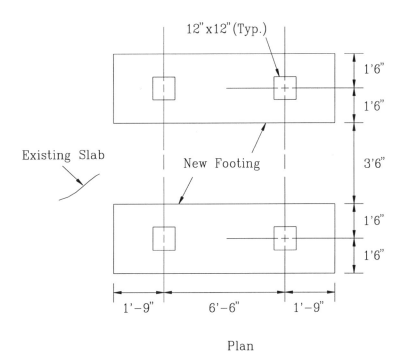

Plan

Fig. P10.9.1 (a)

$f'_c = 3000$ psi

Required:

Verify all shear stresses due to superimposed loading.

Solution

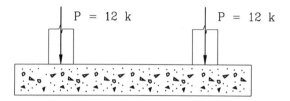

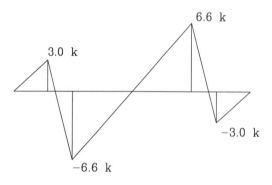

Loading

Shear

Fig. P10.9.1 (b)

Load per pedestal = 48/4 = 12 k

1. One way shear in footing

$$V_u = 1.4 \times 6.6 = 9.24 \text{ kip}$$

$$V_c = 2\sqrt{f'_c} \ b \ d$$

$$= 2\sqrt{3,000} \times 36 \times 7.5 = 29.58 \text{ kip}$$

$$\text{Required } V_u = \frac{9.24}{0.85} = 10.87 \text{ kip} < \frac{V_c}{2} = 14.79 \text{ kip} \quad \text{OK}$$

2. Two way slab shear in footing

$$b_o = 4(12.0 + 7.5) = 78.0 \text{ in.}$$

$$V_c = 4\sqrt{f'_c} \ b \ d$$

$$= 4\sqrt{3,000} \times 78.0 \times 7.5 = 128.2 \text{ kip}$$

$$\text{Required } V_u = \frac{1.4 \times 12.0}{0.85}$$

$$= 19.8 \text{ kip} < V_c \quad \text{OK}$$

3. Two-way slab shear in existing slab (4 in. thick, and d = 2 in.):

$$\text{Weight of footing} = 0.15 \times 3.0 \times 10.0 \times 1.25 = 5.63 \text{ kip}$$

$$\frac{1}{2} \text{ equipment weight} = \frac{1}{2} \times 48 = 24.00 \text{ kip}$$

$$\text{Required } V_u = \frac{1.4}{\phi}(5.63 + 24.0) = \frac{41.5 \text{ kip}}{0.85} = 48.8 \text{ kip}$$

$$b_o = 2(120 + 2) + 2(36 + 2) = 320 \text{ in.}$$

$$V_c = 4\sqrt{f'_c} \, b_o \, d$$

$$= 4\sqrt{3,000} \times 320 \times 2 = 140.2 \text{ kip}$$

$$> 48.8 \qquad \text{OK}$$

10.9.2 P. E. PROBLEM 2 — SPREAD FOOTING FOR TWO COLUMNS

Criteria:

- f'_c = 3000 psi
- f_y = 60 ksi
- q_a = 3000 psf

Column 1	Column 2
DL = 60 kip	DL = 80 kip
LL = 75 kip	LL = 95 kip

Fig. P10.9.2 (a)

Loads given are service loads. Ignore weight of footing

Required:

1. Determine the footing size.

2. Draw shear and moment diagrams.

3. Calculate footing thickness.

4. Design footing reinforcement.

5. Sketch a section of footing to show reinforcement arrangement.

6. Ignore the weight of footing

Solution

Locate resultant of column loads.

Take moment about centerline of column 1:

$$x = \frac{(80 + 95) \times 18.0}{(60 + 75) + (80 + 95)} = 10.16 \text{ ft}$$

1. Calculate footing size:

    Ignore weight of footing (generally the footing weight is not ignored. Use 10% of the total service load as the weight of combined footing.).

    Total load $= (60 + 75) + (80 + 95) = 310$ kip

    At a soil pressure of 3000 lb/ft^2:

    $$\text{Area} = 310/3.0 = 103.3 \text{ ft}^2$$

    Footing length considering no eccentricity:

    $$L = 2 (10.16 + 1.0) = 22.32 \quad \text{Say 22 ft-4 in.}$$

    Width:

    $$b = 103.3/22.35 = 4.63 \qquad \text{Say 4 ft-8 in.}$$

    Use: 4 ft-8 in. $\times$ 22 ft-4 in. footing

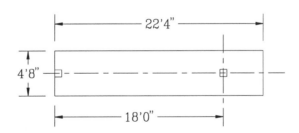

Fig. P10.9.2 (b)

2. Draw shear and moment diagram:

    Factored Load $= (60 \times 1.4 + 75 \times 1.7) + (80 \times 1.4 + 95 \times 1.7)$

    $= 485$ kip

    Equivalent uniform load $= 485/22.33 = 21.72$ kip/ft

    Shear:

    $$V_B = -211.5 + 21.72 \times 2 \qquad\qquad = -168.06 \quad \text{kip}$$

    $$V_C = -168.06 + 21.72 \times 16 \qquad = 179.45 \quad \text{kip}$$

    $$V_D = 179.45 - 273.5 + 21.72 \times 2 = -50.61 \quad \text{kip}$$

Moment:

$$M_B = 1/2\,(168.06)\,(2) = +168 \text{ ft-kip}$$

$$+M_{max} = 1/2\,(168.06)\,(2.0 + 7.74) = +818 \text{ ft-kip}$$

$$M_C = 818 - 1/2\,(179.45)\,(16.0 - 7.74) = +76.9 \text{ ft-kip}$$

$$M_D = 1/2\,(50.61)\,(2.33) = 59.0 \text{ ft-kip}$$

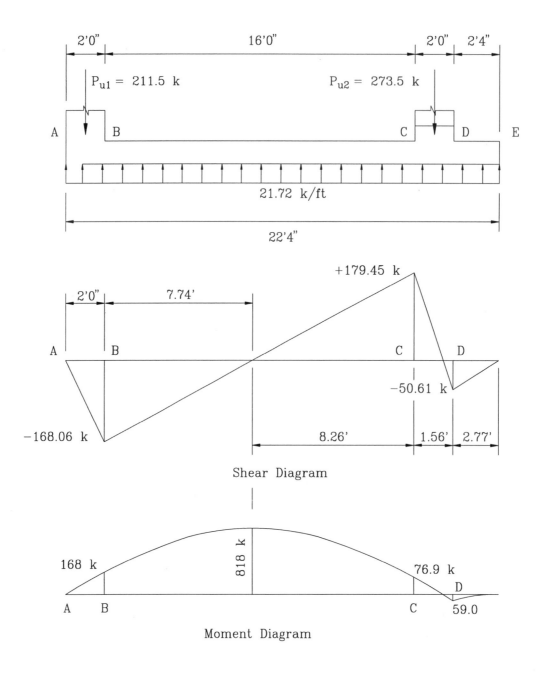

Fig. P10.9.2 (c)

3. Calculate footing thickness:

    Consider:

- D = 24 in.
- d = 24.0 − 3.0 − 1.0 = 20.0 in.
- b = 56.0 ft

Fig. P10.9.2 (d)

One-way shear:

$$\text{Max} \quad V = 179.45 \text{ kip at Column 2}$$

$$\text{At d,} \quad V_u = 179.45 - 21.72 \times (20.0/12) = 143.25 \text{ kip}$$

$$V_c = 2\sqrt{f_c'}bd$$

$$= 2\sqrt{3000} \times 56.0 \times 20.0/1000 = 122.7 \text{ kip} < 143.25 \text{ kip}$$

Need shear reinforcement.

Try #3 @ 9 with four legs:

Fig. P10.9.2 (e) #3 Stirrups with Four Legs

$$V_s = \frac{A_s f_y d}{s} = (4 \times 0.11 \times 60 \times 20.00)/9$$

$$= 58.7 \text{ kip}$$

$$V_n = V_c + V_s = 122.7 + 58.7 = 181.4 \text{ kip}$$

$$\phi V_n = 0.85 (181.4) = 154.2 \text{ kip} > V_u$$

Maximum ϕV_n without shear reinforcement:

$$\phi V_n = \phi V_c = 0.85 \times 122.7 = 104.3 \text{ kip}$$

Minimum A_v:

$$A_v = \frac{50 \ b_w s}{f_u} = \frac{50 \times 56.0 \times 9}{60,000} = 0.42 \text{ in.}^2 \leq 0.44$$

Two-way shear

At Column 1:

V_u = 211.5 kip

b_o = 2(24.0 + 20/2) + (24.0 + 20/2 × 2) = 112.0 in.

V_c = 3 $\sqrt{f'_c}$ b_o d (According to ACI Code 4 $\sqrt{f'_c}$ b_od can be used.)

= [(3$\sqrt{3000}$)/1000] × 112.0 × 20.0 = 368 kip

V_s = 0

ϕV_n = ϕV_c = 0.85 × 368 = 312 kip > V_u

At Column 2:

V_u = 273.5 kip

b_o = 4[24.0 + (20.0/2) × 2] = 176.0 in.

V_c = 4$\sqrt{f'_c}$ b_o d

= [(4$\sqrt{3000}$)/ 1000] × 176.0 × 20.0 = 771 kip

V_s = 0

ϕV_n = ϕV_c = 0.85 (771) = 655 kip > V_u

Extent of shear reinforcement for one way shear

From B, x_1 = [1 − (104.3/168.0)] × 7.74 × 12 = 35.2 in.

From C, x_2 = [1 − (104.3/179.45)] × 8.26 × 12 = 42 in.

Note: Minimum shear reinforcement is not required for:

V_u < ϕV_c See UBC 2611 (f) 5A(i)

4. Design for longitudinal steel between column 1 and 2:

Maximum:

M_u = 818 ft-kip at top of footing

d = 24.0 − 2.0 − 0.4 − 0.6 = 21.0 in.

$F = \dfrac{bd^2}{12000} = \dfrac{56 \times 21.0^2}{12000} = 2.06$

K_n = 818 / 2.06 = 397

Reference SP-17 (84) Flex. 2.1:

a_n = 4.07

$A_s = \dfrac{818}{4.07 \times 21.0} = 9.57$ in.^{2}

Min. $A_s = \dfrac{200\ bd}{f_y} = \dfrac{200}{60000} \times 56.2 \times 25.0 = 3.92$ in.^{2}

Use 8 #10 bars, $A_s = 10.16$ in.^{2}

Cut off four bars and continue the remaining four:

$$a = \frac{4 \times 1.27 \times 60}{0.85 \times 3.0 \times 56} = 2.13 \text{ in.}$$

$$\phi M_n = \phi A_s f_y \left(d - \frac{a}{2}\right)$$

$$= 0.90 \times 10.16 \times 60 \left(21.0 - \frac{2.13}{2}\right) \times \frac{1}{12} = 455 \text{ ft-kip}$$

$$= 455 \text{ ft-kip}$$

Quick Check:

$$A_s = \frac{818 \times 12}{(0.80 \times 21) \times 60} = 9.73 \text{ in.}^2$$

Use eight #10   10.16 in.^{2}

$$F_u = 10.16 \times 60 = 609.6 \text{ kip}$$

$$a = \frac{609.6}{0.85 \times 3 \times 56} = 4.26 \text{ in.}$$

$$M_u = 0.9 \times 609.6 \times \left(21 - \frac{4.26}{2}\right) \times \frac{1}{12}$$

$$= 895 \text{ ft-k} > 818$$

Locate the point where the four #10s are adequate:

From M_{max}, $818 - 21.72 \left(\frac{x^2}{2}\right) = 455$

$$x = 5.78 \text{ ft}$$

From B $x_3 = (7.74 - 5.78)(12) = 23.5$ in.

From C $x_4 = (8.26 - 5.78)(12) = 29.8$ in.

Longitudinal steel at bottom:

$M_u = 59.0$ ft-kip   at D-D

$d = 24.0 - 3.0 - 0.4 - 0.6 = 20.0$ in.

$b = 56.0$ in.

$$F = \frac{56.0 \times 20.0^2}{12000} = 1.87$$

$$K_n = \frac{59.0}{1.87} = 31$$

Minimum:

$$A_s = (200/60{,}000) \times 56.0 \times 20.0 = 3.73 \text{ in.}^2 \quad \text{say four \#9}$$

$$a = \frac{4.0 \times 60}{0.85 \times 3.0 \times 56} = 1.68 \text{ in.}$$

$$\phi M_n = 0.90 \times 4.0 \times 60 \,(20.0 - 1.68/2) \times (1/12)$$

$$= 345 \text{ ft-kip} > M_u$$

Transverse Reinforcement:

$$d = 24.0 - 3.0 - 0.4 - 1.3 - 0.3 = 19.0 \text{ in.}$$

Try #4 @ 12:

$$\phi M_n = 0.90 \times 0.20 \times 60 \,(19.0 - 0.39/2) \times (1/12)$$

$$= 16.92 \text{ ft-kip per ft}$$

At column 2:

$$\text{Effective width} = 24.0 + 2\,(0.75d) = 52.5 \text{ in.}$$

$$\phi M_n = 16.92 \times 52.5/12 = 74.0 \text{ ft-kip}$$

Similarly at column 1:

$$\text{Effective width} = 24.0 + 0.75d = 38.25 \text{ in.}$$

$$\phi M_n = 16.92 \times 38.25/12 = 53.9 \text{ ft-kip}$$

$$\text{Total} \quad \phi M_n = 74.0 + 53.9 = 127.9 \text{ ft-kip}$$

$$M_u = 4.14 \times 22.33 = 92.4 \text{ ft-kip} < \phi M_n \quad \text{OK}$$

5.   Sketch of footing section:

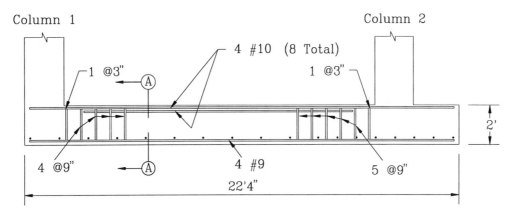

Elevation

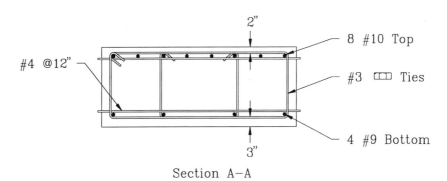

Section A–A

Fig. P10.9.2 (f)

10.10 GRADE BEAMS

10.11 P. E. PROBLEM

10.11.1 P. E. PROBLEM 1 — GRADE BEAM DESIGN

Because of highly expansive soils, exterior walls of the structure shown in Fig. P10.11.1 (a) are carried by a continuous grade beam supported on piles spaced at 18 ft on center

Criteria:

Loads given are service loads.
Uniform dead load   = 65 psf
Uniform live load   = 30 psf
8-in. Block Wall   = 80 psf
4-in. veneer   = 40 psf
Concrete weight   = 150 pcf
Concrete f'_c = 3.0 ksi
Reinforcement f_y = 60 ksi

Required:

A. Determine load per linear foot on the grade beam.

B. Neglecting answer from Part A above, design a typical interior span and an end span of the grade beam shown using an 8000 pounds per linear foot load on the grade beam. Use ACI 318-89 Code provisions.

C. Check beam shear capacity for Part B.

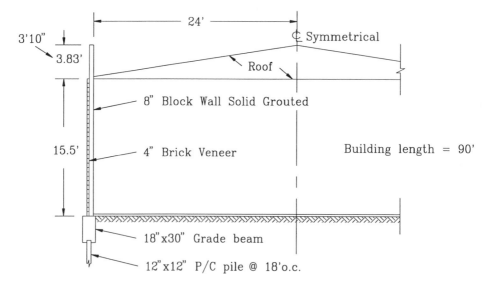

Fig. P10.11.1 (a) Building Section

Solution

A. Determine load on girder.

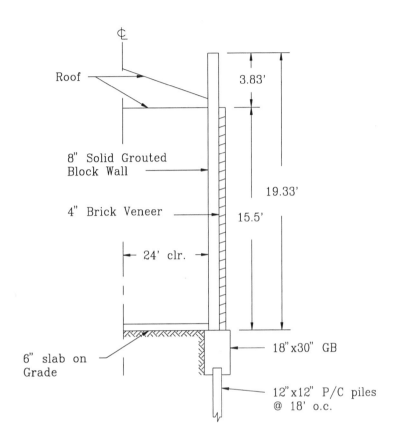

Fig. P10.11.1 (b)

Roof:

DL	$= 65 \times 24$	$= 1,560$ plf
LL	$= 30 \times 24$	$= 720$

Wall :

Block	$= 80 \times 19.33$	$= 1,546$
Veneer	$= 40 \times 15.5$	$= 620$
Grade Beam	$= 18 \times 30 \times \dfrac{150}{144}$	$= 562$

$$2,728 \text{ plf}$$

$$w_D \quad = \quad 1,560 + 2,728 \quad = \quad 4,288$$

$$w_L \quad = \qquad\qquad\qquad = \quad 720$$

$$\overline{\hspace{4cm}}$$

$$w_T \quad = \qquad\qquad\qquad\qquad 5.008 \text{ plf}$$

$$w_u \quad = \quad 4,288 \times 1.4 + 720 \times 1.7$$

$$\qquad = \quad 7,227 \text{ plf}$$

B. Design Grade Beam:

$f'_c = 3.0$ ksi, $f_y = 60$ ksi

Consider given ultimate load $w_u = 8000$ plf and consider grade beams are not integral with precast concrete piles.

Span:

$$L_n \quad = \quad 18.0 \text{ ft} \qquad\qquad\qquad\qquad \text{(ACI Sec. 8.7.1)}$$

$$b_w \quad = \quad 18.0 \text{ in.}$$

$$- d \quad = \quad 30.0 - 2.5 - 0.8 \quad = \quad 26.7 \text{ in.} \quad - F \quad = \quad 1.069$$

$$+ d \quad = \quad 30.0 - 3.5 - 1.0 \quad = \quad 25.5 \text{ in.} \quad + F \quad = \quad 0.975$$

End span:

$$- M_u \quad = \quad \frac{w_u \, L_n^2}{10} \quad = \quad \frac{8.0 \times 18.0^2}{10}$$

$$\qquad\qquad = \quad 259.2 \text{ ft-kip} \qquad\qquad - K_u \quad = \quad 242$$

$$+ M_u \quad = \quad \frac{w_u \, L_n^2}{11} \quad = \quad \frac{8.0 \times 18.0^2}{11}$$

$$\qquad\qquad = \quad 235.6 \text{ ft-kip} \qquad\qquad + K_u \quad = \quad 242$$

$$V_u \quad = \quad 1.15 \, \frac{w_u \, L_n}{2} \quad = \quad \frac{1.15 \times 8.0 \times 18}{2} \quad = \quad 82.8 \text{ kip}$$

$$- A_s \quad = \quad \frac{259.2}{4.23 \times 26.7} \quad = \quad 2.30 \text{ in.}^2$$

$$+ A_s \quad = \quad \frac{235.6}{4.23 \times 25.5} \quad = \quad 2.18 \text{ in.}^2$$

$$V_c = 2\sqrt{f'_c} \; b_w \, d$$

$$= \frac{2 \times \sqrt{3,000}}{1,000} \times 18.0 \times 25.5 = 50.3 \text{ kip}$$

Provide #3 ⊔

$$V_s = \frac{A_v \, f_y \, d}{s} = \frac{0.22 \times 40.00 \times 25.5}{8} = 28.1 \text{ kip}$$

$$V_n = V_c + V_s = 50.3 + 28.1 = 78.4 \text{ kip}$$

Allowable $V_u = \phi \, V_n = 0.85 \times 78.4 = 66.6 \text{ kip}$

$$@ \, d \quad V_u = 82.8 - 8.0 \times \frac{25.5}{12} = 65.8 \text{ kip} < \phi \, V_n \quad \text{OK}$$

Check minimum shear steel $A_v = \dfrac{50 \, b_w \, S}{f_y}$

Interior Span:

$$-M_u = \frac{w_u \, L_n^2}{11} = \frac{8.0 \times 18.0^2}{11} = 235.6 \text{ ft-kip}$$

$$+M_u = \frac{w_u \, L_n^2}{16} = \frac{8.0 \times 18.0^2}{16} = 162.0 \text{ ft-kip}$$

$$V_u = \frac{w_u \, L_n}{2} = \frac{8.0 \times 18.0}{2} = 72.0 \text{ kip}$$

$$-K_n = \frac{235.6}{1.069} = 220$$

$$-A_s = \frac{235.6}{4.27 \times 26.7} = 2.07 \text{ in.}^2$$

$$+K_n = \frac{162.0}{0.975} = 166$$

$$+A_s = \frac{162.0}{4.33 \times 25.5} = 1.47 \text{ in.}^2$$

$$\text{\#3 @12} \quad V_s = \frac{0.22 \times 40.0 \times 25.5}{12} = 17.7 \text{ kip}$$

$$V_n = V_c + V_s = 50.3 + 18.7 = 69.0 \text{ kip}$$

Allowable $V_u = \phi \, V_n = 0.85 \times 69.0 = 58.6 \text{ kip}$

$$@ \, d \quad V_u = 72.0 - 8.0 \times \frac{25.5}{12} = 55.0 < \phi \, V_n$$

C.

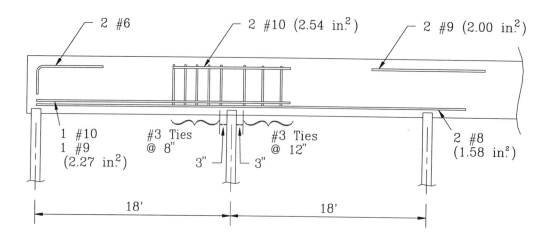

Fig. P10.11.1 (c) Elevation Showing Reinforcement Details

APPENDIX
DESIGN AIDS

The following are sample tables of design aids from the ACI *Design Handbook*.

For complete set of tables, please refer to the current publictions of ACI. The examination may specify that values from Design Tables are not acceptable. However, the Design Tables still serve a valid purpose in checking the answers and to verify that they are within "ball-park".

REINFORCEMENT 1–Nominal cross section area, weight, and nominal diameter of ASTM standard reinforcing bars

Bar size designation	Nominal cross section area, sq in.	Weight, lb per ft	Nominal diameter, in.
#3	0.11	0.376	0.375
#4	0.20	0.668	0.500
#5	0.31	1.043	0.625
#6	0.44	1.502	0.750
#7	0.60	2.044	0.875
#8	0.79	2.670	1.000
#9	1.00	3.400	1.128
#10	1.27	4.303	1.270
#11	1.56	5.313	1.410
#14	2.25	7.650	1.693
#18	4.00	13.600	2.257

Current (1981) ASTM Specifications cover bar sizes #7 through #18 in A 615 Grade 60 and in A 706 only.

FLEXURE 2.1–Coefficients for design of rectangular beams with tension reinforcement only, $f'_c = 3000$ psi

Reference: ACI 318-83, Sections 9.3.2, 10.2, 10.3.1–10.3.3, and Commentary Section 10.3.1(A)(1)

$$\phi M_n \geq M_u$$

$$\phi M_n = K_n F, \text{ ft-kips}$$

where $K_n = \phi f'_c \omega j_n$

$$\omega = \rho \frac{f_y}{f'_c}, \phi = 0.90,$$

and $F = bd^2 / 12{,}000$ (from FLEXURE 6)

Also $\phi M_n = A_s d a_n (A_s \text{ in sq in.})$
where $a_n = \phi f_y j_n / 12{,}000$

$$c/d = 1.18 (\omega / \beta_1)$$
$$a/d = \beta_1 (c/d)$$
$$\beta_1 = 0.85$$
$$j_n = 1 - (a/2d)$$
$$= 1 - 0.59\omega$$

		$f'_c = 3000$								
		$f_y = 40{,}000$		$f_y = 50{,}000$		$f_y = 60{,}000$				
ω	K_n	ρ^*	a_n	ρ^*	a_n	ρ^*	a_n	c/d	a/d	j_n
0.020	53	0.0015	2.96	0.0012	3.71	0.0010	4.45	0.028	0.024	0.988
0.030	80	0.0023	2.95	0.0018	3.68	0.0015	4.42	0.042	0.035	0.982
0.040	105	0.0030	2.93	0.0024	3.66	0.0020	4.39	0.056	0.047	0.976
0.050	131	0.0038	2.91	0.0030	3.64	0.0025	4.37	0.069	0.059	0.971
0.060	156	0.0045	2.89	0.0036	3.62	0.0030	4.34	0.083	0.071	0.965
0.070	181	0.0053	2.88	0.0042	3.60	0.0035	4.31	0.097	0.083	0.959
0.080	206	0.0060	2.86	0.0048	3.57	0.0040	4.29	0.111	0.094	0.953
0.090	230	0.0068	2.84	0.0054	3.55	0.0045	4.26	0.125	0.106	0.947
0.100	254	0.0075	2.82	0.0060	3.53	0.0050	4.23	0.139	0.118	0.941
0.110	278	0.0083	2.81	0.0066	3.51	0.0055	4.21	0.153	0.130	0.935
0.120	301	0.0090	2.79	0.0072	3.48	0.0060	4.18	0.167	0.142	0.929
0.130	324	0.0098	2.77	0.0078	3.46	0.0065	4.15	0.180	0.153	0.923
0.140	347	0.0105	2.75	0.0084	3.44	0.0070	4.13	0.194	0.165	0.917
0.150	369	0.0113	2.73	0.0090	3.42	0.0075	4.10	0.208	0.177	0.912
0.160	391	0.0120	2.72	0.0096	3.40	0.0080	4.08	0.222	0.189	0.906
0.170	413	0.0128	2.70	0.0102	3.37	0.0085	4.05	0.236	0.201	0.900
0.180	434	0.0135	2.68	0.0108	3.35	0.0090	4.02	0.250	0.212	0.894
0.190	455	0.0143	2.66	0.0114	3.33	0.0095	4.00	0.264	0.224	0.888
0.200	476	0.0150	2.65	0.0120	3.31	0.0100	3.97	0.278	0.236	0.882
0.210	497	0.0158	2.63	0.0126	3.29	0.0105	3.94	0.292	0.248	0.876
0.220	517	0.0165	2.61	0.0132	3.26	0.0110	3.92	0.305	0.260	0.870
0.230	537	0.0173	2.59	0.0138	3.24	0.0115	3.89	0.319	0.271	0.864
0.240	556	0.0180	2.58	0.0144	3.22	0.0120	3.86	0.333	0.283	0.858
0.250	575	0.0188	2.56	0.0150	3.20	0.0125	3.84	0.347	0.295	0.853
0.260	594	0.0195	2.54	0.0156	3.17	0.0130	3.81	0.361	0.307	0.847
0.270	613	0.0203	2.52	0.0162	3.15	0.0135	3.78	0.375	0.319	0.841
0.280	631	0.0210	2.50	0.0168	3.13	0.0140	3.76	0.389	0.330	0.835
0.290	649	0.0218	2.49	0.0174	3.11	0.0145	3.73	0.403	0.342	0.829
0.300	667	0.0225	2.47	0.0180	3.09	0.0150	3.70	0.416	0.354	0.823
0.310	684	0.0233	2.45	0.0186	3.06	0.0155	3.68	0.430	0.366	0.817
0.320	701	0.0240	2.43	0.0192	3.04	0.0160	3.65	0.444	0.378	0.811
0.330	718	0.0248	2.42	0.0198	3.02			0.458	0.389	0.805
0.340	734	0.0255	2.40	0.0204	3.00			0.472	0.401	0.799
0.350	750	0.0263	2.38					0.486	0.413	0.794
0.360	766	0.0270	2.36					0.500	0.425	0.788
0.370	781	0.0278	2.35					0.514	0.437	0.782
ρ_{max}		0.0278		0.0206		0.0160				

*Values of ρ above light rule are less than ρ_{min}; $\rho_{min} = 200/f_y$ as provided in Section 10.5.1 of ACI 318-83.

FLEXURE 4.1–Coefficient a_n'' for rectangular beams with compression reinforcement in which $f_s' < f_y$; $f_c' = 3000$ psi

Reference: ACI 318-83, Sections 9.3.2, 10.2, 10.3.1–10.3.4, and Commentary Sections 10.3.1(A)(1) and 10.3.3

$$a_n'' = \frac{\phi M_{n2}}{A_s' d} = \phi \left[\frac{87{,}000}{12{,}000} \left(1 - \frac{d'/d}{c/d} \right) \left(1 - \frac{d'}{d} \right) - \frac{0.85}{12{,}000} f_c' \left(1 - \frac{d'}{d} \right) \right]$$

$$\phi = 0.90$$

c/d	0.025	0.050	0.075	0.100	0.125	0.150	0.175	0.200	0.225	0.250	0.275	0.300
0.04	2.20	—	—	—	—	—	—	—	—	—	—	—
0.05	2.99	—	—	—	—	—	—	—	—	—	—	—
0.06	3.52	0.85	—	—	—	—	—	—	—	—	—	—
0.07	3.90	1.59	—	—	—	—	—	—	—	—	—	—
0.08	4.18	2.14	0.20	—	—	—	—	—	—	—	—	—
0.09		2.58	0.83	—	—	—	—	—	—	—	—	—
0.10		2.92	1.33	—	—	—	—	—	—	—	—	—
0.11		3.20	1.74	0.36	—	—	—	—	—	—	—	—
0.12		3.44	2.08	0.81	—	—	—	—	—	—	—	—
0.13		3.63	2.37	1.19	0.05	—	—	—	—	—	—	—
0.14		3.80	2.62	1.51	0.44	—	—	—	—	—	—	—
0.15		3.95	2.84	1.79	0.78	—	—	—	—	—	—	—
0.16		4.08	3.03	2.03	1.08	0.19	—	—	—	—	—	—
0.17		3.19	2.25	1.34	0.49	—	—	—	—	—	—	—
0.18		3.34	2.44	1.57	0.76	—	—	—	—	—	—	—
0.19		3.47	2.61	1.78	1.01	0.26	—	—	—	—	—	—
0.20		3.59	2.77	1.97	1.23	0.51	—	—	—	—	—	—
0.21		3.70	2.91	2.14	1.42	0.74	0.10	—	—	—	—	—
0.22		3.80	3.03	2.30	1.60	0.94	0.32	—	—	—	—	—
0.23		3.89	3.15	2.44	1.77	1.13	0.53	—	—	—	—	—
0.24		3.97	3.26	2.57	1.92	1.30	0.72	0.17	—	—	—	—
0.25			3.35	2.68	2.06	1.45	0.89	0.36	—	—	—	—
0.26			3.44	2.79	2.19	1.60	1.05	0.53	0.05	—	—	—
0.27			3.53	2.90	2.31	1.73	1.20	0.69	0.22	—	—	—
0.28			3.61	2.99	2.42	1.86	1.34	0.84	0.38	—	—	—
0.29			3.68	3.08	2.52	1.97	1.47	0.98	0.54	0.10	—	—
0.30			3.75	3.16	2.61	2.08	1.59	1.11	0.68	0.25	—	—
0.32			3.87	3.31	2.79	2.28	1.81	1.35	0.93	0.53	0.16	
0.34				3.44	2.94	2.45	2.00	1.56	1.16	0.76	0.41	
0.36				3.56	3.08	2.61	2.17	1.75	1.36	0.98	0.63	
0.38				3.66	3.20	2.74	2.32	1.91	1.53	1.17	0.83	
0.40					3.76	3.31	2.87	2.46	2.06	1.70	1.34	1.01
0.42						3.41	2.98	2.58	2.20	1.84	1.49	1.18
0.44						3.50	3.08	2.70	2.32	1.97	1.63	1.32
0.46						3.58	3.18	2.80	2.43	2.09	1.76	1.46
0.48						3.65	3.26	2.90	2.54	2.20	1.88	1.58
0.50							3.34	2.98	2.63	2.31	1.99	1.70
0.52							3.41	3.06	2.72	2.40	2.09	1.80
0.54							3.48	3.14	2.80	2.49	2.18	1.90
0.56							3.54	3.21	2.88	2.57	2.27	1.99
0.58								3.27	2.95	2.64	2.35	2.08

Left-side boundary notes: $f_s' = 40$ ksi (at c/d ≈ 0.04), $f_s' = 50$ ksi (at c/d ≈ 0.05), $f_s' = 60$ ksi (at c/d ≈ 0.08).

Right-side boundary notes: $f_s' = 40$ ksi (near c/d ≈ 0.54–0.56), $f_s' = 50$ ksi and $f_s' = 60$ ksi (at bottom).

COLUMNS 2—Effective length factor *k* for columns in braced and nonbraced frames

References: ACI 318R Section 10.11.2; *Steel Structures: Design and Behavior*, by C. G. Salmon and J. E. Johnson, 2nd Ed., Harper & Row Publishers, New York, 1980, pp. 843–851

BRACED FRAMES		UNBRACED FRAMES
$\Psi = \dfrac{-2k}{\pi}\ \tan\dfrac{\pi}{2k}$		$\Psi = \dfrac{6k}{\pi}\ \cot\dfrac{\pi}{2k}$
k	Ψ	k
0.50	0.00	1.00
0.61	0.25	1.08
0.69	0.50	1.16
0.74	0.75	1.24
0.77	1.00	1.32
0.82	1.50	1.46
0.86	2.00	1.59
0.88	2.50	1.71
0.89	3.00	1.82
0.92	4.00	2.03
0.93	5.00	2.23
0.96	10.00	3.01
1.00	∞	∞

BRACED FRAMES   UNBRACED FRAMES

Ψ = relative column stiffness = ratio of $\Sigma(EI/l_c)$ of column to $\Sigma(EI/l)$ of beams, in a plane at one end of a column.

COLUMNS 8.22—Basic limits of factored axial load and factored moment for C4-60 columns (Design load and moment strengths)

References: ACI 318-83, Sections 9.3.2.2, 10.2, and 10.3; ACI Publication SP-7, pp. 152–182

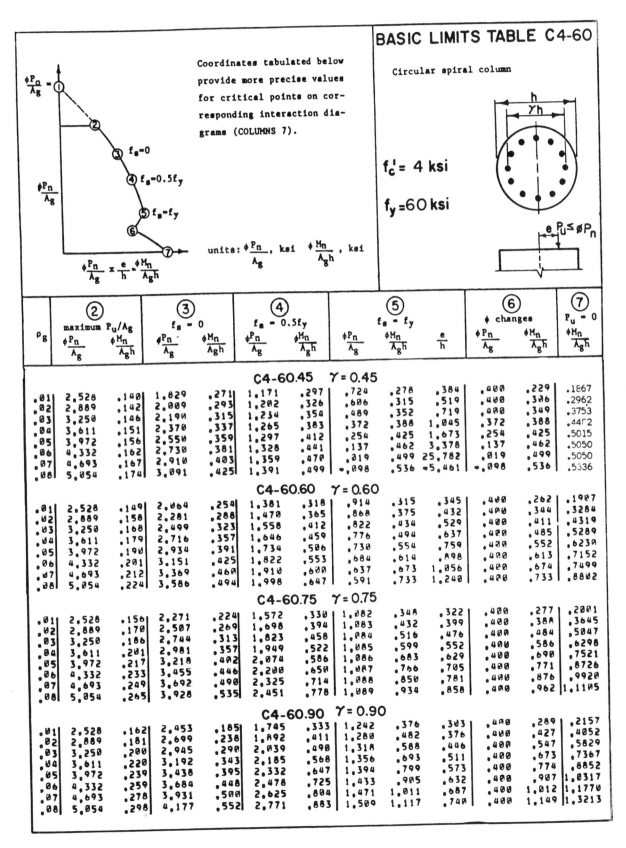

BASIC LIMITS TABLE C4-60

Circular spiral column

$f_c' = 4$ ksi

$f_y = 60$ ksi

Coordinates tabulated below provide more precise values for critical points on corresponding interaction diagrams (COLUMNS 7).

units: $\dfrac{\phi P_n}{A_g}$, ksi $\dfrac{\phi M_n}{A_g h}$, ksi

ρ_g	② max P_u/A_g $\dfrac{\phi P_n}{A_g}$	② $\dfrac{\phi M_n}{A_g h}$	③ $f_s=0$ $\dfrac{\phi P_n}{A_g}$	③ $\dfrac{\phi M_n}{A_g h}$	④ $f_s=0.5f_y$ $\dfrac{\phi P_n}{A_g}$	④ $\dfrac{\phi M_n}{A_g h}$	⑤ $f_s=f_y$ $\dfrac{\phi P_n}{A_g}$	⑤ $\dfrac{\phi M_n}{A_g h}$	⑤ $\dfrac{e}{h}$	⑥ ϕ changes $\dfrac{\phi P_n}{A_g}$	⑥ $\dfrac{\phi M_n}{A_g h}$	⑦ $P_u=0$ $\dfrac{\phi M_n}{A_g h}$
C4-60.45 γ=0.45												
.01	2.528	.140	1.829	.271	1.171	.297	.724	.278	.384	.400	.229	.1867
.02	2.889	.142	2.009	.293	1.202	.326	.606	.315	.519	.400	.306	.2962
.03	3.250	.146	2.190	.315	1.234	.354	.489	.352	.719	.400	.349	.3753
.04	3.611	.151	2.370	.337	1.265	.383	.372	.388	1.045	.372	.388	.4402
.05	3.972	.156	2.550	.359	1.297	.412	.254	.425	1.673	.254	.425	.5015
.06	4.332	.162	2.730	.381	1.328	.441	.137	.462	3.378	.137	.462	.5050
.07	4.693	.167	2.910	.403	1.359	.470	.019	.499	25.782	.019	.499	.5050
.08	5.054	.174	3.091	.425	1.391	.499	-.098	.536	-5.461	-.098	.536	.5336
C4-60.60 γ=0.60												
.01	2.528	.149	2.064	.254	1.381	.318	.914	.315	.345	.400	.262	.1907
.02	2.889	.158	2.281	.288	1.470	.365	.868	.375	.432	.400	.344	.3284
.03	3.250	.168	2.499	.323	1.558	.412	.822	.434	.529	.400	.411	.4319
.04	3.611	.179	2.716	.357	1.646	.459	.776	.494	.637	.400	.485	.5289
.05	3.972	.190	2.934	.391	1.734	.506	.730	.554	.759	.400	.552	.6230
.06	4.332	.201	3.151	.425	1.822	.553	.684	.614	.898	.400	.613	.7152
.07	4.693	.212	3.369	.460	1.910	.600	.637	.673	1.056	.400	.674	.7499
.08	5.054	.224	3.586	.494	1.998	.647	.591	.733	1.240	.400	.733	.8802
C4-60.75 γ=0.75												
.01	2.528	.156	2.271	.224	1.572	.330	1.082	.348	.322	.400	.277	.2001
.02	2.889	.170	2.507	.269	1.698	.394	1.083	.432	.399	.400	.388	.3645
.03	3.250	.186	2.744	.313	1.823	.458	1.084	.516	.476	.400	.484	.5047
.04	3.611	.201	2.981	.357	1.949	.522	1.085	.599	.552	.400	.586	.6298
.05	3.972	.217	3.218	.402	2.074	.586	1.086	.683	.629	.400	.690	.7521
.06	4.332	.233	3.455	.446	2.200	.650	1.087	.766	.705	.400	.771	.8726
.07	4.693	.249	3.692	.490	2.325	.714	1.088	.850	.781	.400	.876	.9920
.08	5.054	.265	3.928	.535	2.451	.778	1.089	.934	.858	.400	.962	1.1105
C4-60.90 γ=0.90												
.01	2.528	.162	2.453	.185	1.745	.333	1.242	.376	.303	.400	.289	.2157
.02	2.889	.181	2.699	.238	1.892	.411	1.280	.482	.376	.400	.427	.4052
.03	3.250	.200	2.945	.290	2.039	.490	1.318	.588	.446	.400	.547	.5829
.04	3.611	.220	3.192	.343	2.185	.568	1.356	.693	.511	.400	.673	.7367
.05	3.972	.239	3.438	.395	2.332	.647	1.394	.799	.573	.400	.774	.8852
.06	4.332	.259	3.684	.448	2.478	.725	1.433	.905	.632	.400	.907	1.0317
.07	4.693	.278	3.931	.500	2.625	.804	1.471	1.011	.687	.400	1.012	1.1770
.08	5.054	.298	4.177	.552	2.771	.883	1.500	1.117	.749	.400	1.149	1.3213

COLUMNS 8.3—Basic limits of factored axial load and factored moment for R3-60 columns (Design load and moment strengths)

References: ACI 318-83, Sections 9.3.2.2, 10.2, and 10.3; ACI Publication SP-7, pp. 152–182

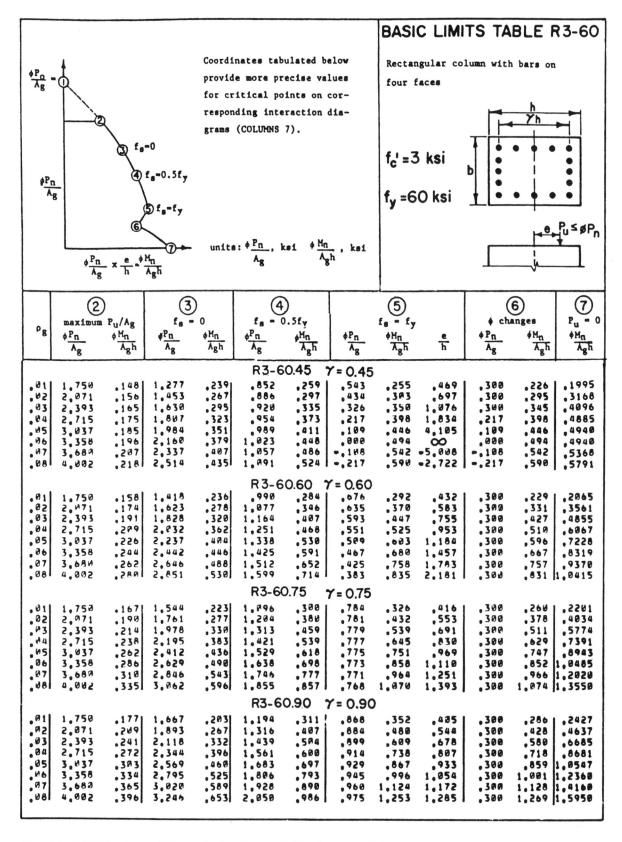

ρ_g	② maximum P_u/A_g $\phi\frac{P_n}{A_g}$	$\phi\frac{M_n}{A_gh}$	③ $f_s = 0$ $\phi\frac{P_n}{A_g}$	$\phi\frac{M_n}{A_gh}$	④ $f_s = 0.5f_y$ $\phi\frac{P_n}{A_g}$	$\phi\frac{M_n}{A_gh}$	⑤ $f_s = f_y$ $\phi\frac{P_n}{A_g}$	$\phi\frac{M_n}{A_gh}$	$\frac{e}{h}$	⑥ ϕ changes $\phi\frac{P_n}{A_g}$	$\phi\frac{M_n}{A_gh}$	⑦ $P_u = 0$ $\phi\frac{M_n}{A_gh}$
					R3-60.45		$\gamma = 0.45$					
.01	1.750	.148	1.277	.239	.852	.259	.543	.255	.469	.300	.226	.1995
.02	2.071	.156	1.453	.267	.886	.297	.434	.303	.697	.300	.295	.3168
.03	2.393	.165	1.630	.295	.920	.335	.326	.350	1.076	.300	.345	.4096
.04	2.715	.175	1.807	.323	.954	.373	.217	.398	1.834	.217	.398	.4885
.05	3.037	.185	1.984	.351	.989	.411	.109	.446	4.105	.109	.446	.4940
.06	3.358	.196	2.160	.379	1.023	.448	.000	.494	∞	.000	.494	.4940
.07	3.680	.207	2.337	.407	1.057	.486	-.108	.542	-5.008	-.108	.542	.5368
.08	4.002	.218	2.514	.435	1.091	.524	-.217	.590	-2.722	-.217	.590	.5791
					R3-60.60		$\gamma = 0.60$					
.01	1.750	.158	1.418	.236	.990	.284	.676	.292	.432	.300	.229	.2865
.02	2.071	.174	1.623	.278	1.077	.346	.635	.370	.583	.300	.331	.3561
.03	2.393	.191	1.828	.320	1.164	.407	.593	.447	.755	.300	.427	.4855
.04	2.715	.209	2.032	.362	1.251	.468	.551	.525	.953	.300	.519	.6067
.05	3.037	.226	2.237	.404	1.338	.530	.509	.603	1.184	.300	.596	.7228
.06	3.358	.244	2.442	.446	1.425	.591	.467	.680	1.457	.300	.667	.8319
.07	3.680	.262	2.646	.488	1.512	.652	.425	.758	1.783	.300	.757	.9370
.08	4.002	.280	2.851	.530	1.599	.714	.383	.835	2.181	.300	.831	1.0415
					R3-60.75		$\gamma = 0.75$					
.01	1.750	.167	1.544	.223	1.096	.300	.784	.326	.416	.300	.260	.2201
.02	2.071	.190	1.761	.277	1.204	.380	.781	.432	.553	.300	.378	.4034
.03	2.393	.214	1.978	.330	1.313	.459	.779	.539	.691	.300	.511	.5774
.04	2.715	.238	2.195	.383	1.421	.539	.777	.645	.830	.300	.629	.7391
.05	3.037	.262	2.412	.436	1.529	.618	.775	.751	.969	.300	.747	.8943
.06	3.358	.286	2.629	.490	1.638	.698	.773	.858	1.110	.300	.852	1.0485
.07	3.680	.310	2.846	.543	1.746	.777	.771	.964	1.251	.300	.966	1.2020
.08	4.002	.335	3.062	.596	1.855	.857	.768	1.070	1.393	.300	1.074	1.3550
					R3-60.90		$\gamma = 0.90$					
.01	1.750	.177	1.667	.203	1.194	.311	.868	.352	.435	.300	.286	.2427
.02	2.071	.209	1.893	.267	1.316	.407	.884	.480	.548	.300	.428	.4637
.03	2.393	.241	2.118	.332	1.439	.504	.899	.609	.678	.300	.580	.6685
.04	2.715	.272	2.344	.396	1.561	.600	.914	.738	.807	.300	.718	.8681
.05	3.037	.303	2.569	.460	1.683	.697	.929	.867	.933	.300	.859	1.0547
.06	3.358	.334	2.795	.525	1.806	.793	.945	.996	1.054	.300	1.001	1.2360
.07	3.680	.365	3.020	.589	1.928	.890	.960	1.124	1.172	.300	1.128	1.4160
.08	4.002	.396	3.244	.653	2.050	.986	.975	1.253	1.285	.300	1.269	1.5950

INDEX

NOTES

NOTES

VOLUME III

P. E. (Civil) License Review Manual

CONCRETE MATERIALS AND MIX DESIGN
Section 5

Geoffrey D. Hichborn, Sr., B. S., P. E.
Principal
Hichborn Consulting Group
Orange, California

ABOUT
THE AUTHOR

Mr. Hichborn is presently principal of Hichborn Consulting Group, a small civil engineering firm. He continues as a consultant to the cement and concrete industries and to local engineering firms.

His previous positions include Director, Materials Engineering — Testing and Inspection, Schaefer Dixon Associates, Inc.; President, Arche Engineering Laboratories; Executive Vice President, Osborne Laboratories, Inc.; and Manager of Technical Services, Riverside Cement Company.

He has been actively involved in the manufacture of cement, testing and evaluation of concrete and other cement containing products, aggregates, asphalt and the distress of materials used in construction; he has provided expert assistance in the specification, testing, analysis, failure and use of cement and concrete.

He obtained his BSCE from University of California, Irvine.

Mr. Hichborn is a member of ASCE, ACI, SEAOSC, and ASTM and is a Registered Civil Engineer in the State of California.

ACKNOWLEDGEMENTS

THIRD EDITION

The author wishes to thank the many people and organizations who were motivating forces toward the preparation of these notes. First acknowledgements go to Dr. R.L. Alexander, upon whose previous course notes this section was created. These notes were prepared during the author's employment with Riverside Cement Company. Without their assistance, encouragement, allocation of staff and typing time, and general blessing to pursue this project, it would not have been accomplished.

C.V. Chelapati, project editor, has poured countless hours into the entire project, and has patiently guided the preparation of these notes: "CV" is also acknowledged with gratitude. Howard McGinnis, a business associate, who was with the Portland Cement Association for many years, has provided valuable suggestions for improvement of these notes. Thanks also go to the many engineers who have used the earlier editions of these notes and brought errors and corrections or points of clarification to the attention of the author. Finally, without the help and support of family including spouse, Kathy, and kids, and father, a de facto technical writer and editor, these notes may never have been completed.

The author and editor have exercised care in the preparation of these notes, but the information contained herein must be used with appropriate judgement since it may not include sufficient data for all users or for all problems. Although these notes are prepared in accordance with generally accepted or recognized engineering and construction principles, it must be recognized that they are only class notes and that they contain general information only; they are not intended for specific project use, and are no substitute for professional engineering analysis. No liability is assumed by the editor or author in connection with the use of or information contained in these notes.

Finally, these notes are dedicated to you, the reader, with the author's hope that you earn your civil registration upon taking your exam the first time.

FOURTH EDITION

The editor wishes to express his appreciation to Mr. Hichborn for making revisions and Mr. Jeffrey Ament who proofed the fourth edition.

TABLE OF CONTENTS

CHAPTER 4
METHODS OF PLACEMENT

CHAPTER 5
SITE CONDITIONS AND DURABILITY OF EXPOSED CONCRETE

PART II
CONCRETE-MAKING MATERIALS

CHAPTER 6
CEMENTS FOR CONCRETE MIXTURES

CHAPTER 7
CONCRETE AGGREGATES

CHAPTER 13
METHODS OF PROPORTIONING CONCRETE MIXTURES

INDEX

NOTES

LIST OF FIGURES

LIST OF TABLES

ALPHABETICAL LIST OF SOLVED PROBLEMS

TRUE−FALSE PROBLEMS

TERMINOLOGY

CONCRETE INGREDIENTS MATERIALS

Required

    Portland Cement or Blended Cement

    Water

    Fine Aggregate (Sand)

    Coarse Aggregate (Rock)

Optional

    Chemical Admixtures

        Water Reducers

        Set Retarders

        Set Accelerators

        Air Entrainers

        Super Plastisizers

    Mineral Admixtures

        Fly Ash (Classes F and C)

        Natural Pozzolans

        Silica Fume

        Slag

        Color

PROPERTIES OF FRESH CONCRETE

Slump:

    The amount of fall of a conically shaped 12-in. high sample of fresh concrete upon demolding; a measure of workability, consistency and water content.

Time of Setting:

    The time required to achieve a condition of no workability measured starting when water mixes with cement.

Pumpability:

The ease of a fresh mixture to flow through a concrete pump.

Finishability

Consistency

Cohesiveness

Segregation

Unit Weight

Air Content

PROPERTIES OF HARDENED CONCRETE

Strength

Compressive

Flexural

Tensile

Durability

Resistance to sulfates

Resistance to freeze thaw cycles

Resistance to de-icing chemicals

Resistance to acid

Watertightness

(Im)Permeability

Porosity

Air Content

Density

Scaling

Cracking

Heat of Hydration

CONCRETE CONSTRUCTION TERMINOLOGY

Curing

Moist Curing

Fogging

Poly

Ponding

Wet Burlap

Wet Sand

Tilt-up Construction

Formwork

Bug Holes

Rock Pockets

Form Leakage

Mass Concreting

Jointing

    Expansion Joints

    Contraction Joints

    Control Joints

    Cold Joints

    Construction Joints

Ready Mixed Concrete

Central Mixed Concrete

Pre-Cast Concrete

Pre-stressed Concrete

Post-tensioned Concrete

Masonry Grout

Pre-packaged Concrete

Cellular Concrete

Heavy Weight (Radiation Shielding)

USEFUL CONSTANTS

STANDARD UNITS AND MEASURES

1 cubic yard = 27 cubic feet
1 ton   = 2,000 lb

WATER

8.33 lb / gallon
62.4 lb / cubic foot
7.48 gallons / cubic foot

PORTLAND CEMENT (CONVENTIONALLY USED VALUES)

94 lb / sack
94 lb / cubic foot (bulk-loose)
1 cubic foot / sack (bulk-loose)
Specific Gravity 3.15 (unless given)

CONCRETE

	Range of Values
Hardrock Concrete Unit Weight	130-155 lb / cubic foot
Lightweight Concrete Unit Weight Range	105-120 lb / cubic foot

AGGREGATE

	Range of Values
Sand Specific Gravity	2.50-2.65
Coarse Specific Gravity	2.55-2.70

FLY ASH

Class F	2.40-2.60
Class C	2.20-2.50

REFERENCES

1. *Guide to Durable Concrete,* American Concrete Institute, Committee 201, Detroit, MI, 1977.

2 *Recommended Practice for Selecting Proportions for Normal and Heavy-Weight Concrete,* American Concrete Institute, Committee 211, Detroit, MI, 1977.

3. *Guide for Use of Admixtures in Concrete,* (212.2) American Concrete Institute, Committee 212, Detroit, MI, 1981.

4. *Admixtures for Concrete,* (212.1) American Concrete Institute, Committee 212, Detroit, MI, 1981.

5. *Building Code Requirements for Reinforced Concrete,* American Concrete Institute, Committee 318, Detroit, MI, 1983.

6. *Designation C 33, Standard Specification for Concrete Aggregates,* American Society for Testing Materials, Committee C-9, Philadelphia, PA, 1983.

7. *Designation C 94, Standard Specification for Ready-Mixed Concrete,* American Society for Testing Materials, Committee C-9, Philadelphia, PA, 1983.

8. *Designation C 150, Standard Specification for Portland Cement,* American Society for Testing Materials, Committee C-1, Philadelphia, PA, 1983.

9. *Designation C 494, Standard Specification for Chemical Admixtures for Concrete,* American Society for Testing Materials, Committee C-9, Philadelphia, PA, 1982.

10. *Designation C595, Standard Specification for Blended Hydraulic Cements,* American Society for Testing Materials, Committee C-1, Philadelphia, PA, 1983.

11. *Designation C 618, Standard Specifications for Fly Ash and Raw or Calcined Natural Pozzolan for Use as a Mineral Admixture in Portland Cement Concrete,* American Society for Testing Materials, Philadelphia, PA, 1983.

12. *Design and Control of Concrete Mixtures,* 12th ed., and 13th ed., Portland Cement Association, Skokie, IL, 1979.

13. *Concrete Manual,* 8th ed., Revised, United States Dept. of the Interior (Bureau of Reclamation), U.S. Government Printing Office, Washington, D.C., 1975.

14. *Concrete Inspection Manual,* J. J. Waddell, International Conference of Building Officials, Whittier, CA, 1976.

15. *Materials of Engineering Construction,* R. L. Alexander and D. Bourgeois, CSULB Bookstore, 1979.

16. *Composition and Properties of Concrete,* 2nd ed., G. Troxell, M. Davis and J. W. Kelly, McGraw-Hill, 1968.

1

INTRODUCTION

1.1 A WORD TO THE CIVIL LICENSE CANDIDATE

Every NCEE Civil Examination for the past several years has had as one of its 24 problem statements exactly one Portland Cement Concrete question.

This question has typically, but not always, been in the morning. The questions have usually been minor variations on only two basic themes: (1) describe concrete materials and properties in general terms; and (2) perform calculations relative to the proportions of those ingredient materials in a batch or volume.

Mix proportioning questions are asked in only one of two major ways. Either (1) the ratios of the materials (cement, rock, sand, water) are given so that volumetric and weight proportions are required on a "per cubic yard" basis; or (2) some "per cubic yard" variables are given and the rest of the concrete ingredients must be determined. Other basic calculations may be required for both problem types.

More than likely, the student will not be required to make assumptions or judgements should a mix design question be asked, since standardized responses ease exam grading. Search for *all* data given since it will probably be sufficient to solve the questions. The tables provided in these notes are useful to working mix problems in general, but probably will not be necessary in the examination. Glean from these notes principles and procedures; do not get weighed down by the tabular data!

Several sources of information have been cited herein, and deserve comment. The softbound publication from the Portland Cement Association entitled, *Design and Control of Concrete Mixtures,* is the most useful and readable of all publications cited. It is devoted to all aspects of concrete from materials to proportioning, from mixing to placing, from material properties to detailed construction practices. One chapter is devoted to proportioning mixtures, it may further clarify the procedures.

Secondly, the U.S. Department of the Interior, Bureau of Reclamation, publishes the *Concrete Manual,* which is an excellent resource for public works type projects authorized by the Bureau. For a basic text for commercial and industrial concrete construction and proportioning, there is none better than the *Concrete Inspection Manual* by Waddell. Finally, for the determined, the national American Concrete Institute (ACI), the Portland Cement Association (PCA) and the American Society of Testing and Materials (ASTM) each have specific standards, methods, specifications and guidelines for concrete, concrete materials, proportioning and construction. All of these are presented in the "References" section of these notes.

PART I

USE AND DURABILITY CONSIDERATIONS FOR CONCRETE CONSTRUCTION

2

OVERVIEW OF CONCRETE
AS MATERIAL

2.1   USE OF CONCRETE

In 1988, over 10.5 million tons of portland cement, and nearly 135 million tons of construction aggregates were sold in California. This amounts to in excess of $1.3 trillion dollars in material, the majority of which was delivered as one of several forms of concrete. Proportioning of this material therefore is of significant consequence for economic and constructability reasons.

Portland cement concrete is an integral part of the construction industry due to its wide variety of qualities; namely, economy, versatility, strength, hardness and tremendous plastic workability which lends it to innumerable shapes and forms. These notes, then, apply to hydraulic cement concretes which require water to develop strength and which can harden under water.

Concrete in one form or another has been used throughout all of recorded history in areas including Egypt, Rome and Ancient Greece. Structures still standing today testify to its endurance over time. In this sense, concrete started as mixtures similar to presently used lime mortar systems, and evolved to burnt limestone/clay material combinations similar to cement, which are more durable.

2.2   PLACEMENT

Being a very versatile material, concrete can be placed in a wide variety of applications by an equally large variety of methods of conveyance. Simple placement can be made out of a ready-mix truck's chute, or a concrete pump can deliver material hundreds of feet in a single lift. To date, concrete mixtures have been pumped over 1,000 ft in one lift. Furthermore, as many as 15,000 cu yd have been delivered in a single placement in one day using pumps and commercial ready-mix trucks. Finally, strengths to 14,000 psi have been commercially available in some regions of the United States and strengths in excess of 20,000 psi recorded.

2.3   MATERIALS

High volumes of concrete require extensive amounts of raw materials, correctly proportioned for the particular application to achieve successful results. Therefore, the materials engineer must recognize not only the range of properties of the raw materials, but also consider the end use of the concrete, the methods of mixing, placing, consolidating and curing and the special conditions at the site. The latter may include a potentially damaging environment which could seriously reduce the life of the concrete components, and possibly the life of the structure. Therefore the concrete must be durable in its environment (soil, water, freezing-thawing) to last a probable service life of many decades. Finally, the material proportions need to be based not only on these many materials, placement and site conditions, but should be economical as well.

2.4   PROPORTIONING

Concrete is an intimately proportioned mixture primarily containing cement, water, fine aggregates and coarse aggregates. Secondarily, chemical and/or mineral admixtures may be incorporated into the mix to supply additional desirable qualities to both the fresh and hardened mixture. Exposure conditions at the site (sulfates, seawater, freezing-thawing, sewage, etc.) have tremendous bearing on the proportions of materials required to satisfy these circumstances. The reader is encouraged to be familiar with how these materials relate to concrete properties, and what composition these materials have. Typical P. E. Problems are shown in Chapter 10.

Proportioning this mixture, then, is more than selecting a combination of materials whose solid volume sums to 27 cu ft/cu yd and will produce satisfactory strengths. It is the engineer's means of assuring that the owner will have a project easily and economically built which will endure in its environment.

Finally, the engineer realizes that he need not reinvent the wheel with each new concrete project. He will use the known, empirical history of the materials he has chosen, as well as standards and specifications which dictate normal criteria for performance. Mix adjustments may be made during initial stages of field use based on the engineer's judgement, and the material's performance.

2.5   STANDARDS

In concrete, standard practice is set forth by the American Concrete Institute's (ACI) Manual of Concrete Practice which is updated annually and is now in five comprehensive volumes. Additionally, agencies at the city, county, state and federal levels specify certain parameters of concrete performance which are acceptable to them. Many cities, for example, refer to the Uniform Building Code (UBC) which is published by the International Conference of Building Officials (ICBO) or other so-called model codes. Occasionally, a city may have its own acceptance criteria in lieu of, or in addition to, a model code. Counties similarly may accept the provisions of a model code with addenda to reflect their own particular concerns, local practice, or special conditions. States may have many sets of concrete specifications. For example, California has Caltrans requirements for highway work, the Office of the State Architect for state building structures and the California Water Project with its different requirements. At the federal level, the United States Department of Defense-Division of the Army-Corps of Engineers has separate sets of requirements for civilian and military concrete construction. Also, the Department of the Interior, Bureau of Reclamation specifies its own special requirements.

Generally speaking, the ACI documents are widely accepted for practice while standard specifications and standard methods of test are a part of the American Society for Testing and Materials (ASTM). ASTM is a consensus organization of volunteers from industry (users, suppliers/manufacturers, testing organizations/interested parties) and government who continually use, examine and refine these standards.

2.6   DEFINITION OF PORTLAND CEMENT CONCRETE

> Concrete is a heterogeneous system of solid, discrete, typically gradiently sized, inorganic mineral aggregates, usually plutonic (feldspatho-siliceous or ferro-magnesian) or sedimentary-calcareous in origins, embedded in a matrix compound of synthesized polybasic alkaline and alkaloidal silicates held in aqueous solution and coprecipitate dispersion with other amphoteric oxides, this matrix being originally capable of progressive dissolution, hydration, reprecipitation, gelatin and solidification through a continuous and coexistent series of crystalline, amorphous, colloidal and cryptocrystalline states and ultimately subject to thermo-allotriomorphic alteration, the system when first conjoined being transparently plastic during which state it is impressed to a predetermined form into which it finally consolidates, thus providing a structure relatively impermeable and with useful capacity to transmit tensile, compressive and shear stresses.

Figure 2.1 Definition of Concrete

2.7   TRUE-FALSE PROBLEMS

2.7.1   QUESTIONS

(Circle one)

1. T   F   When properly proportioning concrete mixtures, no consideration except achieving the required strength at minimum cost is necessary. Explain.

2. T   F   The shapes and sizes of concrete members must often be limited due to the inability of most concrete to be easily worked, consolidated and cured.

3. T   F   ACI, the American Cement Institute, is not an authority with the ability to accept or reject concrete, but through consensus, issues a standard code document which may be referenced by an engineer, owner or agency for criteria of acceptance or design.

4. T   F   The materials engineer has the responsibility to proportion the mixture for considerations of workability, strength, durability, conveyance, consolidation and its method of transport at a minimum cost.

2.7.2   ANSWERS

Question	Answer	Explanation
1	False	Workability, transportability and durability are also necessary.
2	False	A wide variety of shapes and sizes are possible.
3	False	ACI is the American *Concrete* Institute; it does issue standard documents but has no authority.
4	True	

3

INTENDED CONCRETE UTILIZATION

3.1 INTRODUCTION

The mix proportions depend, to a large part, on the intended use of the concrete. The final usage of the concrete can be very routine in nature such as residential foundations, steps, and walks or can have highly specialized service requirements such as massive continuous placements for a large concrete gravity dam or a high-rise building's mat foundation. This section will attempt to list some of the ways concrete intended "designed in" qualities are related to various types of concrete construction.

3.2 FLATWORK

Flatwork includes residential slabs on grade, warehouse floors, sidewalks and driveways. When a very dense surface is necessary, the mixture must have finishability as well as workability. Minimum cement contents traditionally have been specified by the engineer, often without specifying strength, while limiting only water or slump. For flat work which is specified for strength, it is not unusual for strengths as low as 2,000 to 2,500 psi to be required in the Southern California region. Where the engineer desires to specify minimum cement content, he should also specify a maximum water to cement ratio (or maximum water content) and mandate good finishability with sufficient paste to produce a good, dense, hard, durable surface. Minimum cement content alone does not of itself assure a strong, durable, finishable mix. If the water content is high, the quality of the hardened concrete is jeopardized.

Generally, California codes provide an exception to national practice in allowing strengths as low as 2,000 psi. Normal minimum specified strengths of 3,000 psi apply to other portions of the nation. This assures a level of durability and finishability that a "five-sack minimum", for example, does not necessarily imply. Southern California practice is now changing toward a performance specification (e.g., minimum strength of 3,000 psi or maximum water/cement ratio of 0.55) which is preferable to a prescriptive one (e.g., 4.5 sack mix).

Once the performance criteria is established, concrete for flatwork must be properly delivered to the forms, consolidated, finished and cured to obtain optimum performance. Also, the mix generally should not bleed significantly or be allowed to dry (prior to hardening) by means of winds and/or low relative humidities. Flatwork should always be properly cured by ponding, sprinkling with water or fog nozzles, applying curing compound or using an impervious (plastic) membrane such as Visqueen.

3.3 BUILDINGS, COMMERCIAL AND INDUSTRIAL WORK

For buildings, all exposed concrete will be judged not only on its performance characteristics such as strength and durability, but also will be judged for superior aesthetic quality. Here shear walls, columns, exposed beams and flatwork all require a pleasing appearance. Shear walls should utilize a mixture which helps avoid rock pockets and bug holes. Very workable concrete, usually of higher design strengths, is appropriate for cast-in-place beams and columns. Often a 5-in. or 6-in. slump is required due to concentrated rebar or low form clearance. Gap graded sands should be avoided.

Where steel reinforcing is utilized, the mix proportions must provide for concrete which is both workable and sized (the top size aggregate specified) to flow easily between potentially congested steel or through the low clearances between forms and rebar. Where formed concrete walls or columns will be left exposed and uncovered, a surface with bug holes, rock pockets and cold joints *must* be avoided. Here the proportions must have sufficient paste and workability to be well consolidated in the forms. In addition, some retardation of time of setting through the use of chemical admixtures may be in order to prevent cold joints, and the aggregate (both coarse and fine) must be well graded to minimize bug holes.

Compressive strength at 28 days of age is usually specified in buildings. The most economical concrete in these structures will usually have rounded, typically natural coarse aggregate, an optimal proportion of coarse and fine material, and good cohesion during placement.

3.4 HIGHWAYS AND PAVEMENTS

Unlike buildings, which base concrete acceptance on *compressive* strength, highways and pavements (including warehouse floors) resist stresses which relate more to concrete's flexural strength. In this case, the mix proportions and aggregates will be changed to maximize *flexural* properties. Higher cement factors are usual and the use of manufactured (crushed) aggregates is typical. A harsher mix, though not specifically desired, is not unusual; but since highways in particular have fairly rough finishes, it is not as important. More attention is paid to workability and cohesiveness when highways are slip-formed. Aggregate coatings (usually clay materials, if present) will rapidly reduce the flexural strength of concrete, so aggregate must be well washed or newly fractured. Also, aggregates which are angular or elongated perform better than spherical, natural gravels since they will provide some "aggregate interlock" in pavement placements.

3.5 MASSIVE STRUCTURES

The primary factor of importance in massive concrete work is the effect of heat of hydration which may cause internal thermal stresses, consequent dimensional change and resultant cracking with possible loss of structural integrity. This concern may be further complicated by a requirement for "impermeability". For massive structures, such as dams and foundations (characterized by high ratios of volume to surface area) the cement must be chosen and the mix proportioned to minimize the heat generation per cubic yard of concrete. Often the cement will be chosen specifically for minimum heat of hydration. The mix may be designed to include natural pozzolans or fly ash, as they tend to provide increased ultimate strength while minimizing heat. Cement contents are usually lowered when pozzolans are used, since these structures seldom need high early strengths and can wait longer (sometimes up to one year) to achieve the desired design strength.

"Impermeability" characteristics, often required by dams and other facilities, are usually achieved by minimizing the water/cement ratio and/or using pozzolans. Also air entrainment can be used, as well as employing construction techniques which thoroughly consolidate minimum slump fresh concrete. On the other hand, massive concrete placements usually require special conveying techniques for which the proportions may need to be adjusted to accommodate delivery and placement. The engineer must address these conflicting requirements.

Finally, massive structures may incorporate very large top sized aggregates. Some concrete dams have utilized aggregate greater than 1 ft in diameter. Often, large mat foundations for buildings use 1-1/2 or 2-in. top size aggregates, since ready-mix trucks are often unable to handle larger aggregates, or such materials are commercially unavailable.

3.6 ARCHITECTURAL CONCRETE

Concrete used for the dual purpose of architectural design elements of shape and color in combination with structural integrity, requires the most demanding selection of materials: particularly cement, fine aggregate, admixtures and coloring agents. The mix must be proportioned to provide a concrete which will be easily formed into complex, intricate shapes with a high level of relief and which permit special surface treatments such as sandblasting or bush-hammering. The uniformity and source of all ingredient materials must be maintained throughout the project duration.

3.7 SANITARY STRUCTURES

Sanitary structures, as well as hydraulic structures in general, have special durability requirements. Often, to accommodate the requirements of impermeability or the presence of standing water, the water/cement ratio is limited by a maximum value ranging from 0.40 to 0.50 by weight. Sanitary structures also handle materials with varying sulfate and sulfite/sulfide contents which are clearly detrimental to portland cement paste. Well graded aggregates are essential to limiting permeability. Often Type II or V Portland cements are specified in conjunction with a limited water/cement ratio, since they possess sulfate resisting qualities.

Hydraulic structures, for reasons of water-tightness, also specify maximum permissible water/cement ratios. Sulfate exposure can be a consideration too. Often air entrainment is specified for both applications, since "air" will substantially reduce permeability.

3.8 MARINE STRUCTURES

As with sanitary and hydraulic structures, the water/cement ratio will be limited. This limitation reduces the permeability of the structure, increases the durability and provides protection for the embedded reinforcing steel against the action of corrosive salts, particularly chlorides.

Since sulfate exposure is always a factor in marine environments, often Type V cement is specified, but a minimum resistance of Type II is required. Using low water/cement ratios and air entrainment will also improve sulfate resistance.

3.9 TRUE-FALSE PROBLEMS

3.9.1 QUESTIONS

(Circle one)

1. T F Temperature rise due to heat of hydration is an insignificant consideration in mix proportioning.

2. T F The mix proportions are no different for architectural concrete than for other concrete of similar strength.

3. T F Impermeability characteristics of concrete for hydraulic structures depend mainly on the water/cement ratio and air entrainment in normal mixtures using well-graded sands and coarse aggregates.

4. T F Specifying only a minimum cement content assures adequate quality concrete.

5. T F Curing of concrete is not really important to its installed quality.

6. T F Forms for concrete must be:

   A. properly braced

   B. properly trued to line and grade

   C. tight at joints, preventing leakage of water or mortar

   D. removable from hardened concrete while not causing damage to them

   E. able to produce finish and texture desired and

   F. non-absorptive to water.

3.9.2   ANSWERS

Question	Answer	Explanation
1	False	Internal temperature rise in massive structures can easily exceed 70 or 80° F, creating a potential for volume change due to temperature; this can lead to cracking and other forms of concrete distress. Member shape, size, color, and texture all create different material needs than just for strength and durability.
2	False	
3	True	
4	False	
5	False	
6	True	

4

METHODS OF PLACEMENT

4.1 INTRODUCTION

The designed properties required for a fresh concrete mix will differ depending upon the means of transporting the concrete from the mixer to the project.

In general, the concrete needs to be workable enough to be easily transferred by the transporting equipment, but cohesive enough not to segregate during delivery and placement. Also, there should be no loss of workability (commonly called slump loss) due to handling. Finally, bleeding should be kept to a minimum at all stages of placement.

Often, when the means of conveyance is known, the use of special additives can be considered. For example, additives such as fly ash can enhance pumpability, and superplasticizers can yield very high slumps with less tendency to segregate. Also, in the case of pump mixes, the maximum aggregate size must be limited to no more than 40% of the pump line inside diameter and is often lower. Finally, most mixes have better transporting qualities when air is entrained.

4.2 PLACING FROM THE CHUTE

Most concrete is delivered by a mixer truck and put in place with the truck's chute. However, segregation and slump loss should be considered and minimized by the mix proportions and method of placement. The most obvious precaution for this method of delivery is to minimize the drop from the end of the chute to the form. Also, the chute must be steep enough to handle concrete of the least slump expected. If job site conditions do not allow this, then the concrete slump should be reconsidered, the method of placement should be modified, or a ramp be used to elevate the mixer.

4.3   PUMPING CONCRETE

Concrete pumping, particularly for use in high-rise applications which are characterized by moment resisting, ductile-concrete framed structures, continues to grow in popularity as a more efficient and economic way of getting concrete from the mixer to its placement destination.

Normal commercial practice for pumping concrete utilizes fairly high slump concrete (at least 4 in. and often 6 and 7 in.) with:

1. A pea gravel aggregate replacing some or all of the normal mix's 3/4-in. or 1-in. top-size coarse aggregate,

2. A fairly high cement content (usually over 550 lb of cement per yard),

3. Chemical admixtures which lower water requirements while providing identical or better workability and some set retardation and,

4. Fly ash, a spherical, glassy, finely divided mineral pozzolan, which makes the mix ultimately stronger, more pumpable, finishable, durable and economical.

Usually, great attention is paid to the amount of fines in the mix; that is, the aggregate finer than the #50 sieve plus the cement and mineral admixtures (fly ash or other pozzolans). This is because these fines, to a large extent, dictate how slick or pumpable the fresh concrete will be in 4-, 5- or 6-in. diameter steel pump lines. Also, these fines can aid the mix by increasing cohesion, thus reducing any tendency toward segregation of the mix. (Segregation is the separation of the coarse aggregate from the rest of the concrete, often associated with higher slumps).

The cohesion of the mix is also important in preventing packing of rock in the pump line and the pumping of the segregated wet paste or mortar through the pack. Even with the requirements for all of these precautions, pumping remains a preferred way of delivering a steady flow of fairly high volumes of workable, plastic concrete over relatively long distances or great heights, and around obstacles.

4.4   BELT CONVEYORS

Able to deliver high volumes of fresh, lower slump concrete to a central location into a buggy, wheel barrow or bucket, the belt conveyor is used on jobs where the concrete should be moved long distances horizontally to a slightly different level. Unfortunately, the belt conveyor usually is unable to place concrete directly onto or into forms, and care must be taken to prevent segregation at its discharge point. Typically, belt conveyors will convey all concrete proportions with ease, except those of higher slumps which are prone to segregation. Low- or no-slump concrete can be conveyed very effectively by belts.

4.5   BUGGIES, RAIL CARS AND TRUCKS

Both buggies and barrows are labor intensive small loads; they are usually useful only for relatively short, horizontal hauls. Rail cars and trucks, on the other hand, deliver huge volumes quickly and are appropriate only for delivery on large concreting jobs. These include, for example, airfield pavements, flood control channels, dams, large mat foundations, large parking areas, and highways.

The considerations for the mix are the same for all of these methods of transportation; they should be cohesive, should not separate because of the vibration or speed of the equipment and should not lose slump or water from the mix by evaporation. Where sun, temperatures or length dictate, conveyors usually are covered to prevent slump loss of the fresh concrete.

4.6   BUCKETS

Often used because of a placement elevation much higher than the mixer or because of other similar obstacles, a bucket attached to the hook of a mobile or tower-mounted crane will convey a fixed, relatively small volume of concrete repetitively, though often somewhat slowly.

Concrete of all slumps has been placed by the bucket method and no special precautions need be taken except to assure a mix which will not segregate and a bucket with a good control of its discharge of concrete. Also, the drop between bucket and form should be minimized.

4.7   TREMIE PIPES

A tremie (rhymes with 'creamy') is a long, smooth interior pipe with a funnel-shaped hopper at its top to receive concrete. Tremies are used to move concrete vertically downward and are designed to minimize concrete segregation during the drop. They are most effective when placing concrete under water. The fresh concrete must be of higher slump, very cohesive and fairly rich in cement content.

The discharge end of the tremie must rest in previously placed concrete so there is not a *free fall* drop of the fresh concrete through water but rather a low head of concrete which will create a seal to keep out water and permit a flow of concrete. Placement should be continuous, steady and create as little disturbance in the fresh concrete mass as possible.

4.8   TRUE-FALSE PROBLEMS

4.8.1   QUESTIONS

(Circle one)

1. T   F   A primary concern of transporting concrete is segregation of the mix and its prevention.

2. T   F   Belt conveyors can deliver very low-slump concrete.

3. T   F   Concrete pumps can usually handle pumping a high maximum aggregate size, harsh, fairly low-slump mix.

4. T   F   Precautions should be taken to minimize slump loss (and evaporation) through the method of delivery.

4.8.2 ANSWERS

Question	Answer	Explanation
1	True	
2	True	
3	False	Slumps are usually higher, maximum aggregate size is lower and mixes are usually more cohesive.
4	True	While good *concreting practice* will minimize slump-loss, and the method of delivery will inherently affect the slump, no amount of preventive effort or precaution will change the amount of slump loss experienced due to conveying, through say, a pump. However a shaded belt conveyor will reduce slump loss on hot sunny days, or by drying wind across the concrete surface.

5

SITE CONDITIONS AND DURABILITY OF EXPOSED CONCRETE

5.1 INTRODUCTION TO CONCRETE DURABILITY REQUIREMENTS

In general, concrete is expected to provide long durable service in an entire range of services and applications, from a concrete bridge exposed to freezing and thawing plus de-icing chemicals, to a manufacturing plant for bottling wine; from use in a dairy to an offshore concrete platform for oil exploration and production; from the aggressive wastes on the inside of a concrete sewer pipe to the soils on its outside. All of the above situations can be detrimental to improperly proportioned concrete. (Note: lactic acid from milk and acetic acid from wine are both aggressive liquids which react with concrete, specifically attacking the cement paste. In addition, sulfate from soils and sewage wastes can also attack the cement pastes in concrete.)

Concrete in place is exposed to innumerable environmental exposure conditions such as:

1. Weather; which includes freezing and thawing, normal precipitation and temperature extremes;

2. Soils; (including ground water) which contain chlorides, sulfates and sulfides and, in rare conditions, high acidity;

3. Sea water; also containing sulfates and chlorides;

4. Sewage, with common sulfate and sulfide components, corrosives and caustics, plus the whole range of manufacturing waste which (legally or illegally) finds its way into the sewer system;

5. Aggressive chemical exposure, including acids or other materials (organic and inorganic) deleterious to concrete.

Most site conditions should be known (or investigated) before the concrete is designed. Invariably, the concrete can be proportioned and specified to eliminate, or at least to minimize, the potential for damage to the concrete. When it cannot be made sufficiently resistant to attack, coatings are mandatory. The above list of conditions is by no means exhaustive nor are the recommended procedures herein for dealing with them. For further information, the ACI publication No. 201.2 entitled, *Guide to Durable Concrete*, is a fine reference and has an exceptional bibliography of additional references.

5.2   FREEZE-THAW CYCLES

Though seldom considered by the layman in Southern California, vast areas in the United States are affected by many annual freezings and thawings, even the local mountain areas of California are affected. As all engineers know, frozen water occupies a larger volume than water in its liquid state. Due to this fact, classically it was felt by most authorities that expansion of free water in the pores of the cement paste expanded in freezing environments causing a compressive stress resulting in innumerable fractures in the exposed concrete. It was asserted that repetitive cycles finally would cause enough internal distress that the concrete would spall and fail, roughly in layers from the outside, progressively inward.

Current thinking and research holds that expansion of the moisture is not the principal cause of failure of concrete exposed to cyclic freezing and thawing. Rather, the term osmotic pressure is used to describe the circumstances of failure. Since the free interstitial moisture is an alkali-laden solution, when freezing begins it initially supercools the liquid, then ice crystals develop in the larger colder exposed pores of the cement paste. Since the thus frozen ice is pure water, this leaves the same alkali content in a smaller volume of water, resulting in an increase of alkalinity. Adjacent pores, which have not yet supercooled, send additional water under pressure to dilute this higher alkaline solution through an "osmotic potential" set up by the difference in alkalinity. Finally, this newly delivered water freezes on the previously crystallized water, again increasing the alkalinity in an ongoing set of reactions. The osmotic pressure drawing the liquid water out of adjacent pores is believed to cause failure by the tensile stresses created by a high local pressure reduction in the paste. Some evidence suggests that as this moisture redistributes itself through the capillaries and pores in the cement paste, freezing conditions cause local formations of a semi-amorphorous solid, also, resulting in high internal stresses which can lead to failure.

Regardless of the cause of failure in freeze-thaw environments, the way to protect the cement paste from this condition is to entrain numerous, small, well-distributed air bubbles (or voids) into it. Seemingly contrary to logic or intuition, these air voids are said to compete with the natural capillaries and pores for the free, unfrozen water, preventing or greatly reducing the development of internal stresses occurring in the capillaries.

Typically, effective air entrainment can range from 2.0% to 7.5% (by volume of concrete). The recommended air contents increase as exposure conditions grow in severity and as the maximum aggregate size decreases. These spherically-shaped voids should have a spacing factor of less than 0.0008-in.

ASTM C 457 provides the definition of spacing factor as "a useful index related to the maximum distance of any point in the cement paste from the periphery of an air void".

The foregoing discussion only applies to freeze-thaw in the cement paste, not to the aggregate in the mix. Generally, the liquid to ice, water-phase change, pressure-of-expansion theory is used to explain failure in aggregate in freeze-thaw conditions. Air entrainment is not useful in mitigating this mode of failure. On the other hand, this kind of failure is less common, more gradual, and generally less severe. Air entraining admixtures will be discussed in another section.

De-icing chemicals (usually salts of sodium chloride or calcium chloride) are also responsible for pitting and scaling concrete surfaces. These chemicals create the same osmotic pressures in the paste as described previously for freezing and thawing, but are more severe. Additionally, the chlorides will corrode any reinforcing steel which is exposed to it, such as at cracks and areas of unprotected or insufficiently concrete-covered steel. Since corroded steel can occupy up to seven times the volume of the base, refined metal, spalling of concrete at the steel interface is the natural result of insufficiently protected reinforcement. Where corrosion may be a problem, the mix design is proportioned for very low permeability using a low water/cement ratio, air entrainment and well-graded, coarse and fine aggregates.

Both freezing-thawing and de-icing salt environments attack concrete gradually after many cycles. Similarly, if air entrainment is present, the same air void system will continue to resist damage unless special other exposure conditions cause the filling of the air voids by solids or water.

In summary, durable frost resistance of concrete structures is achieved by:

1. Minimizing concrete's exposure to water (especially standing water) by design for drainage, etc.,

2. As in Item #1 above, minimize conditions which would saturate the concrete in and with water,

3. Use of a low water/cement ratio (0.45 − 0.50) paste,

4. Use of the lowest necessary air entrainment,

5. Suitable, durable, sound coarse and fine aggregate,

6. Adequate coverage of steel by concrete,

7. Good construction practices (proper consolidation and complete curing),

8. Minimized chloride ion ($C\ell^-$) in mix where there is steel reinforcement.

5.3   SULFATE ATTACK (GENERAL)

The portland cement portion of concrete is attacked by sulfate ions (SO_4^{-2}) and water. Whether from the soil, wastes, ground or surface water or other exposure conditions, an investigation should be made and precautions should be taken to minimize this detrimental effect of sulfates on concrete.

Usually the two most common sources of exposure are from soil (and its groundwater) and marine environments.

Precautions can include removing the source of sulfates or the source of water, using a more sulfate resistant portland cement, reducing the ability of sulfate laden water to penetrate the concrete by reducing its permeability and water/cement ratio, or some combination of all of these methods.

5.3.1   SULFATE EXPOSURE

The source of natural sulfate minerals in soils include the sulfates of calcium, magnesium, sodium and potassium. Their names are more familiar as gypsum $(CaSO_4 \cdot 2H_2O)$, glauberite $(Na_2SO_4/CaSO_4 \cdot nH_2O)$ and epsomite (or Epsom Salt, $MgSO_4$). When these dissolve in groundwater and come in contact with concrete, cycles of wetting and evaporation create a sulfate concentration which then reacts with the exposed concrete and a water source in three identified ways:

1. The sulfate, with any calcium which is present, combines with water and the aluminum crystal phases of the cement. Water and sulfate combine with the tricalciumaluminate, C_3A, and to a lesser extent with the tetracalcium aluminoferrite, C_4AF, to form ettringite $(C_3A \cdot CaSO_4 \cdot 31H_2O)$, also called calcium sulfoaluminate. This reaction product occupies a much larger volume than the reactants, causing local expansion and the resultant degradation of the paste. Ettringite at one time was called "cement bacillus", because of its method of attack, and crystalline shape.

2. Free calcium hydroxide from the cement combines with the external sulfates and water to form gypsum, also occupying a greater volume and causing degradation due to expansion.

3. The crystallization or re-crystallization of gypsum from the sulfates, and the resultant stresses developed by it in the pores can damage the paste.

Note:

The previous discussion used standard chemical symbols in conjunction with standard cement industry shorthand. For example, C_3A is shorthand for $(CaO)_3 \cdot A\ell_2O_3$ and C_4AF denotes $(CaO)_4 \cdot (A\ell_2O_3) \cdot (Fe_2O_3)$. Some symbols include: $C = CaO$, $A = A\ell_2O_3$, $F = Fe_2O_3$ and $S = SiO_2$. (Further discussion appears in the section on cements.)

These mechanisms of sulfate reactions apply to sulfate attack in soils and fresh water as well as sulfate attack from sea water. Often the expansive forces develop sufficiently to fracture, destroy and crack the concrete in web-like or deep map patterned cracking. Sometimes the concrete disintegrates into very small rubble or just turns to mush. In any event, over time sulfate attack will destroy improperly proportioned concrete well before the end of its intended service life.

Counter measures to this attack include taking provision: (1) to lessen the porosity of concrete paste so the sulfates cannot penetrate it as easily; (2) to lower the aluminum crystal phase(s) of the cement; (by using a different brand); and (3) to minimize exposure to water. The amount of sulfate present in the environment dictates how the porosity (by water/cement ratio) and C_3A and/or C_4AF in the cement will be specified. Typically, for moderate sulfate conditions, a maximum recommended water/cement ratio is 0.50 with cement having a C_3A maximum of 8%. For severe or very severe conditions, it would be 0.45 with a maximum cement C_3A of 5% and the sum of C_4AF plus twice the C_3A not to exceed 20%. Quite frequently, a Class F fly ash or an appropriate natural pozzolan will be used in the mix, as these materials can assist in providing superior sulfate resistance, and provide concurrent reduction in permeability and porosity.

The following Table 5.1 is the ACI-318 requirement for concrete proportions where sulfate exposure is known for water or soil conditions.

Table 5.1 Requirements for Concrete Exposed to Sulfate-Containing Solutions

(Adapted from ACI-318, Table 4.5.3)

Sulfate Exposure	Water Soluble Sulfate (SO_4^{-2}) in Soil, (% by weight)	Sulfate (SO_4^{-2}) in Water, (ppm)	Cement Type	Normal Weight Aggregate Concrete	Lightweight Aggregate Concrete
				Maximum Water-Cement Ratio, by Weight*	Minimum Compressive Strength, f'_c psi*
Negligible	0.00-0.10	0-150	—	—	—
Moderate†	0.10-0.20	150-1500	II,IP(MS), IS(MS)	0.50	3750
Severe	0.20-2.00	1500-10,000	V	0.45	4250
Very severe	Over 2.00	Over 10,000	V plus pozzolan‡	0.45	4250

A lower water/cement ratio or higher strength may be required for water-tightness or for protection against corrosion of embedded items or freezing and thawing (Table 4.5.2).

† *Seawater*

‡ *Pozzolan that has been determined by test or service record to improve sulfate resistance when used in concrete containing Type V cement.*

5.3.2   SOIL SULFATES

As previously described, sulfate attack occurs by virtue of soluble sulfates in the soil, carried by groundwater to the concrete. ACI-318 specifies four ranges of exposure as *negligible, moderate, severe* and *very severe*. For increasing exposure, the recommended maximum water/cement ratio and C_3A of the cement is lowered. For severe or very severe environments, the use of pozzolans is recommended. Table 5.1 in Section 5.3.1 entitled, Requirements for Concrete Exposed to Sulfate Containing Solutions, capsulizes the recommendations. Some specifiers use air entrainment also to reduce permeability.

5.3.3 SEA WATER

Sea water also contains amounts of sulfate harmful to the cement paste; however, generally it is only moderately aggressive to concrete. The precautions for sulfates in soils above are also recommended for structures exposed to sea water (Table 5.1). Although the concentration of sulfates in sea water would suggest severe or very severe exposure levels, researchers suggest that the combined presence of both sodium and magnesium sulfates in sea water somehow reduces their individual effects.

5.3.4 SEWAGE

Concrete pipe is exposed potentially to sulfates in the soils and groundwater outside the pipe, in addition to sulfides and sulfites flowing within. Oxidation of hydrogen sulfide, which occurs to some extent in virtually every sewer system, results in the formation of sulfuric acid, which is very detrimental to portland cement concrete. (Cement paste is fully soluble in sulfuric acid) Bacteria present in the system contributes to the acid's formation. At one time, design procedures provided for sacrificial carbonate aggregates in the pipe to be preferentially dissolved in the acid's presence, thus, ignoring the paste. Today, coatings on the pipe's interior surface now are used extensively in concrete sewer pipes, and sulfate resistant Type V (low C_3A cement, often specified under 5%) is still frequently used with a low water/cement ratio for exterior, soil sulfate resistance.

5.4   ACIDS

As can be seen from Table 5.2, many acids cause rapid attack to concrete. In fact, no unprotected portland cement concrete can endure continuous acid exposure very long. The best protection for mild or infrequent exposure is a low water/cement ratio paste and a dense mix. Typically, the acids attack the calcium portions of the cement paste, but when limestone or dolomitic aggregates are used, they will also be attacked. Usually a coating will be specified in aggressive acid environments.

5.5   SUMMARY

In summary, it is necessary to know the exposure conditions of the concrete in order to proportion materials to produce a satisfactory mixture which will resist or endure its environment. Usually, as the conditions worsen, the mix should have a lower water/cement ratio, lower porosity and higher density. Additionally, the cement composition may be restricted, and the use of additional materials such as pozzolans may be desired. The aggregates may also be restricted for soundness or mineralogy (no carbonate aggregates, for example).

Table 5.2 Effect of Commonly Used Chemicals on Concrete (Durability).

(From ACI-201, Table 2.1)

Rate of Attack at Ambient Temperature	Inorganic Acids	Organic Acids	Alkaline Solutions	Salt Solutions	Miscellaneous
Rapid	Hydrochloric Hydrofluoric Nitric Sulfuric	Acetic Formic Lactic	—	Aluminum chloride	—
Moderate	Phosphoric	Tannic	Sodium hydroxide — > 20 %*	Ammonium nitrate Ammonium sulfate Sodium sulfate Magnesium sulfate Calcium sulfate	Bromine (gas) Sulfite liquor
Slow	Carbonic	—	Sodium hydroxide 10-20 %* Sodium hypochlorite	Ammonium chloride Magnesium chloride Sodium cyanide	Chlorine (gas) Seawater Softwater
Negligible	—	Oxalic Tartaric	Sodium hydroxide < 10 %* Sodium hypochlorite Ammonium hydroxide	Calcium chloride Sodium chloride Zinc nitrate Sodium chromate	Ammonia (liquid)

Avoid siliceous aggregates because they are attacked by strong solutions of sodium hydroxide.

5.6   TRUE-FALSE PROBLEMS

5.6.1   QUESTIONS

(Circle one)

1. T   F   Freeze-thaw conditions over many cycles will damage non-air entrained concrete.

2. T   F   Very few precautions can be taken to reduce sulfate attack of concrete. Explain.

3. T   F   The silicate minerals that are in portland cement are subject to sulfate attack.

4. T   F   Sea water is more severe than very sulfated soils for sulfate attack considerations.

5. T   F   Air entrainment will help concrete resist damage from both freeze-thaw and sulfate attack by reducing permeability.

6. T   F   Properly proportioned concrete is resistant to acid attack.

7. T   F   Sewers contain sulfides which can convert to sulfuric acid which attacks unprotected concrete.

8. T   F   Site conditions will usually not mandate changes in mix design. Explain.

9. T   F   Mixes should be proportioned to provide sufficient durability for the worst exposure conditions expected.

5.6.2 ANSWERS

Question	Answer	Explanation
1	True	
2	False	Lowering water/cement ratio, using low C_3A cement, and using a well-graded sand, increasing density, reducing porosity, using air entrainment using fly ash, all increase concrete's resistance to sulfate attack.
3	False	The aluminate minerals are principally attacked by water borne sulfates, namely, C_3A and C_4AF
4	False	
5	True	
6	False	
7	True	
8	False	Site conditions, water, sulfates, freeze-thaw, etc., will always necessitate special mix considerations.
9	True	

PART II

CONCRETE-MAKING MATERIALS

6

CEMENTS FOR CONCRETE MIXTURES

6.1 CEMENTS

Since evaluation of performance and conformance to specifications is generally more easily done for components of the concrete than for the mix itself, extensive investigation into a given single material or class of materials is evident in the literature and in the volumes of standard specifications which are used.

Generally, the performance of concrete can be judged by the qualities and proportions of its ingredients; namely, cement, aggregate, water, chemical admixtures and natural and/or artificial mineral additives.

Since the topic is so large, only a brief summary is possible for each material.

6.1.1 HYDRAULIC CEMENTS

ASTM C 94 (Ready-Mixed Concrete) recognizes two major types of cements for use in concrete: Portland cement and blended cement. Both materials are said to be hydraulic cement, that is, they: (1) need water to develop strength by chemical reaction; and (2) are able to cure or harden and strengthen while immersed in water. To be sure, many other materials have cementing action such as asphalt or plaster of paris $(CaSO_4 \bullet 1/_2 H_2O)$, the hemihydrate form of gypsum, but no others can harden in conjunction with and under water.

The basis for hydraulic cement's chemistry is the selection, proportioning and burning of raw materials, producing artificial minerals with (semi) crystalline configurations. These include basically the families of calcium silicates and calcium-aluminates. Several hundred different (artificial, manufactured) mineral compounds have been identified in these cements.

To produce cement, either limestone, marl, dolomite and seashells contribute the calcium source; clay, shale and bauxite (among numerous others) provides the alumina source; iron ore, mill scale and tailings can provide the iron source; while silica is abundant in sand and as impurities in many of the formerly mentioned materials.

Once the raw materials are proportioned, blended, ground and burned, portland cement clinker is produced. Portland cement is made when clinker is blended with 3 to 5% gypsum and ground to a fineness of between 2,800 and 6,000 square centimeters of surface area per gram of cement, finer than face powder. This property of specific surface is known as "Blaine units" when measured by air permeability. The finer the cement is ground, the earlier its strength will develop and the faster the heat of hydration will be generated. (Hydration is the name of the chemical reaction between cement and water.) The amount of gypsum added controls the time of setting. Blended cements are made by intergrinding clinker, gypsum and either fly ash, pozzolan, slag or other granulated material.

6.1.2   PORTLAND CEMENTS

The manufacturing of portland cement consists of grinding, burning in a kiln, and grinding again a properly proportioned, completely and uniformly blended mixture of materials containing calcium, silica, alumina and various oxides of iron. The heating (almost melting) action at temperatures exceeding $2700°F$ produces an intermediate product called clinker. Intergrinding clinker with gypsum produces portland cement. The exact proportions of the mixture vary depending upon the type of portland cement desired.

The first modern cements were produced in 1824 in England by stone-mason/inventor Joseph Aspin. They were named because the concrete made from them resembled the color of limestone on the bluffs of the nearby Isle of Portland.

Owing to the enormous quantities of materials, particularly limestone, in the manufacture of cement (over 85 million tons of annual cement capacity in the United States) there are certain ingredients which find their way into the composition which are potentially detrimental impurities, and whose presence must be limited. These impurities include magnesium, usually occurring naturally with calcium bearing minerals, and alkalies (that is Na_2O and K_2O) which are widely distributed through nature.

The *Standard Specifications for Portland Cement*, ASTM C 150, provides for five different types of portland cement; three of which may optionally be air entraining. (See Table 6.1 for their requirements. General practice in recent years has greatly reduced the demand for; and, therefore, manufacture of, air entraining cements.) These cements are:

Type I   General purpose cement.

Type II   Developed for moderate sulfate resistance, often can meet optional low heat or moderate of hydration requirements.

Type III   High early strength cement developed for applications which require early service, quick release of forms or rapid heat evolution and strength in cold weather concreting.

Type IV   Low heat of hydration cement. This was developed for massive structures to minimize both the rapid and total evolution of heat, minimizing possible distress from restrained volume change due to temperature. This cement is rarely manufactured and may not even be available by special order. (Some Type V cements will meet Type IV requirements.)

Type V   High sulfate resistant cement was developed for use in severely sulfated soils or marine environments. This may have low or moderate heat of hydration properties also.

Portland Cement is the product obtained by finely pulverizing clinker produced by heating to incipient fusion an intimate and properly proportioned mixture of argillaceous and calcareous materials with no additions subsequent to calcination except water and gypsum.

Figure 6.1 Definition of Portland Cement

Table 6.1 Mandatory Requirements of ASTM C 150

Chemical		Cement Type				
		I	II	III	IV	V
SiO_2	(min.)	—	20.0	—	—	—
Al_2O_3	(max.)	—	6.0	—	—	—
Fe_2O_3	(max.)	—	6.0	—	6.5	—
MgO	(max.)	6.0	6.0	6.0	6.0	6.0
SO_3	(max.)					
if $C_3A < 8\%$		3.0	3.0	3.5	2.3	2.3
if $C_3A \geq 8\%$		3.5	—	4.5	—	—
Loss on Ignition,	(max.)	3.0	3.0	3.0	2.5	3.0
Insoluble Residue,	(max.)	0.75	0.75	0.75	0.75	0.75
C_3S	(max.)	—	—	—	35	—
C_2S	(max.)	—	—	—	40	—
C_3A	(max.)	8	8	15	7	5
$C_3A + 2(C_4AF)$		—	—	—	—	20
Physical (Partial List)						
Air Content of Mortar by Volume, (%)	(max.)	12	12	12	12	12
Fineness, (sq cm/gm)	(min.)	2800	2800	—	2800	2800
Soundness, (%)	(max.)	0.80	0.80	0.80	0.80	0.80
Strength, (psi)	(min.)					
1 Day		—	—	1800	—	—
3 Days		1800	1500	3500	—	1200
7 Days		2800	2500	—	1000	2200
28 Days		—	—	—	2500	3000
Time of Setting, by Vicat, (Minutes)						
Initial	(min.)	45	45	45	45	45
Final	(max.)	375	375	375	375	375

Cement chemistry involves an enormous set of inorganic chemical combinations. For convenience, a shorthand set of symbols was developed to denote oxides of various elements into a standard format. Hence, $A\ell_2O_3$ becomes "A," while CaO becomes "C." It follows that C_3A is 3 CaO combined in a mineralogical form with 1 $A\ell_2O_3$ or $(CaO)_3 \cdot A\ell_2O_3$ or $Ca_3A\ell_2O_6$. Cement chemical requirements are expressed both ways: (1) by limiting individual oxides (e.g., $MgO \leq 6.0\%$), and; (2) by limiting mineral compounds (e.g., $C_3A \leq 5\%$).

The four primary compounds of concern are:

C_3S — $(CaO)_3(SiO_2)$

C_2S — $(CaO)_2(SiO_2)$

C_3A — $(CaO)_3(A\ell_2O_3)$

C_4AF — $(CaO)_4(A\ell_2O_3)(Fe_2O_3)$

and the shorthand is:

C   — CaO

S   — SiO_2

A   — $A\ell_2O_3$

F   — Fe_2O_3

M   — MgO

$\overline{S}$ — SO_3

N   — Na_2O

K   — K_2O

H   — H_2O

Cement researcher, R. H. Bogue, who initially investigated these chemical compounds, is credited with the equations used to calculate them. ASTM C 150 identifies the way in which these so-called Bogue Compounds are calculated.

In addition to the mandatory requirements on Table 6.1, several optional physical and chemical requirements may be specified by using ASTM C 150; namely,

Optional Chemical Requirements:

Moderate Sulfate Resistance	Type III only	$C_3A \leq 8\%$
High Sulfate Resistance	Type III only	$C_3A \leq 5\%$
Moderate Heat of Hydration	Type II only	$C_3A + C_3S \leq 58\%$
Total Alkalies	All types	$Na_2O + 0.658K_2O \leq 0.60\%$

Optional Physical Requirements:

- False Set (all types) 50% minimum

- Heat of Hydration (based on physically tested heat evolution, not chemistry, at 7 and/or 28 days, Type II or IV)

- 28-day Strength (Types I and II only, 4,000 psi)

- Sulfate Expansion (based on an expansion test in sulfate environment, not cement chemistry, Type V only)

- Air Content (Types I, II and III only, designated as IA, IIA and IIIA with air: $16\% \leq AIR \leq 22\%$)

In California, where a mild to severe sulfate condition exists in much of the state, where there is extensive coastline and marine environments and potentially alkali reactive aggregate is frequently used in concrete construction, most cement used in concrete is ASTM C 150 meeting both Types I and II (and optionally) low alkali. (Alkali-Aggregate reactions will be covered in the next section.)

Portland cement has a specific gravity (solids) of 3.15 which is fairly constant. However, its bulk density is about 94 lb/cu ft (bulk). A sack of portland cement is accepted as a nominal bulk cubic foot weighing 94 lb, although bulk density does vary significantly with the fineness of the cement.

White cement is also portland cement and usually meets the requirements of ASTM C 150 low alkali, Type I or Type III, depending on fineness and strength properties. White cement contains only very small (trace) amounts of iron in the raw materials, as iron compounds contribute to the gray color in cements. Often the alumina and calcium contents are higher in white cements and there is a greater trace amount of titanium.

6.1.3 BLENDED CEMENTS

C 595 is the ASTM specification for blended cements. These are hydraulic cements. Generally, blended cements are interground combinations of portland cement clinker and either pozzolans or quenched, granulated, blast furnace slags. Twelve different materials are defined in ASTM C 595, but can be summarized by recognizing Types IS, P and IPM.

IS refers to portland blast-furnace slag cement which must contain between 25% and 70% slag by weight. P refers to portland-pozzolan cement which contains between 15% and 40%, by weight, of pozzolan while IPM (pozzolan modified) contains 15% or less. Each of these is permitted by ASTM C 94, *Standard Specification for Ready Mixed Concrete* and ACI 318, *Building Code Requirements for Reinforced Concrete*.

All blended cements may be air entraining, and the suffix "A" would so designate it. Thus, IS is a non-air entraining slag cement while ISA is air entraining. Also, the suffixes MH, MS and LH are optional requirements referring to moderate heat of hydration (MH), moderate sulfate resistance (MS) and low heat of hydration characteristics (LH), respectively.

Generally similar to ASTM C 150, the mandatory and optional, chemical and physical requirements are also specified in C 595.

Blended cements are used and widely accepted all over the world, but have received little attention in the United States for a number of reasons. Availability of suitable slags and pozzolans, until just recently, has been limited. Also, there has been little perceived economic advantage in them. Their use has been unfairly judged as detrimental for strength and shrinkage properties.

Finally, a common stigma has plagued their wide acceptance; namely, the concept of using essentially waste products interground with cement clinker, has caused reservation about use of blended cements in structural applications. This is unfortunate since both slag and pozzolan blended cements do possess some superior qualities for particular uses, including sulfate resistance, lower heats of hydration and sometimes superior strengths. Finally, the government has recently mandated the use of these manufacturing waste by-products where possible, practical and economical.

Blended cements range in specific gravity from 2.8 to 3.2 and in bulk density from 70 to 105 pcf.

6.2 TRUE-FALSE PROBLEMS

6.2.1 QUESTIONS

(Circle One)

1. T F Cements have been documented to continue to hydrate and increase in strength (under favorable curing conditions) for over 50 years.

2. T F The alkali content of cement is of little real consequence in proportioning concrete mixtures.

3. T F Sulfate resistance of a cement is partly dependent upon its chemistry.

4. T F Portland cement Types I through III can be designated for air entrainment properties, requiring a manufacturing addition at the cement plant.

5. T F Strength gain of cements *only* occurs if there is sufficient moisture present.

6. T F The chemistry and fineness of a cement primarily control its total heat evolution and the rate of heat generation.

7. T F White cement is not a "true" portland cement.

6.2.2 ANSWERS

Question	Answer	Explanation
1	True	
2	False	– The alkali content must be limited in the case of potentially reactive aggregates to reduce the likelihood of deleterious reactions in the concrete.
3	True	– The water/cement ratio and porosity of the concrete also govern the sulfate resistance of *concrete*.
4	True	
5	True	
6	True	
7	False	

6.3 EXAMPLE PROBLEMS

6.3.1 EXAMPLE PROBLEM 1 — HYDRATION OF PORTLAND CEMENT

Does portland cement concrete of normal workability contain enough mix water to hydrate the cement? Explain.

Solution

Yes. A typical, workable portland cement concrete mix contains about twice as much water as is needed to hydrate all of the particles of cement. For this reason a typical portland cement concrete can be cured simply by keeping the water within the hardening structure by use of an impervious membrane.

Cement needs between 22% and 30% of its weight of water for complete hydration. Typical concretes have water/cement ratios of 0.45 to 0.80.

6.3.2 EXAMPLE PROBLEM 2 — STRENGTH GAIN OF PORTLAND CEMENT WITH TIME

On the axes provided, sketch the shape of the probable curve of compressive strength gain with time of moist cure for a 4,000 psi f'$_c$ normal (Type I) portland cement concrete at room temperature (70°F).

Solution

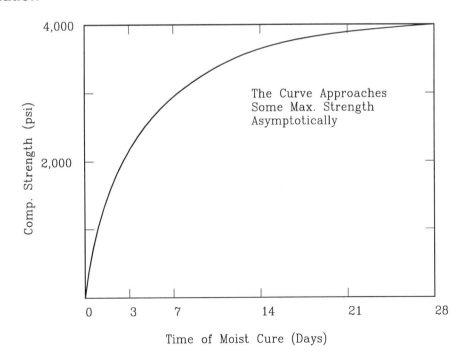

Fig. P6.3.2 (a) Strength Gain of Concrete

7

CONCRETE AGGREGATES

7.1 AGGREGATES, GENERAL PROPERTIES

ASTM C 33 entitled standard specification for aggregates for use in portland cement concrete governs the use and acceptance of both coarse and fine aggregates for use in portland cement concrete. Generally thought of as only a requirement for the sieve gradation for aggregates, the ASTM standard specification actually addresses or mandates a wide range of aggregate characteristics including:

1. Bulk Density
2. Unit Weight
3. Voids Content
4. Fineness Modulus
5. Deleterious Substances:
    A. Organic Impurities
    B. Reactive Aggregate
        1) Alkali-Silica Reactions
        2) Alkali-Carbonate Reactions
6. Soundness (expansion in a sulfate environment)
7. Lightweight Pieces (chert)
8. Abrasion Resistance
9. Clay Lumps
10. Friable Pieces

Documents used in tandem with ASTM C 33 contain tests for other important properties:

1. Specific Gravity
2. Absorption
3. Descriptive Nomenclature
   A. Shape
   B. Size
   C. Color
   D. Surface Texture
   E. Mineral Composition/Geologic Origin

ASTM C 33 deals only with so-called hard rock aggregates used in normal weight concrete; lightweight aggregates are specified according to ASTM C 330 and will not be considered further in these review notes.

Generally, local aggregates are commercially available and have a long history of use. A reputable supplier will know and advise users of any special characteristics which may render his materials unusable in certain circumstances such as freeze-thaw environment or other detrimental conditions, extreme abrasion or "where (the) surface appearance of the concrete is of importance."

Alkali-aggregate reaction is a potentially detrimental, relatively slow, chemical reaction between some classes of aggregates, the alkalies in the cement, and water from the environment. Usually in silica bearing minerals, these forms of aggregate minerals are known to be reactive: "opal, chalcedony, tridymite, . . . cristobalite; (and) volcanic glass (such as) rhyolite, andesite or dacite and certain heulandites and phyllites." The appendix of ASTM C 33 provides a good summary of potentially reactive aggregates.

In addition to the alkali-silica reactions listed above, certain alkali-carbonate reactions occur which can destroy concrete. Testing and prior use will validate the materials' suitability for use in particular applications.

Alkali-aggregate reactions cause destruction of concrete by having reaction products with volumes larger than the combined volumes of the reactants (or general in gradients). The concrete is either destroyed by local cone-shaped expansion of the individual reactive particle at the concrete's surface, known as a pop out, or destroyed by relatively uniform volumetric expansion of the entire restrained section. The use of low alkali cement is essential when using potentially reactive aggregates. Also, some pozzolans will minimize the aggregate-alkali reaction, when correctly proportioned. More simply, such aggregates can be avoided for critical work.

Several standard test methods exist for evaluating the reactivity of aggregate. ASTM C 289 entitled, *Standard Test Method for Potential Reactivity of Aggregates (Chemical Method)* is a commonly used procedure which rates aggregate as "innocuous", "potentially deleterious" and "deleterious", based upon the solubility of silica of the aggregate in the sodium hydroxide.

ASTM C 227 *Test Method for Potential Alkali Reactivity of Cement — Aggregate Combinations (Mortar-Bar Method)* is preferable if the cement brand and type intended for use on the project is known and available for testing with the aggregate. This method provides for actual measurement of length change of mortar samples made with the cement planned for the job.

The mix proportions of the concrete will be based on the following characteristics of the aggregates:

1. Maximum size of the coarse aggregate;

2. Fineness modulus of the sand (F.M.);

3. Bulk unit weight of aggregate larger than 3/8-in. (including possible combinations of, for example, pea gravel and 1-in. coarse.);

4. Shape, gradation and texture (Note: manufactured *crushed* aggregates are usually angular, clean, sharp and sometimes elongated, while natural gravel is often characterized as somewhat rounded, smooth and compact.)

Generally, the cement paste bonds more readily to rough, angular manufactured aggregates than to rounded, natural ones; however, more paste (thus cement) to coat the particle and fill interstitial volumes is usually required also. Hence, manufactured aggregates are considered superior for use in making higher flexural strength concrete, while minimum cement contents for the similar compressive strength are usually achieved with natural coarse aggregates, which tend to be rounded, smooth and of a continuous gradation.

Bulk unit weight or bulk density is the amount of material to fill a unit of specified volume, usually expressed in pounds per cubic foot. Bulk refers to the combined volumes filled by air and solids. For most standard aggregates this ranges from 75 to 110 lb per cu ft. The higher the density for a given specific gravity the more economical the mix.

Owing to the characteristics of the particular aggregate, its mineralogy, cleavage, age, etc., the internal structure of an aggregate particle has both solids and voids such as pores, microscopic fractures and other internal, empty spaces having the ability to be filled with water. Therefore, there are four generally accepted states of moisture conditions, and both specific gravity and bulk density can be stated for those various water contents of the aggregate; namely,

1. Oven Dry (or "Bone Dry");

2. Air Dried or partially water-filled, interstitial aggregate particle pore volumes;

3. Saturated, Surface Dry (or SSD), which have totally filled interstitial aggregate spaces, while dry (moist) on the surface;

4. Damp or Wet, which is a condition of saturation plus additional free moisture.

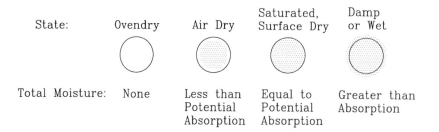

Figure 7.1 Moisture Conditions of Aggregates

The moisture needed to achieve SSD conditions, *expressed as a percentage of the dry weight of aggregate*, is known as the *absorption* of the aggregate.

Some relationships:

dry weight (1 + absorption) = SSD weight

dry weight (1 + absorption + free moisture) = wet weight

absorption + free moisture = moisture content

and if absorption is low, an approximation can be made:

SSD weight (moisture content) ≅ free moisture

This is sometimes done as a practical, "quick check" in the field.

The specific gravity of an aggregate is the ratio of its solids weight to the weight of an equal volume of water. This value is necessary in mix proportioning calculations, though generally not for determination of the quality of the aggregate. This value usually ranges from 2.60 to 2.80 for normal aggregates.

Aggregate gradation can be plotted on several kinds of graphs as shown in Section 7.4 Example Problems. It is generally accepted that those aggregates with *smooth* gradations, that is those which produce smooth curves on standard gradations charts, are best for use in concrete. A smooth, ideal gradation will have no excess or deficiency on any sieve in the nest of sieves, and will usually produce a concrete with minimal bleeding. Coarse sands usually produce harsher working and very bleeding mixes, while very fine sands have higher water demands and, consequently, require more cement per cubic yard, making the concrete less economical.

These curves can be based on amount passing each sieve or on the amount retained on each sieve or between adjacent sieves.

7.2   COARSE AGGREGATES

ASTM 33 defines the gradation of coarse aggregate as the amount of material (by weight) passing through each sieve in a nest of standard square sieve openings. The maximum (top size) of the aggregate is defined as the smallest standard sieve size through which all of the material will pass. The nominal size of the aggregate is defined as the next smaller standard size; and, typically, only a small portion of the material will be retained on that sieve. Table 7.2.1 shows a listing of standard sieve sizes and numeric designation. C 33 provides for several coarse aggregate types, predicated on top size and gradation.

Table P7.2.1 Standard Sieve Sizes and Numeric Designations (Coarse)

Sieve	Size
#16	1.18 mm
# 8	2.36 mm
# 4	4.75 mm
3/8 in.	9.50 mm
1/2 in.	12.50 mm
3/4 in.	19.00 mm
1 in.	25.00 mm
1-1/2 in.	38.10 mm
2 in.	50.00 mm
2-1/2 in.	63.00 mm
4 in.	100.00 mm

The major aspect of coarse aggregate which will be required in the proportioning of the concrete mix is the bulk unit weight. The procedure to determine this is:

1. to dry the coarse aggregates to oven dry conditions;

2. to use a constant volume, non deformable bucket of known (calibrated) volume and tare weight;

3. fill the bucket with the oven dried aggregate in 3 lifts of equal height, each lift being rodded, or densified, by use of a blunt nosed smooth 1/2-in. diameter steel rod forced into the layer and, for the last two lifts, partially penetrating the previous layer;

4. strike off the top layer such that the aggregate is still compacted, but not extending above the top of the bucket; so that the aggregate fills up to the interior limits of the bucket;

5. weigh the full bucket, subtract the empty bucket tare, and determine the weight of the aggregate;

6. divide the material weight by the volume of the bucket to determine the oven−dry, rodded bulk unit weight.

Typical values of oven dry, rodded bulk unit weights of aggregate range from 75 to 110 pounds per cubic foot. Bulk unit weight is also known as bulk density.

7.3 FINE AGGREGATES

Fine aggregate, such as natural and manufactured sand, is also qualified for C 33 by gradation limits. The sieve sizes and acceptable gradations are shown by Table 7.1.

Table 7.1 ASTM C 33 Gradation Requirements for Fine Aggregates

Sieve Size	(Minimum) Percent Passing	(Maximum) Percent Passing
3/8 (9.5 mm)	100	—
#4 (4.75 mm)	95	100
#8 (2.36 mm)	80	100
#16 (1.18 mm)	50	85
#30 (600 μm)	25	60
#50 (300 μm)	10	30
#100 (100 μm)	2	10

Adjustments are permitted on these limitations due to air entrainment or very rich concrete mixtures (cement content over 500 lb/cu yd of concrete) and where experience has shown that exceptions to this gradation will not be detrimental to the properties of the fresh or hardened concrete.

The fineness modulus (F.M.) is defined as the sum of the percentages *retained* on each standard sieve divided by 100, and in ASTM C 33 is not allowed to vary 0.20 from the normal F.M. on a load-to-load basis.

For example, if there was a fine aggregate which had a gradation "down the middle" of the specification such as:

Table 7.2 Example Gradation of a Fine Aggregate

Sieve size	Percent Passing		Percent Retained
	Spec.	Actual	
3/8 in.	100	100	0
#4	95-100	98	2
#8	80-100	90	10
#16	50-85	67	33
#30	25-60	43	57
#50	10-30	20	80
#100	2-10	6	94
			Sum = 276

$$\text{F.M.} = \frac{\text{Sum}}{100} = \frac{276}{100} = 2.76$$

Then, to obtain the fineness modulus, first the percent retained would be calculated by subtracting the amount passing for each sieve from 100%. The algebraic sum of the amounts retained on each sieve would next be determined and divided by 100, resulting in the F.M. **The larger the F.M., the coarser the sand; the smaller the F.M., the finer the sand.**

Often a manufacturer of aggregates will combine material from two (or more) sources to obtain an optimal blend. Such a blend may be strictly for economic reasons or for the purpose of meeting the particular specification, though it is probably to produce materials for very workable concrete.

The two means of analysis for combined gradation of two materials are the graphical and algebraic methods.

7.4   EXAMPLE PROBLEMS

7.4.1   EXAMPLE PROBLEM 1 — SAND BLENDING FOR ECONOMICAL GRADATION

Use a graphical method to find a blended fine aggregate (sand product) which needs to be within specification which combines natural sand, N, and manufactured fines, M, to make the most economical blend of these materials, N and M:

Table P7.4.1 (a)

Sieve Size	Material		Specification Limits
	Percent Passing Natural N	Percent Passing Manufactured M	
3/8 in.	100	100	100
#4	98	92	95-100
#8	90	88	80-100
#16	67	80	50-85
#30	43	60	25-60
#50	10	35	10-30
#100	0	25	2-10

(For this example, assume that the manufactured sand is cheaper.)

Solution

Using the graphical method, the percent passing is plotted for each material, one material on each vertical axis (side). Then *for each sieve* size a line is drawn representing all of the possible combinations of materials M and N and is labeled for that sieve size. Finally, the specification limits are identified by heavy solid dots for each sieve size.

The range of solutions of suitable blends of N and M is determined for each sieve size and is shown by dashed blend lines between the heavy solid dots. Solid lines show out-of-specification combinations. The blend of N and M which can be combined to form an in-specification blend is chosen where the blend line is dashed for all sieve sizes.

From the graph, the two heavy vertical lines show the boundary (shaded area) for all possible solutions. These limits are the range of combinations of N and M which will meet specification. The minimum is $X_M = 8\%$ ($X_N = 92\%$) while the minimum of $X_N = 60\%$ ($X_M = 40\%$). Any combination of M and N within these limits will meet specification.

Finally, when considering costs, the only solution is the one which uses the least of the more expensive material, in this case using less natural sand, N.

Numerically, it is easy to see that *both* sands meet specification for sieves #8, #16 and #30. Hence, *any blend* of these two sands would also meet the specification for those sieves. Also, it follows that the blend must be based on meeting the requirement for #4, #50 and #100 gradations. Therefore, if X_M is the percent blend of M and X_N the percent blend of N, the following describes their requirements:

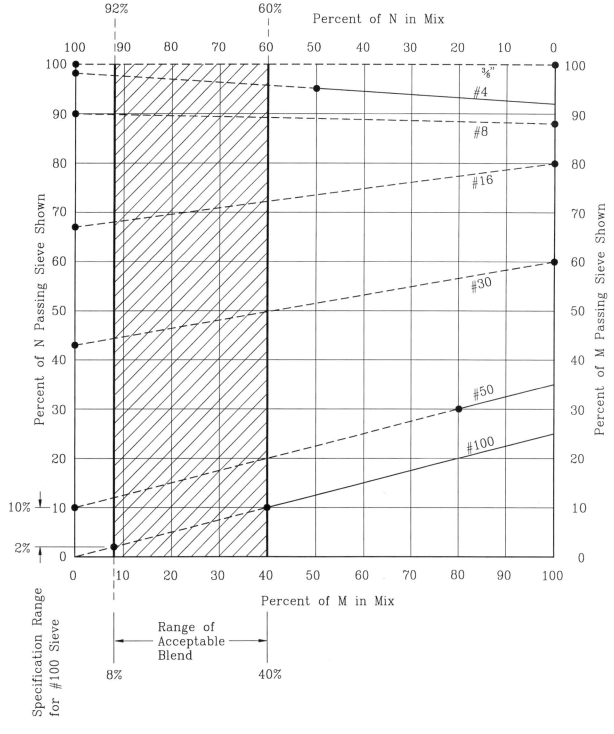

Fig. P7.4.1 (b) Graphical Solution

Verifying Calculation Methods:

#4 Sieve:

1. $0.98\,X_N + 0.92\,X_M \geq 95\%$, and
2. $X_N + X_M = 100\%$

Solving by substitution,

$$0.98\,(100 - X_M) + 0.92\,X_M \geq 95$$

$$X_M \leq \frac{98 - 95}{0.06}$$

Therefore, $\quad\quad\quad\quad X_M \leq 50.0$

And Resubstituting $\quad\quad X_N \geq 100 - X_M \geq 50.0$

$$X_N \geq 50$$

#50 Sieve:

1. $0.10\,X_N + 0.35\,X_M \leq 30\%$, and $\quad\quad 0.10\,X_N + 0.35\,X_M \geq 10\%$
2. $X_N + X_M = 100\%$

Solving by simultaneous equations,

$0.10\,X_N + 0.35\,X_M \leq 30\%$	and	$0.10\,X_N + 0.35\,X_M \geq 10\%$
$-\,(0.10\,X_N + 0.10\,X_M = 10\%)$		$-\,(0.10\,X_N + 0.10\,X_M = 10\%)$

$$0.25\,X_M \leq 20\% \quad\quad\quad\quad\quad 0.25\,X_M \geq 0$$

Therefore, $\quad X_M \leq 80\% \quad\quad\quad\quad\quad X_M = 0\%$

$$X_N \geq 20\% \quad\quad\quad\quad\quad\quad X_N = 100\%$$

#100 Sieve:

1. $0.00\,X_N + 0.25\,X_M \leq 10\%$ and $\quad\quad 0.00\,X_N + 0.25\,X_M \geq 2\%$
2. $\quad\quad\quad X_N + X_M = 100\%$ $\quad\quad\quad\quad\quad X_N + X_M = 100\%$

Therefore, $\quad X_M \leq 40\%$ $\quad\quad\quad\quad\quad\quad X_M \geq 8\%$

$$X_N \geq 60\% \quad\quad\quad\quad\quad\quad X_N \leq 92\%$$

Recapping, the minimum (i.e., least cost) amount of fine material N necessary to produce an in specification blend is:

Table P7.4.1 (c)

Sieve No.	Minimum % X_n	Corresponding % X_m	Minimum % X_m
#4	50	50	0
#50	20	80	0
#100	60	40	8

And for all sieves to be in specification *concurrently*, a minimum amount of 60% of the blend must be material N. It is obvious that except for the #100 sieve, the maximum amount of N is 100% since N meets all the specification gradation requirements for each sieve except #100. This fact confirms the previous graphical analysis.

7.4.2 EXAMPLE PROBLEM 2 — FINENESS MODULUS OF A BLENDED SAND, CALCULATIONS

Determine the fineness modulus, F.M., of the resulting material in the previous problem by using a three-step process:

1. Determine the blend's resultant gradation
2. Find the percent retained per sieve
3. Sum the retained values and divide by 100

The following example illustrates by using the values of the previous example, using the 60% N, 40% M solution:

Solution

Table P7.4.2 (a)

Sieve Analysis (Percent Passing)						
Initial Values					(Sum)	Percent
Sieve Size	N $\boxed{1}$	M $\boxed{2}$	.60 N	.40 M	Blend $\boxed{3}$	Retained
3/8 in.	100	100	60.0	40.0	100.0	0.0
#4	98	92	58.8	36.8	95.6	4.4
#8	90	88	54.0	35.2	89.2	10.8
#16	67	80	40.2	32.0	72.2	27.8
#30	43	60	25.8	24.0	49.8	50.2
#50	40	35	6.0	14.0	20.0	80.0
#100	0	25	0.0	10.0	10.0	90.0

ASTM C 33 Specification Limits		
	Acceptable Range (%)	
Sieve Size	Minimum Passing $\boxed{4}$	Maximum Passing $\boxed{5}$
3/8 in.	100	—
#4	95	100
#8	80	100
#16	50	85
#30	25	60
#50	10	30
#100	2	10

Note: The number in □ at the top of each bolded column corresponds to the graph which follows. Bolded numbers are plotted on graph as shown.

Sum of 'Percent Retained' sieve column = 263.2

$$F.M. = \frac{Sum\ Retained}{100}$$

$$= \frac{263.2}{100}$$

$$= 2.63$$

And these materials, N, M and B (the blend) would be presented graphically within the specification limit upper and lower boundaries as follows:

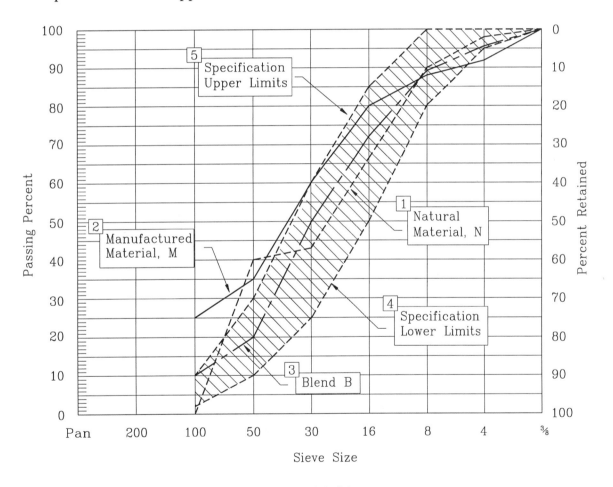

Fig. P7.4.2 (b)

7.4.3 EXAMPLE PROBLEM 3 — FINENESS MODULUS OF BLENDED SAND, COMPLIANCE

Does Blend B from the previous problem meet the ASTM C 33 requirements for fineness modulus?

Solution

The calculated F.M. from the previous example was 2.63. The ASTM C 33 limit is F.M.: $2.3 \leq F.M. \leq 3.1$. This blend meets the requirements.

Figures P7.4.3 (a), P7.4.3 (b) and P7.4.3 (c) may be useful in evaluating blends and sieve analysis for aggregates.

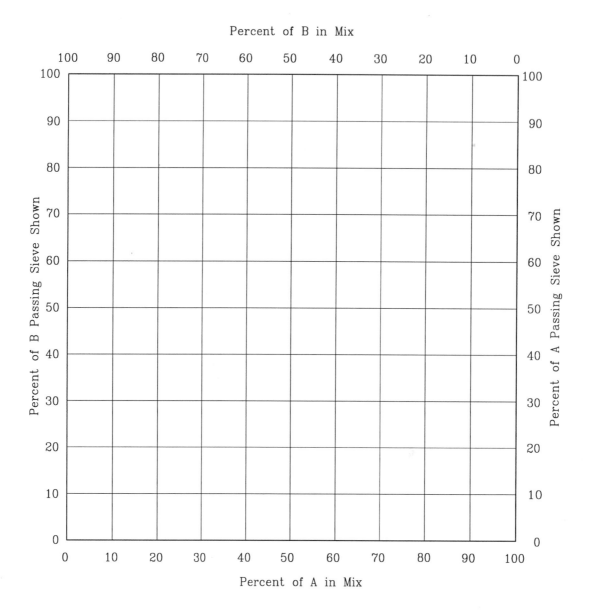

Fig. P7.4.3 (a)

Alternate Method:
Graphic Representation of Sieve Analysis of Sand

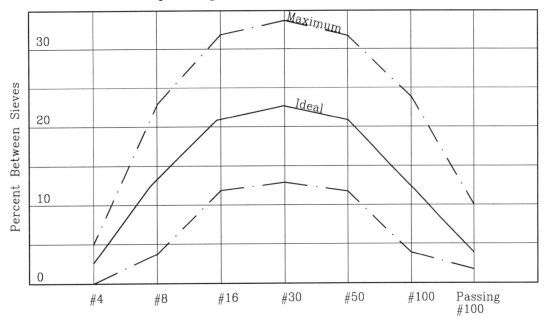

Fig. P7.4.3 (b)

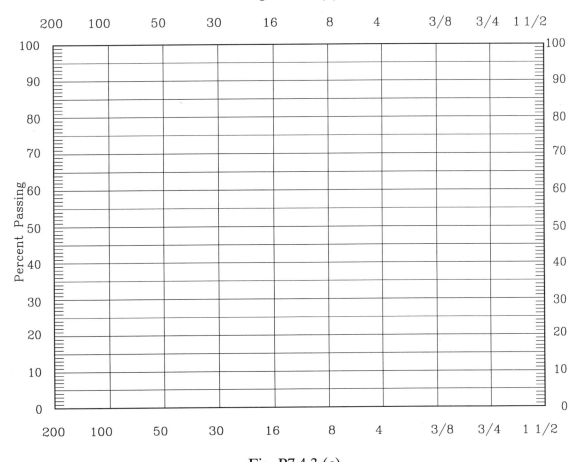

Fig. P7.4.3 (c)

7.5   P. E. PROBLEMS

7.5.1   P. E. PROBLEM 1 — COMBINED GRADATION OF AGGREGATES (NUMERICAL SOLUTION)

Two aggregates "A" and "B" are to be combined and the only requirement you need conform to is that between 20 and 40% of their mixture must pass the #8 sieve.

If "A" is cheaper than "B", and if "A" contains 60% and "B" contains 10% passing the #8, calculate the most economical mixture that meets that one requirement.

Solution

Since there are only two aggregates, A + B = 100%

Also, it is true that:

$$0.6A + 0.1B = 40\% \text{ and that } 0.6A + 0.1B = 20\%$$

Solving the equations simultaneously will yield the allowable range under the specifications.

Upper Limit	Lower Limit
$0.1A + 0.1B = 10\%$	$0.1A + 0.1B = 10\%$
$0.6A + 0.1B = 40\%$	$0.6A + 0.1B = 20\%$
$A = 60\%$	$A = 20\%$

Use more of A since A is cheaper:

> use 60% A and 40% B

7.5.2 P. E. PROBLEM 2 — COMBINED GRADATION OF AGGREGATES (GRAPHICAL SOLUTION)

Rework previous Problem 2 using a graphical method.

Solution

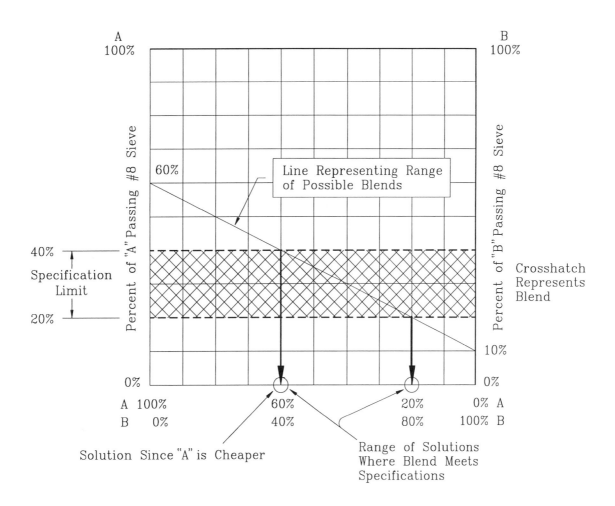

Fig. P7.5.2 (a)

7.5.3 P. E. PROBLEM 3 — COMBINED GRADATION OF AGGREGATES

If the maximum allowable percentage of the less expensive of two aggregates is used in a blend, a minor variation in one direction will place the mix beyond the specification band.

For example, assume that the conveyor belts shown on Fig. P7.5.3 (a) are feeding aggregates "A" and "B" to the #4 sieve. Assume further that each belt (or the bin feeding each belt) can feed each aggregate at + or −5% of the rate for which each is set.

Let aggregate "A" be more expensive than aggregate "B". Select the most economical mix of the two that will allow a variation of + or −5% of either aggregate to pass the sieve and still meet the specification.

In this case, the specification states that between 30% and 50% of the mixture is required to pass the #4 sieve.

20 percent of "A" passes the #4 and

75 percent of "B" passes the #4 sieve.

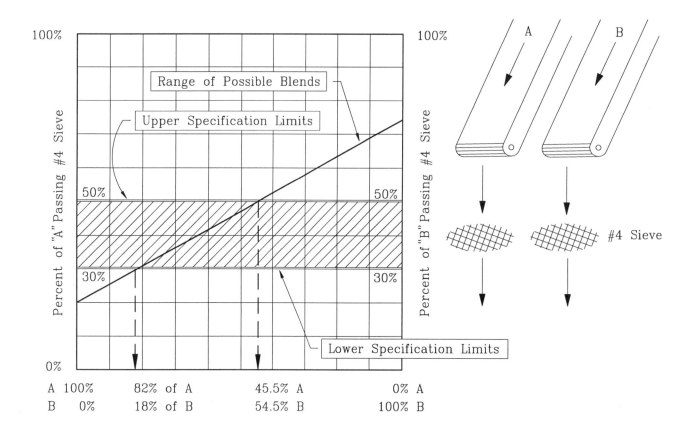

Fig. P7.5.3 (a)

Solution

The specification limits for the #4 sieve are shown as double horizontal lines.

Assume first that both aggregates have the same unit costs and that there is no variation in the feed rates. The cross-hatched region shows permissible specification limits. The diagonal line connects 20% of "A" and 75% of "B" as all possible blends.

For the cross-hatched specification limit of 30% to 50% imposed on the blend line, the diagonal line indicates that the allowable range of the mixes is from 82% of "A" and 18% of "B" to 45.5% of "A" and 54.5% of "B".

However, if "A" is more costly than "B", then the most economical solution is to use 45.5% of "A" and 54.5% of "B".

Now consider that the feed rate of "A" could decrease by 5% while that of "B" could increase by 5% at the same time; this is the worst possible condition.

Try 48% of "A" and 52% of "B":

$$\frac{0.95\ (48\%)}{0.95\ (48\%)\ +\ 1.05\ (52\%)} \ = \ 45.5\% \ \text{of A which is OK}$$

Use 48% of "A" and 52% of "B" to satisfy the worst case feed rate error.

7.5.4   P. E. PROBLEM 4 — COMBINED GRADATION OF AGGREGATES (NUMERIC SOLUTION)

Materials A and B, gradations shown, are to be combined to meet the specifications.

Table 7.5.4(a)

Sieve Size	% Passing		Spec. Limits (% Passing)
	Material "A"	Material "B"	
1-1/2 in.	100	100	100
3/4 in.	87	100	75-100
#4	70	100	45-85
#10	40	100	35-70
#40	10	68	20-35
#200	2	26	9-22

A. Find the minimum % to the nearest whole number of Material "A" that could be used to produce a mix meeting the specification. Show calculations and reasoning. (Note that this problem is based upon gradations for asphaltic concrete, not for portland cement concrete.)

B. Compute the gradation of the combined mix.

Solution

A. It can be seen by examining the plot on Figure P7.5.4 (a) that Material "B" cannot affect the composition of the blend of "A" and "B" on any sieve specified except the #200 and the #40.

To meet the specification, a minimum of 0% of "A" must be retained on the 1-1/2 in. and the 3/4-in. sieves and a minimum of 15% of "A" must be retained on the No. 4 sieve because a maximum of 85% is allowed to pass. A minimum of 30% of "A" must be retained on the No. 10 sieve because a maximum of 70% is allowed to pass. In determining the minimum percentages of "A" that are allowed on the No. 40 and No. 200 sieves, it must be understood that material "B" is also involved. There are an infinite number of combinations of materials "A" and "B" (within certain limits) that can meet the specification on each of these sieves taken one at a time. It is necessary to find the limits for each sieve.

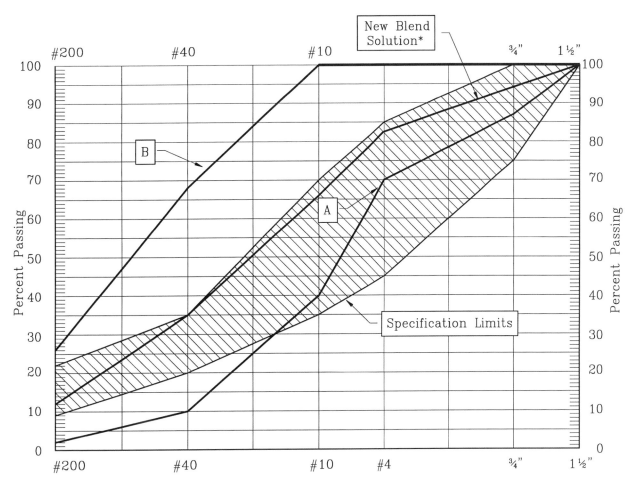

Solution mixture contains 57% "A" and 43% "B".

Fig. P7.5.4 (a) Percent Passing Graphed on Specification A and B

Consider sieve No. 40: 10% of A plus 68% of "B" may contain as little as 20% or as much as 35% passing the sieve; but since only two materials are being mixed, "A" plus "B" must equal 100%. So there are two unknowns and two equations; subtract one from the other:

$$0.10A \; + \; 0.68B \; = \; 20\%$$
$$\underline{0.10A \; + \; 0.10B \; = \; 10\%}$$
$$0.58B \; = \; 10\%$$
$$B \; = \; 17\% \; (\text{maximum})$$
$$A \; = \; 83\% \; (\text{minimum})$$

Likewise for the No. 40 sieve upper limit:

$$0.10A + 0.68B = 35\%$$
$$\underline{0.10A + 0.10B = 10\%}$$
$$0.58B = 25\%$$
$$B = 43\% \text{ (minimum)}$$
$$A = 57\% \text{ (maximum)}$$

Similar calculations for the No. 200 sieve yield:

$$B = 29\% \qquad\qquad B = 83\%$$
$$A = 71\% \qquad\qquad A = 17\%$$

To determine the minimum percentage of material "A" that could be used and still meet the specifications, note that sieves 1-1/2 in., 3/4 in., No. 4, No. 10, No. 40, and No. 200 require a minimum of 15%, 30%, 57%, and 17%, respectively. Therefore, 57% is the minimum percentage of material "A" allowed by specification.

B. The combined mix gradation is determined as follows:

Table 7.5.4(b)
Cumulative Percent Passing Through Each Sieve

Sieve Size	Material A	Material B	57% × A	43% × B	Proposed Blend
3/2 in.	100	100	57	43	100
3/4 in.	87	100	50	43	93
#4	70	100	40	43	83
#10	40	100	23	43	66
#40	10	68	6	29	35
#200	2	26	1	11	12

As would be expected, the mix is on the borderline of the specification at the No. 40 sieve.

7.5.5   P. E. PROBLEM 5 — FINENESS MODULUS OF SAND

A portland cement concrete (PCC) sand is sieved with the following percentages retained on each sieve indicated. Calculate the FM (used in the ACI method of mix design).

#	4	6%
#	8	11%
#	16	22%
#	30	25%
#	50	23%
#	100	13%

Solution

The fineness modulus is defined as the sum of the percentages of the sample *Coarser* than each sieve in the standard series, divided by 100.

Table P7.5.5 (a)

Sieve Size	% Coarser Than
#4	6
#8	17
#16	39
#30	64
#50	87
#100	100
100 × F.M.	313%

$$FM = \frac{1}{100} \sum \% \text{ Coarser than each sieve in the nest}$$

$$FM = \frac{313}{100} = 3.13$$

8

MIXING WATER

8.1 MIXING WATER FOR CONCRETE

Both ASTM C 94 and ACI 318 refer to the quality of the batch water in relatively simple terms such as "clear and apparently clean" and "clean and free from injurious amounts of oils, acids, alkalies, salts, organic materials or other substances that may be deleterious to concrete or reinforcements."

Where the water quality is questionable, the standards mandate that the water produce mortar of identical or better strength than potable water without an appreciable change in the mortar's time of setting characteristics.

Special precautions are taken in the event the concrete might contain embedded aluminum or strands of pre-stressing steel. Here a limit is placed on the chloride ion ($C\ell^-$) content of both the concrete and its mixing water.

Generally, these requirements are applied to water reclaimed from the ready mix operation, as most other fresh water will easily meet the requirements of Table 8.1.

Table 8.1 Chemical Requirements for Mixing Water

Constituent in Mixing Water	Maximum Limit (ppm)
Chloride as Cl^-, ppm	
For Prestressed Concrete	500
For Concrete with Moist Environment, Embedded Aluminum or Galvanized Metals	1000
Sulfate as SO_4^{-2}, ppm	3000
Total Alkalies as (Na_2O) +0.658 K_2O),	600
Total Solids	50,000

Finally, water for concrete should be free from substances which make it taste or smell suspect or discolor it, particularly rusty water.

A disclaimer in ASTM C 94 provides that if such materials meet the above limits and still are suspect, the water may be used if it can be proved that it is not harmful to the quality of the hardened concrete.

9

CHEMICAL ADMIXTURES FOR CONCRETE

9.1 KINDS OF CHEMICAL ADMIXTURES

In addition to fine and coarse aggregate, cement and water, chemical admixtures are often specified and used to impart additional qualities to fresh and/or hardened concrete. Slump, or workability, enhancement and control of the time of setting are examples of properties of fresh concrete which are often desirable to modify and control. Increased strength and an effective air void system (for freeze-thaw resistance) can be controlled by chemical admixtures, helping those qualities of hardened concrete.

ASTM C 494 defines seven types of chemical admixtures according to their use or purpose:

1. Type A   Water reducing admixtures (reduces total water required to produce similar workability)
2. Type B   Retarding admixtures (slows time of setting)
3. Type C   Accelerating (advances or speeds time of setting) admixtures
4. Type D   Water reducing *and* retarding admixtures
5. Type E   Water reducing *and* accelerating admixtures
6. Type F   Water reducing, high range (also known as super-plasticizers)
7. Type G   Water reducing, high range and retarding (also known as super-plasticizers)

Types A and F must not change the setting characteristics appreciably and are often referred to as "normal set water reducers".

Types B, D and G must purposely retard (lengthen) the time of setting while Types C and E must accelerate it.

ASTM C 260 defines air entraining admixtures. Without becoming too detailed, the following is a description of the use of and the raw materials which constitute these chemical additives to concrete.

9.2 NORMAL-RANGE WATER REDUCERS

In order to achieve strength, minimal shrinkage, durability and increase the general quality of hardened concrete, it is necessary to use the lowest reasonable water/cement ratio. Contractors usually prefer the maximum workability generally obtained by using additional water. Special chemicals are available to maintain the lowest reasonable water to cement ratio while creating maximum workability without adding extra water, losing strength and increasing shrinkage.

Therefore, water reducers increase the strength of concrete (for otherwise identical proportions of materials) by reducing the water/cement ratio. Less water is used for the same weight of cement at a similar slump.

Materials used as water reducers include:

1. Salts of lignosulfonic acids (either calcium or magnesium based)
2. Derivatives of lignosulfonates
3. Salts of hydroxylated carboxylic (H-C) acids
4. Derivatives of H-C acids
5. Carbohydrates
6. Hydroxylated polymers, including sugars, polysaccharides, fructose and sucrose
7. Cellulose ethers
8. Melamine formaldehydes
9. Naphthalene formaldehydes

Generally, the major constituents of commercially available (normal range) water reducers include lignosulfates, hydroxylated carboxylic acids and polymers, especially sugars or corn syrups, sometimes with traces of the other materials. Each will have its own characteristics of use, such as bleeding and times of setting, which may dictate its use or avoidance. Generally, water reducers disperse the cement particles in the mix. The less agglomeration of cement particles, the more workability and additional cement hydration is achieved.

Water reducers of the normal range must reduce the total mix water by at least 5% to meet specifications while high-range water reducers must reduce it by at least 12% for the same slump or workability.

9.3 HIGH-RANGE WATER REDUCERS

Types F and G, while in the specification are called high range, received a more common, descriptive name in the industry as so-called super-plasticizers and are often used to increase workability (plasticity or slump of fresh concrete) significantly at the same water/cement ratio. Often a recommended dosage will increase a 2- or 3-in. slump to over 7 in., which is a real advantage not only to the contractor, but also results in the reduction of bug holes and rock pockets in the formed, hardened concrete, where there may be a congestion of reinforcing steel. Of course, the shrinkage expected would correspond to the water for the 2-3-in. slump, *not* the 7-in. slump.

9.4 SET RETARDERS

Generally, set retarders are the same chemical products used for water reduction but used in higher concentration and/or dosage; the previous section applies to this topic as well.

9.5 SET ACCELERATORS

Calcium chloride in concrete is generally used for accelerating the time of setting of concrete. Usually, setting characteristics need to be hastened in cold weather or when early strengths are desirable.

Chemical accelerators include:

1. Calcium chloride
2. Other soluble chlorides
3. Certain soluble carbonates
4. Silicates
5. Fluorosilicates
6. Alkali hydroxides
7. Tri-ethanolamine (TEA)

Some considerations for their use include:

1. Faster setting times, earlier finishing
2. Slightly lower air contents
3. Faster and higher total heat of hydration
4. Earlier strength development
5. Higher shrinkage
6. Reduced durability
7. Reduced sulfate resistance
8. Speeds and increases severity of alkali-aggregate reactions, if present
9. Increases corrosion of embedded metals

9.6   AIR ENTRAINING AGENTS

Although primarily used to increase hardened concrete's resistance to cycles of freezing and thawing, air entraining chemicals generally increase fresh workability as well. This permits using a lower water content and water/cement ratio, although, due to the air void system, the resulting strengths are lower.

Materials which are used for entrainment of air include:

1. Salts of wood resins (e.g., Vinsol resin)

2. Some synthetic detergents

3. Some salts of lignosulfonates

4. Salts of petroleum acids

5. Protein salts

6. Fatty acids and resins

7. Organic salts of hydrocarbons

By far the most popular agents contain wood resins, though others are commercially available.

The most important aspects of the air entraining agent are the size, number, arrangement and thorough dispersion of the air voids it produces. This is known as the air void system. When the voids are too large or too small, they are ineffective; when their collective volume (usually 3-8% of the mixture) is too high, excessive loss of strength occurs. Finally, they must be well dispersed throughout the entire load or batch of fresh concrete.

Generally, a good air void system will have very few air voids of greater than 1 or 2 millimeters (mm) and more than 90% of them smaller than 100 microns (μm) or 4 millions of an inch. The mean distance between any two nearby voids is preferably less than 0.20 mm or 0.008 in. It is preferable that each void is distinct and spherical and that it is not interconnected with another.

Finally, for reasons of not only protection from the effects of freezing and thawing, but also for reduced permeability of concrete to moisture, chlorides, and sulfate ions, the admixture may also be useful in lean (lower cement content) concrete due to its ability to lessen the harshness of workability and finishability often associated with lean mixes.

Air entrainment should not be confused with air entrapment. Some entrapment occurs as a natural function of mixing and agitating concrete materials into fresh concrete. Entrapment, air entrapped by mechanical means rather than chemical, is a function of the maximum size of the aggregate. Entrapped air provides negligible freeze-thaw protection.

10

MINERAL ADMIXTURES
FOR CONCRETE

10.1 MINERAL ADMIXTURES

Meeting the requirements of ASTM C 618, mineral admixtures classically have included fly ashes and natural pozzolans, as well as recognized clays, opaline cherts and shales, tuffs and pumicites. They may also include somewhat exotic materials such as silica fume, ground quartz and ground limestone or other common materials like bentonite (clay) and talc.

10.2 POZZOLANS

> Pozzolans are siliceous or siliceous and aluminous materials which in themselves possess little or no cementitious value but will, in finely divided form and in the presence of moisture, chemically react with calcium hydroxide at ordinary temperatures to form compounds possessing cementitious properties.

Figure 10.1 Definition of Pozzolans

Natural pozzolans are mined natural minerals. They are sometimes calcined (burned in a kiln), resulting in a chemical composition similar to fly ashes. When natural pozzolans meet the requirements of ASTM C 618, they are called Class N, natural pozzolans. All pozzolans, (natural, calcined natural or fly ash, a purely synthetic pozzolans) react with moisture and CaO in lime or cement to develop cementitious properties.

All of these materials are siliceous, or siliceous and aluminous, while the fly ashes are spherically shaped and glassy. Mineralogically the natural pozzolans can be amorphous or crystalline, or exist in some combination. Generally, they all react with alkalies (usually from the cement), and thus tend to mitigate the longer term alkali-aggregate reaction by reacting with all available cement alkalies before the aggregate has time to do so. Further, the use of Class F ashes, and many natural pozzolans, helps increase the sulfate resistance of concrete. Strength benefits often are the result of using good mineral admixtures (and good proportioning) and, as such, can reduce cement contents for similar strengths, also reducing the heat of hydration.

Depending on the properties required, mineral admixtures are usually proportioned at about one fifth the cement content, by weight. Pozzolans have been used in amounts from 20 to 400 lb/yd, and up to 50% of the weight of cementitious material (cement plus ash).

10.3 FLY ASH

> **Fly Ash** is the finely divided residue that results from the combustion of ground or powered coal. Class F and Class C fly ashes are pozzolans which meet the requirements of ASTM C 618.
>
> **Class F** — Fly ash normally produced from burning anthracite or bituminous coal that meets the applicable requirements for this class . . . and has pozzolanic properties.
>
> **Class C** — Fly ash normally produced from lignite or subbituminous coal that meets the applicable requirements for this class . . . and in addition to having pozzolanic properties, may also have some cementitious properties. Some Class C fly ashes may contain lime (Calcium Oxide, CaO) contents higher than 10%.

Figure 10.2 Definition of Fly Ash

ASTM C 618 deals with two types of fly ash traditionally classified by the type of coal burned to create the ash. (Fly ash is the light residue produced by burning coal in a furnace for a steam turbine in an electrical generating facility. Fly ash, then, is the finely divided, flying, mineral residue trapped from those vented gases of combustion.)

Class C ash is said to possess cementitious properties (hardens when mixed with water) while Class F is said to have pozzolanic properties only. That is, pozzolanic materials don't harden with water, but will harden in the presence of moisture and calcium hydroxide, $Ca(OH)_2$, an extremely active reaction product in limes portland and blended cements. Class F ashes have specific gravities range from 2.25 to 2.40.

Generally, Class C fly ashes have fairly high CaO contents (20-30%) while Class F ashes are lower (0-10%). Class F ashes are evaluated for the sum of Fe_2O_3 plus SiO_2 plus $A\ell_2O_3$, which by specification must be above 70%, while Class C ashes must sum above 50%. Class C ashes have specific gravities ranging from 2.10 to 2.40.

10.4 SLAGS

Slags for use in concrete must be quenched and granulated blast furnace slags. They can provide superior sulfate resistance and good strength properties, though some are thought to increase drying shrinkage. Ground slag as an admixture increases the fines content, reduces alkali-aggregate reactions, and increases sulfate resistance while decreasing the porosity of the mix.

10.5 COLORING AGENTS FOR CONCRETE

Often architectural concrete will require shades of color different from natural cement colors. Mineral pigments, natural or synthetic, ground finer than cements, are used in small amounts to impart shades of color to white or gray cement-based concretes.

They should be pure mineral oxides, insoluble in water, free of soluble acids, colorfast and chemically resistant to both weak acids and alkalies. They should contain NO soluble sulfates or chlorides. Usually, manufactured synthetic mineral oxides are superior to natural ones, especially in uniformity.

It is recommended that they not be proportioned as more than 10% of the weight of the cement. Usually they constitute 1/2 to 1% by weight of cement. Often the cement content will be raised slightly to accommodate the extra water necessary to coat the oxide.

All colors will produce cleaner, brighter tones and hues when used with white cement, but results are usually acceptable when used with grey cement, though a higher percentage of pigment will be necessary to produce the intensity of the color.

MATERIALS PROBLEMS REVIEW

11.1 TRUE-FALSE PROBLEMS

11.1.1 QUESTIONS

(Circle one)

1. T F Both silicious and carbonate aggregates can be reactive.

2. T F Both reactive aggregates and organic impurities in aggregates are potentially deleterious to concrete.

3. T F A higher fineness modulus (F.M.) indicates a finer material.

4. T F For reinforced and prestressed concrete work, the separate and combined chloride contents of the batch or mixing water, all chemical additives and the concrete must be limited.

5. T F Water with high amounts of suspended solids may be used in concrete if it can be proven that it will not affect the strength, color or time of setting characteristics of the concrete compared to similar concrete made with potable water.

6. T F Fly ash and granulated, blast furnace slag, even though they meet ASTM requirements, should not be used in concrete, since they are waste by-products.

7. T F Pozzolans provide no benefit to concrete except for the economic value of reducing cement content.

8. T F Type III cement is often used where early strengths are desirable for early form removal or for faster, higher heats of hydration and time of setting.

9. T   F   Of types I through $\overline{V}$, Type V, low alkali cement would be best suited for severe sulfate environments (at appropriate w/c ratios) in concrete made with potentially reactive aggregates.

10. For massive concrete structures, where the heat of hydration is of concern:
    A. What portland cement type was developed specifically for this use?
    B. What portland cement type and optional requirement may be substituted if the cement in (A) is unavailable?

11. For moderate sulfate conditions, which cement type should be specified?

12. When flexural strength is required, is it best to use rounded, smooth (natural gravel) coarse aggregate or manufactured, crushed, angular, rough and very clean ones?

13. If chemical admixtures are unavailable, how can damage from freeze-thaw conditions be minimized?

14. What blended cement optional requirement(s) should be specified for use in a moderate sulfate and severe freeze-thaw environments?

15. What optional requirement should be specified for the cement when it is to be used with potentially reactive aggregates?

16. What can be done to adjust the time of setting characteristics of concrete?

17. If 1,000 lb of aggregate has 5% free moisture and 0.7% absorption, find its (A) *oven dry* and (B) *SSD* weights.

18. What can be done to reduce the water demand of a proportioned concrete mixture, once the cement content and fine and coarse aggregates quantities are chosen?

19. Calculate the F.M., and plot the gradation curve and specification values of the following material:

Table P11.1.1 (a)

Sieve Size	Percent Passing	Spec. Limits (% Passing)
3/8 in.	100	100
#4	97	95-100
#8	85	80-100
#16	75	50-85
#30	34	25-60
#50	20	10-30
#100	5	2-10
#200	1	0-2

20. Assuming the #16 sieve was either improperly tested or its value was incorrectly reported, what is the range of F.M.s possible for this material? (Use the material from Question 19 above.)

21. The following two materials, A and B, must be blended to meet specifications.

    A. What is the range of blends possible to meet specifications?

    B. If Material A is cheaper and the possible error in manufacturing is ±5% (that is any sieve can be % value ±5%, what blend should be used for economy while still assuring an in specification blend?

    C. Calculate the grading and F.M. of the blended material:

Table P11.1.1 (b)

Sieve Size	Percent Passing		
	A	B	Specification
3/8 in.	100	100	100
#4	92	100	95-100
#8	76	100	80-100
#16	48	90	50-85
#30	20	70	25-60
#50	8	34	10-30
#100	0	15	2-10

Note: Use either graphical or algebraic methods. Determine all values to the nearest tenth percent.

11.1.2 ANSWERS

Question	Answer	Explanation
1.	True	
2.	True	
3.	False	
4.	True	
5.	True	
6.	False	Properly proportioned concrete mixtures will benefit from using ASTM C618 pozzolans, and ASTM C 595 blended (slag) cement.
7.	False	They can increase ultimate strength, durability, watertightness, workability sulfate resistance, pumpability, and other significant properties.
8.	True	
9.	True	

10. (A) Type IV; (B) Types II or V, (low heat)

11. Type II, at an appropriate maximum water/cement ratio.

12. Usually manufactured aggregates are superior for flexural strength.

13. Using air entraining cements like ASTM C150 Types IA, IIA or IIIA or ASTM C 595 ISA, IPA, MPA

14. MS for moderate sulfate and A for air entraining

15. Low alkali

16. Use chemical accelerators or retarders as a first choice, change cement content or source if admixtures are not available.

17. A. By definition:

oven dry weight $\times$ (1 + absorption) = SSD weight

oven dry weight $\times$ (1 + absorption + free) = field weight

$$\text{oven dry weight} = \frac{\text{field weight}}{1 + \text{abs} + \text{free}}$$

$$= \frac{1000 \text{ lb}}{1 + 0.007 + 0.05}$$

oven dry weight = 946 lb

B. By definition:

oven dry weight $\times$ (1 + absorption) = SSD weight

946 lb $\times$ (1 + 0.007) = 953 lb

SSD weight = 953 lb

Question	Answer	Explanation

18. Use normal and/or high-range chemical water reducing admixtures in the mix.

19. F.M. = 2.84 calculated percent retained (i.e., percent coarser than) for each sieve, sum and divide by 100.

  $$[(0 + 3 + 15 + 25 + 66 + 80 + 95)/100].$$

A plot follows.

(Copied for reader convenience)

Sieve Size	ASTM
3/8''	100
#4	95 to 100
#8	80 to 100
#16	50 to 85
#30	25 to 60
#50	10 to 30
#100	2 to 10
#200	0 to 2

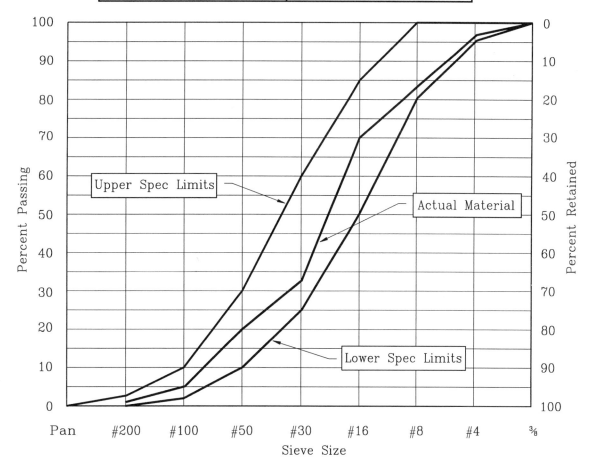

Fig. P11.1.2 (a)

Question	Answer	Explanation
20.		F.M.: $2.72 \leq$ F.M. ≤ 3.23 If #16 sieve is suspect (and #8 and #30 are not), then its true value can range between the #8 and #30 sieve values, or between 85% and 34%. Calculate the F.M. both ways:

Table P11.1.2 (b)

Sieve	Passing	Retained
3/8 in.	100	0
#4	97	3
#8	85	15
#16	?	15 to 51
#30	34	66
#50	22	78
#100	5	95

2.72 to 3.08

Therefore the FM can range between 2.72 and 3.08 if the #16 Sieve is in error. (*Note* that since we *know* that 66% of the sample *was larger than* the #30 Sieve, and also 15% of it is larger than #8, a maximum 66%-15% is available to be present on the #16 Sieve, and thus represents the extreme range of possibilities.)

21.   The solution can be found graphically by using blending graph.

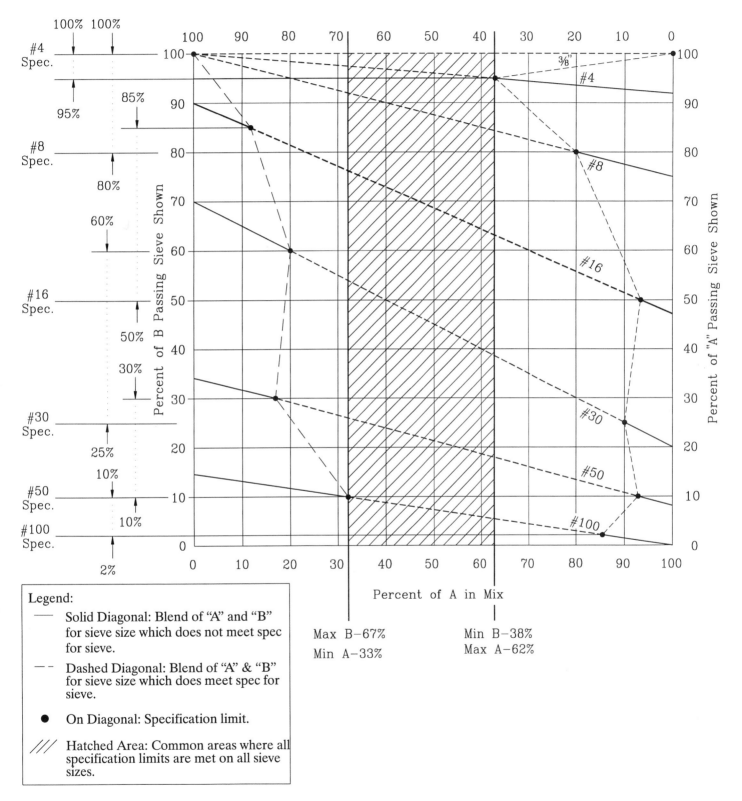

Fig. P11.1.2 (c)

21. (Solution continued)

A. Area shaded shows range of blends of A & B which will meet specification. Heavy dot shows sieve in which specification controls blend limits.

It is possible to see the range of blends from 38% to 67% of B or from 33% to 62% of A for *all sieves of blend* to meet requirements.

By individual sieves:

Table P11.1.2 (d)

Sieve Size	Minimum B	Maximum B
3/8 in.	—	—
#4	38%	100%
#8	17%	100%
#16	4%	88%
#30	10%	80%
#50	8%	85%
#100	13%	67%

B. Since "A" is cheaper, use the maximum possible of material "A" minus 5% for blending error,

$$A = 62\% - 5\% = 57\%$$

C. The blended material is:

Table P11.1.2 (e)

Sieve Size	Original Material A	Original Material B
3/8 in.	100	100
#4	92	100
#8	76	100
#16	48	90
#30	20	70
#50	8	34
#100	0	15

Table P11.1.2 (f)

Sieve Size	Factored Material/Combined (Percent Retained)		
	0.57A	0.43B*	Blend
3/8 in.	57.0	43.0	100.0
#4	52.4	43.0	95.4
#8	43.3	43.0	86.3
#16	27.4	38.7	66.1
#30	11.4	30.1	41.5
#50	5.6	14.6	20.2
#100	0.0	6.5	6.5

note: 0.43 = 1.00 − 0.57

Table P11.1.2 (g)

Sieve Size	Percent Passing, Blend
3/8 in.	0.0
#4	4.6
#8	13.7
#16	33.9
#30	58.5
#50	79.8
#100	93.5

Σ of % Passing = 284

F.M. = 284/100 = 2.84

A plot of materials A, B and the blend follows:

Table P11.1.2 (h)

Sieve Size	ASTM C 33 Spec Limits
3/8''	100
#4	95 to 100
#8	80 to 100
#16	50 to 85
#30	25 to 60
#50	10 to 30
#100	2 to 10

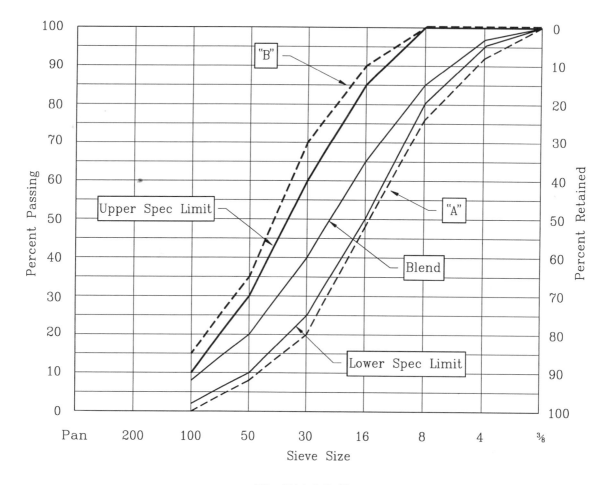

Fig. P11.1.2 (i)

11.2   P. E. PROBLEMS

11.2.1   P. E. PROBLEM 1 — DEFINITIONS IN CONCRETE MATERIALS

You have been requested to advise an engineering company based in a foreign country as to California practices connected with cements and concrete. The following questions are pertinent to your consultation:

A.   Identify five types of portland cement that may be used. List the distinguishing characteristics for each, and give one example of a construction application for which each is particularly suited.

B.   What is false set? What causes it, and how can it be corrected?

C.   What is a pozzolan? Give two examples of pozzolans, and state two advantages that accrue from their use in concrete.

D.   What factors are important in seeking a good concrete cure? What occurs when concrete cures under proper conditions?

E.   What common type of aggregate is preferred? Why?

F.   What is an alkali-aggregate reaction, and how can it be prevented?

G.   How do the following changes in concrete mixes and curing conditions affect the early and late compressive strengths of concrete?

1.   High temperature during placing and initial curing

2.   High water content in concrete mix

3.   Low cement factor

4.   Addition of an air entraining admixture to concrete mix

5.   Curing concrete under water

Solution

A.   Portland cement is available in five basic types, as follows:

Type I is called normal or general purpose and is usually available from most cement plants on request. It is suitable for concrete used in locations not subjected to extreme climatic and chemical effects where ordinary strength gain characteristics are acceptable.

Type II is called modified general purpose. In some parts of the nation it may have to be ordered in advance from the plant. However, in Southern California, Type II is commonly used in place of Type I due to the presence of sulfate-bearing soils and waters in much of this area. Some plants in the area produce material called

Type I-II, low alkali, which can be thought of as general purpose with sulfate resistant properties. Type II would be specified for flatwork and foundations (in contact with soil) where moderate resistance to sulfate soils or waters is required.

Type III is called high-early strength and is usually available from local cement plants. It is used when seven- or ten-day strength is required in just two or three days. An example is a structure from which the forms must be stripped early in order to meet a construction deadline, or when cold weather slows strength gain and type III compensates.

Type IV is called low-heat and normally requires a special order for delivery. The heat of hydration from the cement is generated at a lower rate than the others. It is used in massive structures such as reservoir walls and very thick foundations where excessive rise in temperature could cause subsequent structural problems due to thermal expansion.

Type V is called sulfate-resistant and sometimes requires a special order. It is used in especially arid desert areas of the state where Type II would not meet the requirements of resisting sulfate attack to concrete in contact with the soil or water.

B. False set is the rapid gain in stiffness of a portland cement concrete without the normally anticipated high generation of the heat of hydration. It can be caused by the gypsum (ground with the cement to prevent too rapid stiffening) recrystallizing and temporarily not performing its function. False set can be overcome by additional mixing to break down the recrystallization, but the contractor should not be permitted to use additional water.

C. A pozzolanic material is siliceous in nature, and when combined with source of calcium hydroxide (like lime) in the presence of water, forms a compound which hardness in the pressure of water. Pumicite, diatomaceous earth, fly ash, and blast furnace slag are examples. Some pozzolans are less expensive than portland cement and are used to replace part of the requirement. In a lean portland cement concrete mix, the pozzolan may improve workability and reduce bleeding and segregation. Provided that prolonged moist curing can be supplied, pozzolan admixtures can reduce rapid heat of hydration (by reducing cement content) and reduce the harmful effects of reactive aggregates. Finally, they will often increase concrete's resistance to sulfate attack.

D. The two major curing factors are:
    1. maintaining the portland cement concrete at a moderate temperature, and
    2. providing a means of retaining the mix water within the mass so that hydration of the portland cement can occur. Hydration of the hydraulic cement occurs during the curing period. Specifically, a gel is formed, water combines with the cement particles and results in the final set of the paste. After the final set occurs, further chemical reactions and crystallization occur; this is how gain in

strength occurs in cement. Under ideal curing conditions, portland cement concrete tends to reach some maximum attainable strength asymptotically.

E. The igneous type of aggregate, such as granite, is one of the most popular because it can be obtained economically, can be properly cleaned and crushed, given a desirable shape, is often structurally and chemically sound, and bonds well with the portland cement paste.

F. Some cements have excessive amounts of alkalies (Na_2O and K_2O), and these combine with the silica (SiO_2) in the aggregate, resulting in expansive forces that can disrupt the portland cement concrete. The problem can be prevented by:

   1. Limiting the alkali content of the hydraulic cement,

   2. Avoiding the use of aggregates that have a known history of reactivity, and

   3. Using an admixture such as fly ash that will combine with the alkalies immediately and mitigate expansion later on.

G. Effect on early and late strengths of portland cement concrete:

   1. High temperature during placing and initial curing tends to increase early strength and decrease late strength.

   2. High mixing water content lowers both early and ultimate strength.

   3. Low cement factor contents reduces both, though affects early strength more adversely.

   4. Addition of an air entraining admixture (other things being held constant) would lower both; however, if the air entrainer permits use of less water, the effect on strength may be less significant.

   5. Curing concrete under water raises early strength a little and raises late strength more.

Further information can be obtained from the textbook by Troxell, Davis, J.W. Kelly, *Composition and Properties of Concrete,* 2nd Edition, McGraw-Hill, 1968 (Ref. 16), or PCA's *Design and Control of Concrete Mixtures, any editor.*

11.2.2 P. E. PROBLEM 2 — DEFINITIONS OF ADMIXTURES IN CONCRETE

A new employee was hired into your geotechnical engineering office. Explain these basic concrete materials used in portland concrete mix designs and give examples of how and when they are used.

A. Describe accelerators and one type of construction in which they would be used.

B. Describe retarders and one type of construction in which they would be used.

C. Describe air entrainment and one type of construction in which they would be used.

D. Describe water-reducers and one kind of construction in which they would be used.

E. Describe workability agents and one kind of construction in which they would be used.

Solution

General Answer:

All materials in this list A through E are admixtures for concrete. A-D are chemicals, usually in a liquid form, which alter the performance of both fresh and hardened concrete.

"Workability agents" can be chemical or mineral admixtures. Each of their uses are described as follows:

Specific Answers:

A. Accelerators are technically called "time of setting accelerators" or commonly, set accelerators. They are chemicals added to or batched with fresh concrete to speed the setting or early hardening time of the concrete. Since cooler temperatures delay the setting time of concrete, the use of accelerators in cool or cold weather can speed the setting time to a rate normally expected for regular weather.

Accelerators are usually composed of calcium chloride (CC) or triethanol-amine (TEA).

Both cold weather construction and applications where early, rapid strength gain are desirable (e.g,. precast concrete, early form removal, tilt-up construction, early application of load) benefit from the proper use of accelerators.

B. Retarders are "time of-set" retarders and are used to retard or delay the setting and early hardening characteristics of concrete. Hot weather concreting operations benefit from the use of retarders to offset the effect of higher temperature on concrete. Heat speeds the chemical reaction between the batched water and cement. The presence of the proper dose of retarding chemical admixtures delays the reaction to normal setting rates. Usually, retarding chemical admixtures help reduce the water required for producing a certain workability and therefore, retarders can: 1) reduce water demand, which decreases water/cement ratio, which increases strength; or 2) creates higher slump (more workability at same water content, water/cement ratio and strength).

Delaying the setting time of concrete is helpful in hot weather concreting, and on long pours where a delay in finishing is helpful or required. Slowing the times of setting and heat of hydration are often helpful on mass concreting, such as dams and large mat foundations.

C. Air entrainment is the process of adding billions of properly sized tiny air bubbles to concrete. When hardened, and at the appropriate "air content" (% of concrete volume containing air voids), air entrainment:

    1.   Increases the durability of concrete to cycles of freezing and thawing;

    2.   Increases the resistance of concrete exposure to sulfates and seawater; and

    3.   Generally reduces the permeability of concrete in structures.

Therefore, the use of air entrainment chemical admixtures benefit concrete construction exposed to the extreme environmental conditions of freezing, sulfated soils and water, and marine structures.

D. Water reducers are chemicals which reduce the water required to achieve the same slump of a non-water reduced fresh concrete mix. The water reduction for "regular" water reducers is usually at least 5%, while for "high range water reducers" or super plasticizers it is at least 20%.

Water reducers can be used for their water reducing properties to:

    1.   Achieve much lower water contents, leading to lower water/cement ratios, leading to high concrete strengths at identical slumps;

    2.   Use lower water contents, identical slumps and water/cement ratios, thereby reducing cement contents and cement cost; and

    3.   Using identical water and cement contents, the same water/cement ratio and higher slumps with their attendant increase in workability and placability. (This is particularly helpful where there are relatively small reactions or highly congested reinforcing steel.)

The latter use is also beneficial where labor costs are high (fewer workers are needed for placing high slump concrete) or production schedules are aggressive. Higher strength can be achieved with lower water/cement ratios using placable mixes.

E. Workability agents increase the plasticity of concrete, which is a combination of slump and consistency of fresh concrete. Workability agents can be chemical or mineral admixtures. Of mineral admixtures, fly ash and natural pozzolans (diatomaceous earth, opaline cherts and shales; tuffs, volcanic ashes or pumicites, etc.) are the most prevalent. The most frequently encountered reason for using "workability agents" is to produce a pumpable fresh concrete mix. Sometimes if finishing properties of concrete are harsh, workability agents can increase workability and finishability as well. The color of hardened concrete can also be altered by using mineral admixtures.

PART III

PROPORTIONING MATERIALS IN A CONCRETE MIXTURE

12

THEORY OF MIX PROPORTIONING

12.1 RATIONALE OF ECONOMY IN MIX DESIGNS

Once the end use and method(s) of placement and special durability conditions are known, proper selection of the appropriate materials is made. Proportioning those materials is based on empirically derived tables plus direct experience, if any, with the specific materials chosen. Several principles apply to choosing materials and their relative content in the mix. The empirical tables were developed based upon these principles.

12.1.1 PRINCIPLES OF MIX DESIGN

Strength and durability of the concrete are the two key requirements of the owner and engineer. Additionally, the engineer is charged to produce the required strength and durability of workable concrete at the least cost. Least cost in this section of notes means least cost of ingredient materials. (The engineer *in reality* should examine the least *installed* cost, factoring in other considerations such as the costs of conveying, placing and finishing concrete, shrinkage, formwork, rebar concentrations, etc. Such considerations are beyond the scope of these notes.) Cement is by far the most costly ingredient of concrete, so it behooves the engineer to use the least amount required for the strength and durability needed.

Strength and durability are directly relatable to the ratio of water to cement, not to the total cement content. The combination of water and cement is called paste. For the same water/cement ratio, when the paste content of concrete is minimized, so is the cement content and, therefore, the cost of materials.

The required paste content in turn is dependent upon the total surface area all of the aggregates and their amount of voids. Surface area is minimized by using the highest coarse aggregate size practical and the least amount of fines. A continuously graded aggregate usually needs the least amount of paste to fill its voids.

Convention has related the coarse aggregate bulk density and the fine aggregate F.M. to the water demand of the mixture. With a larger top size, water demand decreases; with a finer (lower) F.M., the water demand increases. Conversely, when the water demand increases, the cement needed to obtain the same water/cement ratio also increases, as does the cost.

The engineer must balance the need for cost and workability. (For example, a higher slump has a higher water content and for a constant w/c, increases cement content, thus cost).

12.1.2 PRINCIPLE OF STRENGTH OF CONCRETE

Compression strength of concrete, for any given set of materials, is proportional to the porosity of the cement paste. Porosity of the cement paste is inversely related to the weight ratio of water to cement. Therefore, the highest strength concrete mixes are those which use the least amount of water relative to cement. This concept is known as Abrams' Law, after Duff Abrams, who initially investigated strength producing properties of concrete. Specifically, Abrams' law states that for a given class and source of materials (rock, sand, cement) which are sound and clean the strength and other desirable qualities of fully consolidated concrete under similar conditions are governed by the amount of batch water per unit of cement.

12.1.3 PRINCIPLE OF LEAST PASTE CONTENT

Paste is the combination of cement and water; cement being the most costly ingredient in concrete. Using the least amount of paste to produce the strength and durability required minimizes the costs of material. Therefore, to minimize paste, the voids or empty spaces between particles of aggregate (both coarse and fine) must be minimized. In addition to filling the voids, the aggregate surface area needs to be coated with paste. Surface area depends on particle shape and is minimized as they become spherical.

Therefore, theoretically, a combination of coarse and fine aggregate should be chosen to minimize both the total surface area of the aggregate combination and its voids content.

12.1.4 PRINCIPLE OF MAXIMUM COARSE AGGREGATE SIZE

In order to minimize the surface area of the aggregate combination, the maximum top size and amount of coarse aggregate should be used as long as it will still provide a workable fresh mix. (Mixes with too much coarse are known as *harsh* or *bony* and should usually be avoided except for some applications such as foundations, where superior workability is not essential.) Here, it should be recalled that the surface area per unit weight is inversely proportional to the mean diameter of the aggregate particle. Hence, using the highest possible quantities of the maximum top-sized (well-graded) coarse aggregate assures least total surface area and probably the smallest paste content as well. Of course, the more rounded, smooth and spherical the shape and texture of the material, the less surface there is to coat.

12.1.5 PRINCIPLE OF WATER DEMAND

Finally, the primary requirement for water in a mix is governed by the surface area of the sand which needs to be coated and whose voids need filling. Obviously, for a greater slump, more water is necessary. Additionally, voids between aggregate particles require more paste and, hence, more water and cement. Also, water content directly affects shrinkage of the concrete. Therefore, the lowest water content usually results in the lowest shrinkage.

12.1.6 SUMMARY OF PRINCIPLES

Once aggregates are chosen for concrete, the slump requirement and the water/cement ratio are known, empirical tables show the water requirement of the mix based on maximum size coarse aggregate the mix can use and the fineness of the sand. Once the water demand is known, the cement content is calculated by using the water/cement ratio. Based on the fineness modulus of the sand and dry-rodded unit weight of the coarse material, the solids volume or weight of coarse per yard of concrete is found. Knowing the volumes of water, cement, coarse aggregate and entrained air, if any, their sum is calculated, and the difference between that sum and 27 cu ft results in the volume of sand per yard of concrete.

12.2 PROPERTIES OF CONCRETE MIXTURES

12.2.1 SELECTION OF CONCRETE PROPERTIES

The maximum size of the aggregate, the water/cement ratio, the design slump of the concrete and its air content need to be determined before proportioning begins. Also, for the durability considerations of the concrete, the appropriate cement type should be chosen along with pozzolans, chemical admixtures and an integral coloring agent if desired.

The proportioning of materials is based on ACI Standard Tables found in ACI 318 and ACI 211. (Use of trial batches or actual experience gives more reliable results.) When actual water/cement ratio versus strength curves are known for the materials at slumps actually expected and used, those values may be used for proportioning in lieu of ACI Tables, which can only serve as a starting point.

12.2.2 SLUMP

Generally, concrete is specified for the least slump which can be conveyed, worked and placed for a given application. Least slump has traditionally meant least water and highest strength and durability. Past experience with the application, or the Standard Tables, can be used to determine normal slump recommendations. It should be noted that the contractor's labor costs increase with lower slumps, as does the potential for rock pockets, bug holes, poor consolidation, or incomplete and possibly poor bond between reinforcement and concrete. On the other hand, shrinkage of hardened concrete increases with the water content. Higher shrinkage may lead to unsightly random drying shrinkage cracking because of higher shrinkage forces.

Figure 12.1 shows the concrete in a cone for measuring slumps. Cone should be filled with concrete in three layers with each layer containing about one third of the total volume (Reference 14).

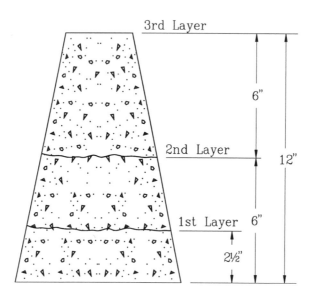

Figure 12.1 Filling Concrete in Slump Cone

High Slump or Low Slump refers to the number of inches the standard fresh concrete conically shaped specimen "slumps" or subsides when the cone is removed. Figure 12.2 shows the high slump and low slump concretes. Concrete A is referred to as "high slump", "wet", fluid or flowable, whereas Concrete B is referred to as "low slump", "dry" or "stiff" concrete. Table 12.1 is a list of recommended, *not* mandated, slumps for different applications. The engineer's judgment and job site requirements will determine the specified slump.

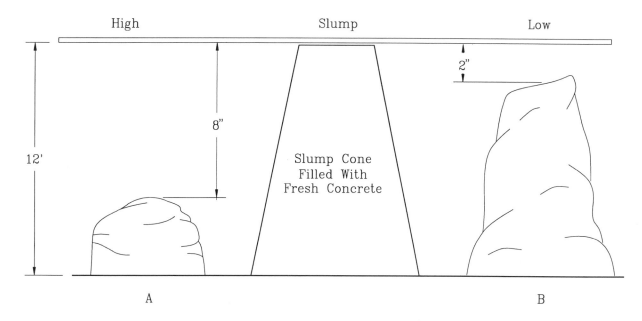

Figure 12.2 High and Low Slump Concretes

Table 12.1 Recommended Slumps for Various Types of Construction
(Adapted from ACI 211)

Types of Construction	Slump (in.)	
	Maximum*	Minimum
Reinforced foundation walls and footings	3	1
Plain footings, caissons, and substructure walls	3	1
Beams and reinforced walls	4	1
Building columns	4	1
Pavements and slabs	3	1
Mass concrete	2	1

May be increased by 1 in. for methods of consolidation other than vibration

12.2.3 STRENGTH

Though usually specified as compressive strength, concrete can be designed for flexural strength as well. For compressive strengths up to 4,500 psi, the water/cement ratio is the primary concern and must be limited to a maximum permissible according to Table 12.2. For higher compressive strengths and for flexural strengths, the water/cement ratio is just as important, but other factors such as aggregate quality (particularly coatings, bulk density, strength and gradation), air entrainment and cement type become equally important. At lower compressive strengths, failure from stress occurs primarily in the hydrated cement paste. At higher strengths, the bond between the coarse aggregate and paste fails. Finally, the highest strength concretes will fail through the aggregate particle itself. Minimizing aggregate to paste bond failure is even more important to flexural strength. There are standard equations which relate flexural strength to compressive strength. One such equation is

$$f_f = K\sqrt{f'_c}$$

where

f_f = flexure strength of concrete

f'_c = compressive strength of concrete

K = factor where

7 < K < 11 in general, and depends upon the materials used.

Table 12.2 shows the water/cement ratio requirements for compressive strength in concrete used when no history of local materials is available. Note that a water/cement ratio of 0.25 is generally accepted as the minimum amount necessary to hydrate the cement. Additional water is used for the needs of placement and workability.

Concrete will gain strength, given proper curing, for at least 100 days and usually longer. Strength versus time curves are asymptotic, and theoretically never stop gaining strength.

Table 12.2 Maximum Permissible Water/Cement Ratio
(Adapted from ACI 318)

Specified Compressive Strength (f'$_c$, psi)*	Absolute Water/Cement Ratio by Weight	
	Non-air-entrained Concrete	Air-entrained Concrete
2500	0.67	0.54
3000	0.58	0.46
3500	0.51	0.40
4000	0.44	0.35
4500	0.38	†
5000	†	†

*28-day strength. With most materials, water/cement ratios shown will provide average strengths greater than indicated in Section 4.3.2 as being required.

† For strengths above 4,500 psi (non-air-entrained concrete) and 4,000 psi (air-entrained concrete) concrete proportions shall be established by methods of Section 4.3.

Strength, unless otherwise specified, is assumed to be based on tests conducted on 28-day old concrete specimens. When earlier or later strength specifications are utilized, appropriate factors for strength gaining relationships are usually used to estimate strength at other ages. For example, if an engineer wants 3,000 psi at 7 days and knows that the 7-day strength for similar mixes and materials is 65% of the 28-day strength, he may use the water/cement ratio interpolated for $3,000 \div 0.65 = 4,615$ concrete at 28 days.

12.2.4 DURABILITY

Durable concrete resists freeze-thaw environments as well as sulfate exposure. Therefore, to provide durability in concrete:

1. Choose an air content from Table 12.3 to produce frost resistance for the expected severity of exposure.

Table 12.3 Total Air Content for Frost Resistant Concrete
(Adapted from ACI 318)

Nominal Maximum Aggregate Size (in.)*	Air Content (Percent)	
	Severe Exposure	Moderate Exposure
3/8	7-1/2	6
1/2	7	5-1/2
3/4	6	5
1	6	4-1/2
1-1/2	5-1/2	4-1/2
2†	5	4
3†	4-1/2	3-1/2

See ASTM C 33 for tolerances on oversize for various nominal maximum size designations

† These air contents apply to the total mix, as for the preceding aggregate sizes. When testing these concretes, however, aggregate larger than 1-1/2 in. is removed by handpicking or sieving and air content is determined on the minus 1-1/2 in. fraction of mix. (Tolerance on air content as delivered applies to this value.) Air content of total mix is computed from value determined on the minus 1-1/2 in. fraction.

2. Choose a water/cement ratio from Tables 12.4 and 12.7 for the kind of application and moisture exposure expected.

Table 12.4 Maximum Permissible Water/Cement Ratios for Concrete in
Severe Exposures*
(Adapted from ACI 211)

Type of Structure	Structure Wet Continuously or Frequently and Exposed to Freezing and Thawing†	Structure Exposed to Sea Water or Sulfates
Thin sections (railings, curbs, sills, ledges, ornamental work) and sections with less than 1 in. cover over steel	0.45	0.40‡
All other structures	0.50	0.45‡

*Based on report of ACI committee 201, "Durability of Concrete in Service," previously cited.

† Concrete should also be air-entrained

‡ If sulfate resisting cement (Type II or Type V of ASTM C 150) is used, permissible water/cement ratio may be increased by 0.05

3. Choose a water/cement ratio from Table 12.5 for the expected sulfate environment. Also, determine the cement type and if pozzolans are required or recommended for sulfate resistance.

Table 12.5 Requirements for Concrete Exposed to Sulfate-Containing Solutions
(Adapted from ACI 211)

Sulfate Exposure	Water Soluble Sulfate (SO_4) in Soil (% by weight)	Sulfate (SO_4) in Water, (ppm)	Cement Type	Normal Weight Aggregate Concrete	Lightweight aggregate concrete
				Maximum Water/Cement Ratio (by weight)*	Minimum Compressive Strength (f'_c psi)*
Negligible	0.00-0.10	0-150	—	—	—
Moderate†	0.10-0.20	150-1,500	II,IP(MS), IS(MS)	0.50	3,750
Severe	0.20-2.00	1500-10,000	V	0.45	4,250
Very Severe	Over 2.00	Over 10,000	V plus pozzolan‡	0.45	4,250

A lower water/cement ratio or higher strength may be required for water-tightness or for protection against corrosion of embedded items or freezing and thawing (Table 4.5.2).
† Seawater
‡ Pozzolan that has been determined by test or service record to improve sulfate resistance when used in concrete containing Type V cement.

4. Compare these water/cement ratios and use the lowest water/cement value, since it will produce concrete which resists the most severe condition.

12.2.5 MAXIMUM AGGREGATE SIZE

Table 12.6 provides a guide to the maximum aggregate size for different applications. The basis for it is that it provides for the largest aggregate which can be worked between concentrated reinforcement, narrow forms or in the pump.

Table 12.6 Maximum Aggregate Size

Maximum size of aggregate should not exceed:	
1/5	The overall dimension of non-reinforced members
or 3/4	The clear space between reinforcement
or 1/3	The depth of the slab
or 2/5	The inside diameter of pump line

Table 12.7 Requirements for Special Exposure Conditions

Exposure Condition	Maximum Water/ Cement Ratio, Normal Weight Aggregate Concrete	Minimum f'_c, Lightweight Aggregate Concrete
Concrete intended to be water-tight: (a) Concrete exposed to fresh water (b) Concrete exposed to brackish water or seawater	0.50 0.45	3,750 4,250
Concrete exposed to freezing and thawing in a moist condition: (a) Curbs, gutters, guard rails or thin sections (b) Other elements (c) In presence of deicing chemicals	0.45 0.50 0.45	4,250 3,750 4,250
For corrosion protection for reinforced concrete exposed to deicing salts, brackish water, seawater or spray from these sources	0.40*	4,750*

If minimum concrete cover required by Section 7.7 is increased by 0.5 in., water/cement ratio may be increased to 0.45 for normal weight concrete, or f'_c reduced to 4,250 psi for lightweight concrete.

13

METHODS OF PROPORTIONING CONCRETE MIXTURES

13.1 TRIAL BATCH METHOD OF PROPORTIONING

As previously noted, mixes are proportioned on the basis of water/cement ratio and workability. Trial batching in a laboratory is a way of designing mixes based on the visual, tested appearance of fresh concrete. A trial batch is started in a laboratory mixer using a fixed water/cement ratio and known weights of cement and water. Measured amounts of coarse and fine aggregate of known, preferably SSD, moisture conditions, are added until the desired workability is achieved. Often several different trials are needed to get the appropriate coarse content (or coarse to fine ratio), for the slump and workability needed. The mix is calculated on the basis of the weights of materials added and is characterized by its slump and strength. A strength was presumed initially and a water cement ratio selected for testing which was expected to achieve it. The trial batch verifies the strength, workability, air content (if tested) and slump.

13.2 PROPORTIONING CONCRETE MIXTURES — EMPIRICAL

13.2.1 COOKBOOK METHODS OF PROPORTIONING

Prior to the advent and wide-spread use of automated weigh batching equipment, concrete was batched by fairly arbitrary though useful ratio proportions. For example, a 1:2:3½ "standard mix" contained 1 part cement, 2 parts sand, 3½ parts coarse aggregate. These could either be bulk volumetric proportions or relative weights. Tables were developed showing various ratios and applications where they might be used.

Even though the use of this ratio method of proportioning has been largely abandoned, reference to it shows up with regularity on the P.E. Exam. Usually the context of this problem requires conversion from these ratios (cement:sand:rock) to a set of standard weights and solids volumes.

Should this sort of problem be offered, the procedure is to convert the ratio for an assumed (or sometimes given) amount of cement (or other ingredient, if given) which will act as a basis for the other materials. Then sand, rock and water weights and solid volumes are determined. A review of the solutions to Problems 13.9.1 and 13.13.3 will be helpful to understand the methodology involved.

In addition to proportioning by trial batches using a fixed water/cement ratio, two basic methods, each with innumerable variations, are available for selecting approximate mix proportions. These methods are called the *absolute volume* and (total) *weight methods*. They are based on *average* materials with empirical starting points for water demand, coarse aggregate, air content and fresh unit weights. The absolute volume method relies on the fact that all the solid volumes sum to 27.0 cu ft. The weight method is similar in that all materials must sum to an empirically estimated weight per (average) yard of concrete. These methods are known as the ACI Methods.

Table 13.2 presents several points of useful data. Its purpose is to provide a starting point for the amount of batch water needed in a mix for various slumps and maximum aggregate sizes. The table is divided into sections for water demand of non air entrained and air entrained concrete mixtures. In addition, for the non air entrained concrete (top) portion of the table, expected air entrapment values are noted. These are used for the "air content" calculation in the absolute volume method because significant over yielding of fresh concrete is possible, despite the fact that this "air" is of no benefit in resisting destructive cycles of freezing and thawing. Also, for the air entrained (bottom) portion of the table, recommended target air entrainment values are provided for each severity condition normally encountered; obtaining such air entrainment will rely on treating the concrete with an admixture whose dosage will produce the air content needed.

Water demands are shown for every typical combination of slump, air entrainment need, and maximum aggregate size. The values are in pounds of water per cubic yard of concrete. Older tables are around and similar tabular values have been presented in past P. E. examinations which show these values in gallons. The water demand figure is based upon **saturated surface dried** (SSD) aggregates which are clean, continuously graded and well shaped. The ACI method of mix design by the absolute volume method adjusts the weight of coarse aggregate according to its absorption in order to put it into standard mix design form using SSD values. Once the absolute volume of sand is calculated, the moisture content difference between dry and SSD is inconsequential, so the weight of the SSD sand is taken as: SSD weight = absolute volume of sand/(specific gravity of sand * 62.4 lb/cu ft). Technically, this calculation determines the dry weight, although the conversion from dry to SSD is rarely performed in practice, and the value is taken as SSD.

Table 13.3 presents values which are used to determine the amount of coarse aggregate which can be used in one cubic yard of fresh concrete. This depends on how finely graded the sand in the mix will be (that is, the fineness modulus, FM, of the sand) and the maximum size of the coarse aggregate itself. The table was created with a concept which basically proposed to put in as many cubic feet of *bulk* coarse aggregate as would fit in 27 cubic feet of concrete utilizing a certain sand. This table presents the ratio of *bulk* cubic feet of coarse aggregate to the total (bulk) volume of concrete. Each value therefore is a ratio, or a value less than one (or unity). The laboratory weight of one cubic foot of (lab) oven dried rodded coarse aggregate is known as its "bulk oven dry unit weight;" the fact that this aggregate has voids throughout its mass and the measuring bucket's calibrated gross volume is used, not the solids volume of the aggregate, accounts for the term "bulk." The concepts of bulk and absolute solids volume must be firmly understood.

The calculation is straightforward: Enter the table's column with the FM of the sand and determine the volume of coarse aggregate for the concrete using the aggregate's maximum size to locate the proper row. For sand with an FM of 2.60, the bulk volume of 1 in. MSA aggregate should occupy 0.69 of the volume of concrete. For a cubic yard of concrete, 69% of its volume should be bulk 1-in. aggregates. A ratio of 0.69 times 27 cubic feet equals 18.63 cubic feet of bulk, 1 in. MSA oven dried aggregate. If the oven dry aggregate weighs 103 pounds per cubic foot, 18.63 cubic feet of it weighs 1919 pounds. At a specific gravity of 2.58 this will occupy a solids volume of 11.92 cubic feet of absolute volume. Summarizing, in the 18.63 cubic feet of bulk volume, there are 11.92 cubic feet of solid material and $18.63 - 11.92 = 6.71$ cubic feet of air voids. If another test is run to determine the 1 in. aggregate's absorption, it is possible to calculate its SSD weight. If the aggregate has an absorption of 1.98% and is allowed to absorb moisture (the saturated condition weighing $1 + 1.98/100$ times the dry) and it becomes saturated, 1919 pounds of dry aggregate will weigh 1919 times $1.0198 = 1957$ pounds in the SSD condition.

In the following diagram and example, some amount of oven dried, bulk coarse aggregate will "fit" in one cubic yard of concrete. The distinction between bulk volume and absolute volume is also shown.

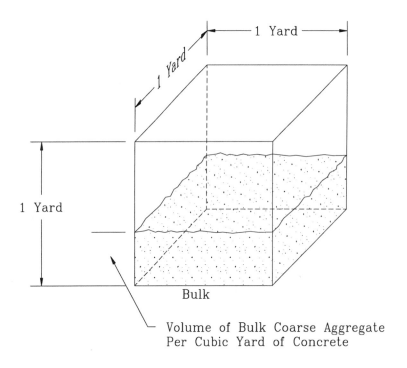

Bulk

Volume of Bulk Coarse Aggregate
Per Cubic Yard of Concrete

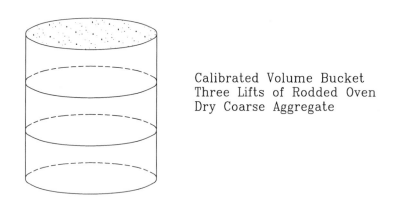

Calibrated Volume Bucket
Three Lifts of Rodded Oven
Dry Coarse Aggregate

Figure 13.1 Oven-Dried, Bulk Coarse Aggregate

EXAMPLE

$$\text{Bulk Unit Weight} = \frac{\text{Weight of Oven-Dry Aggregate}}{\text{Volume of Bucket}}$$

Find oven-dry bulk unit weight, absolute solids volume and voids content of aggregate.

- Weight of Empty Bucket: 12.21 lb
- Weight of Full Bucket: 39.19 lb
- Volume of Bucket: 0.257 ft^3
- Specific Gravity: 2.62

$$\text{Bulk Unit Weight} = \frac{39.19 - 12.21}{0.257} \frac{\text{lb}}{\text{ft}^3}$$

$$= 105 \text{ lb/ft}^3 \underline{\text{Bulk}}$$

$$\text{Absolute Solid Volume} = \frac{105 \text{ lb coarse}}{(62.4 \text{ lb/ft}^3)(2.62)} = 0.642 \text{ ft}^3$$

$$\text{Voids Content} = \frac{1.0642 \text{ ft}^3}{1.000 \text{ ft}^3} = 0.358 = 35.8\%$$

Therefore:

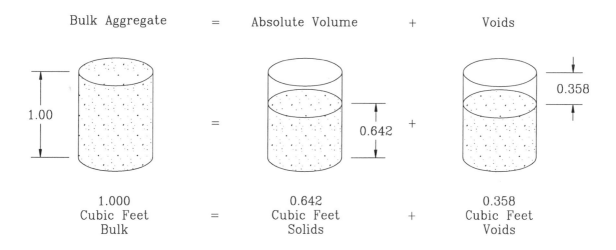

Figure 13.2 Solid and Void Contents of Bulk Aggregate

13.2.2 ABSOLUTE VOLUME METHOD

Once the desired properties of the concrete are specified and the available materials are known, tables based on empirical relationships are employed to determine per yard weights or volumes of all combined ingredients except sand. Weights and bulk volumes are then converted to absolute volumes. Finally, the air content is calculated in cubic feet per cubic yard of concrete. Air is based on requirements for *air entrainment* to achieve minimum durability. If the entrained air is not required, the *entrapped value* should be used. The sand's absolute volume is the remaining volume which, when combined with the other absolute volumes, sums to a cubic yard or 27.00 cu ft.

Convention says that the absorption of the sand is small in comparison to either quantity of aggregate or the batch water. Therefore, the conversion of sand from cubic feet (remaining to fill the cubic yard) to pounds *assumes* the weight to be in saturated surface dry (SSD) condition.

The steps shown in the following tables outline the absolute volume method:

Table 13.1 Table Outline of Absolute Volume Method

Step	Operation	Unknown
1	Find slump (from Table 12.1) or slump or judge from experience	Slump (in.)
2	Calculate (from Table 12.6) or verify suitability of available aggregate	Maximum size of coarse aggregate (in.).
3	Find [from Tables 12.3 (entrainment) and 13.2 (entrainment or entrapment)]	Air content (percent). Use entrained, if necessary; entrapped, if not.
4	Determine, compare, from Table 12.2 for strength, Tables 12.4 and 12.7 for durability, and Table 12.5 for sulfate resistance.	Maximum allowable water/cement ratio. W/C should be lowest of the three. Cement Type may be specified, also.
5	Find (from Table 13.2) water requirement in lb/cy	Convert water requirement from lb to cubic feet.
6	Calculate, from water/cement ratio and water content	Cement content (pounds) and absolute volume (cubic feet)
7	Find cement content minimum if any, compare to value from w/c calculation	Cement content from water/cement ratio against cement content minimum specified, if any. Use larger value.
8	Using known F.M. of sand find (from Table 13.3)	Quantity of coarse aggregate, absolute volume (cubic feet)
9	Calculate air. Convert % to ft^3	Air content (cubic feet)
10	Calculate sum	Sum of water, air, cement and coarse aggregate (cubic feet) from 27.00 cu ft
11	Calculate coarse aggregate SSD weight	Coarse dry weight $\times$ 1 + absorption
12	Calculate difference	Sand content, absolute volume. Subtract absolute volume sum from 27.00 cubic feet.

Table 13.2 Approximate Mixing Water and Air Content Requirements for Different Slumps And Nominal Maximum Sizes of Aggregates (Adapted from ACI 211)

Slump in.	Water, lb per cu yd of concrete for indicated nominal maximum sizes of aggregate							
	3/8 in.*	½ in.*	3/4 in.*	1 in.*	1-½ in.*	2 in.†*	3 in.†‡	6 in.†‡
Non-air entrained concrete								
1 to 2	350	335	315	300	285	260	220	190
3 to 4	385	365	340	325	300	285	245	210
6 to 7	410	385	360	340	315	300	270	—
Approximate amount of entrapped air in non-air entrained concrete, percent	3	2.5	2	1.5	1	0.5	0.3	0.2
Air-entrained concrete								
1 to 2	305	295	280	270	250	240	205	180
3 to 4	340	325	304	295	275	265	225	200
6 to 7	365	345	325	310	290	280	260	—
Recommended average§ total air content, percent for level of exposure:								
Mild exposure	4.5	4.0	2.5	2.0	2.5	2.0	1.5**††	1.0**††
Moderate exposure	6.0	5.5	5.0	4.5	4.5	4.0	3.5**††	3.0**††
Extreme exposure‡‡	7.5	7.0	6.0	6.0	5.5	5.0	4.5**††	4.0**††

These quantities of mixing water are for use in computing cement factors for trial batches. They are maxima for reasonably well-shaped angular coarse aggregates graded within limits of accepted specifications.

† The slump values for concrete containing aggregate larger than 1½ in. are based on slump tests made after removal of particles larger than 1½ in. by wet-screening.

‡ These quantities of mixing water are for use in computing cement factors for trial batches when 3 in. or 6 in. nominal maximum size aggregate is used. They are average for reasonably well-shaped coarse aggregates, well-graded from coarse to fine.

§ Additional recommendations for air-content and necessary tolerances on air content for control in the field are given in a number of ACI documents, including ACI 201, 345, 318, 301, and 302. ASTM C 94 for ready-mixed concrete also gives air content limits. The requirements in other documents may not always agree exactly, so in proportioning concrete consideration must be given to selecting an air content that will meet the needs of the job and also meet the applicable specifications

** For concrete containing large aggregates which will be wet-screened over the 1½ in. sieve prior to testing for air content, the percentage of air expected in the 1½ in. minus material should be as tabulated in the 1½ in. column. However, initial proportioning calculations should include the air content as a percent of the whole.

†† When using large aggregate in low cement factor concrete, air entrainment need not be detrimental to strength. In most cases mixing water requirement is reduced sufficiently to improve the water/cement ratio and to thus compensate for the strength reducing effect of entrained air concrete. Generally, therefore, for these large maximum sizes of aggregate, air contents recommended for extreme exposure should be considered even though there may be little or no exposure to moisture and freezing.

‡‡ These values are based on the criteria that 9 percent air is needed in the mortar phase of the concrete. If the mortar volume will be substantially different from the determined in this recommended practice, it may be desirable to calculate the needed air content by taking 9 percent of the actual mortar volume.

Table 13.3 Volume of Coarse Aggregate per Unit of Volume of Concrete
(Adapted from ACI 211)

Maximum Size of Aggregate (in.)	Volume of Dry-rodded Coarse Aggregate* per Unit Volume of Concrete for Different Fineness Moduli of Sand			
	2.40	2.60	2.80	3.00
3/8	0.50	0.48	0.46	0.44
1/2	0.59	0.57	0.55	0.53
3/4	0.66	0.64	0.62	0.60
1	0.71	0.69	0.67	0.65
1½	0.75	0.73	0.71	0.69
2	0.78	0.76	0.74	0.72
3	0.82	0.80	0.78	0.76
6	0.87	0.85	0.83	0.81

Volume are based on aggregates in dry-rodded condition as described in ASTM C 29 for Unit Weight of Aggregate.

These volumes are selected from empirical relationships to produce concrete with a degree of workability suitable for usual reinforced construction. For less workable concrete such as required for concrete pavement constructions, they may be increased about 10 percent. For more workable concrete see Section 5.3.6.1.

13.2.3 WEIGHT METHOD

Compared with the absolute volume method, the weight method of proportioning is simpler to use, though less accurate, due to the nature of estimating the total weight of a standard cubic yard of concrete. However, it is a good starting point for mixes, especially since most mixes are adjusted and revised based on actual field experience or firsthand knowledge of the materials.

The steps for the weight method are shown in Table 13.4.

Table 13.4 Outline of Weight Method

Step	Operation	Unknown
1	Find (from Table 12.1) or slump judge from experience	Slump (in.)
2	Calculate or verify suitability of available aggregate (from Table 12.6)	Maximum size of coarse aggregate (in.)
3	Find (from Table 12.3 for entrainment and Table 13.2 for entrainment or entrapment)	Air content (percent). Use entrained, if necessary; entrap-ped, if not
4	Determine and compare for strength (Table 12.2), for durability (Tables 12.4 and 12.7) and for sulfate resistance (Table 12.5).	Maximum allowable water/cement ratio. W/C will be the lowest of the three cement values; select cement type.
5	Find (from Table 12.2)	Water requirement (pounds)
6	Calculate, from water/cement ratio and water content	Quantity of cement (pounds)
7	Compare	Cement content from water/ cement ratio against minimum cement content specified, if any. Use higher value.
8	Find (from Table 13.3)	Dry quantity of coarse aggregate, (converted to pounds).
9	Find (from Table 13.5)	Approximate weight of 1.0 cu yd of fresh concrete for similar materials (pounds)
10	Calculate sum	water, coarse aggregate and cement (pounds)
11	Calculate difference between cubic yard estimated weight and sum of water, coarse and cement.	Dry sand content. Subtract sum of other materials from estimated weight of concrete (pounds).
12	Convert to SSD conditions	Adjust coarse and fine aggregate from dry to SSD by adding absorbable water.

Table 13.5 First Estimate of Weight of Fresh Concrete
(Adapted from ACI 211)

Maximum Size of Aggregate (in.)	First Estimate of Concrete Weight, lb per cu yd*	
	Non-air-entrained Concrete	Air-entrained Concrete
3/4	3840	3691
1/2	3890	3760
3/4	3960	3840
1	4010	3900
1½	4070	3960
2	4120	4000
3	4160	4040
6	4230	4120

Values calculated by Eq. (5-1) for concrete of medium richness (550 lb of cement per cu yd) and medium slump with aggregate specific gravity of 2.7. Water requirements based on values for 3 to 4 in. slump in Tables 5.3.3. If desired, the estimated weight may be refined as follows if necessary information is available: for each 10 lb difference in mixing water from the Table 5.3.3. values for 3 to 4 in. slump, correct the weight per cu yd 15 lb in the opposite direction, for each 100 lb difference in cement content from 550 lb, correct the weight per cu yd 15 lb in the same direction, for each 0.1 by which aggregate specific gravity deviates from 2.7, correct the concrete weight 100 lb in the same direction.

13.3 EXAMPLE PROBLEMS

13.3.1 EXAMPLE PROBLEM 1 — CONCRETE MIXTURE FOR TILT-UP WALLS

Part A:

The Los Angeles basin is known for its mild climate, potentially reactive aggregates (in some areas) and moderate sulfate conditions, particularly in the coastal communities.

Design a concrete mixture using a maximum ½-in. aggregate size (105 pcf, dry-rodded weight) and a high slump. The absorption of the rock is 1.0%. The concrete will be used in "tilt-up" wall construction.

The only sand available has an F.M. of 2.80. Both the aggregates have specific gravities of 2.65. The structural engineer specifies a minimum compressive strength of 3,000 psi at 28 days.

Part B:

What is the unit weight of the fresh concrete proportioned in the previous example?

Solution

Part A:

Table 13.2 shows that 385 lb of water are necessary to produce a 6 to 7 in. (high) slump. Moderate sulfate resistance requires using a Type II cement while potentially reactive aggregates demand it to be low alkali; however, tilt-up construction is generally not exposed to soils so sulfates are not really an issue. From Table 12.2, 3,000 psi concrete dictates a maximum water/cement ratio of 0.58. Therefore, 385 lb/0.58 = 664 lb of cement will be required. Based on F.M. of sand of 2.80, and coarse bulk dry density of 105 lb/cu ft, the coarse aggregate bulk volume is 0.55 of a cu yd or 14.85 cu ft bulk volume. (See Table 13.3.) This bulk volume of aggregate weighs:

$$14.85 \text{ cu ft} \times 105 \text{ lb/cu ft} = 1559 \text{ lb}$$

and occupies a solids volume of

$$\frac{1559 \text{ lb (dry)}}{62.4 \text{ lb/cu ft} \times 2.65} = 9.43 \text{ cu ft}$$

The cement occupies a solids volume of

$$\frac{664 \text{ lb}}{62.4 \text{ lb/cu ft} \times 3.15} = 3.38 \text{ cu ft}$$

Also, the water occupies $\frac{385 \text{ lb}}{62.4 \text{ lb/cu ft}} = 6.17 \text{ ft cu of space.}$

The entrapped air occupies 2.5% of the volume which is 0.025×27.00 or 0.675 ft^3

Recapping:

Material	Weight (pounds)	Volume (cubic feet)
Water	385	6.17
Cement (Type II, Low Alkali)	664	3.38
½-in. Coarse Aggregate (dry)	1559	9.43
Air (2.5% Entrapped)	—	0.68
Subtotal	2608	19.66

And the sand occupies the remaining solids volume. Thus,

27.00 cu ft − 19.66 cu ft = 7.34 cu ft

which is absolute volume of sand required. Converting from absolute solids volume to weight, the sand weighs

7.34 cu ft × 62.4 lb/cu ft × 2.65 = 1214 lb (SSD, by convention)

Also, since the weight of the coarse material is dry and its absorption is 1.0%, it should be adjusted to SSD basis. Therefore, the mix contains the following proportions:

Material	Weight (pounds)	Volume (cubic feet)	Other Units
Cement	664	3.38	7.06 Sack
Water	385	6.17	46.2 Gallons
Coarse (SSD)	1575	9.43	
Fine (SSD)	1214	7.34	
Air	—	0.68	2.5%
Total	3838	27.00	1 cu yd

Note that when the conversion of coarse aggregate from dry to SSD occurred, the weight increased (1559 lb × 1.01 = 1575 lb) but the absolute volume did not since an additional volume material was not added, but got absorbed into the same volume of rock.

Water/Cement Ratio:

Weight 385 lb/664 lb = 0.58 or 46.2 gal/7.06 sacks = 6.54 gallons per sack

Part B:

Unit weight is expressed in pounds per cubic foot and is the total weight divided by total volume or 3838 lb / 27.00 cu ft = 142.1 lb/cu ft

13.3.2 EXAMPLE PROBLEM 2 — MIX ADJUSTMENT FOR TRIAL BATCH

The previous mix was calculated and a trial batch was made according to the design, except that only 360 lb of water per batch were necessary to produce the desired slump. Also, it was found that the mix only contained 1.5% entrapped air. Recalculate the actual mix proportions according to what was batched. Also, find the new water/cement ratio and fresh unit weight.

Solution

With the reduction in volumes of air and water, the combination of materials now sums to less than 27.00 cu ft. The volumes batched will be summed, and all materials will be increased proportionately to determine ingredients on a cubic yard basis.

Material	Weight	Volume
Cement	664	3.38
Water	360	5.77
Coarse (SSD)	1575	9.43
Fines (SSD)	1214	7.34
Subtotal (Solids)	3813	25.92
Air Content (1.5%)	—	0.41
Total Batch	3813	26.33

This represents the actual material mixed. The solids volume will need to be increased by a ratio of

$$\frac{27.00 - 0.41}{25.92} = 1.0258$$

to achieve a 27.0 cu ft mix. (Since the air is known and based upon the fresh volume achieved, it is not subject to adjustment.)

Adjusted by factor: 1.0258

Material	Weight (lb)	Volume (cu ft)
Cement	681	3.47
Water	369	5.92
Coarse (SSD)	1616	9.67
Fines (SSD)	1245	7.53
Air (1.5%)	—	0.41
Total	3911	27.00

New water/cement ratio by weight: 369/681 = 0.54

$$\text{gal/sack:} \quad \frac{369 \text{ lb water}/8.33 \text{ lb/gal}}{681 \text{ lb cement}/94 \text{ lb cement/sk}} = 6.1 \text{ gal/sack}$$

unit weight: 3911/27.0 = 144.9 lb/cu ft

13.3.3 EXAMPLE PROBLEM 3 — MIX DESIGN USING WEIGHT METHOD

An old rule of thumb says 6-6-6-4000. That is, 6 sacks, 6 gallons per sack, 6-in. slump and 4,000 pounds per cubic yard. Although no longer used, find the approximate mix proportions based on these criteria. Assume 1 in. maximum sized coarse aggregate, 100 lb/cu ft dry bulk density with a specific gravity of 2.65, natural sand with an F.M. of 2.80 and a specific gravity of 2.63 and a mild climate — no sulfate exposure. The coarse absorption is 0.5% and the fine, 0.7%.

Solution

Using the weight method:

Step:

1. Slump = 6 in.

2. Aggregate = 1 in. top size

3. Air content = 1.5% (entrapped). No air entrainment.

4. Water/cement = 6 gal/sack = $\dfrac{8.33 \text{ 1b/gal} \times 6.0 \text{ gal/sk}}{94 \text{ 1b/sk}}$ = 0.53

   Note: Water/cement is fixed by conditions of problem. However, based on water/cement = 0.53, strengths above 4,000 psi can readily be expected; sulfate resistance, freeze-thaw and other durability considerations would not warrant lowering it.

5. Water is dictated at 6 gallons per sack times 6 sacks per yard

   6 × 6 = 36 gal; 36 gal × 8.33 lb/gal = 300 lb/cu yd

   Checking Table 13.2, 340 lb may be more realistic, but use 300 due to instructions.

6. Cement content is fixed by problem statement at 6 sacks

   6 sk × 94 lb/sk = 564 lb/cu yd

7. From Table 13.3, this concrete should contain 0.67 of its volume as (bulk) coarse aggregate or

   27.00 cu ft/cu yd × 0.67 = 18.09 cu ft
   18.09 cu ft × 100 pcf = 1809 lb (dry)

8. Use 4,000 lb per cubic yard from problem statement. (Table 13.5 says a better approximation is 4,010.)

9. Recapping:

Water	300 lb
Cement	564 lb
Coarse(dry)	1809 lb
Subtotal	2673 lb

10.

4000 lb	(per yard, given)
−2673 lb	(solids except sand)
1327 lb	Sand content (dry)

11. Coarse SSD   =   Coarse (dry) × 1.005 = 1818 lb (SSD)
    Fine SSD   =   Fine (dry) × 1.007 = 1336 lb (SSD)

Answer: The mix is as follows:

Material	Dry Weight (lb)	SSD Weight (lb)	
Cement	564		564
Water	300		300
Coarse (dry)	1809	Coarse (SSD)	1818
Fine (dry)	1327	Fine (SSD)	1336
Total	4000		4018

13.3.4 EXAMPLE PROBLEM 4 — WEIGHT METHOD ACCURACY

To determine how close the previous mix is in volume to 1.00 cubic yard, each weight should be converted to the volume it occupies. (Remember, the approximation from empirical data suggests that one yard of this mix should weigh *about* 4,000 to 4,010 lb.) Verify how much volume the customer received if this material was batched using the weights from the previous example:

Solution

Table P13.3.4 (a)

Material	Weight (lb)	Volume (cu ft)	
Cement	564	$\dfrac{564}{62.4 \times 3.15}$	$= 2.87$
Water	300	$\dfrac{300}{62.4}$	$= 4.81$
Coarse 1 in. (dry)	1809	$\dfrac{1809}{62.4 \times 2.65}$	$= 10.94$
Fine (dry)	1327	$\dfrac{1327}{62.4 \times 2.63}$	$= 8.09$
Air (entrapped)		$27.0 \times 0.015 =$	$\underline{0.41}$
	Total		27.12

Hence, the customer was delivered more concrete than the 1.0 cubic yard ordered or

$$\frac{27.12}{27.00} = 1.0044$$

This is 0.44% more than ordered, but usually acceptable, since the error is less than the mechanical accuracy of weight batchers required by governing codes.

13.4   P. E. PROBLEMS

13.4.1   P. E. PROBLEM 1 — MIX DESIGN FOR EXPOSED BEAM

Use the American Concrete Institute (ACI) method of mix design to design a portland cement concrete (PCC) mix for the following conditions.

Data Provided by the Structural Engineer:

The members being cast are spandrel beams which are exposed external members in a multi-story building which will be exposed to severe and frequent cycles of freezing and thawing in air. The concrete will be compacted by high frequency vibrators. A cross section of the beams is shown, and their design 28-day compressive strength (f'_c) is 4,000 psi.

Data Provided by the Testing Laboratory:

The portland cement has a specific gravity (SG) of 3.15. The coarse aggregate (CA) is well shaped angular material with a SG of 2.65, a dry-rodded unit weight of 105 pcf, a saturated surface-dry (SSD) moisture content of 1.1%, and a field moisture content of 1.0%. The fine aggregate (FA) is a natural sand with a fineness modulus (FM) of 3.0, a SG of 2.65, a SSD moisture content of 4.0%, and a free water content of 2.0% in the field. (Free moisture is water in the sand *beyond* SSD)

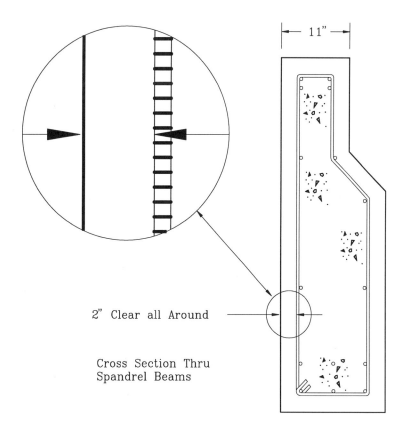

2" Clear all Around

Cross Section Thru
Spandrel Beams

Fig. P13.4.1 (a) Cross Section through Spandrel Beams

Solution

1. Enter Table 12.1 with beam and read that the slump can range from 3 in. to 5 in.; select 3 in. if minimum bleeding and drying shrinkage are necessary. Note that slump can be increased 1 in. when HF vibrators are used.

    Slump: Use 4 in. slump (Judgment)

2. Enter Table 12.6 with minimum dimension of the beam = 11 in. and minimum clearance of 2 in. all around. Calculate the maximum size of CA to be 1½ in.; select 1½ in. for high density, least paste and maximum economy. A smaller size is permissible and very desirable for pumping and workability though more cement will be required. Verify that 1½ in. maximum size also meets form dimension and bar spacing requirements.

    Max Size of CA: Use 1½ in. maximum CA (¾ of clear distance)

3. Enter Table 12.3 with fact that beams will be exposed to severe freeze thaw environment and note that 5.5% air entrainment should be used. Enter Table 13.2 with 4 in. slump, entrained air, and 1½ in. maximum CA.

    Free Mix Water: Use 275 lb per cu yd

4. Enter Table 12.3 or 13.2 with 4 in. slump and 1½ in. maximum CA and read that recommended average total air content is 5.5% for severe freeze-thaw conditions.

    Air Content: 5.5% by volume of fresh concrete

5. Enter Table 12.4 with beam ("thin sections") exposed to freeze-thaw in air and read maximum w/c = 0.45. Enter Table 12.2 with f'c and entrained air and read maximum w/c = 0.35.

    w/c ratio: Use 0.35 lb water/lb cement

6. Calculate cement content using a water/cement (w/c) ratio of 0.35 and a water content of 275 lb.

    PC Content: Use $\dfrac{275 \text{ lb}}{0.35}$ = 786 lb, use Types I or II

                               Same as $\dfrac{786}{94}$ = 8.36 sacks PC

7. Enter Table 13.3 with 1½ in. maximum CA and FA FM = 3.00 and read proportions (cu yd per cu yd) of PCC of dry-rodded CA. (Other tables express this value as cu ft/cu yd)

    CA Quantity: Use 0.69 cu yd of bulk CA per cu yd

8. Use the method of solid (absolute) volumes to calculate the quantity of FA in one cubic yard of fresh concrete.

The course aggregate quantity (CA) is :

$$\frac{0.69(27.00 \text{ cu ft}) \times 105 \text{ lb (dry) per cu ft}}{2.65 \times (62.4 \text{ lb/cu ft})} \qquad = \quad 11.83 \text{ cu ft (dry)}$$

$$\text{Water} \quad = \quad \frac{275 \text{ lb}}{62.4 \text{ lb/cu ft}} \qquad = \quad 4.41 \text{ cu ft}$$

$$\text{PC} \quad = \quad \frac{786 \text{ lb/cu ft}}{3.15(62.4 \text{ lb/cu ft})} \qquad = \quad 4.00 \text{ cu ft}$$

Air = 0.055 (27.00 cu ft) = 1.49 cu ft

Subtotal = 21.73 cu ft

FA = 27.00 − 21.73 = 5.27 cu ft sand solid volume per cu yd of PCC

9. Note that the volumes of the aggregates found in Steps 7 and 8 of the ACI Method assume the CA and the FA to be dry.

Weight of dry CA = 11.83 cu ft (2.65) 62.4 lb per cu ft. = 1956.2 lb

Weight of dry FA = 5.27 cu ft (2.65) 62.4 lb per cu ft. = 871.4 lb

SSD weights:

A. PC = (8.36 sacks per cu yd)(94 lb per sack) = 786.0 lb

B. CA = 1.011 (1956.2 lb) = 1977.7 lb SSD

C. FA = 1.04 (871.4 lb) = 906.3 lb SSD

D. Water = 4.41 cu ft (1.0) 62.4 lb per cu ft = 275.0 lb

Subtotal = 3945.0 lb

This problem statement says "a SSD moisture content of 4.0% for sand, 1.1% for coarse". These are vague ways of expressing absorption.

10. Field Moisture Weights:

A. PC = 786.0 lb

B. CA = 1.010 (1956.2 lb) = 1975.7 lb

C. FA = (1.0 + 0.04 + 0.02) × (871.5 lb) = 923.8 lb
   = (1.0 + absorption + free)

D. Water = 275.0 lb + (0.001) (1956.2 lb) − (0.02)(871.4 lb)
   = Batch + Adjustment for dry − surplus coarse material
                                   from fine material
   = 259.5 lb

Subtotal = 3945.0 lb

In summary,

Task	Item	Answer	Units
1	Slump of the PCC	4	inches
2	Maximum Size of CA	1.5	inches
3	Free Mix-Water Requirement	275	lb per cu yd
4	Air Content	5.5	percent
5	W/C Requirement	0.35	lb water per lb cement
6	PC Content	8.36	sacks per cu yd
7	CA Quantity (Dry Rodded Volume)	0.69	cu yd per cu yd
8	FA Quantity (Dry Solid Volume)	5.27	cu ft per cu yd
9	Weight of Materials for SSD Aggregates:		
	A. PC	786.0	lb per cu yd
	B. CA	1977.7	lb per cu yd
	C. FA	906.3	lb per cu yd
	D. Water	275.0	lb per cu yd
10	Weight of Materials for Field Moisture Conditions:		
	A. PC	786.0	lb per cu yd
	B. CA	1975.8	lb per cu yd
	C. FA	923.7	lb per cu yd
	D. Water	259.5	lb per cu yd

Note: The ACI method generally does *not* distinguish between dry and SSD sands. This was done for extra precision in this problem. Usually the calculation:

$$5.27 \text{ ft}^3 \text{ required} \times 62.4 \times 2.65 = 871 \text{ lb}$$

Assume SSD is sufficient to determine SSD sand weight.

13.4.2 P. E. PROBLEM 2 — MIX DESIGN

Statement:

Rework the PCC Mix Design P. E. Problem 1 (Section 13.4.1) using the ACI Method with the following changes in the design conditions:

1. The beams are all interior and are fully protected from the weather.

2. The 28 day f'_c is 4,500 psi.

3. The maximum size of the only locally available coarse aggregate is 3/4 in.

4. The FM of the FA is 2.60.

5. It is raining at the batch plant and the aggregate stock piles are not covered. The field moisture condition of both the coarse and the fine is quite high. The free moisture (moisture above SSD condition) of the coarse is 1.2%; of the fine 13.1%.

Table P13.4.2 (a)

Item	Answer		Units
Slump of the PCC	(Table 12.2)	4	inches
Maximum Size of CA	(Given)	3/4	inches
Free Mix-Water Requirement	(Table 13.2)	340.0	lb per cu yd
Air Content (Entrapped)	(Table 13.2)	2.0	percent
W/C Requirement for Durability (Tables 12.2, 12.4, 12.5 No Max w/c)	(Table 12.2)	0.38	lb per lb
PC Content	340 / 0.38 = 895		lb per cu yd
CA Quantity (Dry Rodded Volume)	(Table 13.3)	0.64	cu yd per cu yd

Table P13.4.2 (b)

Item	Solid Volume Calibration (ft^3)	Batch Volume (ft^3)	Batch Weights*		
			Oven-Dry Aggregates (lb)	SSD (lb)	Field (lb)
CA	$\dfrac{0.64 \times 27 \times 105}{2.65 \times 62.4}=$	10.97	$10.97 \times 2.65 \times 62.4$ $= 1814$	1814×1.01 $= 1834$	$1814 \times (1.01 + 0.0012)$ $= 1858$
Batch Water	$\dfrac{340}{62.4}=$ (Table assumes SSD)	5.45	$340 + (1834 - 1814)$ $+ (945.9 - 909.5)$ $= 396.4$	340	$340 + (1858 - 1834)$ $- (1065 - 945.9)$ $= 196.9$
PC	$\dfrac{894}{3.15 \times 62.4}=$	4.54	894	894	894
Air	$0.02 \times 27 =$	0.54	—	—	—
FA	$10.97 + 5.45 + 4.54$ $27.00 - 21.5 =$	21.5 5.50	$5.50 \times 2.65 \times 62.4$ $= 909.5$	909.5×1.04 $= 945.9$	$909.5(1.04 + 0.131)$ $= 1065.0$

*Weights of materials if batched in these moisture conditions.

**Oven-dry aggregates should not be batched. The concrete performance will be hindered.

Table P13.4.2 (c)

Weight of Materials for Aggregates with Field Moisture Conditions:			
A.	PC	894.0	lb per cu yd
B.	CA	1814.0	lb per cu yd
C.	FA	909.5	lb per cu yd
D.	Water	196.9	lb per cu yd
Weight of Materials for SSD (Design) Conditions:			
A.	PC	894.0	lb per cu yd
B.	CA	1858.0	lb per cu yd
C.	FA	1065.0	lb per cu yd
D.	Water	340.0	lb per cu yd

13.4.3 P. E. PROBLEM 3 — AIR-ENTRAINED CONCRETE MIX DESIGN

A batch of air-entrained portland cement concrete (PCC) contains the following quantities of materials with the properties shown below:

Material	Batch Quantities / Field Conditions
Portland Cement	32 sacks
Fine Aggregate (sand)	6,200 lb (dry)
Coarse Aggregate	11,400 lb (at 1% excess moisture over SSD)
Batch Water Added	140 gal
Air Content	4.0%

Note:

(1) The absorption of sand is 2.0%

(2) The coarse aggregate contains 1.0% free moisture, absorption unknown.

(3) Specific gravity of sand: 2.60

(4) Specific gravity of course: 2.65

(5) Specific gravity of cement: 3.15

Calculate:

A. The volume of fresh concrete, in cubic yards, that will be produced by the combination of the materials with these properties.

B. The water/cement ratio or water content in gallons per sack, as a weight ratio, and in gallons per yard.

C. The cement factor, or cement content per cubic yard, for the batch.

D. The fresh unit weight of the mixture.

Solution

Cement:

Weight: 32 sacks $\times$ 94 lb/sack = 3,008 lb

Solid Volume: 3,008 lb/(3.15 $\times$ 62.4 lb/cu ft) = 15.30 cu ft

Sand:

Dry wt = 6200 lb of sand which will absorb 2% more water to become SSD

SSD Weight: SSD   = 6200 lb (1.0+0.02) = 6324 lb

Volume: Sand Vol = 6324 lb/(2.60 $\times$ 62.4 lb/cu ft) = 38.98 cu ft

Note: This requires 124 lb of water (6324 − 6200) which will be absorbed into the sand from the batch water added, thus reducing the actual (calculated) volume of water available to react with the cement, and used to calculate the w/c ratio.

Coarse:

SSD Weight: 11,400 lb of coarse which contains 1.0% free moisture above SSD (Approximate solution, coarse absorption not given, assumed low:

Weight (SSD)11,400/(1.0 + 0.01) $\qquad$ = 11,287 lb*

Excess Water $\qquad$ 11,400 lb − 11,287 lb $\quad$ = 113 lb

Volume: 11,287 lb/(2.65 × 62.4 lb/cu ft) $\qquad$ = 68.26 cu ft

*An approximation since absorption is unknown but assumed very low.

Water:

Batch Water added: $\qquad$ 140 gal (from problem statement)

Weight: $\qquad$ 140 gal × 8.33 lb/gal $\qquad$ = 1,166.2 lb

Deduct water required to saturate sand (which is dry) $\quad$ = − 124.0 lb

Add excess, or free, water in coarse (above S.S.D.) $\quad$ = + 113.0 lb

Therefore, total water weight available to cement $\qquad$ = 1,152.2 lb

Volume: Convert weight of 1,152.2 lb to volume
1,152.2 lb/(62.4 lb/cu ft) $\qquad$ = 18.46 cu ft

Sub Total of the above Solids SSD Weight and absolute volumes are shown below:

Table P13.4.3 (a)

Material	SSD Weight (lb)	Absorption Volume (cu ft)
Cement	3,008.0	15.30
Sand	6,324.0	38.99
Coarse	11,287.0	68.26
Water	1,152.2	18.46
Sub Total (Solids)	21,774.2 lb	141.01 cu ft

This weight and volume represents the total solids of the combined mixture, or the full volume of fresh concrete produced, not including the air content.

Since there is 4% air, the solids represent 100% − 4%, or 96%, of the total concrete volume; therefore:

The total volume of concrete: $\qquad$ 141.01 cu ft/0.96 $\qquad$ = 146.89 cu ft

Air:

Weight of air,	= 0.0 lb
Volume of Air:	
(the difference of total and solids volume)	
Total volume	= 146.89 cu ft
Solids volume	= $-$141.01 cu ft
Therefore, Air volume	= 5.88 cu ft
Note: to check air volume = (4/96) (141.01)	= 5.88 cu ft

Checks

A. The volume of the fresh batch of concrete in cu ft is 146.89 (say 147) cu ft

The volume of concrete in cu yd is 146.89 cu ft/(27.0 cu ft/cu yd) = 5.44 cu yd

B. The water/cement ratio is total water in batch *when all aggregate is at SSD:*

Batch water	= 1,166.20 lb
Less required by sand	= $-$ 124.00 lb
Plus excess in coarse	= +113.00 lb
	1,155.20 lb
or 1,155.2 lb/(8.33 lb/gal)	= 138.68 gal
recall cement wt.	= 3,008 lb
in sacks	= 32

Water/cement ratios:

138.68 gal/32 sacks	= 4.33 gal/sack
1,155.2 lb/3,008 lb	= 0.38 lb/lb
138.68 gal/5.44 cu yd	= 25.5 gal/cu yd
(a *very low* water content)	

C. The cement content is:

32 sacks cement/5.44 cu yd	= 5.88 sk/cu yd
5.88 sk/cu yd $\times$ 94 lb/sk	= 553 lb/cu yd

D. The fresh unit weight is batch weight/batch volume:

21,774.2 lb/146.89 cu ft	= 148.2 lb/cu ft
	Answer (seems reasonable)

13.4.4 P. E. PROBLEM 4 — CONCRETE PROPORTIONS

A concrete mix design is being evaluated for use by a city engineer who is required to assess many of its characteristics. The following information is presented about the mix and its ingredients:

Cement

> Specific Gravity: 3.15

Fine Aggregate

> Fineness Modulus: 2.89
> Specific Gravity: 2.56
> Absorption: 3.0%

Coarse Aggregate

> Specific Gravity: 2.73
> Dry Bulk Density: 110 pcf
> Absorption: 0.5%

Concrete Properties

> Slump: 6 in.
> Water: 4.7 gal/sack
> Coarse Aggregate: 0.42 cu ft/cu ft (bulk)
> Air Content: 5%
> Cement Content: 6.1 sack mix

Multiple Choice Questions:

1. What is the dry weight of the coarse aggregate in one cubic yard of concrete, most nearly?

    (a) insufficient data given

    (b) 1151 lb

    (c) 1217 lb

    (d) 1247 lb

    (e) 1305 lb

2. What is the absolute volume of the coarse aggregate in one cubic yard of concrete, most nearly.

    (a) insufficient data given

    (b) 7.21 cu ft

    (c) 7.14 cu ft

    (d) 7.32 cu ft

    (e) 7.66 cu ft

3. What is the water/cement ratio, most nearly?
    (a) 0.42
    (b) 0.46
    (c) 0.47
    (d) 0.50
    (e) 0.58

4. What is the weight of cement in one cubic yard of fresh concrete, most nearly?
    (a) 545 lb
    (b) 573 lb
    (c) 602 lb
    (d) 612 lb
    (e) 671 lb

5. What is the absolute volume of fine aggregate in one cubic yard of fresh concrete, most nearly?
    (a) 10.23 cu ft
    (b) 11.58 cu ft
    (c) 12.93 cu ft
    (d) 13.10 cu ft
    (e) 14.45 cu ft

6. What is the SSD weight of the sand in one cubic yard of fresh concrete, most nearly?
    (a) 1634 lb
    (b) 1906 lb
    (c) 2065 lb
    (d) 2093 lb
    (e) 2308 lb

7. Assuming that the mix is calculated on SSD weights, and that proper water adjustments are used, and if free moisture is 5.0% in the fine aggregate and 0.7% in the coarse aggregate, what is the total (combined) weight of coarse aggregate, fine aggregate and free water *batched* per cubic yard of concrete, most nearly?
    (a) insufficient data given
    (b) 2785 lb
    (c) 3165 lb
    (d) 3336 lb
    (e) 3695 lb

8. What is the absolute volume of the cement in one cubic yard of this fresh concrete, most nearly?

    (a) 2.92 cu ft

    (b) 3.18 cu ft

    (c) 3.37 cu ft

    (d) 3.59 cu ft

    (e) 3.70 cu ft

9. What is the volume of water designed for use in one cubic yard of fresh concrete, most nearly?

    (a) 0.61 cu ft

    (b) 1.35 cu ft

    (c) 1.96 cu ft

    (d) 3.64 cu ft

    (e) 3.83 cu ft

10. If the oven-dry weight of the coarse aggregate was 1050 lb, how much water would it need to absorb to reach SSD conditions?

    (a)   5.3 lb

    (b)   31.5 lb

    (c)   52.5 lb

    (d) 1055.3 lb

    (e) 1055.3 lb

Solutions

1(d)   Dry weight of coarse is

        110 lb/cu ft $\times$ 27.00 cu ft $\times$ 0. 42 = 1247 lb (dry)

2(d)   Absolute volume of the coarse aggregate in this mix

        1247 lb (dry)/(2.73 $\times$ 62.4 lb/cu ft) = 7.32 cu ft

3(a)   Water/cement ratio is

$$\frac{4.7 \text{ gal/sk} \times 8.33 \text{ lb/gal}}{94 \text{ lb/sk}} = 0.42$$

4(b)   Weight of cement per cubic yard

        6.1 sk/cu yd $\times$ 94 lb/sk = 573 lb/cu yd

5(b)   Absolute volume of sand per cubic yard of concrete

V_{sand} = 1 cu yd − (combined volumes of air, cement, water, and coarse)

so V_{air} = 0.05 × 27 cu ft

= 1.35 cu ft/cu yd

and V_{cement} = $\dfrac{573 \text{ lb/cu yd}}{3.15 \ (62.4 \text{ lb/cu ft})}$

= 2.92 cu ft/cu yd

V_{water} = $\dfrac{4.7 \text{ gal/sk} \times 6.1 \text{ sk/cu yd} \times 8.33 \text{ lb/gal}}{62.4 \text{ lb/cu ft}}$

= 3.83 cu ft/cu yd

and V_{coarse} = 7.32 cu ft

so V_{sand} = 27.0 − (1.35 + 2.92 + 3.83 + 7.32)

= 11.58 cu ft/cu yd

6(b)   What is the weight of SSD sand per cubic yard?

11.58 cu ft × (2.56 × 62.4 lb/cu ft) = 1850 lb

$W_{SSD \ sand}$ = $W_{Dry \ sand}$ × (1 + 0.030)

$W_{SSD \ sand}$ = 1906 lb

Note that this is the exact answer. The dry sand weight, W_{dry} is W_{dry} = (absolute volume sand, cu ft) × (sand specific gravity) × (62.4 lb/cu ft). W_{SSD} = W_{dry} × (1 + absorption). However, in practice, the difference between W_{SSD} and W_{dry} is so small compared to the batch water volume and the sand weight that $W_{SSD} \approx W_{dry}$. Since this problem asked specifically, the exact answer has been given.

7(c)   Since proper water adjustments and SSD conditions are assumed the total of sand, rock and water weights will be constant for any set of moisture contents.

	Dry Weight (lb)	SSD Weight (lb)	Field Weight (lb)
Coarse	1,247	1,253	1,262
Find	1,850	1,906	1,998
Batch Water Added	301	239	139
	3,398	3,398	3,398

8(a)   Absolute volume of cement

$$V_c = \frac{6.1 \text{ sacks/cu yd} \times 94 \text{ lb/sk}}{3.15 \ (62.4 \text{ lb/cu ft})}$$

V_c = 2.92 cu ft (see Part 5)

9(e)   Volume of water

$$V_w = \frac{4.7 \times 6.1 \times 8.33}{62.4} \quad \text{see Part 5}$$

$$= 3.83 \text{ cu ft}$$

In summary, mix has following:

Table P13.4.4 (a)

Mix Materials	Weight (lb)	Volume (cu ft)
Cement	573	2.92
Water	239	3.83
Coarse Aggregate	1,247	7.32
Sand (SSD)	1,850	11.58
Air (5%)	0	1.35
Total	3,909	27.00

10(a)   If coarse aggregate

oven dry = 1,050 lb

Find absorption (in pounds)

absorption = 0.5%

Wt of absorbed water   =   0.005 (1050) lb

=   5.25 lb

rounded to 5.3 lb

13.5 FINAL ADJUSTMENTS

Once initial mix proportions are determined by weight or absolute volume methods, adjustments will usually be required in the field or lab to adjust the slump, workability, harshness, bleeding, over sanded conditions, etc., if necessary.

Depending on the particular conditions of the mix, small changes in coarse and/or fine aggregate contents will be made and usually the water will be adjusted, also, to provide more or less workability as needed.

After these (judgement based) changes are made, the mix is re-computed, usually by the absolute volume method, particularly if the air content is tested.

After the SSD proportions are finalized by the preceding slight modifications, batching can be done. However, the moisture conditions of the fine and coarse aggregates at the batch plant probably will differ from the SSD conditions considered by the mix design. Therefore, any moisture excess in the aggregates (over SSD) will require batching a higher weight of (wetter) aggregate and a correspondingly lower amount of mixing water. Should aggregates be drier than SSD, more batch water will be required to compensate for the volume (or weight) absorbed into the aggregates.

13.6   P. E. PROBLEM

13.6.1   P. E. PROBLEM 1 — MIXTURE ADJUSTMENTS AND FIELD CALCULATIONS

A mix is given with proportions of cement: sand: coarse rock = 1.0:2.7:1.7 (by weight). It is desired to proportion a concrete mixture with the following characteristics, using materials with the following specific gravities.

Mix Properties	Specific Gravities		
3% air	Coarse rock	=	2.65
5.5 gal H₂O/sack cement	Cement	=	3.15
	Sand	=	2.60

Required:

A. Calculate weight of cement, sand, coarse aggregate and water for 1 cubic yard of mix.

B. If sand has 3% free moisture and rock is SSD, calculate amount of batch water required.

C. If this mix is used for concrete pavement, discuss two ways of curing to obtain a durable surface.

D. Discuss two methods for installation of transverse joints in pavement.

Solution

A. First, the weight of water will be determined for 1 lb of cement using the water/cement ratio, converted from gallons per sack to pounds per pound. Then, the weights will be converted to corresponding volumes for this mix based on a batch containing 1.0 lb of cement. 3% air content will be added to find the total volume of fresh concrete for these weights of materials. These volumes will be inflated by a factor to bring them to the volume of 1 cu yd or 27.0 cu ft. Finally, the weights of materials will be determined for the volumes of material required in one yard.

Convert from weight to volume:

Weight (lb)				Volume (cu ft)
1.0 lb	Cement	1 lb cement/(3.15 × 62.4 lb/cu ft)		= 0.00508
	Water	$\dfrac{(5.5 \ \text{gal/sack}) \ (8.33 \ \text{lb/gal})}{94 \ \text{lb/sack} \times \text{sack}} = 0.4874 \ \text{lb}$		
0.4874		0.4874 lb H_2O/62.4 lb/cu ft		= 0.00781
1.7	Coarse	1.7 lb rock/(2.65 × 62.4 lb/cu ft)		= 0.01028
2.7	Sand	2.7 lb sand/(2.60 × 62.4 lb/cu ft)		= 0.01664
5.8874		Solid Materials	Subtotal	= 0.03981

Since, of the total concrete volume,

3% is air and 97% is solids, $\dfrac{0.03981}{0.97}$ Total   = 0.04104

less solids $= -0.03981$

and air content is difference between
total volume and solids volume   Air   = 0.00123 cu ft

This mix has a unit weight of 5.8874 lb/0.04104 cu ft = 143.5 lb/cu ft. Since there are 27.00 cu ft in 1 cu yd, the total volume should be 27.00 cu ft. A volume inflation factor, 27.00/0.04104 = 657.89 is required to inflate each component volume for a cubic yard mix volume.

Material			Batch Volume for 1 cubic yard (cu ft)
Cement	657.89 × 0.00508	=	3.342
Water	657.89 × 0.00781	=	5.138
Coarse	657.89 × 0.01028	=	6.763
Sand	657.89 × 0.01664	=	10.947
Air	657.89 × 0.00123	=	0.810
		=	27.000

Convert volume to SSD yard weight, (Vol × SG × 62.4)

Material		Cubic Yard Mix Weight(lb)
Cement	$3.342 \times 62.4 \times 3.15$	= 657
Water	$5.138 \times 62.4 \times 1.0$	= 321
Rock	$6.763 \times 62.4 \times 2.65$	= 1118
Sand	$10.947 \times 62.4 \times 2.60$	= 1776
	Therefore total lb/cu yd mix	= 3872

To check, see if fresh unit weight is the same: $3872 \text{ lb}/27.00 \text{ ft}^3 = 143.4 \text{ lb/ft}^3$

143.4 equals 143.5. Considering rounding error, calculation checks.

B. From part A, the batch weight of sand is 1776 lb SSD. Since 3% is free moisture, that is moisture *above* SSD, 1776 lb/0.97 or 1831 lb of actual wet material is batched, of which $3\%(1831 \times 0.03)$ or 55 lb is water.

Rock weight is SSD, so no adjustment is required.

The calculated lb H_2O from part A, 321 lb, must be adjusted:
$321 - 55 = 266$ lb water should be batched, which supplements batch water for mixing:

Material	Batch Weight (lb)
Cement	657
Water	266
Rock	1118
Sand(3% H_2O)	1831
Air	0
	3872 lb

C. Two methods which can be used to cure fresh concrete pavements include any of the following:

1. Sprayed on curing compound applied in two coats perpendicular to each other, after the finishing operation is complete.

2. Using an impervious barrier (plastic, visqueen, tarp, etc.) covering the pavement which would be covering a thin film of free moisture.

3. Continuous sprinkling of water onto the pavement surface by a mist sprayer or a sprinkler.

4. Use of moist hay, straw or sand on the pavement to assure continuous moisture.

5. Complete ponding of water around pavement by built-up earth berms.

Any method which prevents the drying out of the surface for the first 3 to 7 days is acceptable. The longer the curing duration, the better the concrete pavement.

D. Any of the following methods for installation of transverse joints in pavement can be used: Joints can be saw cut into the concrete the day after placement, or can be installed during placement by using plastic inserts, or joints can be tooled to a depth of about 1/4 to 1/3 the slab thickness.

13.7 BATCHING

One consideration which sets concrete apart from other materials is that it is ordered, purchased, sold and used by volume. However, it is batched by weight. The purpose of the licensed engineer in this process is to verify that the conversions between weight and volume are accurate. The yield of concrete, therefore, is of concern to both supplier and purchaser to verify the delivered volume of materials for purposes of fair commerce. Yield, usually expressed in cubic yards, is calculated as the sum of the batched weights (or weight of the loaded mixer truck less its tare, or self weight) divided by the tested unit volume weight.

$$Y = \frac{WT}{27.00\ (UW)}$$

where

Y = yield (cubic yards); usually called "truck yield" if the fully-loaded mixer truck is weighed.

WT = sum of and the batch weights of all materials loaded including aggregate, water, cement and others, if any (pounds);

[Or, the loaded mixer truck weight less its empty weight];

UW = fresh concrete's tested unit weight (pounds per cubic foot).

(*Note:* Unit weight is tested using the tared weight of fresh concrete in a volume calibrated bucket.)

Final adjustments of water in the batch weights compensate for the variation in moisture contents of the aggregate. When the moisture content of the aggregate is higher than SSD, that extra water should count as mixing water. Therefore, the batched amount of water should be correspondingly reduced, while the batched weight of the aggregate is increased to deliver an identical solids volume and dry material weight.

13.8   TRUE-FALSE EXAMPLES

13.8.1   QUESTIONS

(Circle one)

1. T   F   In order to assure its in-place quality, concrete needs at least to be all of the following:
   a) properly proportioned,
   b) properly batched,
   c) properly mixed,
   d) properly transported and placed,
   e) properly consolidated,
   f) properly finished and
   g) properly cured.

2. T   F   Proper proportions of concrete mixtures are largely independent of the final use.

3. T   F   Concrete should never be proportioned for providing greater than a 5-in. slump.

4. T   F   Higher water/cement ratios assure greater strengths.

5. T   F   More cement in a mix will always assure higher strengths.

6. Does the lowest practical water content assure an economical mix? Why?

7. Does using the maximum practical coarse aggregate size assure an economical mix? Why?

8. Does a well-graded aggregate usually assure an economical mix? Why?

9. What maximum water/cement ratio and cement type should be specified for concrete exposed to moderate sulfate attack and severe freeze-thaw (Using a 3/4- in. top size aggregate.)?

10. If a mix shows strength gain from 7 days to 28 days of 50%, find an appropriate water/cement ratio to produce 3,000 psi concrete at 7 days? (Note: Table 6-2 shows water/cement ratios based on 28-day strengths.)

11. A structural engineer requires a 4,000 psi concrete mix (28 days) for interior building columns and beams. Free clearance between rebars and forms is 2 in., between separate rebar 1½ in. The engineer will permit 6- to 7-in. slump if the strength is not lowered. Buckets will be used for placement. (This slump range will accommodate heavily congested steel reinforcement.)

    The testing laboratory reports that only two coarse aggregates are available: a 2-in. top sized and a 3/4-in. top sized. Both have 105 lb/cu ft bulk densities and are well graded, each with a specific gravity of 2.65. The fine aggregate has a specific gravity of 2.60 and an F.M. of 2.80.

Design an appropriately proportioned concrete mixture.

12. For the kind of mix designed in Problem (11):

A. A water reducing admixture claims it can replace 5% of the water at a dosage rate of 5 oz per 100 lb of cement. Recalculate the mix based on 5% water reduction. What dosage of admixture is necessary per yard, and how did the cement content (in sacks per yard) change?

B. If no water reducer was used but the slump was changed from 7 in. to 4 in., what would happen to the cement content?

C. If *both* the slump was changed (7 in. to 4 in.) and a water reducer used, how would the cement content change?

13.8.2　ANSWERS

1. True

2. False

3. False — Concrete in tremie placements and in heavily congested rebar are but two examples of valid uses of high slump concrete.

4. False

5. False — If the amount of water added increases and the cement remains constant, then the water/cement ratio increases and the strength decreases.

6. Lowest water contents at similar water/cement ratios mean the lowest cement contents. Lowest cement content means least material cost.

7. Using the maximum coarse size usually lowers water demand, thereby lowering cement costs, if transportation, mixing, placement, etc., can still be achieved.

8. A well-graded aggregate assures least paste content because of fewer voids in aggregate. Least paste means least cement costs.

9. The concrete should contain a Type II cement, using an air content of 6.0% and a water/cement ratio not higher than 0.50.

10. 3,000 psi at 7 days plus 50% means 3,000 x 1.5 = 4,500 psi at 28 days. Therefore, the water/cement ratio should be 0.38, according to design chart.

11. Use absolute volume method:

Step	Find
1.	Slump = 7 in.
2.	Max. aggregate size = 3/4 in. (2 in. is too big)
3.	Air content = 2% (entrapped)
4.	w/c (strength) = 0.44

w/c (sulfate) — No exposure

w/c (freeze-thaw) — No exposure

Use Type I or II cement.

Water content 360 lb (from table)

$$360 \text{ lb } = 360 \text{ lb } / 8.33 \text{ lb/gal } = 43.2 \text{ gal}$$

$$\frac{360 \text{ lb}}{62.4 \text{ lb/cf}} = 5.77 \text{ cu ft}$$

5.   360 lb / 0.44 = 818 lb cement

$$\frac{818 \text{ lb}}{3.15 \times 62.4 \text{ lb/cu ft}} = 4.16 \text{ cu ft}$$

6.   No cement content minimum

$$818 \text{ lb } = \frac{818 \text{ lb}}{94 \text{ lb/sk}} = 8.70 \text{ sack}$$

7.   Quantity of coarse aggregate

$$27.0 \times 0.62 = 16.74 \text{ cu ft (bulk volume)}$$

$$16.74 \text{ cu ft } \times 105 \text{ lb/cu ft } = 1758 \text{ lb}$$

$$\frac{1758 \text{ lb}}{2.65 \times 62.4 \text{ lb/cu ft}} = 10.63 \text{ cu ft absolute volume}$$

8.   Air content = 27.0 × 0.020 (No intentional entrainment, no freeze thaw exposure expected)

Air = 0.54 cu ft (entrapped)

9.

Table P13.8.2 (a)

Recap Weight Sand Volumes	Wt (lb)	Vol (cu ft)
Water	360	5.77
Cement	818	4.16
Coarse	1758	10.63
Air	—	0.54
Subtotal	2936	21.10

10 .   Sand Volume   =   27.00 cu ft − 21.10 cu ft

                           =   5.90 cu ft

              $5.90 \times 2.60 \times 62.4 = 957$ lb sand

11 .

Table P13.8.2 (b)

Recap Again	Wt (lb)	Vol (cu ft)
Water	360	5.77
Cement	818	4.16
Coarse	1758	10.63
Fine	957	5.90
Air		0.54
Total	3893	27.00

Unit weight = 3893 lb/27.00 cu ft

           = 144.2 lb/cu ft

12 .   (A)   Slump = 7 in.

              Max. Aggregate Size = 3/4 in.

              Air Content = 2%

              Water/Cement Ratio = 0.44

              Cement Type I or II

              Water = 360 lb

              Water Revised = 360 − 5% (360) or (1 − 0.05) 360

              360 − 18 = 342 lb

$$342 \text{ lb} = \frac{342 \text{ lb}}{62.4 \text{ lb/cu ft}} = 5.48 \text{ cu ft}$$

$$\text{Cement} = \frac{342 \text{ lb}}{0.44} = 777 \text{ lb}$$

$$777 \text{ lb} = \frac{777 \text{ lb}}{3.15 \times 62.4 \text{ lb/sk}} = 3.95 \text{ cu ft}$$

$$777 \text{ lb} = \frac{777 \text{ lb}}{94 \text{ lb/sk}} = 8.27 \text{ sacks}$$

              Coarse   = 1758 lb

                       = 10.63 cu ft

              Air   = 0.54 cu ft

Table P13.8.2 (c)

Recap:	Wt (lb)	Vol (cu ft)
Water	342	5.48
Cement	777	3.95
Coarse	1758	10.63
Air	—	0.54
Subtotal	2877	20.60

$$\text{Sand} = 27.00 \text{ cu ft} - 20.6 \text{ cu ft} = 6.40 \text{ cu ft}$$

$$6.40 \text{ cu ft} \times 2.60 \times 62.4 \text{ lb/cu ft} = 1038 \text{ lb}$$

Revised Recap:

Table P13.8.2 (d)

Mix Design	Wt (lb)	Vol (cu ft)
Water	342	5.48
Cement	777	3.95
Coarse	1758	10.63
Fine	1038	6.40
Air	—	0.54
Total	3915	27.00

Unit weight 3915 lb/27.00 cu ft

Unit weight = 145.0

(B) Original Cement Content   8.70 sk

Revised Cement Content   − 8.27 sk

Difference   0.43 sk

(C) 777 lb of cement at 5 oz admixture per 100 lb

$$777 \text{ lb} \times \frac{5 \text{ oz}}{100 \text{ lb}} = 38.85 \text{ oz}$$

Use 39 oz.

(D)   A 4-in. slump usually requires 340 lb water, or 20 lb less than a 7-in.

Therefore, the savings on cement from 7-in. to 4-in. slump (at identical w/c) is:

$$\frac{360 - 340}{360} = 5.6\% \text{ less water, } 5.6\% \text{ less cement}$$

Combined savings from slump reduction and using the water reducer is:

$$\frac{360 - 340(.95)}{360} = 10.3\% \text{ less water, } 10.3\% \text{ less cement}$$

Note: Remember these cement contents are based on empirical standards for w/c. Trial batches will probably show lower water and cement contents.

13.9 EXAMPLE PROBLEM

13.9.1 EXAMPLE PROBLEM 1 — BATCH WATER ADJUSTMENTS FOR MOISTURE CONDITION OF AGGREGATES

Suppose the design specified calls for:

Material	Weight (lb)
Cement	500
Water	300
Coarse (SSD)	1900
Fine (SSD)	1300
Total	4000

But at the batch plant, the coarse contains 1.0% free water, and the sand contains 3.0% free water. (Free water is moisture above SSD conditions.) Adjust the batch weights for the water and aggregates to produce this mix.

Solution

The following is an *inexact* method since the absorption of the materials is not given. The SSD weight is used as a basis for the free moisture and the absorption is assumed very low.

1900 lb Coarse Aggregate SSD

(Use SSD $\times$ (1 + free moisture) = batch weight)

   1900 lb $\times$ (1.01) = 1919 wet; containing 19 lb water

1300 lb Fine Aggregate SSD

   1300 $\times$ (1.03) = 1339 wet; containing 39 lb water

Since 19 lb + 40 lb = 59 lb additional water introduced through aggregate, then batch water is reduced to 300 − 58 = 242 lb.

Therefore,

Mix Design	Batch Weights (lb)	
Cement	500	500
Water	300	242
Coarse (SSD)	1900	1919 at 1% moisture
Fine (SSD)	1300	1339 at 3% moisture
Total	4000	4000

If the absorption of the materials had been provided then the following solution is exact, using the <u>dry</u> material weight as a basis for both the absorption and the free moisture, as follows:

Assume: Coarse absorption of 0.5%

Fine absorption of   2.0%

Coarse

1900 lb coarse SSD weight / 1.005 = 1890.5 dry material

1890.5 lb [1 + 0.01 (free) + 0.005 (absorbed)] coarse <u>wet</u> weight

= 1918.9 lb wet weight ≅ 1919

Note that for low absorption the previous (inexact) method has reasonable accuracy.

Fine

1300 lb Fine SSD weight / 1.020 = 1274.5 dry material

= 1274.5 lb Fine <u>Dry</u>

1274.5 lb × [1 + 0.03 (free) + 0.02 (absorbed)] fine wet weight

1338.2 lb Fine <u>Wet</u> weight

Note that as absorption of material <u>increases</u> the inexact, previous method becomes less accurate, as

1339 lb   −   1338.2 lb   =   0.8 lb

(inexact method)   (exact method)

(absorb. unknown)   (absorb. known)

If the problem gives absorption, use the exact method shown. If the absorption is not given, either assume one and calculate by exact method *or preferentially* use inexact method and state why it is an approximate answer.

13.10 P. E. PROBLEMS

13.10.1 P. E. PROBLEM 1 — RATIO METHOD OF MIX DESIGN

You have been asked to approve another engineer's mix design. The mix given used ratios to express the relative amounts of cement and fine and coarse aggregates.

This design called out the following:

Portland Cement

    Specific Gravity: 3:15

    Cement Content: 6.28 sks/cu yd

Water

    Water batched: 225.8 lb/cu yd

Mix Ratio (of field condition aggregates)

    1: 21/4: 31/4 cement : sand : rock (weight ratio)

Field Conditions of Aggregate

    Fines   5.0 Moisture Content (in field), absorption unknown

    Coarse   1.0 Absorption (bone dry in field)

The engineer asserts that this mixture will yield a fresh volume of concrete of 1 cu yd.

1.   What is the combined weight of batched materials?
2.   What is the expected fresh unit weight?
3.   How much extra water was added to the mix by using the moist sand?
4.   How much mixing water was absorbed by the coarse aggregate?

Solution

1.   Since the ratio (expressed as cement:sand:rock) given is based upon <u>field condition weights</u>, we determine the cement batch weight, and the corresponding weights of fine and coarse aggregate, as follows:

Material	Calculation	Weight (1b)
Cement	6.28 sk/cy × 94 lb/sk	590
Sand	590 lb × 2.25 lb/lb	1328
Rock	590 lb × 3.25 lb/lb	1918
	Material Subtotal	3836
Water batched	226 lb	226
Combined material weight in batch		4062

2. We are advised that this combination produces exactly one cubic yard (1 cu yd) of fresh concrete. Therefore, the fresh unit weight is weight of material batched divided by volume of material batched.

$$\text{Unit weight} = 4062 \text{ lb/cu yd}$$
$$= 4062 \text{ lb/27.00 cu ft}$$
$$= 150.5 \text{ lb/cu ft}$$

3. We batched 1328 lb of (5%) moist sand whose absorption is unknown. This weight includes sand solids and water as follows:

dry weight of sand × (1 + moisture content) = field weight

Therefore, we will find total moisture in sample. (If absorption is assumed, "free moisture" can be calculated. In this case we assume that absorption is low compared to the free and our answer is approximate without considering absorption.)

dry weight (1 + 0.05) = field weight

$$\text{dry weight} = \frac{1328 \text{ lb}}{1.05}$$
$$= 1265 \text{ lb}$$

water weight = field weight − dry weight

water weight = 1328 lb − 1265 lb
$$= 63 \text{ lb}$$

(Note how close this is to a less accurate approximation of 5% × 1328 lb = 66 lb.)

Any known absorption will reduce the 63 lb value some, but this is the best approximation with data given. Equally valid would be an assumption of 1% absorption.

4. SSD_{rock} = dry weight rock × (1 + absorption)
   SSD_{rock} = 1918 lb × (1 + 0.01)
   SSD_{rock} = 1937 lb

water required to saturate rock = SSD weight − dry weight

water required = 1937 lb − 1918 lb
$$= 19 \text{ lb from mix}$$

(Alternately we could have skipped a step in the solution and noted that water absorbed from mix = dry weight times absorption, 1918 lb × 0.01 = 19 lb.)

13.10.2 P. E. PROBLEM 2 — SPECIFIC GRAVITY CALCULATIONS AND BATCH PROPORTIONS

Your ready mix concrete company is moving into a new quarry area for which aggregate material properties have not yet been determined. You obtain the following specific gravity test data on samples of available coarse and fine aggregates:

COARSE AGGREGATES

Oven dry weight in air,	A_c =	4998 gms
Saturated surface dry weight in air,	B =	5002 gms
Saturated weight submerged in water,	C =	3129 gms

FINE AGGREGATES

Oven dry weight in air,	A_f =	495.02 gms
Volume of pycnometer,	V =	500 ml
Weight of water added to pycnometer containing saturated surface dry sample,	W =	305.64 gms
Saturated surface dry weight,	B =	500 gms

Cement weighs 94 lb/sack and has a specific gravity of 3.15.

Job specifications require the concrete mix with the following properties:

The solid volume of coarse aggregate required is 43%; the cement factor is 6.4 sacks/cy, the water requirement is 34 gal/cu yd, and 5.5% air should be entrained.

A. Calculate the bulk specific gravity, bulk saturated surface dry specific gravity, and absorption of both the coarse and fine aggregates.

B. Calculate the batch weights on a <u>dry</u> basis for CA, FA, cement, and water for a cubic yard of concrete.

Solution

Part A

For Coarse Aggregate:

Bulk SG = $A_c/(B - C)$	=	4998/1873 = 2.668	$\cong$ 2.67
Bulk SSD SG = $B/(B - C)$	=	5002/1873 = 2.671	$\cong$ 2.67
Absorption(%) = $(B - A_c)/A_c \times 100$	=	$(4/4998) \times 100$	= 0.08

For Fine Aggregate:

Bulk SG = $A_f/(V - W)$	=	495.02/194.36	= 2.547
Bulk SSD SG = $B/(V - W)$	=	500/194.36	= 2.573
Absorption (%) = $(V - A)A \times 100$	=	$(4.98/495.02) \times 100$	= 1.01%

Part B.

From the problem statement we are not certain if "43% Coarse Aggregate" is 43% of the volume of all aggregate or if it is 43% of the volume of the entire concrete mix. The solution presented here then, solves for all possible cases, and generates the comparison.

In local practice "43% Coarse" normally would mean 43% Coarse/57% Fine. (Case #1). In national practice 43% Coarse often means by volume of all batched materials (43% Coarse = 0.43 × 27.00 cu ft = 11.61 cu ft *solid* coarse aggregate material per cu yd of fresh concrete). Case #3, *the most likely possibility*, assumes that 43% means 11.61 cu ft *bulk volume* but requires a corresponding bulk density (not given) for the coarse material which is assumed.

Case #1

Assume that the required 43% coarse aggregate solid volume is of *total aggregate in the mix* and that *dry* means oven dry.

Solid Volumes for 1 cu yd of portland cement concrete (PCC).

Portland Cement	=	(6.4 × 94)/(3.15 × 62.4)	=	3.06 cu ft
Air	=	5.5% × 27 cu ft	=	1.49 cu ft
Water	=	34 gal/7.48 gal/cu ft	=	4.55 cu ft
			Total =	9.10 cu ft
Aggregate	=	27.00 − 9.10	=	17.90 cu ft

Batch Weights on a Dry Basis for Coarse Aggregate and Fine Aggregate

Coarse	=	0.43 × 17.90 × 2.67 × 62.4	=	1282	lb/cu yd (dry)
Fine	=	0.57 × 17.90 × 2.55 × 62.4	=	1624	lb/cu yd (dry)
Cement	=	6.4 sacks × 94 lb/sack	=	602	lb/cu yd
Water	=	4.55 cu ft × 62.4 lb/cu ft	=	284	lb/cu yd
Absorption(Coarse)	=	1282 lb × .08%	=	1	lb/cu yd
Absorption (Fine)	=	1624 lb × 1.01%	=	16	lb/cu yd
		Water Subtotal	=	301	lb (per cu yd)
		Total weight	=	3809	lb/cu yd

Case #2

Now assume in Part B the coarse aggregate requirement is 43% of the solid volume of the *total concrete mix*:

Solid Volumes for 1 cu yd batch

Cement	=	$(6.4 \times 94)/(3.15 \times 62.4)$	=	3.06 cu ft
Air	=	$5.5\% \times 27.00$ cu ft	=	1.49 cu ft
Coarse	=	0.43×27.00 cu ft	=	11.61 cu ft
Water	=	34 gal/7.48 gal/cu ft	=	4.55 cu ft
		Total	=	20.71 cu ft
Fine	=	$27.00 - 20.71$	=	6.29 cu ft

Batch Weights on a Dry Basis (1 cu yd batch)

Coarse	=	$11.61 \times 2.67 \times 62.4$	=	1934 lb (dry)
Fine	=	$6.29 \times 2.55 \times 62.4$	=	1001 lb (dry)
Cement	=	6.4 sk/cy $\times$ 94 lb/sk	=	602 lb
Water	=	4.55×62.4 lb/cu ft	=	284 lb
Absorption (Coarse)	=	$1934 \times 0.08\%$	=	2 lb water
Absorption (Fine)	=	$1001 \times 1.01\%$	=	10 lb water

Total of 296 lb of
water per cu yd of   3833 lb/cu yd
PCC

Case #3

Assume that 43% of the volume *really means* that the *bulk volume* of the coarse aggregate is 43% of 1 cubic yard. With this assumption we must also assume a bulk density of the coarse material. A reasonable assumption is 105 lb/cu ft.

Therefore:

$$0.43 \times 27 \text{ cu ft} \times 105 \text{ lb/cu ft} = 1219 \text{ lb (SSD)}$$

$$\frac{1219}{62.4 \text{ lb/cu ft} \times 2.67} = 7.32 \text{ cu ft (solids)}$$

From Cases 1 and 2, and these coarse aggregate amounts:

Material	Weight (lb)	Volume (cu ft)
Cement	602	3.06
Water	284	4.55
Air	00	1.49
Coarse	1219	7.32
Subtotal	2105	16.42

So sand volume fills the remainder of the cubic yard:

27.00 cu ft (concrete) − 16.42 (materials except fine aggregate)
= 10.58 cu ft (solids) fines.

Summary:

The problem statement was *very* ambiguous. If it had said 43% coarse volume *and* had provided a coarse *bulk* density, the correct answer is Case #3 without question. The 43% ratio corresponds to the information we get from Table 12.5 and the procedure for determining coarse aggregate contents. Case #2 is a mathematically correct answer but produces in reality a *very* harsh mix with so much coarse aggregate that it probably would not be workable. [This you *could not possibly* be expected to know.]

Case #1 is also mathematically correct and corresponds to local Southern California practice of using coarse to fine ratios, but is least likely to satisfy the national examination where the practice is accustomed to determine coarse aggregate content using Table 12.5 (or ones like it), the bulk coarse aggregate density, a weight conversion and a solid volume conversion (Case #3). The student is strongly encouraged to be *certain* of the problem statement, the information given and the procedures which apply to the problem solution requirements. In the event of ambiguous problems, state assumptions clearly and explain your logic fully.

13.10.3 P. E. PROBLEM 3 — YIELD CALCULATIONS OF FRESH MIXTURES

A batch of air-entrained portland cement concrete contains the following:

Cement	1950 lb	
Fine aggregate	4250 lb	(Contains 3% free moisture)
Coarse Aggregate	7500 lb	(will absorb 1.1% moisture)
Water	86 gal	
Air	4.5%	

The apparent specific gravity of the cement is 3.15. The SSD specific gravity of the fine aggregate is 2.65; for the coarse aggregate is 2.69. Cement weighs 94 lb/ sack.

Determine the following:

A.   Volume of concrete in cubic yards produced by these weights.

B.   Water/cement ratio in gal/sack

C.   Cement factor in sks/cubic yards

D.   Unit weight of fresh concrete

Solution

The field or <u>batch</u> condition of the coarse aggregate is implied as being in a state drier than SSD. The absorptions of CA and FA are not stated but are not needed since the SSD specific gravities are given. [Recall that apparent Specific gravity = (weight of solids)/(volume of solids), whereas SSD Specific gravity = (weight of solids + weight of water filling permeable voids)/(volume of solids + volume of permeable voids)].

A. Convert batch weights to volume:

Cement	1950 lb/ (3.15 × 62.4 lb/cu ft) lb/cf	= 9.92 cu ft
Fine:	4250 lb/ 1.03 =	
	4126 lb (SSD Wt.) / (2.65 × 62.4 lb/cu ft)	= 24.95
Coarse:	7500 lb × 1.011 = 7582.5 lb (SSD)	
	7582.5 lb (SSD Wt.)/(2.69 × 62.4) lb/cu ft	= 45.17
Water:	Added to batch: 86 gal × 8.33 lb/gal	
	= 716 lb / 62.4 lb/ft^3	= 11.48
	Free in Fines: (4250 − 4126) lb	
	= 124 lb / 62.4 lb/cu ft	=+1.99

Deduct abs. by Coarse Aggregate:
(7500 − 7582.5) lb

$$= −82.5 \text{ lb} / 62.4 \text{ lb/cu ft} \qquad = −1.32$$

Subtotal (Solids)		= 92.19 cu ft

Solids occupies 100 − 4.5 = 95.5%;

	Solids + Air Volume 92.19/0.955	= 96.53 cy
Air	96.53 cu ft × 0.045	= 4.34
Total Fresh Concrete		= 96.53 cu ft

Therefore, Volume of concrete in "yards":

$$96.53 \text{ cu ft} / 27 \text{ cu ft/ cu yd} \qquad = 3.53 \text{ cu yd}$$

B. W/C   Ratio (water not assuming SSD aggregate/cement)

Added (or batched water)		= 86 gal
Free (from fine): 124 lb / 8.33 lb/gal		= +14.89 gal
Absorbed by coarse: 82.5 lb / 8.33 lb/gal		= − 9.90 gal
Total water available to hydrate cement		= 90.99 gal
Therefore, W/C ratio = 90.99 gal/(1950 lb / 94 lb/sk)		= 4.39 gal/sk

C. Cement factor   = (1950 / 94) sks/3.57 cu yd   = 5.81 sk/cu yd

D. Unit weight $= \dfrac{(1950 + 4250 + 7500 + 716)}{96.34 \text{ cu ft}}$ = 149.6 lb/cu ft

13.10.4 P. E. PROBLEM 4 — DESIGN A MIX TO GIVEN SPECIFICATIONS

Design a mix in accord with the specifications, order materials for the project, and adjust the mix for air entrainment and slump requirements.

Problem:

195 cubic yards of air entrained concrete are required for a certain project. Calculate a one cubic yard batch volume and weights per the following instructions. Calculate total material volumes and weights for the entire project. Discuss the consequences to the concrete performance should various changes be made to the mix, and what will happen to various properties of the mix?

MIX SPECIFICATIONS and related KNOWN INFORMATION:

- The batch shall contain two times as much Fine Aggregate than Coarse Aggregate by dry material weight;
- The water to cement ratio shall be 0.58, (w/c = 0.58;)
- The Air Entrainment of the fresh concrete shall be 5.0%;
- The water content shall be 30 gal/cubic yard.

Material Properties:

- Coarse Aggregate

  Specific Gravity, SpG. $_{CA}$ = 2.70

  Absorption   Abs. $_{CA}$ = 1.00%

- Fine Aggregate

  Specific Gravity, SpG. $_{FA}$ = 2.65

  Absorption   Abs. $_{FA}$ = 3.00%

- Portland Cement

  Specific Gravity,   SpG. $_{PC}$ = 3.15

All material shall be considered to be in **Saturated Surface Dry (SSD)** condition upon shipping, delivery, and batching.

Part 1

Design and present the mix for 1 cubic yard of volume; then calculate the minimum required weights of each material for the entire project. (Assume that no extra material is required.)

Part 2

Should the air entrainment admixture fail to be added and the air content not reach 5.00% (so that the air content of fresh concrete is tested at 1.00%,) which of the various properties of the **fresh concrete** will be affected, and how will they change? Explain.

Part 3

Should the air entrainment admixture fail to be added and the air content not reach 5.00% (so that the air content of fresh concrete is tested at 1.00%,) which of the various properties of the **hardened concrete** will be affected, and how will they change? Explain.

Part 4

If a higher slump is intended for this mix, what changes can be made to the mix to maintain its strength and to preserve its general proportions? Explain.

Solution

Part 1:

Find the mix proportions and material requirements:

Since the w/c ratio is 0.58 and there are 30 gallons of water per cubic yard of fresh concrete, then:

30 gal water/cy concrete × 8.33 lb water/gal water = 249.9 lb water/cy concrete

249.9 lb water/cy concrete / 0.58 lb water/lb cement = 430.86 lb cement/cy concrete

Since the problem statement indicates that the air content is 5.00% we can also determine the volume of the entrained air per cubic yard of fresh concrete:

5.00% air/cy concrete × 27.00 ft^3 / cy concrete = 1.35 ft^3 air/cy concrete

Converting the solids to absolute volume and summarizing all of these ingredient materials, for each cubic yard of fresh concrete, we have:

Material (lb)	Weight	Volume (cf)
Cement	430.9	2.19
Water	249.9	4.00
Air (5%)	—	1.35
Subtotal	680.8	7.54

Because 7.54 cf of the 27.00 cubic foot yard of this mix is water, cement and air (collectively called paste,) then the rest of it is sand and rock. Therefore

27.00 cf − 7.54 cf = 19.46 cf

The absolute volume of fine aggregate (sand) and coarse aggregate (rock) is 19.46 cubic feet.

In the mix design, the weight ratio of sand to rock is 2.00 per the problem project specifications.

Since the specific gravities of materials compare the *weights* between equal volumes of the material, then the ratio of their inverses is their *volumetric* ratio. The volumetric ratio for the available sand to the available rock is $(1/2.65)/(1/2.70)$ or 1.0189.

This means that the volumetric ratio of sand to rock *in the mix* is 2.00×1.0189 or 2.0377.

The combined dry volumes of fine and coarse aggregates as noted earlier is 19.46 cf, with 1 part rock to 2.0377 part sand. Simple ratios show that:

For the coarse aggregate volume:

$1/(1+2.0377) \times 19.46$ cf $= 6.406$ cf

For the fine aggregate volume:

$2.0377/(1+2.0377) \times 19.46$ cf $= 13.054$ cf

Checking

Coarse Aggregate	6.406 cf
Fine Aggregate	13.054 cf
Sub−Total	19.46 cf *(checks)*

The dry weights for these materials is as follows:

Rock	6.406 cf $\times$ 2.70 $\times$ 62.4 lb/cf $=$ 1,079 lb (dry)
Sand	13.054 cf $\times$ 2.65 $\times$ 62.4 lb/cf $=$ 2,158 lb (dry)

Rounding and recapping for all materials:

Material (lb)	Weight	Volume (cf)
Cement	431	2.19
Water	250	4.00
Rock (dry)	1,079	6.41
Sand (dry)	2,158	13.05
Air (5%)	—	1.35
Total	3,918	27.00

Checking again we note that:

- the ratio of the dry weights of sand and rock is

  2,158 lb/ 1,079 lb $=$ 2.00 *(ok)*

- the w/c ratio is

  250 lb/ 431 lb $=$ 0.58 *(ok)*

- the air content is

  1.35 cf/ 27.00 cf $=$ 0.05 $=$ 5.00% *(ok)*

- the water content is

  250 lb/ 8.33 lb/gal $=$ 30 gal *(ok)*

Finally we need to adjust the mix weight to put it into standard form which records the **SSD** weights of materials (recalling that the volumes do not change when the material becomes saturated):

Rock (dry) =	1,079 lb
Rock (ssd) =	1,079 lb $\times$ (1 + 0.01) = 1,090 lb
Sand (dry) =	2,158 lb
Sand (SSD) =	2,158 lb $\times$ (1 + 0.03) = 2,223 lb

Summarizing:

Material (lb)	Weight	Volume (cf)	Other Units
Cement	431	2.190	4.59 Sacks
Water	250	4.00	30 gallons
Rock (ssd)	1,090	6.41	
Sand (ssd)	2,223	13.05	
Air	—	1.35	5.00%
Total	3,994	27.00	1 cubic yard

The material required to produce 195 cubic yards is simply 195 times the one cubic yard mix:

1 cy Material (lb)	Weight	195 cy Weight (lb)	Other Units
Cement	431	84,045	895 Sacks
Water	250	48,750	5850 gallons
Rock (ssd)	1,090	212,550	
Sand (ssd)	2,223	433,485	
Air	– – –	– – –	5.00%
Total	3,994	778,830	195 cu yds

Part 2:

If the air content is tested at 1% instead of the intended 5% and all the other materials are batched as intended, what properties of the fresh concrete will change and what will those changes be?

Examine any of the water demand tables (from ACI, PCA or any other standard concrete reference) which present the water requirement for each combination of slump and coarse aggregate size for both air entrained and non air entrained concrete. For any single slump and aggregate size, note the difference in water required between the air and non air entrained mix. As a general rule of thumb, 20% less water is required in an air entrained mix than a non air mix.

Because of this, removing the air from the mix is like removing, say, 20% of the water. Therefore, the single most noteworthy change to the fresh concrete mix is a huge reduction of workability or slump. The mix would not be nearly as pumpable or workable. It is likely that the concrete will not mix thoroughly and will demand more mixing time and effort. Secondarily, if the concrete is installed as batched, and because 4% (5% − 1%) less volume is present in the mix, the total amount of fresh concrete cubic yards batched and delivered will be 4% less, so 4% more cement, rock, sand and water will be required on the project. (This is known as a reduction in concrete *yield*). Also, once the concrete is installed and ready to be trowelled and finished, the concrete surface will be more easily trowelled and less sticky than the concrete which was air entrained.

Part 3:

If the air content is tested at 1% instead of the intended 5% and all the other materials are batched as intended, what properties of the hardened concrete will change and what will those changes be?

As previously noted, the omission of air entraining admixture will greatly reduce the slump and yield of the fresh concrete. Assuming that the concrete is properly batched, completely mixed and installed as designed, except for the air, then the single greatest concrete property to change is the complete elimination of the intended freeze thaw durability. (Freeze thaw durability is the principal reason for specifying air entrainment.) However, a second major result of the reduction of air is an increase in compressive and flexural strength of the concrete. Since air bubbles have no strength and there is a large reduction of air bubbles, the strength will increase. Another property of the hardened concrete to be affected is also related to the reduced air content. This has to do with the fact that air entrained concrete has lower permeability and higher sulfate resistance than non air entrained concrete. So the concrete erroneously batched without air will be less permeable and somewhat less sulfate resistant.

Part 4:

If a higher slump which preserves the basic mix proportions and materials is desired, what changes should be made to the mix.

Higher slump can be accomplished by increasing the water content of the mix or by using chemical admixtures. Since the basic design intent for the proportions and materials needs to be preserved, and admixtures were not part of the basic mix, they will not be used. This leaves the option of increasing the water content. However, increasing the water content while maintaining the cement content increases the water cement ratio (w/c). This in turn reduces the strength and the character of the mix. So the mix should be changed to: (1) increase the water content to the level required to achieve the desired new slump; and, (2) increase the cement content to the level required to maintain the original w/c ratio. Finally, since the absolute volume of the mix has increased because of more water and more cement, the sand content should be reduced by the amount of the extra cement and water volumes added.

INDEX

NOTES

NOTES

VOLUME III

P. E. (Civil) License Review Manual

STEEL DESIGN
Section 6

Alexander Fattaleh, M.S., S.E.
Senior Vice President
American Bridge Company
Western Region
Long Beach, California

ABOUT
THE AUTHOR

Mr. Fattaleh is presently the Senior Vice President of American Bridge Company, a company that specializes in structural steel fabrication and erection of high-rise buildings, bridges, convention centers, arenas, stadiums, industrial buildings and space-launch facilities. Mr. Fattaleh plans, organizes, staffs, directs and controls the Western Regional office of American Bridge. His office is fully responsible for its marketing, estimating, contract negotiation and construction management operation of structural steel work of major multi-million dollar type projects.

Since 1962, he has been working in the structural steel business. In spite of his busy schedule, he has been teaching the Structural Steel Design course at California State University, Long Beach since 1979.

He obtained his BSCE from U.C., Berkeley and his MSCE from California State University, Long Beach.

He is a member of ASCE, IASE, SEAOSC, Council on Tall Buildings and Urban Habitat, World Trade Center and the Beavers.

Mr. Fattaleh is a Registered Civil and Structural Engineer in the State of California, and is licensed as a General Contractor and Steel Erector Contractor in the State of California.

ACKNOWLEDGEMENTS

The author is very grateful to Dr. C. V. Chelapati for taking the initiative and interest to lead, coordinate and edit the entire examination review series; to California State University Continuing Education Staff for their review and valuable comments and suggestions of this subject matter; to Dr. Plecnik, Professor at California State University for preparing the original Structural Steel Review material; to the American Institute of Steel Construction for the wealth of information they published related to structural steel; and last but not least, to his wife Nancy and daughter Linda for their understanding for the reason and purpose of the many hours spent in preparing this material.

The author acknowledges The James F. Lincoln Arc Welding Foundation for the use of selected tables from the Design of Arc Welded Structures and finally to Paul E. Rice and Edward S. Hoffman for the use of figures and tables from their book, Structural Design Guide to AISC Specifications for Buildings.

TABLE OF CONTENTS

CHAPTER 4
COMPRESSION MEMBERS

CHAPTER 5
ELASTIC DESIGN AND ANALYSIS OF BEAMS

CHAPTER 6
ANALYSES AND DESIGN OF BEAM-COLUMNS

CHAPTER 7
BOLTED CONNECTIONS

INDEX

NOTES

LIST OF FIGURES

LIST OF TABLES

ALPHABETICAL LIST OF SOLVED PROBLEMS

Topics	Problem	Sec.	Page #
Using AISC Ultimate Strength Tables	Example Problem 1	7.18.1	6-172
Warehouse Roof System	P. E. Problem 3	5.25.3	6-117

REFERENCES

1. *Manual of Steel Construction,* 8th ed. and 9th edition, Published by American Institute of Steel Construction, Chicago, 1980 and 1989.

2. *Uniform Building Code,* 1985 and 1988 Editions.

3. *Structural Steel Design,* 4th ed., J. C. McCormac, New York, 1992.

4. *Design of Welded Structures,* Published by James F. Lincoln Arc Welding Foundation.

5. *Practical Steel Design for Buildings 2-20 Stories* by Roy Becker, AISC Publication.

6. *Recommended Lateral Force Requirements and Commentary,* Published by Structural Engineers Association of California.

7. *Basics of Structural Steel Design* by Samuel H. Marcus, 2nd edition, 1981.

8. *Basic Steel Design* by Johnson, Lin, Galambos, 2nd edition.

9. *Designing Steel Structures* by Sol E. Cooper and Andrew C. Chen, 1985.

10. *Steel Structure* by Charles Salmon and John Johnson, 2nd edition 1980.

11. *Structural Steel Design* by Editor Lambert Tall, 2nd edition, 1974.

12. *Design of Steel Structures* by Edwin H. Gaylord, Jr. and Charles N. Gaylord.

1

INTRODUCTION

1.1 INTRODUCTION TO STEEL DESIGN

A brief review summary of some of the main basic information related to the steel design is presented herein for those who are preparing to take the P.E. (Civil) License Examination. It is assumed that the candidate has taken this subject matter in the past. However, for those who have not taken structural steel design, it is strongly suggested that this manual be used in conjunction with some of the texts in steel design listed in the reference section.

The design of structural steel buildings is partly based on the specifications developed by the American Institute of Steel Construction (AISC), and are published in the Manual of Steel Construction. The Manual of Steel Construction consists of five chapters. The first four chapters have reference tables to properties and dimensions of various steel shapes, design aid tables, and design examples. The fifth chapter refers to the specifications and commentary to the specifications. Specifications are written as minimum recommendations for design criteria while commentary to the specifications are written to show the reasons and logic behind the development of the specifications. One should remember that specifications provide the minimum requirements for a certain design. It is up to the designer to design a safe, economical and practical structure.

In addition to the Manual of Steel Construction, the design of steel structures is also governed by building codes adopted by various agencies. Most building codes do refer to the specifications recommended by AISC. The three major building codes are Uniform Building Code (UBC), Southern Building Code (SBC), and Building Officials and Code Administrators (BOCA).

The AISC manual is now in its ninth edition with green cover, published in 1989, and is referred to as Manual of Steel Construction Allowable Stress Design (ASD).

2

STRUCTURAL STEEL

2.1   STEEL PROPERTIES

There are two types of properties related to structural steel. One type of property deals with dimensional figures such as moment of inertia, section modulus and areas. The other type of property deals with the material strength such as yield and ultimate strengths and modulus of elasticity. The yield and ultimate strengths are governed by the type or grade of steel being used, plus the thickness of the material.

The American Society of Testing Materials (ASTM) is an agency that sets the standards for various types and grades of steel such as ASTM A36, A572-50, etc. Each grade has its own certain chemical and physical properties. One should note that local building codes allow only certain types of material to be used in their jurisdictional areas. A partial list of various grades of structural steel is shown in Table 2.1. For a complete list of all other types of material, refer to ASTM publications.

2.2   STRESS-STRAIN DIAGRAM

The tensile stresses and other properties are obtained in a testing laboratory by performing various standard tests. One of the most important properties of steel is its tensile strength.

A tensile load, P, pulling force, is applied to a standard specimen (flat bar) of cross-sectional area A = W × t similar to the one shown below in Figure 2.1.

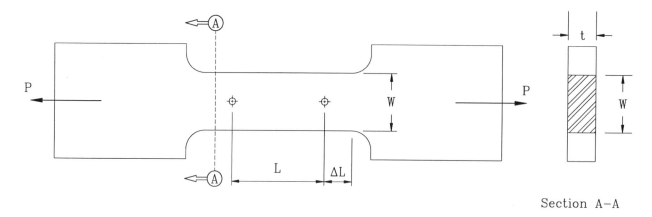

Section A–A

Figure 2.1 Tensile Test Specimen

In performing the standard tensile test, the tensile load and the elongation, ΔL, are recorded throughout the test until the flat bar fails. The recorded readings are then plotted in terms of stress, P/A, versus strain, $\Delta L/L$, to obtain a stress-strain curve, where L is a standard gage length and ΔL is the change in length, L, due to applied tensile load.

Figure 2.2 shows the stress-strain curve for ASTM A36 grade of structural steel.

ASTM A36 steel has an extremely large plastic yielding range, thus contributes to a high ductility feature. Material of high-ductility measure will absorb significant amounts of strain energy which is desired in the structure. Material of strengths higher than A36 are not as ductile and will fail in a brittle type failure.

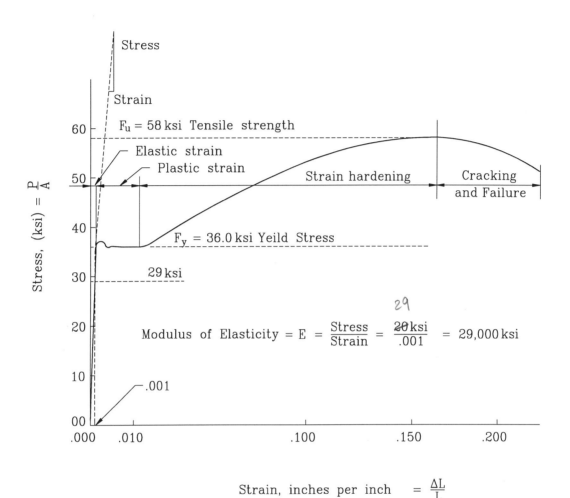

Figure 2.2 Stress-Strain Curve for A36 Steel
(Ref. AISC — Structural Steel Detailing)

2.3   TENSILE STRESSES FOR A GIVEN ASTM

The allowable stresses are equal to the yield stress divided by a safety factor. The safety factor varies by the type of load the member carries and by the type of stress.

Shapes listed in the AISC Manual are subdivided into five different groups as shown in (M1-8). Tensile stresses for a given ASTM material are listed in (M1-7). The shaded areas in (M1-7) indicate that the shapes and plates are available for a certain type ASTM material.

The minimum yield stress, F_y, and ultimate stress, F_u, for a given shape and for a given ASTM designation can be determined as shown below:

1. From (M1-8) determine the group number for the given shape.
2. In (M1-7) look for a shaded area where the given ASTM intersects the group number found in Step 1 above, then read the tensile stresses F_y and F_u.

Note:

1. All shapes are available in A36 material except for plates whose thickness are greater than 8 inches.
2. Steel pipes are available in A36 material.
3. Structural tubes are available with a yield strength of 46 ksi.

Table 2.1 Properties of Structural Steel Considered in AISC

ASTM Designation	Type of steel	Shapes available	Recommended uses	Yield stress psi	Atmospheric corrosion resistance
A36	Carbon	Shapes and bars	Riveted, bolted or welded bridges and buildings, and other structural uses	36,000 up through 8 in. (32,000 above 8 in.)	
A500	"	Cold-formed welded and seamless tubing	"	33,000 for Grade A 42,000 for Grade B	
A501	"	Hot-formed welded and seamless tubing PLs and bars up through $\frac{1}{2}$ in. and some light shapes	Riveted, bolted and welded buildings, and related construction	36,000 42,000	
A440	High-strength	" " "	Riveted and bolted bridges and buildings, and other structural uses; not recommended for welding	50,000 up through $\frac{3}{4}$ in. 46,000 above $\frac{3}{4}$ in. through $1\frac{1}{2}$ in. 42,000 above $1\frac{1}{2}$ in. through 4 in.	Approximately equal to two times that of structural carbon steel
A441	High-strength low-alloy	" " "	May be used for welded, riveted, and bolted structures but primarily intended for welded bridges and buildings	50,000 up through $\frac{3}{4}$ in. 46,000 above $\frac{3}{4}$ in. through $1\frac{1}{2}$ in. 42,000 above $1\frac{1}{2}$ in. through 4 in. 40,000 above 4 in. through 8 in.	"

Table 2.1 (Cont'd.) Properties of Structural Steel Considered in AISC

ASTM	Type	Shapes/use	Purpose	Minimum yield point or yield strength, ksi	Corrosion resistance
A572	"	" " "	Grades 42, 45, and 50 especially intended for riveted, bolted or welded bridges, buildings, and other structures. Grades 55, 60, and 65 especially intended for riveted or bolted bridges, and for other structures which are riveted, bolted or welded	42,000 / 45,000 / 50,000 55,000 60,000 / 65,000 — varying thickness, chemical compositions, etc. (see ASTM)	
A242	Corrosion-resistant High-strength low-alloy	Shapes and bars	Welded, riveted or bolted construction; welding technique very important	50,000 up through $\frac{3}{4}$ in. / 46,000 above $\frac{3}{4}$ in. through $1\frac{1}{2}$ in. / 42,000 above $1\frac{1}{2}$ in. through 4 in.	Approximately equal to four times that of structural carbon steel with copper
A588	"	" " "	May be used for welded, riveted or bolted construction but primarily intended for welded bridges and buildings; welding technique very important	50,000 up through 4 in. / 46,000 above 4 in. through 5 in. / 42,000 above 5 in. through 8 in.	Approximately equal to four times that of structural carbon steel with copper
A514	Quenched and tempered alloy	PLs up through 4 in., and a limited number of shapes	Primarily intended for use in welded bridges and other structures; welding technique very important	100,000 up through $2\frac{1}{2}$ in. / 90,000 above $2\frac{1}{2}$ in. through 4 in.	

Table 2.2 Availability of Structural Shapes
(AISC, M1-7)

TABLE 1
Availability of Shapes, Plates and Bars According to ASTM Structural Steel Specifications

Steel Type	ASTM Designation		F_y Minimum Yield Stress (ksi)	F_u Tensile Stress[a] (ksi)	Shapes (Group per ASTM A6)					Plates and Bars										
					[b]1	2	3	4	5	To ½" Incl.	Over ½" to ¾" Incl.	Over ¾" to 1¼" Incl.	Over 1¼" to 1½" Incl.	Over 1½" to 2" Incl.	Over 2" to 2½" Incl.	Over 2½" to 4" Incl.	Over 4" to 5" Incl.	Over 5" to 6" Incl.	Over 6" to 8" Incl.	Over 8"
Carbon	A36		32	58–80																
			36	58–80[c]																
	A529		42	60–85																
High-strength Low-alloy	A441		40	60																
			42	63																
			46	67																
			50	70																
	A572 Grade	42	42	60																
		50	50	65																
		60	60	75																
		65	65	80																
Corrosion-resistant High-strength Low-alloy	A242		42	63																
			46	67																
			50	70																
	A588		42	63																
			46	67																
			50	70																
Quenched & Tempered Low-alloy	A852[d]		70	90–110																
Quenched & Tempered Alloy	A514[d]		90	100–130																
			100	110–130																

[a]Minimum unless a range is shown.
[b]Includes bar-size shapes.
[c]For shapes over 426 lbs./ft, minimum of 58 ksi only applies.
[d]Plates only.
☐ Available.
☐ Not available.

Table 2.3 Structural Steel Groupings for Tensile Properties
(AISC, M1-8)

TABLE 2 Structural Shape Size Groupings for Tensile Property Classification					
Structural Shapes	Group 1	Group 2	Group 3	Group 4	Group 5
W shapes	W 24×55, 62 W 21×44 to 57 incl. W 18×35 to 71 incl. W 16×26 to 57 incl. W 14×22 to 53 incl. W 12×14 to 58 incl. W 10×12 to 45 incl. W 8×10 to 48 incl. W 6×9 to 25 incl. W 5×16, 19 W 4×13	W 44×198, 224 W 40×149 to 268 incl. W 36×135 to 210 incl. W 33×118 to 152 incl. W 30×90 to 211 incl. W 27×84 to 178 incl. W 24×68 to 162 incl. W 21×62 to 147 incl. W 18×76 to 143 incl. W 16×67 to 100 incl. W 14×61 to 132 incl. W 12×65 to 106 incl. W 10×49 to 112 incl. W 8×58, 67	W 44×248, 285 W 40×277 to 328 incl. W 36×230 to 300 incl. W 33×201 to 291 incl. W 30×235 to 261 incl. W 27×194 to 258 incl. W 24×176 to 229 incl. W 21×166 to 223 incl. W 18×158 to 192 incl. W 14×145 to 211 incl. W 12×120 to 190 incl.	W 40×362 to 655 incl. W 36×328 to 798 incl. W 33×318 to 619 incl. W 30×292 to 581 incl. W 27×281 to 539 incl. W 24×250 to 492 incl. W 21×248 to 402 incl. W 18×211 to 311 incl. W 14×233 to 550 incl. W 12×210 to 336 incl.	W 36×848 W 14×605 to 730 incl.
M Shapes	to 37.7 lb./ft incl.				
S Shapes	to 35 lb./ft incl.				
HP Shapes		to 102 lb./ft incl.	over 102 lb./ft		
American Standard Channels (C)	to 20.7 lb./ft incl.	over 20.7 lb./ft			
Miscellaneous Channels (MC)	to 28.5 lb./ft incl.	over 28.5 lb./ft			
Angles (L) Structural Bar-size	to ½ in. incl.	over ½ to ¾ in. incl.	over ¾ in.		

Notes: Structural tees from W, M and S shapes fall into the same group as the structural shape from which they are cut.
Group 4 and Group 5 shapes are generally contemplated for application as columns or compression components. When used in other applications (e.g., trusses) and when thermal cutting or welding is required, special material specification and fabrication procedures apply to minimize the possibility of cracking. (See Part 5, Specification Sects. A3.1, J1.11 and M2.2 and corresponding Commentary sections)

2.4   COMMON ROLLED-STEEL SHAPES

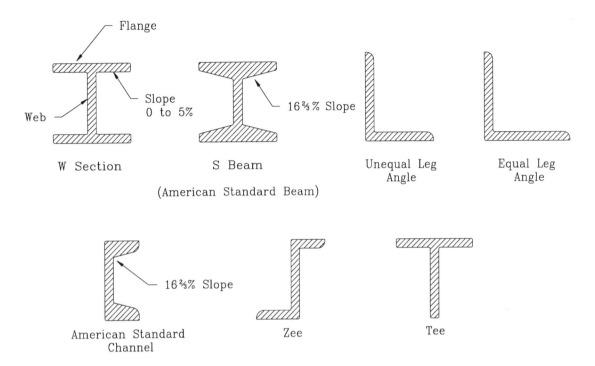

Figure 2.3 Rolled-Steel Shapes

2.5   SECTION PROPERTIES

The following is a partial list of section properties that are used in the design of structural steel.

1. Cross-Sectional Area, A, in.^{2}

2. Moment of Inertia, I, in.^{4}

3   Section Modulus, S, in.^{3}

4. Radius of Gyration, r, in.

5. Neutral Axis, N.A.

Moments of inertia for rectangles, triangles and other common shapes are given in M6-17 to M6-23.

For built-up members consisting of a combination of shapes or plates, the section properties required for the design must be calculated.

2.5.1   MOMENT OF INERTIA

A brief discussion of moment of inertia is given here. The reader is referred to any textbook on statics for detailed information.

Moment of inertia of a cross section of a member is a measure of its resistance to a rotation.

By definition

$$I_x = \int_A y^2 \, dA$$

$$I_y = \int_A x^2 \, dA$$

where

A = area whose moment of inertia is desired.

x and y are the distances of an element, dA, from the y and x axes respectively.

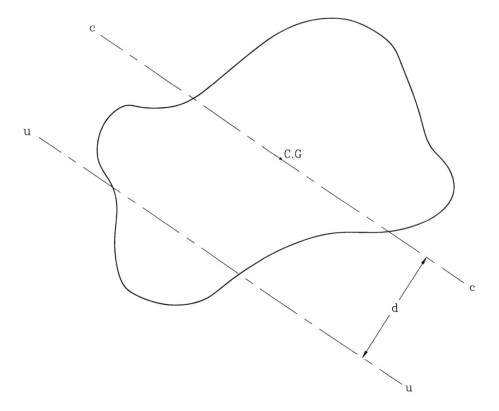

Figure 2.4 Cross Section of a Member

Moment of inertia for built-up shapes must be calculated. The parallel axis theorem is used to calculate the moment of inertia about an axis parallel to the centroidal axis and is given by

$$I_u = I_c + Ad^2$$

where

I_u = moment of inertia about the u-u axis

I_c = moment of inertia about the centroidal axis c-c

A = area whose moment of inertia is desired

d = perpendicular distance between the parallel axes c-c and u-u

2.5.2   SECTION MODULUS

The section modulus is given by

$$S = \frac{I}{c}$$

where

I = moment of inertia of the section

c = distance from c.g. of shape to end of shape or extreme fiber

2.5.3   RADIUS OF GYRATION

The radius of gyration is given by

$$r = \sqrt{\frac{I}{A}}$$

where

I = moment of inertia of section

A = area of cross section

2.5.4   TABULATED SECTION PROPERTIES AND DIMENSIONS

The section properties and physical dimensions of rolled shapes, steel pipes and structural tubes are listed in Part 1 of the AISC Manual.

Table 2.4 Structural Steel Dimensions and Properties (AISC, M1-14)

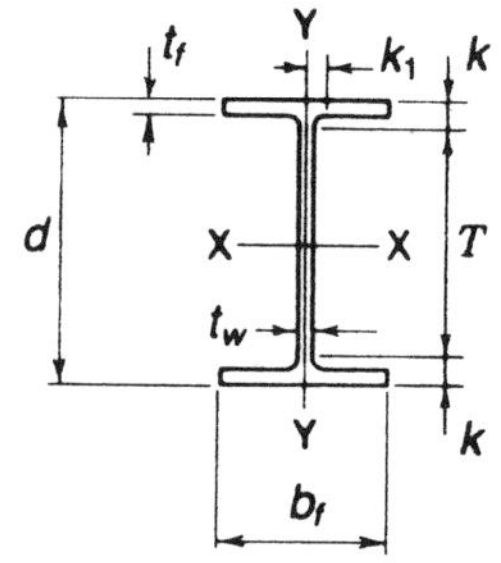

W SHAPES
Dimensions

Designation	Area A	Depth d		Web: Thickness t_w		Web: $\frac{t_w}{2}$	Flange: Width b_f		Flange: Thickness t_f		Distance: T	Distance: k	Distance: k_1
	In.^{2}	In.		In.		In.	In.		In.		In.	In.	In.
W 33×619[a]	181.0	38.47	38 1/2	1.970	2	1	16.910	16 7/8	3.540	3 9/16	29 3/4	4 3/8	1 3/4
×567[a]	166.0	37.91	37 7/8	1.810	1 13/16	1	16.750	16 3/4	3.270	3 1/4	29 3/4	4 1/16	1 11/16
×515[a]	151.0	37.36	37 3/8	1.650	1 5/8	13/16	16.590	16 5/8	2.990	3	29 3/4	3 13/16	1 5/8
×468[a]	137.0	36.81	36 3/4	1.520	1 1/2	3/4	16.455	16 1/2	2.720	2 3/4	29 3/4	3 1/2	1 9/16
×424[a]	124.0	36.34	36 3/8	1.380	1 3/8	11/16	16.315	16 3/8	2.480	2 1/2	29 3/4	3 5/16	1 7/16
×387[a]	113.0	35.95	36	1.260	1 1/4	5/8	16.200	16 1/4	2.280	2 1/4	29 3/4	3 1/8	1 3/8
×354[a]	104.0	35.55	35 1/2	1.160	1 3/16	5/8	16.100	16 1/8	2.090	2 1/16	29 3/4	2 7/8	1 3/8
×318[a]	93.5	35.16	35 1/8	1.040	1 1/16	9/16	15.985	16	1.890	1 7/8	29 3/4	2 11/16	1 5/16
×291	85.6	34.84	34 7/8	0.960	1	1/2	15.905	15 7/8	1.730	1 3/4	29 3/4	2 9/16	1 1/4
×263	77.4	34.53	34 1/2	0.870	7/8	7/16	15.805	15 3/4	1.570	1 9/16	29 3/4	2 3/8	1 3/16
×241	70.9	34.18	34 1/8	0.830	13/16	7/16	15.860	15 7/8	1.400	1 3/8	29 3/4	2 3/16	1 3/16
×221	65.0	33.93	33 7/8	0.775	3/4	3/8	15.805	15 3/4	1.275	1 1/4	29 3/4	2 1/16	1 3/16
×201	59.1	33.68	33 5/8	0.715	11/16	3/8	15.745	15 3/4	1.150	1 1/8	29 3/4	1 15/16	1 1/8
W 33×169[b]	49.5	33.82	33 7/8	0.670	11/16	3/8	11.500	11 1/2	1.220	1 1/4	29 3/4	2 1/16	1 1/8
×152	44.7	33.49	33 1/2	0.635	5/8	5/16	11.565	11 5/8	1.055	1 1/16	29 3/4	1 7/8	1 1/8
×141	41.6	33.30	33 1/4	0.605	5/8	5/16	11.535	11 1/2	0.960	15/16	29 3/4	1 3/4	1 1/16
×130	38.3	33.09	33 1/8	0.580	9/16	5/16	11.510	11 1/2	0.855	7/8	29 3/4	1 11/16	1 1/16
×118	34.7	32.86	32 7/8	0.550	9/16	5/16	11.480	11 1/2	0.740	3/4	29 3/4	1 9/16	1 1/16
W 30×581[a]	170.0	35.39	35 3/8	1.970	2	1	16.200	16 1/4	3.540	3 9/16	26 3/4	4 5/16	1 11/16
×526[a]	154.0	34.76	34 3/4	1.790	1 13/16	1	16.020	16	3.230	3 1/4	26 3/4	4	1 5/8
×477[a]	140.0	34.21	34 1/4	1.630	1 5/8	13/16	15.865	15 7/8	2.950	3	26 3/4	3 3/4	1 9/16
×433[a]	127.0	33.66	33 5/8	1.500	1 1/2	3/4	15.725	15 3/4	2.680	2 11/16	26 3/4	3 7/16	1 1/2
×391[a]	114.0	33.19	33 1/4	1.360	1 3/8	11/16	15.590	15 5/8	2.440	2 7/16	26 3/4	3 1/4	1 7/16
×357[a]	104.0	32.80	32 3/4	1.240	1 1/4	5/8	15.470	15 1/2	2.240	2 1/4	26 3/4	3	1 3/8
×326[a]	95.7	32.40	32 3/8	1.140	1 1/8	9/16	15.370	15 3/8	2.050	2 1/16	26 3/4	2 13/16	1 5/16
×292[a]	85.7	32.01	32	1.020	1	1/2	15.255	15 1/4	1.850	1 7/8	26 3/4	2 5/8	1 1/4
×261	76.7	31.61	31 5/8	0.930	15/16	1/2	15.155	15 1/8	1.650	1 5/8	26 3/4	2 7/16	1 3/16
×235	69.0	31.30	31 1/4	0.830	13/16	7/16	15.055	15	1.500	1 1/2	26 3/4	2 1/4	1 1/8
×211	62.0	30.94	31	0.775	3/4	3/8	15.105	15 1/8	1.315	1 5/16	26 3/4	2 1/8	1 1/8
×191	56.1	30.68	30 5/8	0.710	11/16	3/8	15.040	15	1.185	1 3/16	26 3/4	1 15/16	1 1/16
×173	50.8	30.44	30 1/2	0.655	5/8	5/16	14.985	15	1.065	1 1/16	26 3/4	1 7/8	1 1/16

[a]For application refer to Notes in Table 2.
[b]Heavier shapes in this series are available from some producers.
Shapes in shaded rows are not available from domestic producers.

Table 2.4 (Cont'd.) Structural Steel Dimensions and Properties
(AISC, M1-15)

W SHAPES
Properties

Nom-inal Wt. per Ft	Compact Section Criteria				r_T	$\dfrac{d}{A_f}$	Elastic Properties						Plastic Modulus	
	$\dfrac{b_f}{2t_f}$	F_y'	$\dfrac{d}{t_w}$	F_y'''			Axis X-X			Axis Y-Y			Z_x	Z_y
							I	S	r	I	S	r		
Lb.		Ksi		Ksi	In.		In.^{4}	In.^{3}	In.	In.^{4}	In.^{3}	In.	In.^{3}	In.^{3}
619	2.4	—	19.5	—	4.51	0.64	41800	2170	15.2	2870	340	3.98	2560	537
567	2.6	—	20.9	—	4.46	0.69	37700	1990	15.1	2580	308	3.94	2330	485
515	2.8	—	22.6	—	4.42	0.75	33700	1810	14.9	2290	276	3.89	2110	433
468	3.0	—	24.2	—	4.37	0.82	30100	1630	14.8	2030	247	3.85	1890	387
424	3.3	—	26.3	—	4.33	0.90	26900	1480	14.7	1800	221	3.81	1700	345
387	3.6	—	28.5	—	4.30	0.97	24300	1350	14.7	1620	200	3.79	1550	312
354	3.8	—	30.6	—	4.27	1.06	21900	1230	14.5	1460	181	3.74	1420	282
318	4.2	—	33.8	57.8	4.24	1.16	19500	1110	14.4	1290	161	3.71	1270	250
291	4.6	—	36.3	50.1	4.21	1.27	17700	1010	14.4	1160	146	3.69	1150	226
263	5.0	—	39.7	41.9	4.18	1.39	15800	917	14.3	1030	131	3.66	1040	202
241	5.7	—	41.2	38.9	4.17	1.54	14200	829	14.1	932	118	3.63	939	182
221	6.2	—	43.8	34.5	4.15	1.68	12800	757	14.1	840	106	3.59	855	164
201	6.8	—	47.1	29.8	4.12	1.86	11500	684	14.0	749	95.2	3.56	772	147
169	4.7	—	50.5	25.9	2.95	2.41	9290	549	13.7	310	53.9	2.50	629	84.4
152	5.5	—	52.7	23.7	2.94	2.74	8160	487	13.5	273	47.2	2.47	559	73.9
141	6.0	—	55.0	21.8	2.92	3.01	7450	448	13.4	246	42.7	2.43	514	66.9
130	6.7	—	57.1	20.3	2.88	3.36	6710	406	13.2	218	37.9	2.39	467	59.5
118	7.8	—	59.7	18.5	2.84	3.87	5900	359	13.0	187	32.6	2.32	415	51.3
581	2.3	—	18.0	—	4.34	0.62	33000	1870	13.9	2530	312	3.86	2210	492
526	2.5	—	19.4	—	4.29	0.67	29300	1680	13.8	2230	278	3.80	1990	438
477	2.7	—	21.0	—	4.24	0.73	26100	1530	13.7	1970	249	3.75	1790	390
433	2.9	—	22.4	—	4.20	0.80	23200	1380	13.5	1750	222	3.71	1610	348
391	3.2	—	24.4	—	4.16	0.87	20700	1250	13.5	1550	198	3.68	1430	310
357	3.5	—	26.5	—	4.12	0.95	18600	1140	13.4	1390	179	3.65	1300	279
326	3.7	—	28.4	—	4.09	1.03	16800	1030	13.2	1240	162	3.61	1190	252
292	4.1	—	31.4	—	4.06	1.13	14900	928	13.2	1100	144	3.58	1060	223
261	4.6	—	34.0	57.2	4.02	1.26	13100	827	13.1	959	127	3.54	941	196
235	5.0	—	37.7	46.4	4.00	1.39	11700	746	13.0	855	114	3.52	845	175
211	5.7	—	39.9	41.4	3.99	1.56	10300	663	12.9	757	100	3.49	749	154
191	6.3	—	43.2	35.4	3.97	1.72	9170	598	12.8	673	89.5	3.46	673	138
173	7.0	—	46.5	30.6	3.94	1.91	8200	539	12.7	598	79.8	3.43	605	123

2.6 SHEAR AND BENDING MOMENT DIAGRAMS

The shear and moment diagrams represent the internal forces carried by beams and frames. This topic is discussed extensively in Structural Analysis, Volume 1, Section 1 of this review manual.

Starting on Page M2-293, the AISC Manual gives the shear and bending moment diagrams for most load conditions that one is likely to encounter. For simple loading conditions, the Method of Superposition can be used by combining various loading conditions shown in AISC Tables. An example problem using superposition is given below.

However, for most cases it is preferable to draw the shear and moment diagrams using the methods described in Section 1.

2.7 EXAMPLE PROBLEMS

2.7.1 EXAMPLE PROBLEM 1 — TENSILE STRESS PROPERTIES

Determine the tensile stresses for a W14 $\times$ 132 whose material is ASTM A441.

1. From (M1-8) the group number for W14 $\times$ 132 is 2.
2. From (M1-7) the tensile stresses for the shaded area where group 2 intersects ASTM A441 are as follows:

$F_y = 50$ ksi   and $F_u = 70$ ksi

2.7.2   EXAMPLE PROBLEM 2 — MOMENT OF INERTIA

For the built-up shape shown below, find its moment of inertia about its X-X axis, I_x.

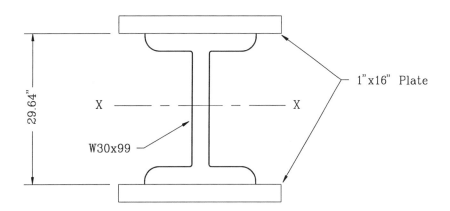

Fig. P2.7.2 (a) Section of Built-Up Shape

Solution

1. By symmetry, the X-X axis passes through the centroid of the entire cross section.

2. The moment of inertia, I_{xw}, about the neutral X-X axis for the W30 × 99 is equal to 3,990 in.^{4} and its cross-sectional area, A_w, is equal to 29.1 in.^{2} obtained from (M1-16).

3. The cross-sectional area, A_p, and the moment of inertia, I_{xp}, of one cover plate about its centroidal axis are as follows:

$$A_p = bt = 16 \times 1 = 16 \text{ in.}^2$$

$$I_{xp} = \frac{b\,t^3}{12} = \frac{16 \times 1^3}{12} = 1.3 \text{ in.}^4$$

4. The moment of inertia for the entire built-up section is as follows:

$$I_x = \Sigma I_{x\text{-}x} + \Sigma Ad^2 = I_{xw} + \Sigma (I_{xp} + A_p d^2)$$

$$I_x = 3,990 + 2 \times 1.3 + 2\,(16 \times 1)\left[\left(\frac{29.64}{2}\right) + \frac{1}{2}\right]^2 = 11,503 \text{ in.}^4$$

Use Tabulate forms.

2.7.3   EXAMPLE PROBLEM 3 — SHEAR AND BENDING MOMENT DIAGRAMS

Find the shear and bending moment for the beam shown below at a point just to the left of A using tabulated values in the AISC Manual.

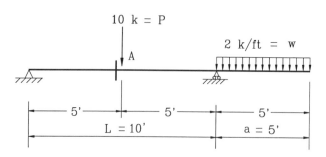

Fig. P2.7.3 (a)

Solution

The loading is divided into two cases for which AISC has provided solutions. The two cases are superimposed. Note the differences in signs of shear and moment for each case. It is recommended that this procedure be used only for very simple cases. Please refer to Volume 1, Section 1, Structural Analysis Section of P.E. (Civil) License Review manual for detailed information on structural analysis.

Case 1: Concentrated Load, P

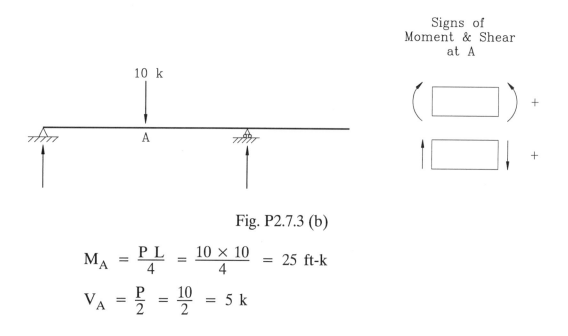

Fig. P2.7.3 (b)

$$M_A = \frac{P\,L}{4} = \frac{10 \times 10}{4} = 25 \text{ ft-k}$$

$$V_A = \frac{P}{2} = \frac{10}{2} = 5 \text{ k}$$

Case 2: Distributed Load, w

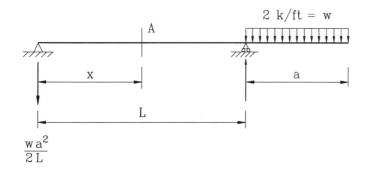

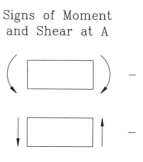

Signs of Moment
and Shear at A

Fig. P2.7.3 (c)

$$M_A = \frac{w\,a^2\,x}{2\,L} = \frac{2 \times 5^2 \times 5}{2 \times 10} = 12.5 \text{ ft-k}$$

$$V_A = \frac{w\,a^2}{2\,L} = \frac{2 \times 5^2}{2 \times 10} = 2.5 \text{ k}$$

Total internal forces at A:

Total moment at A = 25 − 12.5 = 12.5 ft-kip

Total shear just to left of A = 5 − 2.5 = 2.5 kip

3

TENSION MEMBERS

3.1 TENSION MEMBERS

Tension members are members that are subjected to axial tensile loads.

3.2 TENSILE STRESS

$$f_t = P/A \leq F_t$$

where

- f_t is the actual tensile stress
- P   is the axial tensile load
- A   is the cross-sectional area of member. There are several definitions for the area depending upon the context in which it is used. Please refer to symbols page M5-201 and also at end of Part 6 of the AISC Manual.
- F_t is the allowable tensile stress

3.3 ALLOWABLE TENSILE STRESS

In accordance with Section D1 of AISC Specifications (M5-40), the allowable tensile stress for prismatic members subjected to centroidal axial tensile force is summarized as follows:

$F_t = 0.60 F_y$ When taken at the gross (total cross-sectional area), A_g, of the tension member where there are no holes

$F_t = 0.50 F_u$ When taken at the total effective net area, A_n, of the tension member with holes

For pin-connected members:

$F_t = 0.45 F_y$ When taken at the net cross-sectional area, A_n, of a tension member at the pin hole.

For threaded parts:

$F_t = 0.33 F_u$ When taken at the tensile root cross-sectional area, A_D, of a threaded rod.

3.4   DEFINITION OF CROSS-SECTIONAL AREAS

Chapter B, Design Requirements of the AISC Specifications (M5-33)

A_g is the total cross-sectional area of a tensile member taken along a transverse line where no holes are provided. To find A_g for rolled shapes, refer to Part 1 of the AISC Manual. For example, the A_g for a W14 × 132 is equal to 38.8 in.[2] obtained from (M1-26).

To find A_g for a plate, multiply its width by its thickness. For example, the A_g for a plate 12 in. wide by 1/2 in. thick is equal to 12 × 1/2 = 6 in.[2]

A_n is the least net area of a tensile member taken along a line where holes are provided. Holes are provided in a tension member either in a non-staggered pattern or in a staggered pattern. In accordance with the AISC Specifications, Chapter B, A_n shall be obtained as follows:

A_n for a non-staggered condition is:

$$A_n = A_g - \Sigma\, n\, (d+1/8)\, t$$

A_n for a staggered condition is:

$$A_n = A_g - \Sigma\, n\, (d+1/8)\, t + \Sigma \frac{s^2}{4g} t$$

where

n   is the number of holes along a transverse line to the direction of the applied load

d   is the diameter of fastener or bolt

t   is the thickness of material

s   is the longitudinal dimension between two staggered holes (pitch)

g   is the transverse dimension between two staggered holes (gage)

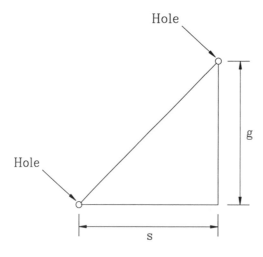

Figure 3.1 Holes and Stagger

3.5   EXAMPLE PROBLEM

3.5.1   EXAMPLE PROBLEM 1 — NET AREA A_n OF FLAT BAR

Determine the net area, A_n, for a flat bar with holes for $7/8$-in.-diameter bolts provided as shown in Fig. P3.5.1 (a).

Solution

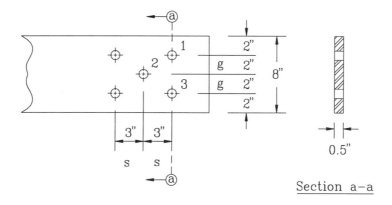

Fig. P3.5.1 (a)

A_n for the non-staggered condition along line (a-1-3-a) is:

$$A_n = A_g - \Sigma n (d+1/8) t$$
$$= 8 \times 1/2 - 2 (7/8+1/8) 1/2$$
$$= 4 - 1 = 3.00 \text{ in.}^2$$

A_n for the staggered condition along line (a-1-2-3-a) is:

$$A_n = A_g - \Sigma n (d+1/8) t + \Sigma \frac{s^2}{4g} t$$

$$= 8 \times 0.5 - 3 (7/8+1/8) (0.5) + 2 \left(\frac{3^2}{4 \times 2}\right) 1/2$$

$$= 4 - 1.5 + 1.125 = 3.63 \text{ in.}^2$$

Therefore, the least A_n is equal to 3.0 in.^{2}

3.6   EFFECTIVE NET AREA, A_e

3.6.1   STRUCTURAL SHAPES

A structural shape consists of elements that make its shape (Figure 3.2). For example, a wide flange shape consists of three elements (two flanges and one web). An angle consists of two elements (one element for each leg).

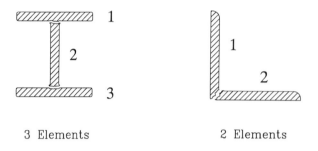

Figure 3.2 Elements of a Section

When the load is transmitted to all the elements of a cross section through connectors, the effective net area, A_e, is equal to net area, A_n.

When the load through the connectors is transmitted to some but not all elements of the section, then the areas are reduced by the reduction coefficient, U.

For members connected by bolted and riveted connections,

$$A_e = U \times A_n$$

For members connected by welded connections,

$$A_e = U \times A_g$$

where

A_e is the total effective net area of a tensile member when the load is transmitted through some but not all the cross-sectional elements of the member.

U   is a reduction coefficient in accordance with the AISC Section B3 (M5-34).

U   = 1.0   When the tensile load is transmitted by bolts through all the cross-sectional elements of a member (Figure 3.3).

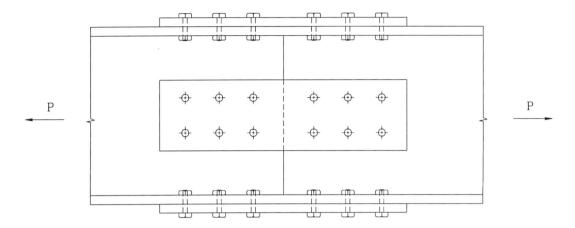

Figure 3.3 Load Transmitted Through All Elements

U = 0.9   When the tensile load is transmitted by bolts through the flanges of W, M, or S shapes with flange widths $b_f \geq 2/3d$, where d is the depth of the member and for structural tees cut from these shapes, provided the connection has at least three bolts in each line parallel to the tensile load (Figure 3.4).

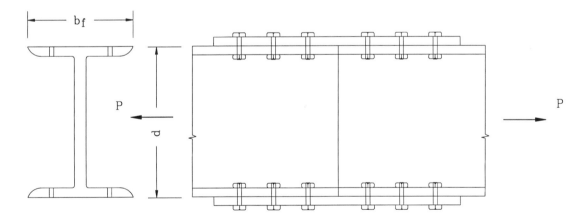

Figure 3.4 Load Not Transmitted Through All Elements

U = 0.85   When the tensile load is transmitted by bolts through some but not all the cross-sectional elements of a member for all shapes not meeting the preceding conditions and provided that the connection has at least three bolts in each line parallel to the tensile load (Figure 3.5).

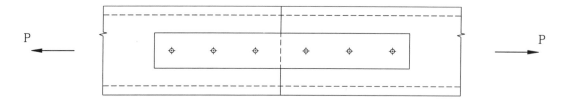

Figure 3.5 Connections with at Least Three Bolts in Each Line.

U = 0.75   When the tensile load is transmitted by bolts through some but not all the cross-sectional elements of a member and with only two bolts in each line parallel to the tensile load (Figure 3.6).

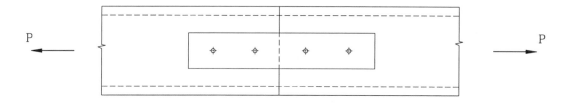

Figure 3.6 Connections with at Least Two Bolts in Each Line.

U values for welded connections as provided in AISC Manual (M5-34) are as follows:

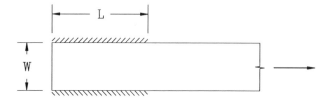

Figure 3.7 Welded Connections

U = 1.00   when L > 2W

U = 0.87   when 2W > L > 1.5W

U = 0.75   when 1.5W > L > W

where

L = weld length, in.

W = plate width (distance between welds), in.

3.6.2 THREADED RODS

A_D is the tensile stress area of a threaded rod based on the gross area of the rod computed with the major thread diameter. For determining A_D refer to Table 3.1 (M4-147).

For example, the tensile stress area of a 2-in.-diameter threaded rod is equal to 3.142 in.^{2}

Table 3.1 Properties of Threaded Fasteners (AISC M4-147)

SCREW THREADS
Unified Standard Series—UNC/UNRC and 4UN/4UNR
ANSI B1.1–1982

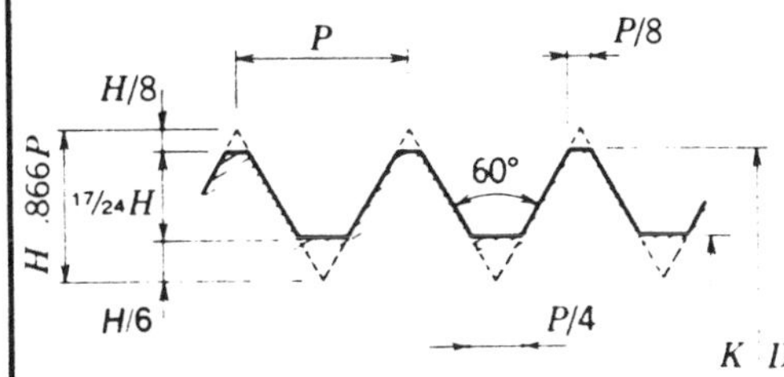

Thread Dimensions 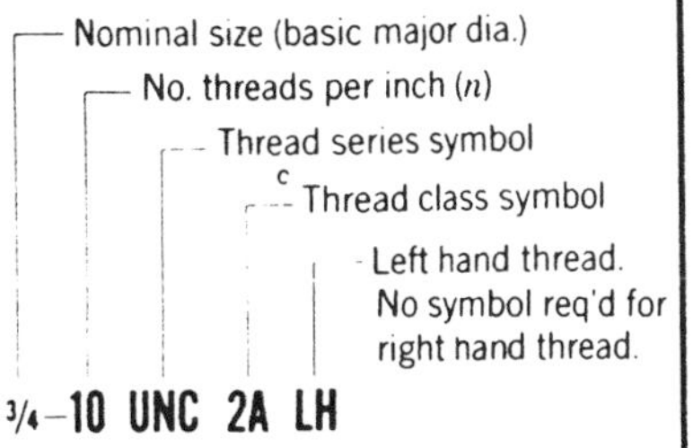 — Standard Designations

¾–10 UNC 2A LH
- Nominal size (basic major dia.)
- No. threads per inch (n)
- Thread series symbol
- Thread class symbol [c]
- Left hand thread. No symbol req'd for right hand thread.

Basic Major D (In.)	Min. Root K (In.)	Gross A_D (In.^{2})	Min. Root A_K (In.^{2})	Tensile[a] Stress (In.^{2})	Th'ds[b] per In. n	Basic Major D (In.)	Min. Root K (In.)	Gross A_D (In.^{2})	Min. Root A_K (In.^{2})	Tensile[a] Stress (In.^{2})	Th'ds[b] per In. n
¼	.189	.049	.028	.032	20	2¾	2.443	5.940	4.69	4.93	4
⅜	.298	.110	.070	.078	16	3	2.693	7.069	5.70	5.97	4
½	.406	.196	.129	.142	13	3¼	2.943	8.296	6.80	7.10	4
⅝	.514	.307	.207	.226	11	3½	3.193	9.621	8.01	8.33	4
¾	.627	.442	.309	.334	10	3¾	3.443	11.045	9.31	9.66	4
⅞	.739	.601	.429	.462	9	4	3.693	12.566	10.71	11.1	4
1	.847	.785	.563	.606	8	4¼	3.943	14.186	12.2	12.6	4
1⅛	.950	.994	.709	.763	7	4½	4.193	15.904	13.8	14.2	4
1¼	1.075	1.227	.908	.969	7	4¾	4.443	17.721	15.5	15.9	4
1⅜	1.171	1.485	1.08	1.16	6	5	4.693	19.635	17.3	17.8	4
1½	1.296	1.767	1.32	1.41	6	5¼	4.943	21.648	19.2	19.7	4
1¾	1.505	2.405	1.78	1.90	5	5½	5.193	23.758	21.2	21.7	4
2	1.727	3.142	2.34	2.50	4½	5¾	5.443	25.967	23.3	23.8	4
2¼	1.977	3.976	3.07	3.25	4½	6	5.693	28.274	25.5	26.0	4
2½	2.193	4.909	3.78	4.00	4						

[a]Tensile stress area $= 0.7854 \left(D - \dfrac{.9743}{n} \right)^2$

[b]For basic major diameters of ¼ to 4 in. incl., thread series is UNC (coarse); for 4¼ in. dia. and larger, thread series is 4UN.

[c]2A denotes Class 2A fit applicable to external threads, 2B denotes corresponding Class 2B fit for internal threads.

MINIMUM LENGTH OF THREAD ON BOLTS
ANSI B18.2.1–1972

Length of Bolt	Diameter of Bolt D, In.																
	¼	⅜	½	⅝	¾	⅞	1	1⅛	1¼	1⅜	1½	1¾	2	2¼	2½	2¾	3
To 6 in. Incl.	¾	1	1¼	1½	1¾	2	2¼	2½	2¾	3	3¼	3¾	4¼	4¾	5¼	5¾	6¼
Over 6 in.	1	1¼	1½	1¾	2	2¼	2½	2¾	3	3¼	3½	4	4½	5	5½	6	6½

Thread length for bolts up to 6 in. long is $2D + ¼$. For bolts over 6-in. long, thread length is $2D + ½$. These proportions may be used to compute thread length for diameters not shown in the table. Bolts which are too short for listed or computed thread lengths are threaded as close to the head as possible.

For thread lengths for high-strength bolts, refer to *Allowable Stress Design Specification for Structural Joints Using ASTM A325 or A490 Bolts.*

3.6.3   GUSSET PLATES

In accordance with Chapter B (M5-33), the effective net area for a gusset plate or other connection fittings subject to tensile force shall be taken as the actual net area but not greater than $0.85 \, A_g$. This is known as the 85% rule.

A_e = minimum value of $\{A_n, 0.85 \, A_g\}$

3.7   SLENDERNESS RATIO

In accordance with Chapter B, Section B7 of the AISC Specifications (M5-37), the maximum slenderness ratio, L/r, of a tension member, other than rods preferably should not exceed the value of 300, where L is the length of member and r is the least radius of gyration.

Remarks:

1. The least radius of gyration for a single angle is r_z.

2. The least radius of gyration for a built-up member is the minimum value obtained from the following equations:

$$r_x = \sqrt{\frac{I_x}{A}} \; ; \; r_y = \sqrt{\frac{I_y}{A}}$$

Least radius of gyration for various shapes are listed in the first portion of AISC Manual.

Note: In accordance with AISC Section D2, (M5-40), built-up tension members separated from one another by intermittent fillers shall be connected at these fillers at intervals such that the slenderness ratio of a single member between the fillers is equal and less than 300.

3.8   PIN-CONNECTED MEMBERS

Pin-connected members consist of eye bars and pin-connected plates. Their design requirements are described in Section D3 of the AISC Specifications (M5-41). Some of the design requirements are listed below.

$$A_n = A_g - \left(d + \frac{1}{32}\right) t$$

3.8.1   EYE BARS

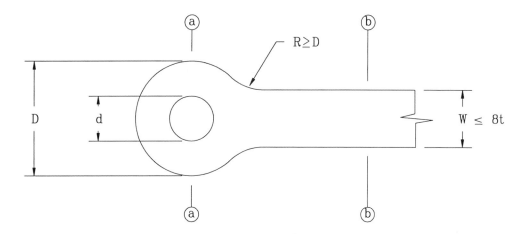

Figure 3.8 Eye Bar

$W \leq 8t$ with $t \geq 1/2$

$A_g = W \times t$

$A_n = A_g - 1 \left(d + \frac{1}{32} \right) t$

$^3/_4 \, W \geq \left(\frac{D - d}{2} \; = \; d_e \right) \geq {}^2/_3 \, W$

Diameter of pin $= \; d_p \geq \frac{7}{8} W$

Diameter of pin hole $= d = d_p + \frac{1}{32}$

Tensile stress along line a-a $= f_t = \dfrac{P}{A_n} \; \leq \; 0.45 F_y$

Tensile stress along line b-b $= f_t = \dfrac{P}{Wt} \; \leq \; 0.60 \; F_y$

3.8.2   PIN-CONNECTED PLATES

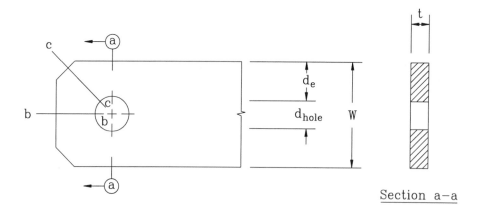

Figure 3.9 Pin-Connected Plates

Diameter of pin $= d_p$

Diameter of pin hole $= d_p + \dfrac{1}{32} = d_{hole}$

$d_e \leq 0.8\, d$

Edge distance from edge of hole $= d_e \leq 4t$

$A_g = W \times t$

A_n along line a-a $= A_g - 1 \left(d + \dfrac{1}{32} \right) t$

A_n along line b-b $\geq$ 2/3 of A_n along line a-a

A_n along line c-c $\geq A_n$ along line b-b

Tensile stress along line a-a $= f_t = \dfrac{P}{A_n} \leq 0.45\ F_y$

Bearing stress at pin hole $= f_b = \dfrac{P}{d\ t} \leq 0.9\ F_y$

3.9 ⚓ DESIGN PROCEDURE FOR TENSION MEMBERS WITH BOLTED CONNECTIONS

Given:

Tensile load, P_t, length of member, L, grade of material, connection details, and desired shape.

Required:

The most economical desired shape

Procedure:

1. Determine the value of F_y and F_u from (M1-7).

2. Determine the required area, A_g.

$$A_g = \frac{P_t}{0.6 \times F_y}$$

3. Select a desired shape from Part 1 of the AISC Manual whose area, A_g, is slightly greater than the required area, A_g, obtained in Step 2 above.

4. Determine A_n and U and calculate the effective area, A_e, for the selected shape.

$$A_e = U \times A_n$$

5. Calculate the actual tensile stress due to the effective area, A_e, and compare it to the allowable tensile stress.

$$f_t = \frac{P_t}{A_e} \leq 0.5 \, F_u$$

6. Calculate the slenderness ratio, L/r_{min}, for the selected member and compare it to the recommended values by the AISC Specifications. The selected shape will be adequate if Steps 5 and 6 above are satisfied. If not satisfied, then select a heavier shape and repeat Steps 4 through 6.

3.10   EXAMPLE PROBLEMS

3.10.1   EXAMPLE PROBLEM 1 — DESIGN OF A TENSILE MEMBER

Design for the lightest W12 shape to support a tensile load of 400 kip. The ends of the member have holes for $7/8$-in.-diameter fasteners in the web and flanges as shown. The length of the member is 20 ft (ASTM A36 material).

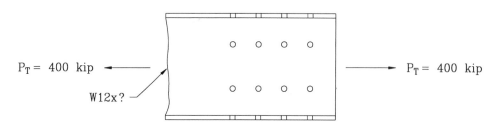

Fig. P3.10.1 (a)

Solution

1. For ASTM A36 material, $F_y = 36$ ksi and $F_u = 58$ ksi

2. A_g required: $\dfrac{P}{0.6\ F_y} = \dfrac{400}{0.6 \times 36} = 18.5$ in.^{2}

3. From M1-24, select a W12 × 65 whose $A_g = 19.1$ in.$^2 > 18.5$ in.^{2}

4. $U = 1.0$, because all elements are connected to transfer the tensile load.

$$A_n = A_g - \sum n \left(d + \frac{1}{8}\right) t$$

$$= 19.1 - \left[4 \left(\frac{7}{8} + \frac{1}{8}\right) \times 0.605\right] - \left[2 \left(\frac{7}{8} + \frac{1}{8}\right) \times 0.39\right]$$

$$= 15.9 \text{ in.}^2$$

$$A_e = U \times A_n = 1.0 \times 15.9 = 15.9 \text{ in.}^2$$

5. $f_t = \dfrac{P}{A_e} = \dfrac{400}{15.9} = 25.16 < 0.5\ F_u = 0.5 \times 58 = 29$ ksi   OK

6. $\dfrac{L}{r} = \dfrac{(20 \times 12)}{3.02} = 79.47 < 300$ OK

3.10.2 EXAMPLE PROBLEM 2 — TENSION MEMBER, THREADED ROD

For the laterally supported frame shown below, design the threaded tie rod. Material is ASTM A307.

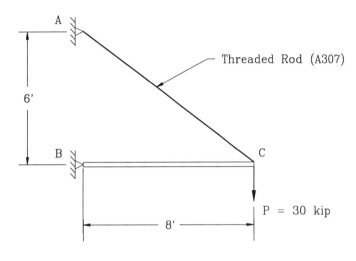

Threaded Rod (A307)

6'

B

C

P = 30 kip

8'

Fig. P3.10.2 (a)

Solution

For ASTM A307 material, $F_u = 60$ ksi   (M4-4)

Using the method of joints at Joint C, obtain the force in the tie rod, AC.

Tensile force, P, in tie rod, AC = 50 kip

Required $A_t = \dfrac{P}{0.33 \times F_u} = \dfrac{50}{0.33 \times 60} = 2.5$ in.^{2}

From M4-147, select a 2-in.-diameter rod.

Note: The slenderness ratio, L/r, does not have to be checked for rods. However, to obtain some kind of rigidity it is a common practice to select a rod whose diameter $\geq$ L/500.

3.11   ALLOWABLE LOADS FOR TENSION MEMBERS

Given:

Shape, length of member, L, grade of material, connection details.

Required:

Find the allowable tensile load, P.

Procedure:

1.   Determine the value of F_y and F_u from M1-7.

2.   Determine the allowable load.

For members with no holes and load being transmitted through all elements

$$P_{all} = 0.6\, F_y\, (A_g)$$

For members with bolt holes

P_{all} = least value of P_1 or P_2
P_1 = $0.6\, F_y\, (A_g)$
P_2 = $0.5\, F_u\, (A_e)$

For pin-connected plates and eye bars, refer to AISC Specification Section D3, M4-147

P_{all} = least value of P_1 or P_3
P_1 = $0.6\, F_y\, (A_g)$
P_3 = $0.45\, F_y\, (A_n)$

For threaded rods

$$P_{all} = 0.33\, F_u\, (A_D)$$

For threaded rods with upset ends   (M4-3)

$P_{all} = 0.6\, F_y A_b \leq 0.33\, F_u A_D$ where A_b is the nominal body area of the rod before upsetting

3.12   EXAMPLE PROBLEMS

3.12.1   EXAMPLE PROBLEM 1 — TENSION MEMBER, WELDED ENDS

Determine the allowable tensile load, P, that can be applied on a single angle $3 \times 3 \times {}^{1}/_{4}$ which is welded to a gusset plate. Material is ASTM A36.

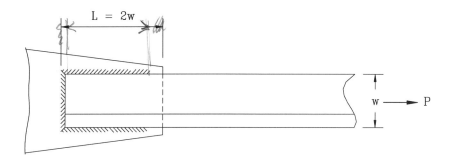

Fig. P3.12.1 (a) Welded Connection

Solution

$F_y = 36$ ksi and $F_u = 58$ ksi

A_g for L $3 \times 3 \times 1/4 = 1.44$ (M1-49).

$P_1 = 0.6\, F_y\, A_g$

$\quad = 0.6 \times 36 \times 1.44 = 31.1$ kip (governs)

$P_2 = 0.5\, F_u\, A_e$

$\quad = 0.5 \times 58 \times U \times A_n$

$\quad = 0.5 \times 58 \times 1.0 \times 1.44 = 41.76$ kip

$U = 1$, because longitudinal welds are $> 2w$ ... M5-34 (see also pg. 6-26)

3.12.2 EXAMPLE PROBLEM 2 — TENSION MEMBER, BOLTED ENDS

Determine the allowable tensile load, P, that can be applied on a single angle $3 \times 3 \times \frac{1}{4}$, which is bolted with a single row of $\frac{7}{8}$-in. bolts. Material is ASTM A36.

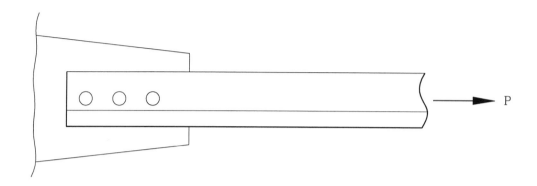

Fig. P3.12.2 (a) Non-Staggered Bolted Connection

Solution

$F_y = 36$ ksi and $F_u = 58$ ksi

$P_1 = 0.6 \, F_y \, A_g$

$\quad = 0.6 \times 36 \times 1.44$

$P_1 = 31.1$ kip

$P_2 = 0.5 \, F_u \, A_e$

$\quad = 0.5 \, F_u \, U \, A_n$

$\quad = 0.5 \, F_u \, U \left[A_g - \sum n \left(d + \frac{1}{8} \right) t \right]$

$\quad = 0.5 \times 58 \times 0.85 \left[1.44 - 1 \left(\frac{7}{8} + \frac{1}{8} \right) \frac{1}{4} \right]$

$P_2 = 29.3$ kip (governs)

The allowable load is equal to 29.3 kip, which is the smaller value obtained from calculating P_1 and P_2.

3.12.3   EXAMPLE PROBLEM 3 — TENSION MEMBER, BOLTED ENDS

Determine the allowable tensile load, P, that can be applied on the member shown below. Material is ASTM A36 and all holes are for $^7/_8$-in.-diameter bolts.

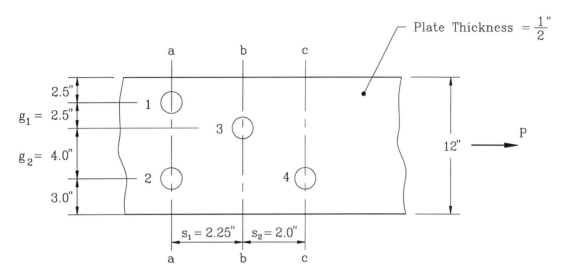

Fig. P3.12.3 (a) Staggered Bolted Connection

Solution

F_y = 36 ksi and F_u = 58 ksi

P_1 = $0.6 \, F_y \, A_g$

$\qquad$ = $0.6 \times 36 \times \left(12 \times \dfrac{1}{2}\right)$

$\qquad$ = 129.6 kip

P_2 = $0.5 \, F_u \, A_e$ = $0.5 \, F_u \, U \, A_n$

U = 1.0 (one element, 3 bolts in a row)

A_n: Along path (a-1-2-a) the holes are non-staggered

$\qquad A_n = A_g - \sum n \left(d + \dfrac{1}{8}\right) t$

$\qquad\quad$ = $12 \times \dfrac{1}{2} - 2 \left(\dfrac{7}{8} + \dfrac{1}{8}\right) \dfrac{1}{2}$

$\qquad\quad$ = 5.0 in.^{2}

A_n: Along path (a-1-3-2-a) the holes are staggered

$\qquad A_n = A_g - \sum n \left(d + \dfrac{1}{8}\right) t + \sum \dfrac{s^2}{4g} \times t$

$\qquad\quad$ = $\left(12 \times \dfrac{1}{2}\right) - \left[3 \left(\dfrac{7}{8} + \dfrac{1}{8}\right) \dfrac{1}{2}\right] + \left(\dfrac{2.25^2}{4 \times 2.5} \times \dfrac{1}{2}\right) + \left(\dfrac{2.25^2}{4 \times 4} \times \dfrac{1}{2}\right)$

$\qquad\quad$ = $6 - 1.5 + 0.25 + 0.16$

$\qquad\quad$ = 4.91 in.^{2}

A_n: Along path (a-1-3-4-c) the holes are staggered:

$$A_n = A_g - \sum n \left(d + \frac{1}{8}\right) t + \sum \frac{s^2}{4g} \times t$$

$$= \left(12 \times \frac{1}{2}\right) - \left[3 \left(\frac{7}{8} + \frac{1}{8}\right)\frac{1}{2}\right] + \left(\frac{2.25^2}{4 \times 2.5} \times \frac{1}{2}\right) + \left(\frac{2^2}{4 \times 4} \times \frac{1}{2}\right)$$

$$= 6 - 1.5 + 0.25 + 0.125$$

$$= 4.9 \text{ in.}^2$$

The least value of A_n is equal to 4.9 in.^{2}

$$P_2 = 0.5 \times 58 \times 1.0 \times 4.9 = 142.1 \text{ kip}$$

Therefore, the allowable load is equal to 129.6 kip which is the smaller value of P_1 and P_2.

3.12.4   EXAMPLE PROBLEM 4 — PIN-CONNECTED PLATE

What is the allowable tensile load, P, that can be applied on the pin-connected plate shown in Figure P3.12.4 (a)? Material is ASTM A441. Pin diameter is 2.5 in. and the thickness of the plate is $^1/_2$ inch.

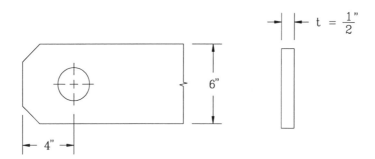

Fig. P3.12.4 (a)

Solution

For ASTM A441 material and a plate thickness of $^1/_2$ in., the values of $F_y = 50$ ksi and $F_u = 70$ ksi obtained from (M1-7).

$$P_1 = 0.6 F_y A_g = 0.6 \times 50 \times 6 \times \frac{1}{2} = 90 \text{ kip}$$

$$P_2 = 0.45 F_y A_n = 0.45 \times 50 \left[6 - 1 \left(2.5 + \frac{1}{32}\right)\right]\frac{1}{2} = 39.02 \text{ kip}$$

Therefore, the allowable tensile load, P, is 39.02 kip.

Need to also look @ pinhole stress. See pg 6-30

3.12.5   EXAMPLE PROBLEM 5 — TENSION MEMBER, WELDED ENDS

Check if member AB in the truss frame shown in Fig. P3.12.5 (a) is adequate for the applied uniform load.

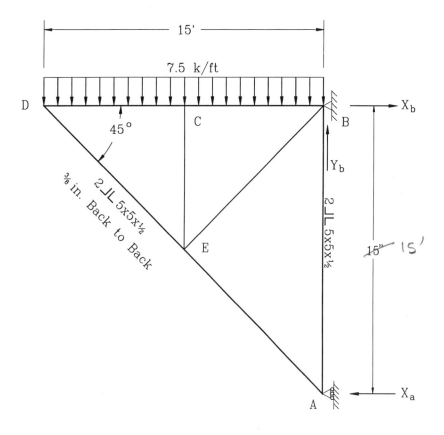

Fig. P3.12.5 (a) Frame with Uniform Load

Solution

Take moments about Joint B

$$M_B = 0 = 7.5 (15) 15/2 = 15 X_A$$
$$X_A = 56.2 \text{ kip, which is the horizontal reaction at A. } (tension)$$

Using the Method of Joints, the forces at Joint A in members AB and AE are obtained

$$T_{AB} = 56.2 \text{ kip (Tension)}$$
$$C_{AE} = 79.5 \text{ kip (Compression)}$$

Assume the truss frame is connected at the joints by welding with no holes.

Member AB is in tension, and $A_g = 9.50$ in.^{2} (M1-76).

For ASTM A36 material, $F_y = 36$ ksi and $F_u = 58$ ksi.

$$f_t = \frac{P}{A_g} = \frac{56.2}{9.50} = 5.92 \text{ ksi} \leq 0.6 F_y = 21.6 \text{ ksi}$$

Therefore, member AB is adequate.

3.12.6   EXAMPLE PROBLEM 6 — PLASTIC DESIGN

A rigid weight, W, is supported by three steel wires as shown. Area of each wire is 1 in.^{2} F_y = 36 ksi. Length of wires 1 and 3 is 10 ft. Length of wire 2 is 5 ft. Find the maximum load, W, that may be applied to the three wires using:

A.   Elastic design method using allowable stress = 0.6 F_y

B.   Plastic design method using a load factor of 1.7

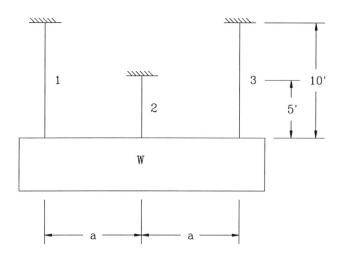

Fig. P3.12.6 (a)

Solution

$E = 29 \times 10^3$ ksi

A.   Elastic Design:

Let σ_1, σ_2, and σ_3 equal to the stress in ksi in each rod respectively.

$$T_1 \ = \ \sigma_1 A_1$$

$$T_2 \ = \ \sigma_2 A_2$$

$$T_3 \ = \ \sigma_3 A_3$$

Let Δ = deflection of weight, W

$$\Delta \ = \ \varepsilon_1 L_1 \ = \ \varepsilon_2 L_2 \ = \ \varepsilon_3 L_3$$

$$\sigma_1 \ = \ E\varepsilon_1 \ = \ \frac{E\Delta}{L_1}$$

$$\sigma_2 \ = \ E\varepsilon_2 \ = \ \frac{E\Delta}{L_2}$$

$$\sigma_3 \ = \ E\varepsilon_3 \ = \ \frac{E\Delta}{L_3}$$

Since $L_2 < L_1 = L_3$, Bar 2 has maximum stress.

$$\sigma_2 = \frac{E\Delta}{5 \times 12} \le 0.6 \, F_y = 21.6 \text{ ksi}$$

$$\Delta \le \frac{21.6 \times 5 \times 12}{29 \times 10^3} = 0.0448 \text{ in.}$$

$$\sum F_y = 0 \qquad\qquad W = T_1 + T_2 + T_3$$

Fig. P3.12.6 (b) Free-Body Diagram

For $\Delta = 0.0448$ in.:

$$T_1 = \sigma_1 \times A_1 = \frac{E\Delta}{L_1} \times A_1 = \frac{(29 \times 10^3)(0.0448)}{10 \times 12} \times 1 = 10.83 \text{ kip}$$

$$T_2 = \sigma_2 \times A_2 = \frac{E\Delta}{L_2} \times A_2 = \frac{(29 \times 10^3)(0.0448)}{5 \times 12} \times 1 = 21.65 \text{ kip}$$

$$T_3 = \sigma_3 \times A_3 = \frac{E\Delta}{L_3} \times A_3 = \frac{(29 \times 10^3)(0.0448)}{10 \times 12} \times 1 = 10.83 \text{ kip}$$

$$W = 10.83 + 21.65 + 10.83 = 43.31 \text{ kip}$$

Therefore, the maximum load, W, that may be applied for a maximum allowable stress of 0.6 F_y is 43.31 kip. This result was obtained by using elastic design methods.

B. Plastic Design:

Using plastic design method, find the allowable load, W, with a safety factor of 1.7. Some basic concepts concerning plastic design of axially loaded members are reviewed here.

For A36 steel, the approximate or the idealized stress-strain diagram is shown below. Please note that after F_y is attained, increasing strains will not produce increased stresses.

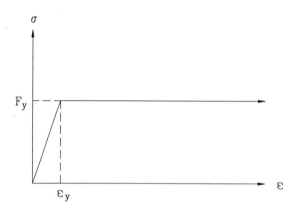

Fig. P3.12.6 (c) Stress-Strain Diagram

In plastic design, it is possible that some members in the structure will yield at the designed allowable loads. However, the structure will not collapse since the remaining members of the structure which have not attained the yielding stage will take the load. That is, redistribution of the stress or moment will occur in the structure.

From Part A, it is concluded that the middle rod has the highest stress. Therefore, this rod will reach the yield stress first. However, even though $\sigma_2 = F_y$, bars 1 and 3 have stresses of $\sigma_1 = \sigma_3 = 0.5\ F_y$. Therefore, bars 1 and 3 are still elastic when bar 2 has attained the yield stress. Let us increase W, and we see that the stress in bar 2 remains the same because A36 steel has the stress-strain diagram shown above. Bars 1 and 3, therefore, must take up the additional load. As W is increased, bars 1 and 3 will also reach the yield stress. When this happens, all three bars have yielded and any additional load will cause collapse of the bar system. The load required to produce yield stress in all three bars is denoted as W_p = plastic load capacity of this system. To obtain the allowable load, we simply divide by the safety factor.

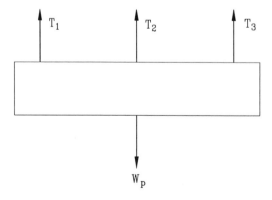

Fig. P3.12.6 (d) Free-Body Diagram

Hence,

$$T_1 = F_y A_1 \quad = 36\,(1) \quad = 36 \text{ kip}$$
$$T_2 = F_y A_2 \quad = 36\,(1) \quad = 36 \text{ kip}$$
$$T_3 = F_y A_3 \quad = 36\,(1) \quad = 36 \text{ kip}$$
$$W_P = T_1 + T_2 + T_3$$
$$W_P = 3\,(36) \quad = 108 \text{ kip}$$

For $W_P = 108$ kip, the three bars have all attained the yield stress and a load of $W_P + \Delta W$ will cause collapse of the bar system. ΔW is a small increment in the load.

The allowable load obtained by using plastic design methods is as follows:

$$W_{allow} \;=\; \frac{W_p}{SF} \;=\; \frac{108}{1.7} \;=\; 63.53 \text{ kip}$$

As you can see, the allowable load obtained by plastic methods is considerably greater than that obtained in the elastic method. In general, the plastic design gives more economical sections than the elastic design, since the reserve strength in a highly indeterminate structure is taken into account.

In a way; this also means that the factor safety under elastic design is decreased.

3.13   P. E. PROBLEM

3.13.1   P. E. PROBLEM 1 — DESIGN OF TIE ROD

For the structure shown in Fig. P3.13.1 (a), select an appropriate W6 section for the beam and design the tie rod. The rod has threads and is attached to the beam as shown. The beam supports a hanging sign from three points and the sign weighs 3,000 lb. Two horizontal supports in the plane of the beam are provided at the same location as the rod. Use A36 steel and latest AISC specifications.

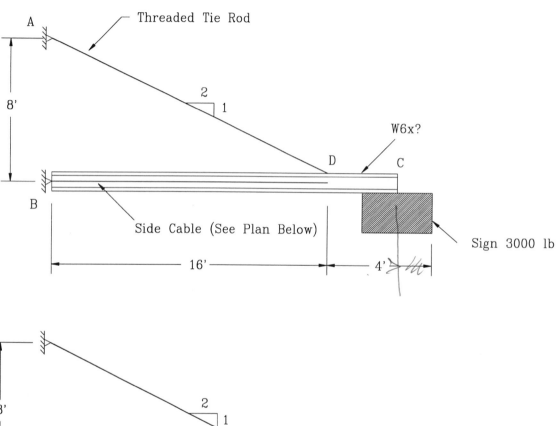

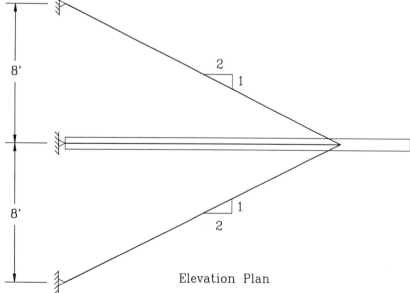

Fig. P3.13.1 (a)

Solution

1. Determine the load in the threaded rod and the W6 beam:

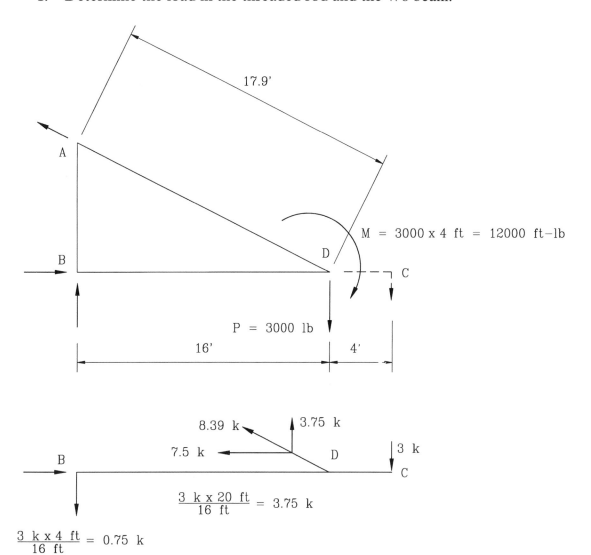

Fig. P3.13.1 (b)

$$\text{Load in AD (threaded rod)} = \frac{3750 \times 17.9}{8} = 8{,}390 \text{ lb}$$

$$\text{Load in BC (W6 beam)} = \frac{3750 \times 16}{8} = 7{,}500 \text{ lb}$$

2.   Determine required size of threaded rod AD:

$$f_t = \frac{P}{A_D} \leq F_t = 0.33F_u$$

$$\frac{P}{F_t} \leq A_D$$

Area required $= \dfrac{8390}{0.33 \times 58,000} = 0.438 \text{ in.}^2$

Select $^3/_4$-in.-diameter threaded rod from M4-147, where

$$A_D = 0.442 \text{ in.}^2 > 0.438 \text{ in.}^2$$

3.   Note slenderness ratio check is not required because cables and rods are excluded from limits imposed by AISC.

4.   Selecting the appropriate W6 section:

The W6 section is subjected to combined axial force, P = 7.5 kip

plus a bending moment = 12 ft-kip as shown below.

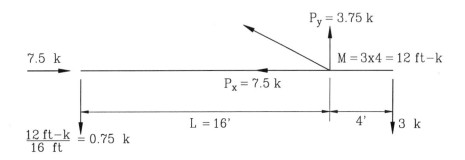

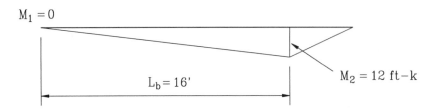

Moment Diagram

Fig. P3.13.1 (c)

Assume both ends of the W6 section are pinned.

Therefore, K = 1.0 and KL = 1.0 × 16 = 16

Since the W6 section is braced and not allowed to sway
Therefore,

$$C_{mx} = 0.6 - 0.4 \; (\delta) \left(\frac{M_1}{M_2} \right) \geq 0.4$$

$$= 0.6 - 0.4 \times (-1) \times \frac{0}{12} = 0.6$$

Trial number 1

$$P_{eff} = P_0 + mM_x + mM_y u$$

$$= 7.5 + 2.2 \times \frac{0.6}{0.85} \times 12 + 0 = 26.135 \text{ kip}$$

Select W6 $\times$ 15 whose $P_{all} = 38 > 26.135$
Trial number 2

$$P_{eff} = P_0 + mM_x + mM_y u$$

$$= 7.5 + 2.0 \times \frac{0.6}{0.85} \times 12 + 0 = 24.44 \text{ kip}$$

again select W6 $\times$ 15 where $P_{all} = 38 > 24.44$
Check W6 $\times$ 15 using the modified equations

$$f_a = \frac{P}{A} = \frac{7.5}{4.43} = 1.69 \text{ ksi}$$

$$F_a = \frac{P_{all}}{A} = \frac{38}{4.43} = 8.57$$

$$\frac{f_a}{F_a} = \frac{1.69}{8.57} = 0.198 > 0.15$$

Therefore, check both equations (H1-1) and (H1-2).

Equation (H1-1) modified

$$7.5 + 0.456 \times 12 \times 12 \times 0.6 \times \frac{8.57}{22} \left(\frac{4.33 \times 10^6}{4.33 \times 10^6 - 6 \times (6 \times 12)^2} \right)$$

$$7.5 \times (1 \times 16 \times 12)^2$$

$$= 22.96 \text{ kip} < 38 \qquad \text{OK}$$

Equation (H1-2) modified

$$7.5 \times \frac{8.57}{0.6 \times 36} + 0.456 \times 12 \times 12 \times \frac{8.57}{22}$$

$$= 28.56 \text{ kip} < 38 \qquad \text{OK}$$

Therefore, W6 $\times$ 15   OK for use

4

COMPRESSION MEMBERS

4.1 COMPRESSION MEMBERS

Compression members are members that are subjected to axial compressive loads. The capacity or strength of compression members are affected by the following:

1. Material imperfections
2. Type of end restraints
3. Initial crookedness
4. Eccentric loads on columns
5. Residual stresses
6. Length of column
7. Type of material
8. Geometric shape

4.2 COMPRESSIVE STRESS

$$f_a = P/A \leq F_a$$

where

f_a = Actual compression stress

P = Axial compression load

A = Cross-sectional area of the member

F_a = Allowable compression stress

4.3 ALLOWABLE COMPRESSION STRESSES

Chapter E of the AISC Specifications, M5-42, provides allowable stresses for the following three types of compression members:

1. Short members
2. Long members

4.3.1 SHORT COMPRESSION MEMBERS

Short compression members are members whose slenderness ratio, KL/r, is less than the value of C_c. Their failures take place because of compression yielding. The allowable stresses for short columns are computed by the AISC Equation E2-1, M5-42 as shown below.

$$F_a = \frac{\left[1 - \frac{(KL/r)^2}{2\,C_c^2}\right]F_y}{\frac{5}{3} + \frac{3\,(KL/r)}{8\,C_c} - \frac{(KL/r)^3}{8\,C_c^3}} \tag{E2-1}$$

$$\text{Where} \quad C_c = \sqrt{\frac{2\pi^2\,E}{F_y}}$$

The value of C_c is equal to slenderness ratio, KL/r, which divides long compression member from short compression member. For example, the C_c value for 36-ksi material is 126.1 and for 50-ksi material is 107.0.

4.3.2 LONG COMPRESSION MEMBERS

Long compression members are those whose slenderness ratio, KL/r, are greater than the value of C_c. Their failures take place because of buckling instability. The allowable stresses for long columns are computed by the AISC Equation E2-2 shown below which is based on Euler analysis.

$$F_a = \frac{12\,\pi^2\,E}{23\,(KL/r)^2} \tag{E2-2}$$

Allowable compressive stresses can be presented as shown in Figure 4.1. Table 4.1, taken from AISC Table C-36 (M3-16), lists the allowable compression stresses for long and short columns for material with 36 ksi as yield stress.

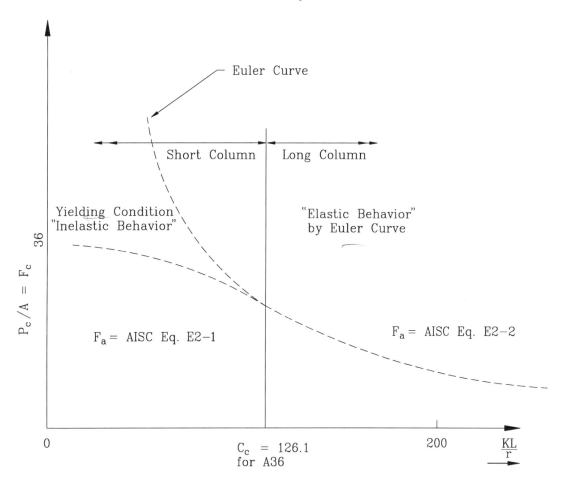

Figure 4.1 Allowable Stresses Curve for Compression Members with Respect to Slenderness Ratio

Table 4.1 Allowable Stress for Compression Members for 36-ksi Material
(AISC Table C-36, M3-16)

Table C-36
Allowable Stress
For Compression Members of 36-ksi Specified Yield Stress Steel[a]

$F_y = 36$ ksi

$\frac{Kl}{r}$	F_a (ksi)	$\frac{Kl}{r}$	F_a (ksi)	$\frac{Kl}{r}$	F_a (ksi)	$\frac{Kl}{r}$	F_a (ksi)	$\frac{Kl}{r}$	F_a (ksi)
1	21.56	41	19.11	81	15.24	121	10.14	161	5.76
2	21.52	42	19.03	82	15.13	122	9.99	162	5.69
3	21.48	43	18.95	83	15.02	123	9.85	163	5.62
4	21.44	44	18.86	84	14.90	124	9.70	164	5.55
5	21.39	45	18.78	85	14.79	125	9.55	165	5.49
6	21.35	46	18.70	86	14.67	126	9.41	166	5.42
7	21.30	47	18.61	87	14.56	127	9.26	167	5.35
8	21.25	48	18.53	88	14.44	128	9.11	168	5.29
9	21.21	49	18.44	89	14.32	129	8.97	169	5.23
10	21.16	50	18.35	90	14.20	130	8.84	170	5.17
11	21.10	51	18.26	91	14.09	131	8.70	171	5.11
12	21.05	52	18.17	92	13.97	132	8.57	172	5.05
13	21.00	53	18.08	93	13.84	133	8.44	173	4.99
14	20.95	54	17.99	94	13.72	134	8.32	174	4.93
15	20.89	55	17.90	95	13.60	135	8.19	175	4.88
16	20.83	56	17.81	96	13.48	136	8.07	176	4.82
17	20.78	57	17.71	97	13.35	137	7.96	177	4.77
18	20.72	58	17.62	98	13.23	138	7.84	178	4.71
19	20.66	59	17.53	99	13.10	139	7.73	179	4.66
20	20.60	60	17.43	100	12.98	140	7.62	180	4.61
21	20.54	61	17.33	101	12.85	141	7.51	181	4.56
22	20.48	62	17.24	102	12.72	142	7.41	182	4.51
23	20.41	63	17.14	103	12.59	143	7.30	183	4.46
24	20.35	64	17.04	104	12.47	144	7.20	184	4.41
25	20.28	65	16.94	105	12.33	145	7.10	185	4.36
26	20.22	66	16.84	106	12.20	146	7.01	186	4.32
27	20.15	67	16.74	107	12.07	147	6.91	187	4.27
28	20.08	68	16.64	108	11.94	148	6.82	188	4.23
29	20.01	69	16.53	109	11.81	149	6.73	189	4.18
30	19.94	70	16.43	110	11.67	150	6.64	190	4.14
31	19.87	71	16.33	111	11.54	151	6.55	191	4.09
32	19.80	72	16.22	112	11.40	152	6.46	192	4.05
33	19.73	73	16.12	113	11.26	153	6.38	193	4.01
34	19.65	74	16.01	114	11.13	154	6.30	194	3.97
35	19.58	75	15.90	115	10.99	155	6.22	195	3.93
36	19.50	76	15.79	116	10.85	156	6.14	196	3.89
37	19.42	77	15.69	117	10.71	157	6.06	197	3.85
38	19.35	78	15.58	118	10.57	158	5.98	198	3.81
39	19.27	79	15.47	119	10.43	159	5.91	199	3.77
40	19.19	80	15.36	120	10.28	160	5.83	200	3.73

[a]When element width-to-thickness ratio exceeds noncompact section limits of Sect. B5.1, see Appendix B5.
Note: $C_c = 126.1$

4.4 EFFECTIVE LENGTH OF A COMPRESSION MEMBER

The effective length of a compression member is equal to the distance between the inflection points of a laterally deflected member. The effective length is KL distance, where L is the actual length of member and K is effective length factor.

Figure 4.2 shows a column with pins at both ends. The location of inflection points of buckled shape are located at the pins. The effective length is equal to actual length. Therefore, the theoretical K-value for such a case is equal to 1.0.

Figure 4.3 shows a column whose ends are fixed. The location of inflection points of a buckled shape are located at quarter points. The effective length is equal to half the actual length. Therefore, the theoretical K-value for such a case is equal to 0.5.

The value of K varies from 0.5 to 1.0 for columns which are prevented from swaying; that is, inhibited. The values of K are greater than 1.0 for columns which are allowed to sway; that is, uninhibited. The value of K is conservatively considered equal to 1.0 for braced columns.

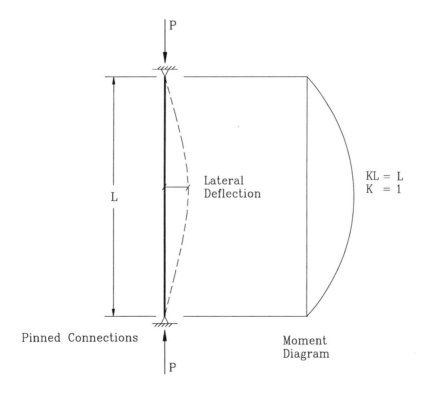

Figure 4.2 Column with Pinned End Connection

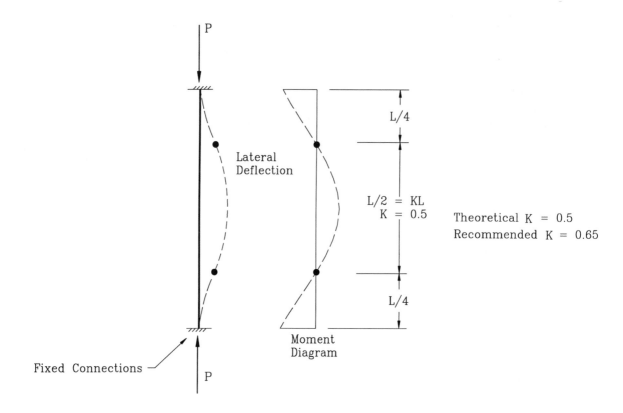

Figure 4.3 Column with Fixed End Condition

4.5 EFFECTIVE LENGTH FACTOR K

Table C-C2.1 in AISC M5-135, gives the value of K for columns whose end restraints are defined. Use the recommended design values when ideal conditions are approximated. The values of K can also be determined from the alignment chart shown in the AISC Manual. The alignment chart in M5-137 is for continuous frames which are allowed to sway; that is, uninhibited. The alignment charts in M3-5 are for continuous frames which are braced or not allowed to sway; that is, inhibited, plus for frames that are allowed to sway. The definition of the parameter G in the alignment charts is as follows:

$$ G = \frac{\Sigma \left(\frac{I_c}{L_c} \right)}{\Sigma \left(\frac{I_g}{L_g} \right)} $$

Where I_c and L_c are the moment of inertia and the unsupported length of a column, respectively. I_g and L_g are the moment of inertia and the unsupported length of a girder or other restraining member, respectively. The moments of inertia are taken about the axis perpendicular to the plane of buckling being considered.

Table 4.2 Effective Length Factor, K
(AISC Table C-C2.1)

	(a)	(b)	(c)	(d)	(e)	(f)
Buckled shapes of column is shown by dashed line						
Theoretical K value	0.5	0.7	1.0	1.0	2.0	2.0
Recommended design value when ideal conditions are approximated	0.65	0.80	1.2	1.0	2.10	2.0
End condition code	Rotation fixed, translation fixed / Rotation free, translation fixed / Rotation fixed, translation free / Rotation free, translation free					

4.5.1   PROCEDURE FOR USING ALIGNMENT CHARTS

1.   Calculate the G value at each end of column.

2.   Enter Alignment Chart with value of G for the top of the column as G_A.

3.   Enter Alignment Chart with value of G for the bottom of the column as G_B.

4.   K-factor is obtained at the point of intersection between the line connecting two G values and K line.

Note that the value for G for a fixed end column is equal to 1.0 and the value for G for a pin end column is equal to 10.0

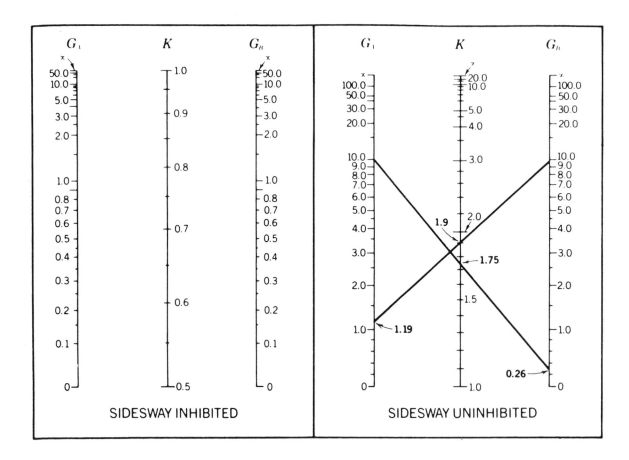

Figure 4.4 Alignment Charts for Braced and Unbraced Frames
(Ref. Lincoln Welding, by Blodgett)

4.6   EXAMPLE PROBLEMS

4.6.1   EXAMPLE PROBLEM 1 — K-FACTORS FOR FRAME WITH NO SIDE-SWAY

For the framing system shown in Fig. P4.6.1 (a), determine K values for columns 1-2 and 2-3. The frame is connected to another building as shown in the sketch. The webs of all the members are located in the plane of the paper.

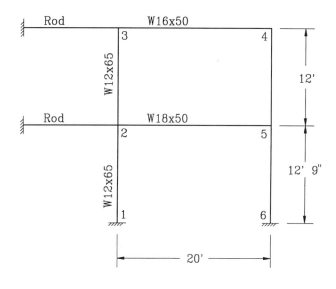

Fig. P4.6.1 (a)

Solution

Column 2-3

Step 1:

Determine the moments of inertia for all members in the frame.

$I_{3\text{-}4} = 659$ in.^{4}

$I_{2\text{-}3} = 533$ in.^{4}

$I_{2\text{-}5} = 800$ in.^{4}

$1_{2\text{-}1} = 533$ in.^{4}

Step 2:

$$G_3 = G_A = \frac{\left(\dfrac{I_{2-3}}{L_{2-3}}\right)}{\left(\dfrac{I_{3-4}}{L_{3-4}}\right)}$$

$$G_3 = G_A = \frac{\dfrac{533}{12 \times 12}}{\dfrac{659}{20 \times 12}} = 1.34$$

Step 3:

$$G_2 = G_B = \frac{\left(\dfrac{I_{2\text{-}3}}{L_{2\text{-}3}}\right) + \left(\dfrac{I_{1\text{-}2}}{L_{1\text{-}2}}\right)}{\left(\dfrac{I_{2\text{-}5}}{L_{2\text{-}5}}\right)}$$

$$G_2 = G_B = \frac{\dfrac{533}{12 \times 12} + \dfrac{533}{12.75 \times 12}}{\dfrac{800}{20 \times 12}} = 2.16$$

Step 4:

Enter sideways inhibited alignment chart with
$G_3 = G_A$ and $G_2 = G_B$ and obtain K = 0.84

Column 1-2

$G_A = G_2 = 2.16$
$G_B = G_1 = 1.00$ (fixed end)
K   = 0.82

4.7 DESIGN PROCEDURE FOR MOST ECONOMICAL COMPRESSION MEMBERS

Design procedure for the most economical compression members that are listed in Part 3 of the AISC Manual:

Given:

Axial compression load, length of member, type of material and end condition.

Required:

Most economical cross section.

Procedure:

Step 1.   Determine value of K from M5-135

Step 2.   Calculate the effective length, KL, in feet.

Step 3.   Refer to the Column Tables in Part 3 of the manual, and select the lightest shape whose P allowable $\geq$ P given.

Note: Wide flange sections, W4 through W14, are used primarily for columns and W16 to W36 are used primarily for beams.

4.8   EXAMPLE PROBLEM

4.8.1   EXAMPLE PROBLEM 1 — FIXED-PINNED COLUMN

Select the lightest W10 column section to support 300 kip of axial compression load. Material is A36 steel. The column is fixed at one end and pinned at the other.

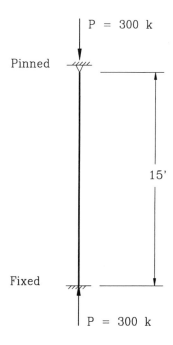

Fig. P4.8.1 (a) Fixed-Pinned Column

Solution

$$K = 0.80 \qquad \text{(M5-135)}$$
$$KL = 0.8 \times 15$$
$$= 12 \text{ ft}$$

For an effective length of KL = 12 and 36-ksi material, select W10 $\times$ 60 from the Column Tables in Part 3 of the AISC Manual (M3-30) whose $P_{allowable}$ = 313 kip, which is just greater than the given P of 300 kip.

Table 4.3 Column Table for W10
(AISC M3-30)

F_y = 36 ksi		
F_y = 50 ksi		

COLUMNS
W shapes
Allowable axial loads in kips

Designation		W10										
Wt./ft		60		54		49		45		39		33
F_y		36	50	36	50	36	50	36	50	36	50	36	50
Effective length in ft KL with respect to least radius of gyration r_y	0	380	528	341	474	311	432	287	399	248	345	210	291
	6	353	482	317	433	289	394	260	351	224	303	189	255
	7	348	472	312	423	284	385	253	340	218	293	184	246
	8	341	461	306	414	279	376	247	328	213	283	179	237
	9	335	450	300	403	273	367	240	316	206	272	173	228
	10	328	437	294	392	268	357	232	303	200	260	167	217
	11	321	425	288	381	262	346	224	289	193	248	161	207
	12	313	412	281	369	256	335	216	274	186	235	155	196
	13	306	398	274	356	249	324	208	259	178	221	149	184
	14	297	383	267	343	242	312	199	243	170	207	142	171
	15	289	368	259	330	235	299	190	227	162	193	135	159
	16	280	353	251	316	228	286	180	209	154	177	127	145
	17	271	337	243	301	221	273	170	191	145	161	120	131
	18	262	320	235	286	213	259	160	172	136	144	112	117
	19	253	303	226	271	205	245	149	154	126	130	103	105
	20	243	285	217	255	197	230	138	139	116	117	95	95
	22	222	248	199	221	180	198	115	115	97	97	78	78
	24	201	209	179	186	161	167	97	97	81	81	66	66
	26	177	178	158	159	142	143	82	82	69	69	56	56
	28	154	154	137	137	123	123	71	71	60	60	48	48
	30	134	134	119	119	107	107	62	62	52	52	42	42
	32	118	118	105	105	94	94	54	54	46	46	37	37
	33	111	111	99	99	88	88	51	51	43	43		
	34	104	104	93	93	83	83						
	36	93	93	83	83	74	74						
Properties												
U		2.55	2.55	2.56	2.56	2.57	2.57	3.25	3.25	3.28	3.28	3.35	3.35
P_{wo} (kips)		99	138	83	116	73	101	79	109	64	89	55	77
P_{wi} (kips/in.)		15	21	13	19	12	17	13	18	11	16	10	15
P_{wb} (kips)		239	282	163	193	127	149	138	163	101	119	79	93
P_{fb} (kips)		104	145	85	118	71	98	86	120	63	88	43	59
L_c (ft)		10.6	9.0	10.6	9.0	10.6	9.0	8.5	7.2	8.4	7.2	8.4	7.1
L_u (ft)		31.1	22.4	28.2	20.3	26.0	18.7	22.8	16.4	19.8	14.2	16.5	11.9
A (in.^{2})		17.6		15.8		14.4		13.3		11.5		9.71	
I_x (in.^{4})		341		303		272		248		209		170	
I_y (in.^{4})		116		103		93.4		53.4		45.0		36.6	
r_y (in.)		2.57		2.56		2.54		2.01		1.98		1.94	
Ratio r_x/r_y		1.71		1.71		1.71		2.15		2.16		2.16	
B_x } Bending		0.264		0.263		0.264		0.271		0.273		0.277	
B_y } factors		0.765		0.767		0.770		1.000		1.018		1.055	
$a_x/10^6$		50.5		45.0		40.6		37.2		31.2		25.4	
$a_y/10^6$		17.3		15.4		13.8		8.0		6.7		5.4	
$F'_{ex} (K_x L_x)^2/10^2$ (kips)		200		198		196		194		189		182	
$F'_{ey} (K_y L_y)^2/10^2$ (kips)		68.5		68.0		66.9		41.9		40.7		39.0	

Note: Heavy line indicates Kl/r of 200.

4.9 DESIGN PROCEDURE FOR BUILT-UP COMPRESSION MEMBER

Given:

Axial compression load, length of member, type of material, desired built-up shape and end condition.

Procedure

Step 1:

Assume the allowable compression stress, $F_a = 18$ ksi

Step 2:

Calculate the required cross sectional area, A_g.
$A_{g \text{ required}} = P/F_{a \text{ assumed}}$

Step 3:

Select the components of the desired built-up shape whose
$A_{g \text{ actual}} \geq A_{g \text{ required}}$

Step 4:

Determine the value of K from Manual (M5-135).

Step 5:

Calculate the moment of inertia and slenderness ratio, KL/r, about the x-x axis and the y-y axis for the built-up shape.

Step 6:

Determine the actual allowable stress for maximum slenderness ratio from the AISC Manual Table C-36 or C-50 as applicable (M3-16 or M3-17).

Step 7:

If $F_{a \text{ actual}} \geq F_{a \text{ assumed}}$ in Step 1, then the selected built-up shape is OK.
If $F_{a \text{ actual}} < F_{a \text{ assumed}}$, then the selected built-up shape is no good, re-select the shape and repeat Steps 2 thru 6 until Step 7 is satisfied.

Step 8:

Tie the components of built-up member together by plates and lacings to prevent local buckling of individual components in accordance with Section B5 and E4 of AISC Specifications M5-35 or M5-43, respectively.

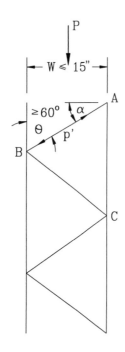
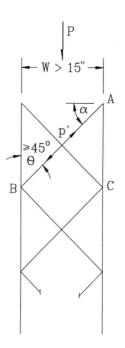

Single Lacing   Double Lacing

Figure 4.5 Lacing Requirements for Compression Members

Single Lacing

$$\left(\frac{L}{r}\right)_{AC} \le \frac{3}{4}\left(\frac{KL}{r}\right)_{B.U.\,Shape}$$

$$\left(\frac{L}{r}\right)_{AB} \le 140$$

$$P' = \frac{1\%\,(P)}{\cos\alpha}$$

Double Lacing

$$\left(\frac{L}{r}\right)_{AC} \le \frac{3}{4}\left(\frac{KL}{r}\right)_{B.U.\,Shape}$$

$$\left(\frac{0.7\,L}{r}\right)_{AB} \le 200$$

$$P' = \frac{1\%\,(P)}{\cos\alpha}$$

4.10   EXAMPLE PROBLEMS

4.10.1   EXAMPLE PROBLEM 1 — DESIGN OF BUILT-UP COLUMN

Select a pair of American Standard channels to support an axial compression load of 400 kip. Use A36 material. The channel's back-to-back dimension is 10 inches.

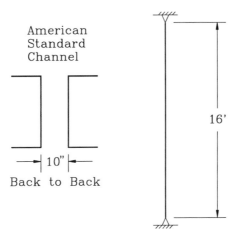

Fig. P4.10.1 (a) Built-Up Column

Solution

Step 1:

Assume F_a = 18 ksi

Step 2:

A_g = P/$F_{a\ assumed}$ = 400/18 = 22.2 in.^{2}

Step 3:

Select two C15 × 40 from M1-40
$A_{g\ actual}$ = 2 × 11.8 = 23.6 > 22.2 in.^{2}

Step 4:

K = 1 from M5-135

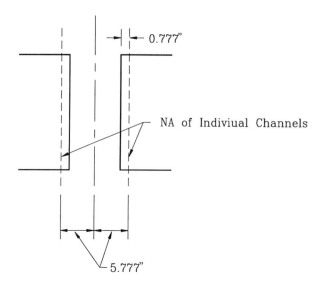

Fig. P4.10.1 (b) Cross Section of Built-Up Column

Step 5:

$$I_x = 2 \times 349 = 698 \text{ in.}^4$$

$$I_y = 2 \times 9.23 + 11.8 \times 5.777^2 \times 2 = 804 \text{ in.}^4$$

$$r_x = \sqrt{\frac{I_x}{A}} = \sqrt{\frac{698}{23.6}} = 5.43 \text{ in.} \quad \dots \text{ governs}$$

$$r_y = \sqrt{\frac{I_y}{A}} = \sqrt{\frac{804}{23.6}} = 5.84 \text{ in.}$$

$$KL/r = \frac{1.0 \times 16 \times 12}{5.43} = 35.4$$

Step 6:

$$F_a = 19.54 \text{ obtained from M3-16}$$

Step 7:

$$F_a = 19.54 > 18.0 \text{ assumed } \dots \text{ OK}$$

Step 8:

Tie the two channels with end tie plates and lacings in accordance with Section E4 (M5-43) of AISC Specifications. See Example Problem 4.12.3 for lacing design of a built-up compression member.

4.11   ALLOWABLE LOADS FOR COMPRESSION MEMBERS

For rolled structural shapes, the AISC Manual gives allowable load column tables for material whose F_y = 36 ksi and 50 ksi. These column tables are valid for buckling about the weak axis only. However, these tables can be used to find the load about the strong axis by utilizing the value of r_x/r_y given in the tables. Refer to Example in M3-4.

For built-up columns, the allowable loads are determined by utilizing the KL/r tables.

$$P_a = F_a \times A_g$$

4.12   EXAMPLE PROBLEMS

4.12.1   EXAMPLE PROBLEM 1 — ALLOWABLE LOAD ON COLUMN

Determine the allowable load on a W10 × 60 column, whose length is 15 ft and its ends are pinned. Material is A36.

Solution

Method 1:

Utilizing column tables

$$\begin{aligned} K &= 1.0 \text{ (pinned ends)} \\ L &= 15 \text{ ft} \\ KL &= 15 \text{ ft} \end{aligned}$$

Enter column tables (M3-30) and determine the value of P as equal to 289 kip with respect to buckling in weak axis of the column.

Method 2:

Utilizing KL/r tables

KL/r = (1 × 15 × 12) / 2.57 = 70.03

Enter Allowable Stresses Table on M3-16 with KL/r = 70 and find the value of F_a equal 16.43 ksi.

Therefore, $P_a = A_g \times F_a$ = 17.6 × 16.43 = 289 kip

As will be noted, the answer to both methods is the same.

To find the allowable load with respect to the strong axis of the column, use the value of r_x/r_y given in the tables as follows:

$$\text{Equivalent length} = \frac{KL}{\frac{r_x}{r_y}} = \frac{1.0 \times 15.0}{1.71} = 8.77 \text{ ft}$$

Enter Column Tables (M3-30) with KL = 8.77 and read P_a = 335 kip.

4.12.2   EXAMPLE PROBLEM 2 — ALLOWABLE LOAD ON FIXED-FIXED COLUMN

Determine the allowable load that can be applied on the column shown below. Material is A36 steel.

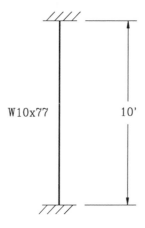

W10x77   10'

Fig. P4.12.2 (a) Fixed-Fixed Column

Solution

(Utilizing AISC column tables)

K = 0.65 from M5-135

KL = 0.65 × 10 = 6.5

P_a = 452 obtained from M3-29 for W10 × 77 and KL = 6.5

(Utilizing KL/r table)

K = 0.65 from M5-135

r_{min} = r_y = 2.60

KL/r = $0.65 \times 10 \times \dfrac{12}{2.60} = 30$

F_a = 19.94 ksi from M3-16

P_a = $F_a \times A_g$ = 19.94 × 22.6 = 452 kip. Same answer as above.

4.12.3 EXAMPLE PROBLEM 3 — BUILT-UP COLUMN

Given:

The built-up column as shown below has an unsupported length of 50 ft, and supports a concentric axial load. Both ends are pinned. Material is ASTM A36.

Required:

    A. What total load can the column safely support?

    B. Design size and spacing of X lacing members.

    C. Show your answer on a sketch and indicate the lacing connections.

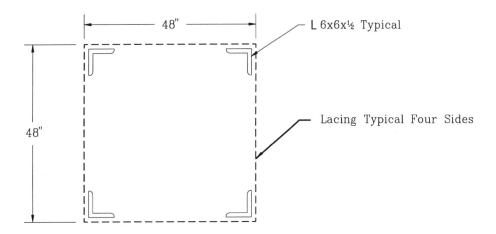

Fig. P4.12.3 (a) Plan View of Built-up Column

Solution

A. 1. Calculate the physical properties of the built-up column.

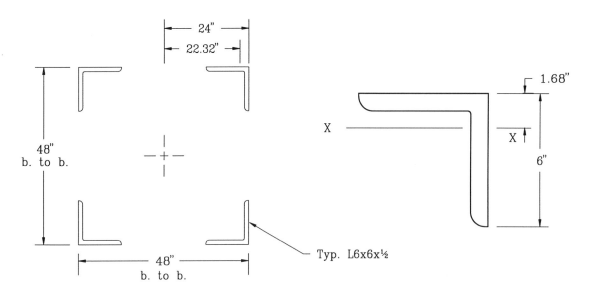

Fig. P4.12.3 (b)

Single angle L 6 × 6 × 1/2

$A = 5.75$ in.^{2}

$r_z = 1.18$ in.

$I_x = I_y = 19.9$ in.^{4}

a) Total moment of inertia

$$I_x = \Sigma I_o + \Sigma A\,(y)^2$$
$$= 4 \times 19.9 + 4\,(5.75 \times 22.32^2)$$
$$= 11{,}538 \text{ in.}^4$$

b) Total area $= 4 \times 5.75 = 23$ in.^{2}

c) $r_x = r_y = \sqrt{\dfrac{I}{A}} = \sqrt{\dfrac{11{,}538}{23}} = 22.4$ in.

2. Slenderness ratio, $KL/r = \dfrac{1.0 \times 50 \times 12}{22.4} = 26.8$

3. Determine F_a from M3-16

for $KL/r = 26.8$, $F_a = 20.15$ ksi

4. Load capacity of built-up column

$$P_a = F_a \times A_g = 20.15 \times 23 = 463.5 \text{ kip}$$

B. Design of X Lacing

 1. Determine the horizontal load on lacing due to axial load, P.

$P_H =$ 1% (P) for each side of built-up column per Section E4 of AISC Specifications (M5-44), or 2 % of load, P, on both sides of a built-up column.

$$= 1\% \, (463.5) = 4.64 \text{ kip}$$

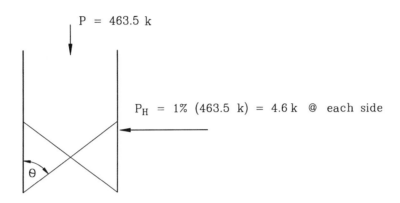

Fig. P4.12.3 (c)

 2. Assume angle $\theta = 60°$ and calculate L/r_z for segment AC.

L/r_z of segment AC shall not be greater than $^3/_4$ KL/r of the entire built-up member.

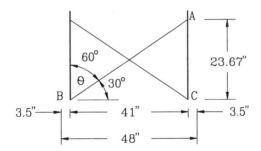

Fig. P4.12.3 (d)

$$L_{BC} \quad = 48 - 2 \, (3.5)$$
$$= 48 - 7 = 41 \text{ in.}$$

$$L_{AC} \quad = 41 \times \tan 30°$$
$$= 41 \times 0.577 = 23.67 \text{ in.}$$

$$L_{AB} \quad = \sqrt{AC^2 + BC^2}$$
$$= \sqrt{23.67^2 + 41^2} = 47.34 \text{ in.}$$

L/r_z of segment AC $= \dfrac{23.67}{1.18} = 20.06 \leq \left(\dfrac{3}{4}\right)(26.8) = 20.10$ of entire built up member . . . OK

3.   Determine axial load in lacing AB

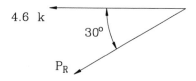

Fig. P4.12.3 (e)

P_R = 4.6/cos 30° = 4.6/0.860 = 5.35 kip
Load on lacing bar   = 5.35 kip
Length of lacing bar = 47.34 in.

4.   Assume F_a in the secondary member AB = 10 ksi

From M3-16 find L/r = 122

Determine r_z of lacing angle:
0.7 (L)/r_z = 122   . . . (M5-53)

$$r_z = \frac{0.7 \times 47.34}{122} = 0.272 \text{ in.}$$

5.   Select L 2 × 2 × 1/4 whose r_z = 0.391 in. > 0.272 in.

C.   Sketch

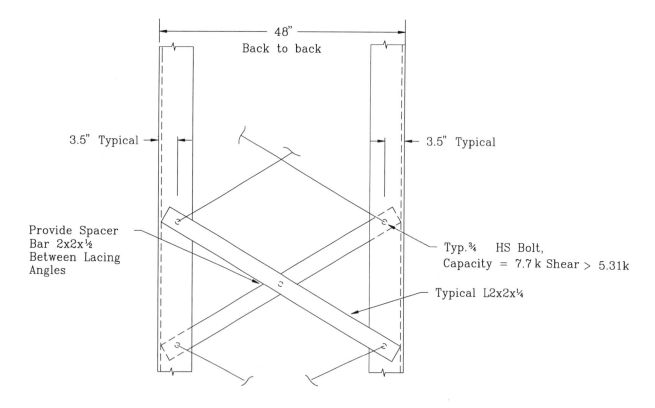

Fig. P4.12.3 (f)

4.13   COLUMN BASE PLATES

Column base plates are plates which spread the load and moments at the base of the columns to the concrete foundation. Base plates are usually welded to the base of the columns and anchored to the foundation by anchor bolts. The top of the base plates must be planed to assure good contact with the bottom of the column. Base plates are initially set in place on steel shims or leveling nuts and not directly on the concrete. Grout is poured below the base plates to fill the gap between the top of the concrete and the bottom of the base plate after the columns are plumbed and guyed.

The length and width of base plates are designed so that the actual bearing pressure does not exceed the allowable bearing pressure of the concrete foundation. The thickness of base plates is determined to prevent the base plates from bending. Figure 4.6 shows the plan view and elevation of a base plate. Figure 4.7 shows bearing pressure distribution for axial load.

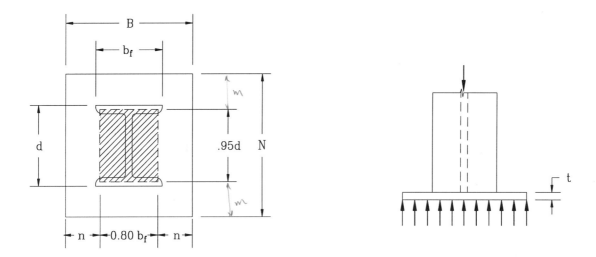

Figure 4.6 Column Base Plate

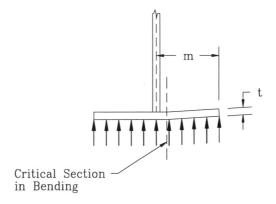

Figure 4.7 Bearing Pressure Distribution on a Base Plate

4.14 DESIGN PROCEDURE FOR COLUMN BASE PLATES SUBJECTED TO AXIAL LOADS

Given:

Size of column, axial load, type of material, allowable bearing pressure of concrete foundation, F_p.

Procedure:

1. Determine the area of base plate, A_1, that is required so as not to exceed the allowable bearing pressure. A_1 is the larger value obtained from the following two equations

$$A_1 = \frac{1}{A_2}\left(\frac{P}{0.35\ f_c'}\right)^2 \text{ and } A_1 = \frac{P}{0.7\ f_c'};$$

where A_2 is the full cross-sectional area of concrete support (in.^{2}) and

$$F_p = 0.35\ f_c'\ \sqrt{\frac{A_2}{A_1}} \le 0.7\ f_c'$$

Note: If A_2 and f_c' are not given on the problem but F_p is given, then determine

$$A_1 = \frac{P}{F_p}.$$

2. Select the length and width of the base plate, in increments of even inches, so that actual area is greater than the area required.

$$A_{actual} = B \times N \ge A_{required}$$

3. Calculate the actual bearing pressure:

$$f_p = P/A_{actual} = P/(B \times N)$$

4. Determine the distances n and m between the edges of the base plate to the edges of the column. See Figure 4.8.

$$m = (N - 0.95\ d)/2$$
$$n = (B - 0.80\ b_f)/2$$

5. Calculate the value of n':

$$n' = \frac{\sqrt{d\ b_f}}{4}$$

6. The thickness of base plate, in increments of 1/8 in., is the largest value calculated by using the following formulas. (See Figure 4.8.)

$$t = m \sqrt{\frac{f_p}{0.25\ F_y}}$$

$$t = n \sqrt{\frac{f_p}{0.25\ F_y}}$$

$$t = n' \sqrt{\frac{f_p\ (bearing\ pressure)}{0.25\ F_y\ (yield\ strength)}}$$

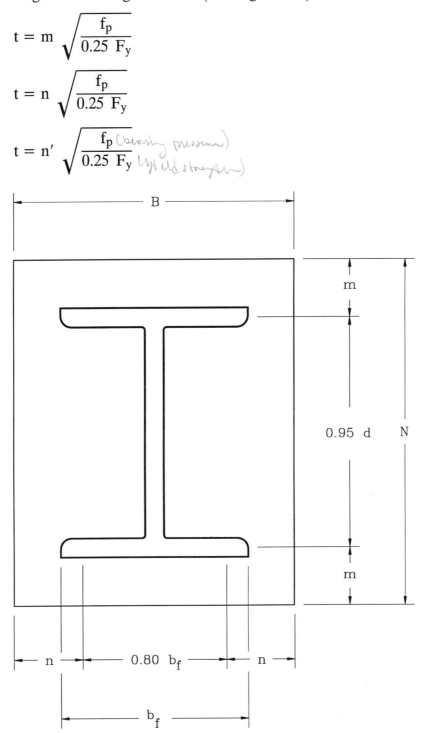

Figure 4.8 Dimension of a Column Base Plate

4.15   EXAMPLE PROBLEM

4.15.1   EXAMPLE PROBLEM 1 — SQUARE BASE PLATE

Design a square base plate for a W14 × 132 column which supports an axial load, P, of 480 kip. Material is A36, $F_p = 1,100$ psi.

Solution

1. $A_{required} = P/F_p = 480 \times 1,000/1,100 = 436.4$ in.^{2}

2.   For square base plates, the length equals the width.

   Select length of base plate N = 22 in.

   Select width of base plate B = 22 in.

   $A_{actual} = N \times B = 22 \times 22 = 484$ in.$^2 > 436.4$ in.^{2}

3. $f_p = \dfrac{P}{N \times B} = \dfrac{480}{22 \times 22} = 0.992$ ksi

4.   Determine the value of m and n

   $$m = \frac{(22 - 0.95 \times 14.66)}{2} = 4.04$$

   $$n = \frac{(22 - 0.80 \times 14.73)}{2} = 5.11 \quad \ldots \text{governs}$$

5.   Determine the value of n′:

   $$n' = \frac{\sqrt{d\, b_f}}{4} = \frac{\sqrt{14.66 \times 14.73}}{4} = 3.67$$

6.   Thickness of base plate, using the maximum value of m, n, or n′ is as follows:

   $$t = n \sqrt{\frac{f_p}{0.25\, F_y}} = 5.11 \sqrt{\frac{0.992}{(0.25 \times 36)}} = 1.69 \text{ in.}$$

   Use thickness, t, equal to $1^3/_4$ inches.

   Dimensions of base plate are $22 \times 22 \times 1^3/_4$ inches.

5

ELASTIC DESIGN AND ANALYSIS OF BEAMS

5.1   INTRODUCTION

Beams are members that support transverse loads. Types of beams are:

- Floor beams
- Girders
- Spandrels
- Stringers
- Joists
- Rafters
- Lintels

Beam sizes are primarily W16 through W36. Part 2 of the AISC Manual provides tables and charts that are very useful in the design and analysis of beams. The following is a partial list that needs to be considered in the design and analysis of beams.

1. Bending stresses
2. Shear stresses
3. Deflections
4. Web crippling
5. Beam bearing plates

5.2   BENDING STRESSES

Bending stresses are computed by using the flexure formula.

$$f_b = \frac{Mc}{I} \ = \ \frac{M}{S} \le F_b$$

Where

f_b = Actual bending stress, ksi

M = Maximum design moment, in.-kip

c   = Distance from the neutral axis to the extreme fiber edge, in.

I   = Moment of inertia, in.^{4}

S   = Section modules, in.^{3}

F_b = Allowable bending stress, ksi

The flexure formula is valid for beams whose ratio of their spans to their depths are greater than 10, and is also limited to stresses in the elastic zone.

5.3   ALLOWABLE BENDING STRESSES

Sections F1, F2 and F3 of the AISC Specifications give the allowable bending stresses for various beam conditions and shapes. In most cases, the allowable bending stresses are as follows, unless noted otherwise by the AISC Specifications.

A. Bending about strong axis

   1) $F_b = 0.66\ F_y$ when beam is compact

   2) $F_b = 0.60\ F_y$ when beam is partial compact

   3) $F_b \le 0.60\ F_y$ when beam is not compact

B. Bending about weak axis

   $F_b = 0.75\ F_y$

5.4   BEAM'S INTERNAL RESISTING MOMENTS

When a beam is subjected to a transverse load, it will deflect vertically, developing an internal resisting moment, and also tends to deflect laterally. The internal resisting moment and stress distributions along the cross section are illustrated in the Figures 5.1, 5.2 and 5.3.

Figure 5.1 shows stress distribution across the section when extreme fiber reaches yield stress. The internal resisting moment, M, is equal to $\frac{C \times 2d}{3}$.

Figure 5.2 shows stress distribution when entire cross section is yielded. The internal resisting moment, known as the plastic moment, M_p, is equal to $\frac{C \times d}{2}$.

Figure 5.3 shows the section with its vertical and lateral deflected shape.

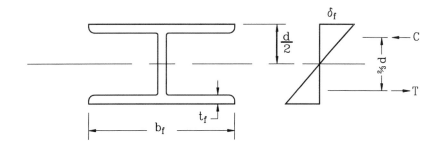

Figure 5.1 Bending Stresses at Elastic Limit

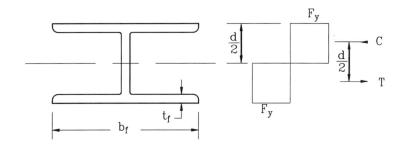

Figure 5.2 Bending Stresses at Plastic Limit

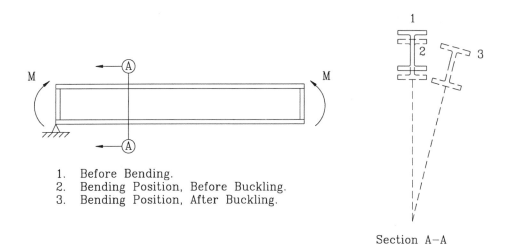

1. Before Bending.
2. Bending Position, Before Buckling.
3. Bending Position, After Buckling.

Section A-A

Figure 5.3 Vertical and Lateral Deflected Shape

5.5   COMPACT SECTION

A compact section is a section that can develop its plastic moment, M_p, before it buckles laterally. A section will develop its plastic moment before it buckles laterally if it meets all the following conditions as applicable:

1. The flanges shall be continuously connected to the web or webs, Section F1.1 M5-45.

2. The width-to-thickness ratio of unstiffened projecting elements of the compression flange, as defined in Section B5 shall not exceed $\dfrac{65}{\sqrt{F_y}}$.

   This requirement is checked by comparing yield stress, F_y, to the value, F'_y. The value of F'_y is listed in the S_x Tables and in Part 1 of AISC Manual.

   If $F_y \le F'_y$, where $F'_y = \left(\dfrac{65 \times 2t_f}{b_f}\right)^2$, then condition No. 2 is satisfied.

3. The width-to-thickness ratio of stiffened elements of compression flanges as defined in Section B5 shall not exceed $\dfrac{190}{\sqrt{F_y}}$. This requirement relates to box shapes used as beams.

4. The depth-thickness ratio of the web or webs shall not exceed the value given by AISC Table B5.1 as applicable.

$$\frac{d}{t_w} \le 640 \frac{\left(\dfrac{1 - 3.74 f_a}{F_y}\right)}{\sqrt{F_y}}, \qquad \text{when } \frac{f_a}{F_a} \le 0.16$$

$$\frac{d}{t_w} \le 640, \qquad \text{when } f_a = 0$$

$$\frac{d}{t_w} \le \frac{257}{\sqrt{F_y}}, \qquad \text{when } \frac{f_a}{F_a} > 0.16$$

   The values of $\dfrac{d}{t_w}$ are listed in Part 1 of the AISC Manual.

   This requirement is checked by comparing the yield stress of the material, F_y, to the value, F_y'''. The value of F_y''' is listed in Part 1 of the AISC Manual.

   If $F_y \le F_y'''$ where $F_y''' = \left(\dfrac{257\, t_w}{d}\right)^2$, then condition No. 4 is satisfied.

5. The laterally unsupported length of compression flange of members other than box members shall not exceed

$$L_c \le \frac{76\, b_f}{\sqrt{F_y}} \quad \text{or} \quad \frac{20,000}{(d/A_f)\, F_y} \qquad \text{AISC Equation F1-2, M5-45}$$

6. The laterally unsupported length of compression flange of a box-shaped member of rectangular cross section whose $d \leq 6b$ and $t_f \leq 2t_w$ is as follows:

$$L_c = \left(1950 + 1200 \, \frac{M_1}{M_2} \right) \frac{b}{F_y} \qquad \text{AISC Eq. F3-2}$$

Where d is depth and b is width of box. M_1 is smaller and M_2 is larger moment at lateral supports.

If a beam meets the above requirements, then the beam is compact and its F_b is equal to $0.66 \, F_y$.

Exceptions:

If a member (except hybrid girders and members of A514 steel) meets the above requirements, except that $\frac{b_f}{2 \, t_f}$ exceeds $\frac{65}{F_y}$ but is less than $\frac{95}{F_y}$, then the allowable bending stress may be designed on the basis of the AISC Equation F1-3.

$$F_b = F_y \left[0.79 - 0.002 \left(\frac{b_f}{2t_f} \right) \sqrt{F_y} \right] \qquad \text{AISC Eq. F1-3}$$

If a member is a doubly-symmetrical I- and H-shaped member bent about its minor axis (except hybrid girders and members of A514 steel) meeting the requirements of Section F1.1 subparagraph 1, except where $b_f/2t_f$ exceeds $65/F_y$, but is less than $95/F_y$, then the allowable bending stress may be designed on the basis of the AISC Equation F2-3.

$$F_b = F_y \left[1.075 - 0.005 \left(\frac{b_f}{2t_f} \right) \sqrt{F_y} \right] \qquad \text{AISC Eq. F2-3}$$

For complete specifications related to bending, refer to Chapter F in AISC Manual.

5.6 PARTIAL COMPACT SECTION

A partial compact section is a section that meets the requirements of a compact section, except where the laterally unsupported length of the compression flange, L_b, is greater than the value of L_c but does not exceed the value of L_u

For most shapes, the value of L_u is equal to $\dfrac{20,000}{12\left(\frac{d}{A_f}\right)F_y}$. (M2-30)

For few shapes, the value of L_u is equal to $\left(\dfrac{\sqrt{102,000}}{F_y}\right)\dfrac{r_T}{12}$. (M2-30)

Therefore, if $L_c < L_b < L_u$, then the allowable bending stress is equal to $0.60\,F_y$.

5.7 NON-COMPACT SECTION

A non-compact section is a section that does not meet the requirements for a compact or a partial compact section. The unsupported length of the compression flange, L_b, is greater than the value of L_u.

Therefore, if $L_b > L_u$, then allowable bending stress is equal to and less than $0.60\,F_y$.

Definitions:

  L   Span of a beam between two vertical supports

  L_b Unsupported length of a compression flange between two lateral supports

  L_c Maximum unbraced length of the compression flange at which the allowable bending stress is $0.66\,F_y$

  L_u Maximum unbraced length of the compression flange at which the allowable bending stress is $0.60\,F_y$

AISC gives values of L_c and L_u for beams in S_x Tables and also in Beam Tables. Values of L_c and L_u for columns are given in column tables as well.

5.8 ALLOWABLE BENDING STRESSES SUMMARY

The allowable bending stresses for wide flange shapes are illustrated in Figure 5.4 and as described below:

$$F_b = 0.66\,F_y \quad \text{if} \quad L_b \le L_c$$
$$F_b = 0.60\,F_y \quad \text{if} \quad L_c < L_b \le L_u$$
$$F_b \le 0.60\,F_y \quad \text{if} \quad L_b > L_u$$

When $L_b > L_u$, then the beam is not compact and its allowable bending stresses are determined as follows.

1. Calculate the value of $\dfrac{L_b}{r_T}$

2. Calculate the value of $\quad B_o \;=\; \sqrt{\dfrac{102 \times 10^3 \times C_b}{F_y}}$

3. Calculate the value of $\quad \sqrt{5}\,B_o \;=\; \sqrt{\dfrac{510 \times 10^3 \times C_b}{F_y}}$

If $\dfrac{L_b}{r_T} \le B_o$, then $F_b = 0.60\,F_y$.

If $\sqrt{5}\ B_o \ge \dfrac{L_b}{r_T} > B_o$, then $F_b = \max\{F_{b1}, F_{b3}\} \le 0.60\,F_y$

If $\dfrac{L_b}{r_T} > \sqrt{5}\ B_o$, then $F_b = \max\{F_{b2}, F_{b3}\} \le 0.60\,F_y$

Where r_T is radius of gyration of a section comprising the compression flange plus 1/3 of compression web area taken about an axis in the plane of web.

$$F_{b1} = \left[\frac{2}{3} - \frac{F_y \left(\frac{L_b}{r_T}\right)^2}{1530 \times 10^3\,C_b}\right] F_y \qquad\qquad \text{AISC Eq. F1-6}$$

$$F_{b2} = \frac{170 \times 10^3\,C_b}{\left(\frac{L_b}{r_T}\right)^2} \qquad\qquad \text{AISC Eq. F1-7}$$

$$F_{b3} = \frac{12 \times 10^3\,C_b}{L_b \left(\frac{d}{A_f}\right)} \qquad\qquad \text{AISC Eq. F1-8}$$

Values of r_T and $\dfrac{d}{A_f}$ are provided in Part 1 of AISC Manual.

Note: For channels bent about their major axis, the allowable compressive stress is determined from Equation F1-8.

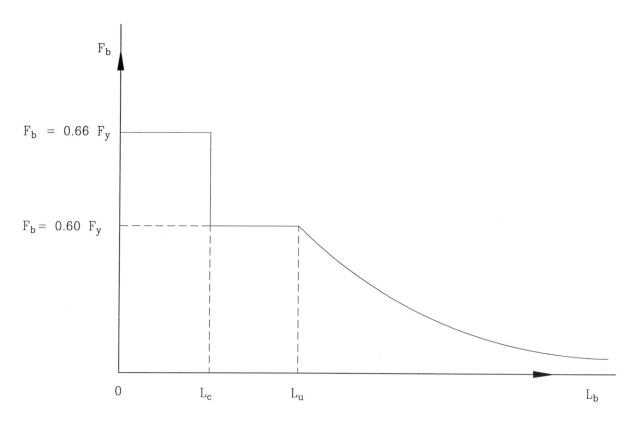

Figure 5.4 Allowable Bending Stresses for Wide Flange Section

5.9   VALUES OF C_b

The term C_b is used to take into consideration the variation of bending moment along the length of beam (AISC Section F1.3, M5-47).

$$C_b = 1.75 + 1.05 \, (\delta) \left(\frac{M_1}{M_2}\right) + 0.3 \left(\frac{M_1}{M_2}\right)^2 \leq 2.3$$

Where,

M_1 = Smaller bending moment at the end of an unbraced length of the compression flange

M_2 = Larger bending moment at the end of an unbraced length of the compression flange

δ = -1 when M_1 and M_2 are acting in opposite directions, thus causing single curvature bending

δ = +1 when M_1 and M_2 are acting in same direction, thus causing double curvature bending

C_b = +1 when the bending moment M_3 at any point within the unbraced length is larger than M_2

C_b = +1 for a cantilever beam

5.10   EXAMPLE PROBLEMS

5.10.1   EXAMPLE PROBLEM 1 — CALCULATION OF C_b OF COMPRESSION FLANGE

Determine the value of C_b for each of the lateral unsupported lengths of the compression flange. The beam is W18 × 50, A36 material. Loaded as shown in Fig. P5.10.1 (a). Lateral supports are located at A, B, C, and D.

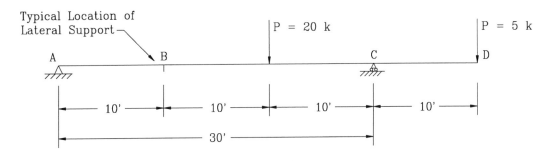

Fig. P5.10.1 (a)

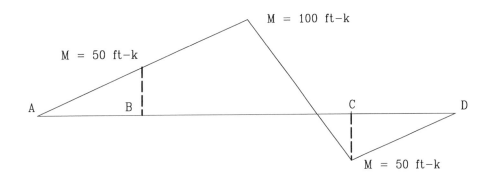

Fig. P5.10.1 (b) Moment Diagram

Solution

Moment diagram for each unsupported length is as follows:

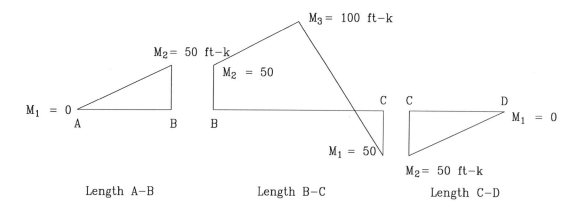

Fig. P5.10.1 (c)

a. C_b for unsupported length, AB:

$$C_b = 1.75 + 1.05 \, (\delta) \left(\frac{M_1}{M_2}\right) + 0.3 \left(\frac{M_1}{M_2}\right)^2 \leq 2.3$$

$$C_b = 1.75 + 1.05 \, (\text{-}1) \left(\frac{0}{50}\right) + 0.3 \left(\frac{0}{50}\right)^2 = 1.75 \ \leq 2.3 \quad \ldots \text{OK}$$

b. C_b for unsupported length, BC:
   $C_b = 1.0$ because $M_3 = 100 > M_2 = 50$

c. C_b for unsupported length, CD:
   $C_b = 1.0$ because length, CD, is a cantilever.

5.10.2 EXAMPLE PROBLEM 2 — C$_b$ OF LATERAL UNSUPPORTED LENGTHS

Determine the value of C$_b$ for each of the lateral unsupported lengths of the compression flange. The beam is W18 × 50, A36 material. Loaded as shown in Fig. P5.10.2 (a). Lateral supports are located at A, B, C, and D.

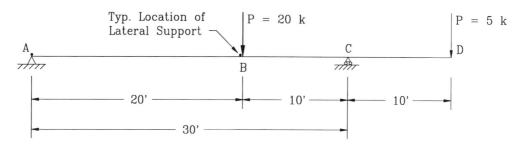

Fig. P5.10.2 (a)

Solution

Bending moment diagram for complete beam is as follows:

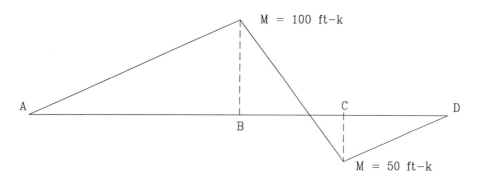

Fig. P5.10.2 (b) Moment Diagram

Moment diagram for each unsupported length is as follows:

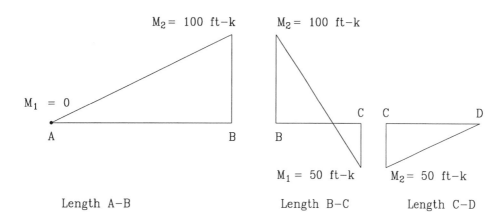

Fig. P5.10.2 (c)

a. C_b for unsupported length, AB:

$$C_b = 1.75 + 1.05\ (\delta)\left(\frac{M_1}{M_2}\right) + 0.3\left(\frac{M_1}{M_2}\right)^2 \leq 2.3$$

$$C_b = 1.75 + 1.05\ (-1)\left(\frac{0}{100}\right) + 0.3\left(\frac{0}{100}\right)^2 = 1.75 \qquad \leq 2.3 \qquad \dots OK$$

b. C_b for unsupported length, BC:

$$C_b = 1.75 + 1.05\ (\delta)\left(\frac{M_1}{M_2}\right) + 0.3\left(\frac{M_1}{M_2}\right)^2 \leq 2.3$$

$$C_b = 1.75 + 1.05\ (+1)\left(\frac{50}{100}\right) + 0.3\left(\frac{50}{100}\right)^2 = 2.35 > 2.3$$

Use $C_b = 2.3$

c. C_b for unsupported length, CD:

$C_b = 1.0$ because length, CD, is a cantilever.

5.11   PROCEDURE TO CHECK BEAM DESIGN IN BENDING

1.   Calculate the reactions for the given loads.

2.   Draw the shear and moment diagrams for the given loads. Refer to M2-294 through M2-311 for beam diagrams and formulas when applicable.

3.   List all laterally unsupported distances, L_b, between consecutive lateral supports of the compression flange.

4.   Find maximum moment for each laterally unsupported distance.

5.   Find the allowable bending stress, F_b, from AISC Sections F1, F2 or F3 for each laterally unsupported distance.

6.   Find actual bending stress, f_b, for each laterally unsupported distance.

$$\text{If } f_b = \left(\frac{Mc}{I}\right) = \frac{M}{S} \leq F_b, \text{ then beam is OK.}$$

$$\text{If } f_b = \left(\frac{Mc}{I}\right) = \frac{M}{S} > F_b, \text{ then beam is NG.}$$

5.12   EXAMPLE PROBLEM

5.12.1   EXAMPLE PROBLEM 1 — ADEQUACY OF SIMPLE BEAM IN BENDING

Check if the given beam is OK when subjected to given loads. Lateral support of the compression flange is provided at beam ends only. A36 material, AISC specifications. Bending about strong axis.

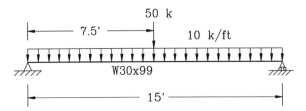

Fig. P5.12.1 (a)

Solution

1.   There is one laterally unsupported length for this beam. $L_b = 15$ ft.

2.   Maximum Moment:

$$M = \frac{(10 + 0.099)\,15^2}{8} + \frac{50 \times 15}{4} = 284 + 188 = 472 \text{ ft-k}$$

3.   Actual Bending Stress:

$$S = 269 \text{ in.}^3 \text{ from M2-10}$$

$$f_b = \left(\frac{Mc}{I}\right) = \frac{M}{S} = \frac{472 \times 12}{269} = 21.0 \text{ ksi}$$

4.   Allowable Bending Stress:

For W30 × 99, obtain the values of L_c and L_u from (M2-10).

$$L_c = 10.9 \text{ ft}$$

$$L_u = 11.4 \text{ ft}$$

$$L_b = 15 \text{ ft}$$

Because $L_b > L_u$, then $F_b \le 0.60\,F_y$.

Calculate the value of $\frac{L_b}{r_T}$:

$$\frac{L_b}{r_T} = \frac{15 \times 12}{2.57} = 70 \qquad \text{(for W30} \times 99, r_T = 2.57, \text{ from M1-17)}$$

Calculate the value of B_o

$$B_o = \sqrt{\frac{102 \times 10^3 \times C_b}{F_y}}$$

$$B_o = \sqrt{\frac{102 \times 10^3 \times 1}{36}} = 53 \qquad (C_b = 1, M_3 > M_2)$$

Calculate the value of $\sqrt{5}\ B_o$

$$\sqrt{5}\ B_o = \sqrt{\frac{510 \times 10^3 \times C_b}{F_y}}$$

$$\sqrt{5}\ B_o = \sqrt{\frac{510 \times 10^3 \times 1}{36}} = 119$$

Because $\sqrt{5}\ B_o \geq \dfrac{L_b}{r_T} > B_o$, $F_b = \max\{F_{b1}, F_{b3}\} \leq 0.60\ F_y$

$$F_{b1} = \left[\frac{2}{3} - \frac{F_y\left(\frac{L_b}{r_t}\right)^2}{1530 \times 10^3\ C_b}\right] F_y$$

$$F_{b1} = \left[\frac{2}{3} - \frac{36 \times 70^2}{1530 \times 10^3 \times 1.0}\right] 36$$

$$= 19.85 \text{ ksi}$$

$$F_{b3} = \frac{12 \times 10^3\ C_b}{L_b\left(\frac{d}{A_f}\right)} \qquad (\text{F1-8})$$

$$= \frac{12 \times 10^3 \times 1}{15 \times 12\ (4.23)}, \qquad (\text{For W30} \times 99,\ d/A_f = 4.23 \text{ from M1-17})$$

$$= 15.8 \text{ ksi}$$

$$F_b = \max\{19.9, 15.8\} \leq 0.60 \times 36 = 22 \text{ ksi}$$

$$= 19.9 \text{ ksi}$$

Beam is not adequate because $f_b = 21$ ksi $> F_b = 19.9$ ksi

5.13   DESIGN PROCEDURE FOR COMPACT BEAMS

Given:

Span, vertical supports, location of lateral supports, type of material and loading.

Procedure:

1.   Calculate the reactions for the given loads.

2.   Draw the shear and moment diagrams for the given loads. Refer to M2-294 through M2-311 for beam diagrams and formulas.

3.   List all laterally unsupported distances, L_b.

4.   Determine the maximum moment for each laterally unsupported distance.

5.   Select a section from S_x Tables in M2-7 through M2-13 of the AISC Manual, that appears in **bold face** type, whose allowable moment, M_R, is equal to or greater than the maximum design moment for each laterally unsupported distance.

6.   The final section to be selected is the section which has the maximum value of M_R.

7.   Check if the final selected section meets the following compactness requirements:

$$L_b \leq L_c$$
$$F_y \leq F'_y$$

If items a and b are met, then the final selected section is good. If items a or b are not met, then the section must be redesigned in accordance with the design procedure for non-compact beams.

8.   Check beam for shear and deflection.

Table 5.1 Allowable Stress Design Selection Table (S_x Table)
(AISC M2-7)

ALLOWABLE STRESS DESIGN SELECTION TABLE
For shapes used as beams S_x

F_y = 50 ksi			S_x	Shape	Depth d	F'_y	F_y = 36 ksi		
L_c	L_u	M_R					L_c	L_u	M_R
Ft	Ft	Kip-ft	In.^{3}		In.	Ksi	Ft	Ft	Kip-ft
16.2	64.1	8720	3170	W 36×848	42½	—	19.1	89.0	6280
16.1	61.7	8200	2980	W 36×798	42	—	19.0	85.7	5900
15.9	56.5	7400	2690	W 36×720	41¼	—	18.8	78.5	5330
15.1	45.7	7120	2590	W 40×655	43⅝	—	17.8	63.4	5130
15.7	51.3	6660	2420	W 36×650	40½	—	18.6	71.2	4790
14.9	41.7	6440	2340	W 40×593	43	—	17.6	57.9	4630
15.6	46.9	6000	2180	W 36×588	39⅞	—	18.4	65.2	4320
15.1	52.1	5970	2170	W 33×619	38½	—	17.8	72.3	4300
14.8	37.9	5750	2090	W 40×531	42⅜	—	17.4	52.6	4140
15.0	48.3	5470	1990	W 33×567	37⅞	—	17.7	67.1	3940
15.4	42.7	5360	1950	W 36×527	39¼	—	18.2	59.4	3860
14.7	34.4	5200	1890	W 40×480	41¾	—	17.3	47.7	3740
14.5	53.8	5140	1870	W 30×581	35⅜	—	17.1	74.7	3700
14.9	44.4	4980	1810	W 33×515	37⅜	—	17.5	61.7	3580
15.3	39.2	4920	1790	W 36×485	38¾	—	18.1	54.5	3540
14.5	31.4	4700	1710	W 40×436	41⅜	—	17.1	43.7	3390
14.3	49.8	4620	1680	W 30×526	34¾	—	16.9	69.1	3330
14.7	40.7	4480	1630	W 33×468	36¾	—	17.4	56.5	3230
15.2	36.2	4460	1620	W 36×439	38¼	—	17.9	50.3	3210
13.7	55.6	4320	1570	W 27×539	32½	—	16.1	77.2	3110
14.4	29.0	4290	1560	W 40×397	41	—	17.0	40.3	3090
14.2	45.7	4210	1530	W 30×477	34¼	—	16.7	63.4	3030
14.6	37.0	4070	1480	W 33×424	36⅜	—	17.2	51.4	2930
15.1	32.7	3990	1450	W 36×393	37¾	—	17.8	45.4	2870
13.5	51.3	3960	1440	W 27×494	32	—	15.9	71.2	2850
14.3	26.5	3910	1420	W 40×362	40½	—	16.9	36.7	2810
14.1	41.7	3800	1380	W 30×433	33⅝	—	16.6	57.9	2730
14.5	34.4	3710	1350	W 33×387	36	—	17.1	47.7	2670
16.0	25.8	3690	1340	W 40×328	40	—	18.9	35.9	2650
15.0	30.0	3630	1320	W 36×359	37⅜	—	17.7	41.7	2610
13.4	47.6	3580	1300	W 27×448	31⅜	—	15.8	66.1	2570
12.6	56.5	3550	1290	W 24×492	29⅝	—	14.9	78.5	2550

5.14   EXAMPLE PROBLEM

5.14.1   EXAMPLE PROBLEM 1 — DESIGN OF A WIDE FLANGE BEAM

Select the lightest wide flange beam shown in Fig. P5.14.1 (a). Material is A36 steel. The compression flange is encased in concrete.

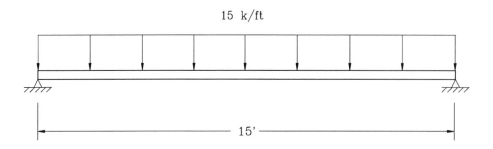

Fig. P5.14.1 (a)

Solution

1. Reactions, shear and moment diagrams are obtained from M2-296.

2. The compression flange is fully supported because it is encased in concrete. Therefore, the laterally unsupported distance, L_b, is equal to 0.

3. $M_{max} = \dfrac{wL^2}{8} = \dfrac{15 \times 15^2}{8} = 421.9$ ft-kip

4. Select W27 × 84 from S_x Table (M2-10), which appears in bold type and it has

    $M_R = 422$ ft-kip $> M_{max} = 421.9$ ft-kip

5. Check for compactness:

    $L_b = 0 < L_c = 10.5$ ft   OK

    $F_y = 36$ ksi $< F_y' \geq 65$ ksi   OK

    Therefore, W27 × 84 is good.

6. Check beam for shear and deflection.

5.15 DESIGN PROCEDURE OF NON-COMPACT BEAMS

Given:

Span, vertical supports, location of lateral supports, type of material and loading.

Procedure:

1. Calculate the reactions for the given loads.

2. Draw the shear and moment diagrams for the given loads. Refer to M2-294 through M2-311 for beam diagrams and formulas.

3. List all laterally unsupported distances, L_b.

4. Determine the maximum moment for each laterally unsupported distance.

5. Determine the value of C_b for each laterally unsupported distance.

6. Determine the equivalent length, L_b', for each laterally unsupported distance.

   $$L_b' = L_b/C_b$$

7. Select a section from the AISC Charts in M2-149 through M2-211 as follows:

   Enter the charts with the equivalent length, L_b', on the bottom scale, then proceed upward to intersect a horizontal line corresponding to the maximum moment. The beam to be selected is the beam that appears in **solid line** directly above or to the right of the point of intersection.

   Note that the charts are provided for $C_b = 1.0$

8. Check the beam for shear and deflection.

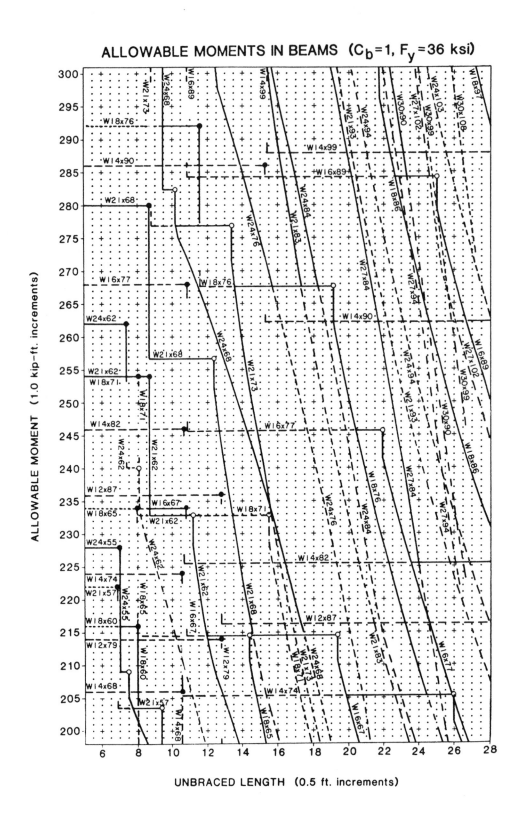

Figure 5.5 Allowable Moments in Beams (C_b = 1.0, F_y = 36 ksi)
(AISC M2-166)

5.16   EXAMPLE PROBLEMS

5.16.1   EXAMPLE PROBLEM 1 — BENDING STRESS CRITERIA

For the beam shown below, design the lightest wide flange section that will satisfy the bending stress criteria. Material is A36 steel. Lateral supports for the compression flange are provided only at the beam ends.

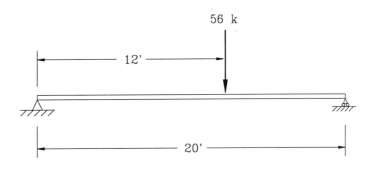

Fig. P5.16.1 (a)

Solution

1. Reactions, shear and moment diagrams are all obtained from M2-298.

2. There is one laterally unsupported distance between the lateral supports. The lateral supports given are to be at the end of the beam. Therefore, $L_b = 20$ ft

3. $M_{max} = \dfrac{56 \times 12 \times 8}{20} = 268.8$ ft-kip say 270 ft-kip

4. $C_b = 1.0$, because $M_3 = 270$ ft-kip $> M_2 = 0$

5. $L_b' = L_b/C_b = 20/1.0 = 20$ ft

6. From AISC Chart M2-166, select W27 $\times$ 84

5.16.2 EXAMPLE PROBLEM 2 — ECONOMICAL WIDE FLANGE

Design the most economical wide flange shape for the beam shown below. Lateral supports of the compression flange are provided at points A, B, C and D. Use A36 steel.

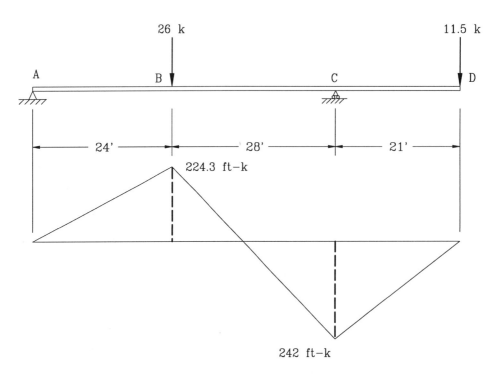

Fig. P5.16.2 (a)

Solution

1. List of laterally unsupported distances:

   $L_{AB} = 24$ ft $\qquad L_{BC} = 28$ ft $\qquad L_{CD} = 21$ ft

2. Maximum moment in each laterally unsupported distance:

   $M_{AB} = 224.3$ ft-k

   $M_{BC} = 242.0$ ft-k

   $M_{CD} = 242.0$ ft-k

3. Values of C_b for each laterally unsupported distance:

$$C_{bAB} = 1.75 + 1.05\,(-1)\left(\frac{0}{224.3}\right) + 0.3\left(\frac{0}{224.3}\right)^2$$

$$= 1.75 < 2.3 \quad \text{OK}$$

$$C_{bBC} = 1.75 + 1.05\,(+1)\left(\frac{224.3}{242}\right) + 0.3\left(\frac{224.3}{242}\right)^2$$

$$= 2.98 > 2.3 \quad \text{NG use 2.3 as maximum.}$$

$C_{bCD} = 1.0$, because it is a cantilever.

4. Equivalent lengths:

$$L_{bAB}' = \left(\frac{L_{bAB}}{C_{bAB}}\right) = \frac{24}{1.75} = 13.7 \text{ ft}$$

$$L_{bBC}' = \left(\frac{L_{bBC}}{C_{bBC}}\right) = \frac{28}{2.30} = 12.2 \text{ ft}$$

$$L_{bCD}' = \left(\frac{L_{bCD}}{C_{bCD}}\right) = \frac{21}{1.00} = 21.0 \text{ ft}$$

5. Select sections for each laterally unsupported distance:

For distance AB: $M_{max} = 224.3$ and $L'_b = 13.7$

Select W21 × 68 from AISC Charts M2-166

For distance BC: $M_{max} = 242.0$ and $L'_b = 12.2$

Select W21 × 68 from AISC Charts M2-166

For distance CD: $M_{max} = 242.0$ and $L'_b = 21.0$

Select W18 × 76 from AISC Charts M2-166

Section to be selected for this beam is W18 x 76 being the heaviest, then check to make sure that $f_b \le F_b$.

5.17   SHEAR STRESSES

Members supporting transverse loads are subjected to two types of shear stresses. One is transverse shear and the other is longitudinal shear.

Transverse shear stress: (AISC Section F4 in M5-49)

$$f_v = \left(\frac{V}{dt_w}\right) \le F_v = 0.4\,F_y$$

Longitudinal shear stress:

$$f_v = \left(\frac{VQ}{It}\right) \le F_v$$

where

f_v = Actual shear stress

V = Shear force

d = Depth of beam

t_w = Thickness of web

F_v = Allowable shear stress

Q = Statical moment about the neutral axis

I = Moment of inertia

t = Width of section where shear stress is considered

Transverse shear stresses may govern the design of a beam if any of the following conditions exist: the span is too short, concentrated loads located near the end supports, beams with very thin webs, or beams with notches or being coped. Spandrels welded to columns will cause tremendous concentrated transverse forces at their flanges. These forces have to be supported by the column webs in shear.

Longitudinal shear stresses are considered in the design of shear connectors, welding re-enforcement plates to beam flanges and other similar problems.

The AISC provides the maximum shear force, V, that a beam can support. These values are shown in Part 2 of the manual under Beam Tables.

5.18   EXAMPLE PROBLEMS

5.18.1   EXAMPLE PROBLEM 1 — SIMPLE BEAM WITH OVERHANG

Find the largest load, P, that can be applied to the W30 × 99 beam shown below. Consider shear stress only. Use A36 steel.

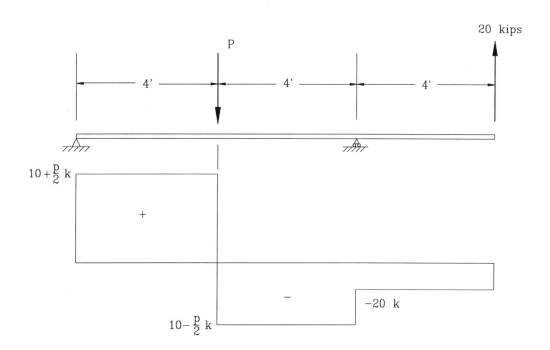

Fig. P5.18.1 (a) Shear Diagram of a Simple Beam with Overhang

Solution

1.   Maximum shear force = V = 10 + P/2

2. $f_v = \left(\dfrac{V}{dt_w}\right) \le 0.40\, F_y$

$$f_v = \frac{\left(10 + \frac{P}{2}\right)}{29.65 \times 0.52} \le 0.40 \times 36$$

3. $P_{all} = \{(0.40 \times 36 \times 29.65 \times 0.52) - 10\}2$

   = 424 kip for shear criteria only.

The beam must be checked for bending to find the allowable load that can be applied.

5.19 DEFLECTION IN BEAMS

Deflection in beams should not exceed the allowable deflection values limited by the building codes or by the designers. Many designers require the beams to be cambered to compensate for the dead loads or live loads deflections. If the problem limits the deflection to very small magnitudes, then the I_x Tables in the AISC Manual (M2-26) are very useful. The I_x Tables are used in the very same way as the S_x Tables are used. That is, select a beam that appears in **bold type** whose I_x is equal to or greater than the moment of inertia, I, required.

5.20 EXAMPLE PROBLEMS

5.20.1 EXAMPLE PROBLEM 1 — SIMPLE SUPPORTED BEAM

A simply supported beam, 30 ft in length, is loaded at the centerline with a concentrated load equal to 100 kip. Determine the size of the beam so that its deflection will not exceed L/1,000.

Solution

1. Allowable deflection = L/1,000

2. Actual deflection $= \dfrac{PL^3}{48\ EI}$

3. Actual deflection $\leq$ Allowable deflection

    $$\frac{PL^3}{48\ EI} \leq \frac{L}{1,000}$$

4. Solve for I, required.

    $$I \ =$$
    $$= \left(\frac{100\ \times\ 30^3\ \times\ 12^3}{48\ \times\ 29\ \times\ 10^3\ \times\ 30\ \times\ 12} \right) 1,000$$
    $$=\ 9,310\ \text{in.}^4$$

5. From M2-26 select W40 $\times$ 149 which appears in bold type and its moment of inertia; I_x is equal to 9,780 in.^{4}

6. The beam must be checked for shear and bending stresses.

5.20.2 EXAMPLE PROBLEM 2 — MEZZANINE STORAGE AREA

Given:

A mezzanine storage area is to be constructed in an existing building area shown in Fig. P5.20.2 (a).

Assume the beam, B1, is pin-supported at lines A and B.

Height requirement allows a nominal beam depth of 10 inches.

Consider alternate span loadings.

State all assumptions and show all work.

Do not check for shear.

Beam laterally supported at lines A and B.

Criteria:

Codes: (UBC) 1991 and (AISC) 9th Edition

Materials: Structural Steel ASTM A36

                    Concrete floor = Non-composite section, 4 in. thick, (wt = 150 pcf)

Loadings:

Live loads   = 175 psf

Ceiling loads   = 10 psf

Steel beam wt   = 50 plf (assumed)

Required:

A. Design the lightest W10 x ? beam (B1) assuming that deflection is not a problem.

B. Design the lightest W10 x ? beam (B1) considering the live load deflection criteria of L/360 in the 15-ft span and limiting the deflection at Line C to $1/4$ inch (up or down).

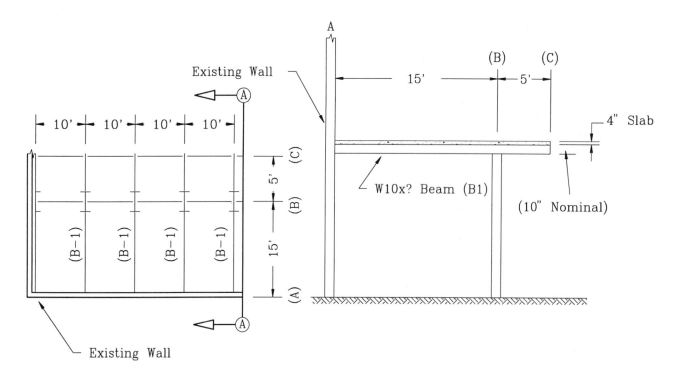

Partial Plan–Mezzanine   Section A–A

Fig. P5.20.2 (a)

Solution

A. Design for lightest 10 x ? Beam (B1),   assuming that deflection is not a problem.

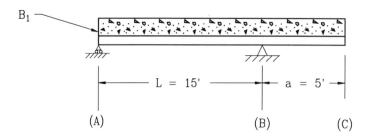

Fig. P5.20.2 (b)

Beam (B1) is spaced typically at 10 ft o.c., therefore the tributary area supported by each beam is equal to 10-ft-wide strip.

DL due to ceiling = 10 psf × 10 ft =   100 plf
DL due to steel beam   =   50 plf
DL due to concrete floor
    10 ft × 4/12 × 1 × 150 pcf   =   500 plf
Total DL   =   650 plf

LL given 175 psf × 10 = 1750 plf

Different Loading Conditions

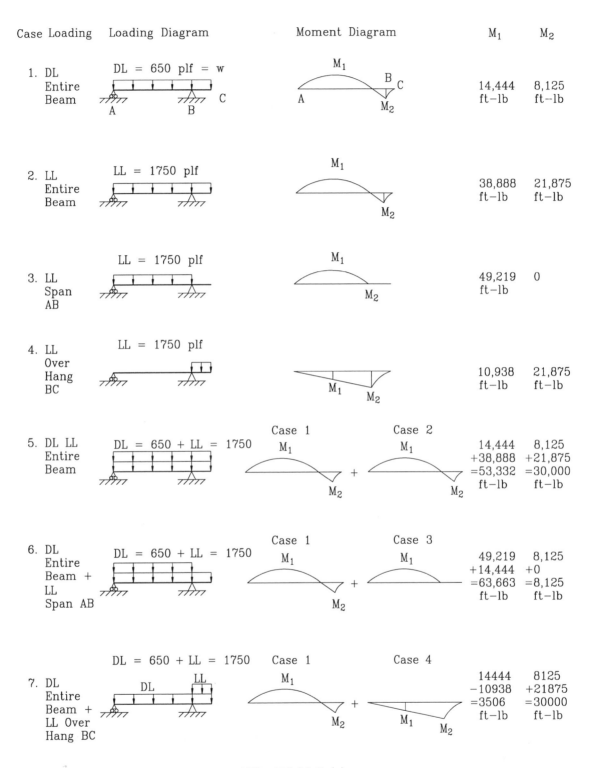

Fig. P5.20.2 (c)

From Fig. P5.20.2 (c), the maximum moment of 63.7 ft-kip in beam (B1) is produced by load combination case number 6.

Note: M_1 and M_2 were calculated by using the equations shown in M2-304 and M2-305.

Design of beam (B1) for maximum moment of 63.7 ft-kip. The compression flange is laterally supported by the concrete.

Solution

Select W10 x 30 from, S_x, Tables (M2-12)

$$M_{max} = 63.7 < M_R = 64 \text{ ft-kip} \qquad \text{OK}$$

$$L_b = 0 < L_c = 6.1 \qquad \text{OK}$$

$$F_y = 36 < F_y' \geq 65 \qquad \text{OK}$$

B. Design for the lightest W10 beam (B1) considering LL deflection criteria of L/360 in the 15-ft span and limiting the deflection of end, C, to maximum value of $1/4$ inch up or down.

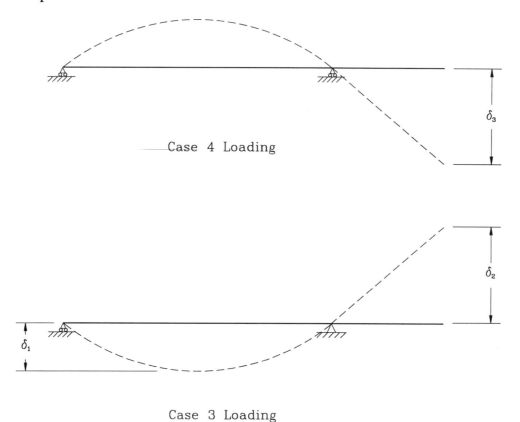

Case 4 Loading

Case 3 Loading

Fig. P5.20.2 (d) Deflected Shape of Beam B1

Maximum deflection in the 15-ft span is produced by loading span AB only with live load. That is load combination Case 3.

Actual deflection:

$$\delta_1 = \frac{5wL^4}{384 \ EI} = \frac{5 \times 1750 \times 15^4 \times 12^4}{384 \times 12 \times 29 \times 10^6 \times I_x}$$

Allowable deflection:

$$\delta_1 = \frac{L}{360}$$

Let the allowable deflection equal actual deflection for δ_1 in the above equations and solve for the unknown moment of inertia, I_x.

$$I_x = 137.5 \text{ in.}^4$$

The maximum upward deflection at the end of the overhang is produced by loading only span AB with the live load. That is load combination Case 3.

Actual deflection:

$$\delta_2 = \frac{wL^3a}{24 \text{ EI}} = \frac{1750 \times (15 \times 12)^3 \times 5 \times 12}{12 \times 24 \times 29 \times 10^6 \times I_x}$$

Allowable deflection:

$$\delta_2 = {}^1\!/_4 \text{ inch}$$

Let the allowable deflection equal actual deflection for δ_2 in the above equations and solve for the unknown moment of inertia, I_x.

$$I_x = 293.3 \text{ in.}^4 \quad \text{governs the design.}$$

The maximum downward deflection at the end of the overhang is produced by loading only the overhang with the live load. That is load combination Case 4.

Actual deflection:

$$\delta_3 = \frac{wa^3 (4L + 3a)}{24 \text{ EI}}$$

$$= \frac{1750 \times (5 \times 12)^3 \times (4 \times 15 \times 12 + 3 \times 5 \times 12)}{12 \times 24 \times 29 \times 10^6 \times I_x}$$

Allowable deflection:

$$\delta_3 = {}^1\!/_4 \text{ inch}$$

Let the allowable deflection equal actual deflection for δ_3 in the above equations and solve for the unknown moment of inertia, I_x.

$$I_x = 162.9 \text{ in.}^4$$

Select from I_x Tables (M2-27) W10 × 54 whose $I_x = 303 \text{ in.}^4 > 293.3 \text{ in.}^4$

5.20.3   EXAMPLE PROBLEM 3 — ECONOMICAL SECTION FOR LOADED BEAM

Given:

Full lateral support of compression flange

Maximum deflection = 1.5 in.

F_{bx} = 20 ksi, E = 29 × 10³ ksi.

Find an economical section for the beam loaded as shown in Fig. P5.20.3 (a).

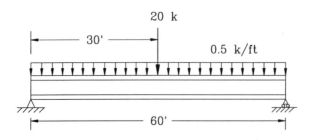

Fig. P5.20.3 (a)

Solution

Please note that the problem does not require the lightest possible section. Since the beam is laterally supported, Paragraph 5, Section F1.1 (M5-45) is automatically satisfied. Hence, there are two possible methods of solving this problem. Also, note the constraint on deflection; this indicates that deflection may be the governing criteria.

Procedure:

Since beam is laterally supported, then assume the beam to be compact.

Step 1:

W_{beam} = 100 lb/ft (Assumption)

W   = 0.5 + 0.1 = 0.6 kip/ft

Step 2:

$$M_{max} = \frac{0.6 \times 60^2}{8} + \frac{20 \times 60}{4} = 270 + 300$$

M_{max} = 570 ft-kip = 6850 in.-kip

Step 3:

F_{bx} = 20 ksi (Given)

Step 4:

$$S_{req} = \frac{6850 \text{ kip-in.}}{20 \text{ ksi}} = 342 \text{ in.}^3$$

Step 5:

Choose W33 × 118 with S = 359 in.³ > 342 in.³

Step 6:

$W_{beam} = 118$ lb/ft

Hence,

$$M_{max} = \frac{0.618 \times 60^2}{8} + \frac{20 \times 60}{4} = 278 + 300 = 578 \text{ ft-kip}$$

$$f_{bx} = \frac{M_{max}}{S_{sup}} = \frac{578 \times 12}{359} = 19.4 \text{ ksi} < 20 \text{ ksi OK}$$

If W33 $\times$ 118 is used, bending stresses OK. Check deflection for W33 $\times$ 118.

$$\delta = \frac{5 \times (0.618/12) \times (60 \times 12)^4}{384EI} + \frac{20 \times (60 \times 12)^3}{48EI}$$

$$= \frac{1}{EI} \left(18.0 \times 10^7 + 15.5 \times 10^7\right)$$

$$= \frac{33.5 \times 10^7}{\left(29 \times 10^3\right) \times I}$$

$$= \frac{1.16 \times 10^4}{I}$$

$$= \frac{1.16 \times 10^4}{5.9 \times 10^3}$$

$$= 1.96 \text{ in.} > 1.5 \text{ in.}$$

Deflection governs: Use the following ratio:

$$\frac{I_{req}}{I_{W33 \times 118}} = \frac{\delta_{W33 \times 118}}{\delta_{allow}}$$

Since deflection is inversely proportional to the moment of inertia about the bending axis.

Therefore,

$$I_{req} = 5,900 \left(\frac{1.96}{1.5}\right) = 7,709 \text{ in.}^3$$

From each depth class, the following beams meet the required 7,709 in.^{3}

Depth Class	Cross Section	I_x
W27 to W16	None	
W30	W30 × 173	8,200
W33	W33 × 152	8,160
W36	W36 × 135	7,800

Since I_{req} = 7,788 in.^{3}, then it appears that W36 × 135 is the lightest possible section which will satisfy both bending stress and deflection requirements.

Note: For a complete solution, you should now go back and analyze W36 × 135 for bending stresses and deflections.

Check of W36 × 135:

For bending stresses:

$$M_{max} = \frac{0.635 \times 60^2}{8} + \frac{20 \times 60}{4} = 286 + 300 = 586 \text{ ft-kip}$$

$$f_{bx} = \frac{586 \times 12}{440} = 16 \text{ ksi} < 20 \text{ ksi}$$

$$\delta = \frac{1}{EI}\left(18.9 \times 10^7 + 15.5 \times 10^7\right) = 34.4 \times 10^7/EI$$

From previous page $EI = \left(29 \times 10^3\right)(7800)$

$$= 1.51 \text{ in.} \cong 1.5 \text{ inch}$$

W36 × 135 is the lightest possible beam for the conditions specified in this problem.

5.21 WEB CRIPPLING DUE TO CONCENTRATED LOADS

Concentrated loads and end reactions will cripple or buckle the web of a beam unless the web is stiffened or the loads are spread over a large area of the flange. Figure 5.6 illustrates the distribution of end reactions and interior loads over a distance, N. The thinnest portion of the web is at the toe of the beams fillets, which is located a distance, k, from the flange faces. Assuming load distribution is at a 45° angle, then the applied concentrated load or reaction will bear on a web whose area is equal to $(N+2.5 k)t_w$ for end reactions and $(N+5 k)t_w$ for interior loads.

In accordance with the AISC Specifications, Section K1.3, the compression stress shall not exceed $0.66 F_y$ to prevent web yielding.

The bearing stress at the end of a beam is as follows:

$$\frac{R}{(N + 2.5 \ k) \ t_w} \leq 0.66 \ F_y$$

The bearing stress at an interior concentrated load is as follows:

$$\frac{P}{(N + 5 \ k) \ t_w} \leq 0.66 \ F_y$$

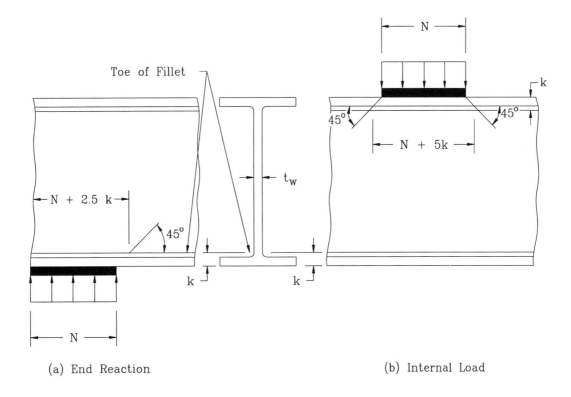

(a) End Reaction   (b) Internal Load

Figure 5.6 Distribution of Reaction and Internal Loads

5.22   EXAMPLE PROBLEM

5.22.1   EXAMPLE PROBLEM 1 — BEAM ON BEARING PLATE

For the beam shown below, what is the minimum bearing length, N_r, at the reactions and the minimum length, N_1, over which the concentrated load must be distributed to prevent buckling of the web? The beam size is W30 × 99. Beam is made of A36 steel.

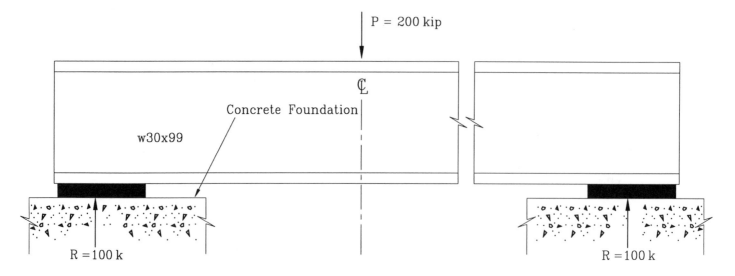

Fig. P5.22.1 (a) Beam on Bearing Plate

Solution

Get the following values from M1-16 for W30 × 99.

$$k = 1\frac{7}{16} = 1.4375 \text{ inch}$$

$$t_w = 0.520 \text{ inch}$$

At beam end reaction:

$$\frac{100}{\left(N_r + 2.5 \times 1\frac{7}{16}\right) \times 0.520} = 0.66 \times 36$$

$N_r = 4.4$ inches   Use 6.0 inches

At concentrated load:

$$\frac{200}{\left(N_c + 5 \times 1\frac{7}{16}\right) \times 0.520} = 0.66 \times 36$$

$N_c = 8.8$ inches   Use 10.0 inches

5.23   DESIGN OF BEAM BEARING PLATES

Bearing plates for beams are designed to avoid web crippling of the beam and high bearing stresses on the foundation. Figure 5.7 shows the dimensions of the bearing plate that need to be determined.

Length of the plate, b, must be greater than N_r in order to avoid crippling of the beam web.

$$b \geq N_r = \left(\frac{R}{0.66 \, F_y \, t_w}\right) - 2.5 \, k$$

Note that $N_r \geq 3.5$ in.

The width, a, of the plate is determined so that the actual bearing stress, f_p, on the foundation does not exceed the allowable bearing stress, F_p.

$$f_p = \frac{R}{a \, b} \leq F_p$$

Solving for $a \geq \dfrac{R}{F_p \, b}$

The thickness of the bearing plate is determined from the following equation:

$$t \geq \sqrt{\frac{3 \, f_p \left(\frac{a}{2} - k\right)^2}{0.75 \, F_y}}$$

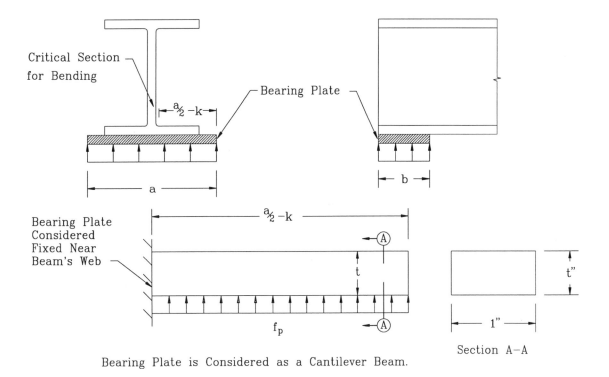

Figure 5.7 Bearing Plate for a Beam

5.24 EXAMPLE PROBLEM

5.24.1 EXAMPLE PROBLEM 1 — BEAM BEARING PLATE

Design a beam bearing plate for a W30 × 99 beam if F_p = 540 psi and F_y = 36 ksi. Maximum reaction at support is 100 kip.

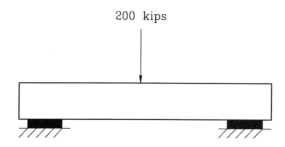

Fig. P5.24.1 (a)

Solution

Length of bearing plate, b:

$$b \geq N_r = \left(\frac{R}{0.66 \ F_y \ t_w}\right) - 2.5 \ k$$

$$= \left(\frac{100}{0.66 \times 36 \times 0.52}\right) - 2.5 \times 1.438 = 4.4 \text{ in.} \quad \text{Use 6 inches}$$

Width of bearing plate, a:

$$a \geq \frac{R}{F_p \ b}$$

$$\geq \frac{100}{0.54 \times 6} = 30.86 \text{ in.}$$

Use a = 32 inches

Actual bearing stress, f_p:

$$f_p = \frac{R}{a \ b} = \frac{100}{32 \times 6} = 0.521 \text{ ksi} \leq 0.54 \ \text{OK}$$

Thickness of bearing plate, t:

$$t \geq \sqrt{\frac{3 \ f_p \ (\frac{a}{2} - k)^2}{0.75 \ F_y}}$$

$$t \geq \sqrt{\frac{3 \times 0.521 \ (\frac{32}{2} - 1.438)^2}{0.75 \times 36}}$$

$$\geq 3.50 \text{ in.}$$

Use t = 3.50 inches

5.25 P. E. PROBLEMS

5.25.1 P. E. PROBLEM 1 — DESIGN OF COVER PLATES

Given:

Beam W30 × 173 is specified but W30 × 124 is delivered. Plates are available to alter W30 × 124. F_b = 18 ksi. Find the size of the cover plates.

Solution

Since only flanges are to be altered and only bending stresses are given, then consider bending only and neglect shear, deflections, and web crippling.

For W30 × 173, S_x = 539 in.^{3} (M1-15).

Thus $M_{max} = S_x F_b$ = 539 (18) = 9702 in.-kip

For W30 × 124, I_x = 5,360 in.^{4} (M1-17).

b_f = 10.52 in.

Use 1-in. plate and find the required width, X.

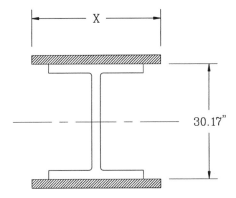

Fig. P5.25.1 (a) Beam with Cover Plates

$$f_{bx} = \frac{9,702 \left(\frac{30.17}{2} + 1.0\right)}{I_{TOT}} \leq 18 \text{ ksi}$$

$$I_{TOT} = 8,669.8 \text{ in.}^3$$

But, $I_{TOT} = I_{W30 \times 124} + I_{plates}$

$$= 5,360 + 2\left(Ad^2 + \frac{bh^3}{12}\right)$$

$$= 5,360 + 2\left(X \times 1 \times 15.58^2 + \frac{X \times 1^3}{12}\right)$$

$$= 5,360 + 485.6 \, X$$

$$X = \frac{8,669.8 - 5,360}{485.6}$$

$$X = 6.8 \text{ in.}$$

Hence, use two plates, each 1 in. $\times$ 7 in.

Note: Since flange width is 10.52 in., we could also use a wider plate.

5.25.2   P. E. PROBLEM 2 — BEAM DESIGN

For the beam loaded as shown in Fig. P5.25.2 (a), select a W section. Lateral supports only at points A and B and at beam ends. Use A36 steel. Use 8th edition of AISC Manual.

Solution

To obtain R_C and R_D:

$$36\ R_C = 90(28) + 63(4)$$

$$R_C = 77\ \text{kip}$$

$$R_D = 76\ \text{kip}$$

Shear and moment diagrams are shown in Fig. P5.25.2 (a) .

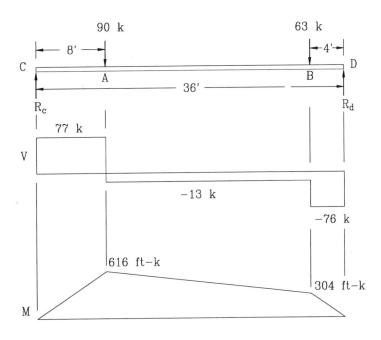

Fig. P5.25.2 (a)

Analyze section AB for bending stresses.

The lightest section is found using the AISC charts in Part 2 of the manual.

From the procedure given in Chapter 5:

Step 1:

Neglect beam weight. $L_{AB} = 24$ ft

Step 2:

$M_{max} = 616$ ft-kip for Section AB

Step 3:

C_b for Section AB

$$C_b \;=\; 1.75 \;+\; 1.05 \; \delta \left(\frac{M_1}{M_2}\right) \;+\; 0.3 \left(\frac{M_1}{M_2}\right)^2 \;\le\; 2.3$$

$$C_{bAB} \;=\; 1.75 \;+\; 1.05 \, (-1) \left(\frac{304}{616}\right) \;+\; 0.3 \left(\frac{304}{616}\right)^2 \;\le\; 2.3$$

$$C_{bAB} \;=\; 1.3$$

Step 4:

Since $C_b > 1$, then $L'_{AB} = 24 \text{ ft}/1.3 = 18.5 \text{ ft}$

From M2-162 for $M_{max} = 616$ ft-kip and $L'_{AB} = 18.5$ ft

Use W33 $\times$ 130.

5.25.3   P. E. PROBLEM 3 — WAREHOUSE ROOF SYSTEM

A typical bay of a warehouse roof system. The warehouse building is braced for lateral loads.

Live load = 40 psf

Dead load = 20 psf

Material is A36.

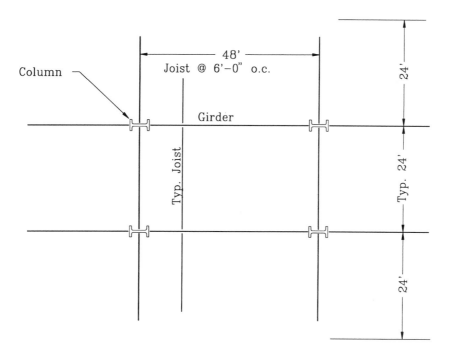

Fig. P5.25.3 (a)

Required:

A. Select the lightest wide flange joist.

(Max deflection due to LL = L/360)

B. Select the lightest wide flange girder.

C. Select the lightest wide flange column.

(K = 1.0, Length = 30 ft)

Solution

Part A:

Design the lightest wide flange joists which are spaced at 6 ft o.c.

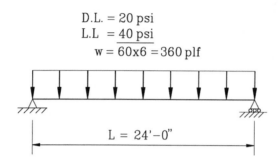

$$\text{D.L.} = 20 \text{ psi}$$
$$\text{L.L} = \underline{40 \text{ psi}}$$
$$w = \overline{60 \times 6} = 360 \text{ plf}$$

$$L = 24'-0''$$

Fig. P5.25.3 (b)

$$\text{Maximum moment} = \frac{wL^2}{8} = \frac{\left(\frac{360}{1000}\right) 24^2}{8} = 25.92 \text{ ft-k}$$

From S_x Table (M2-13), select W12 × 14 that appears in bold type and whose

$$M_R = 30 > 25.92$$

Assuming the joist compression flange is laterally supported.

$$L_b = 0 < L_C = 3.5 \quad \dots \text{OK}$$
$$F_y = 36 < F_y' = 54.3 \quad \dots \text{OK}$$

Selected section is adequate for bending stress criteria.

Check deflection for live load only:

Live load, W, is equal to 40 lb/ft × 6 ft = 240 lb/ft = 0.02 k/in.

$$\delta_{max.} \leq \delta_{allowable}$$

$$\delta_{max} = \frac{5wL^4}{384 \text{ EI}}$$

$$= \frac{5 \times 0.02 \times 24^4 \times 12^4}{384 \times 29 \times 10^3 \times 88.6} = 0.697 \text{ in.}$$

$$\delta_{allowable} = \frac{L}{360} = \frac{24 \times 12}{360} = 0.8 \text{ in.}$$

$$0.697 < 0.8 \quad \dots \text{OK}$$

Part B:

Design of the lightest wide flange girder:

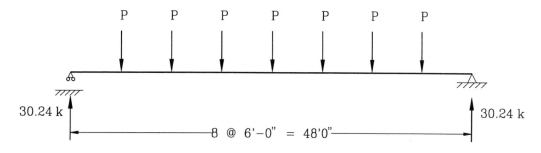

Fig. P5.25.3 (c)

Load P = Load from tributary area on both sides of the girder

  = (40 psf + 20 psf) $\times$ 6 ft $\times$ 12 $\times$ 2

  = 8640 lb or 8.64 kip

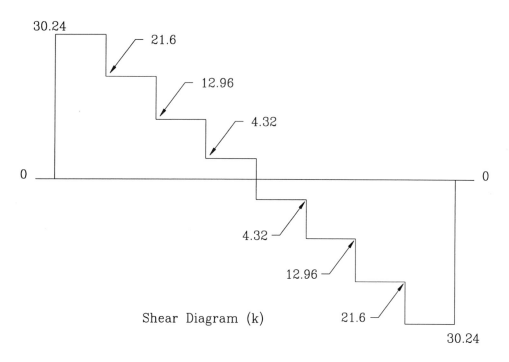

Fig. P5.25.3 (d)

Maximum Moment

  = (30.34 + 21.6 + 12.96 + 4.32) $\times$ 6 ft = 415.32 ft-kip

From S_x Tables (M2-10), select W27 $\times$ 84 that appears in bold type and whose M_R = 422 > 415.32 . . . OK

Check:

Joists are spaced at

$$L_c = 10.5 > 6 \text{ ft} = L_b \quad \ldots \text{OK}$$

$$F_y < F'_y = 65 \quad\quad\quad \ldots \text{OK}$$

Section selected is adequate for bending.

Part C:

Design for the most economical wide flange column:

Length of column = 30 ft

$$K_x = K_y = 1.0 \quad\quad \text{(given)}$$

$$KL = 1.0 \times 30 = 30 \text{ ft}$$

$$P = (48 \text{ ft} \times 24 \text{ ft} \times 60 \text{ lb/in.}^2) = 69.12 \text{ kip}$$

From M3-31, select W8 × 48 whose $P_{all} = 70$ kip > 69.12 kip

5.26   SUMMARY OF ALLOWABLE BENDING STRESSES

1. Rice and Hoffman, in their steel design text, provide an excellent summary of allowable bending stresses for various types of cross sections. This table is provided in the following two pages. Note that only angles are not included.

2   For flexural members made up of single angles, a complex analysis is often required as provided in Reference 5, Chapter 9, for some non-standard type flexural shapes.

3. Note that all flexural analysis assumes that the load is applied through the shear center. Furthermore, if the load is applied to the bottom flange, as in crane rails, the added stability provided by the load may be considered. See Figure 5.8.

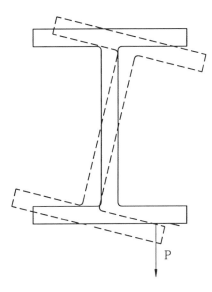

Figure 5.8 Load Applied at Bottom Flange

(Ref: *Structural Design Guide to AISC Specifications for Buildings*, pages 86-87, Rice and Hoffman.)

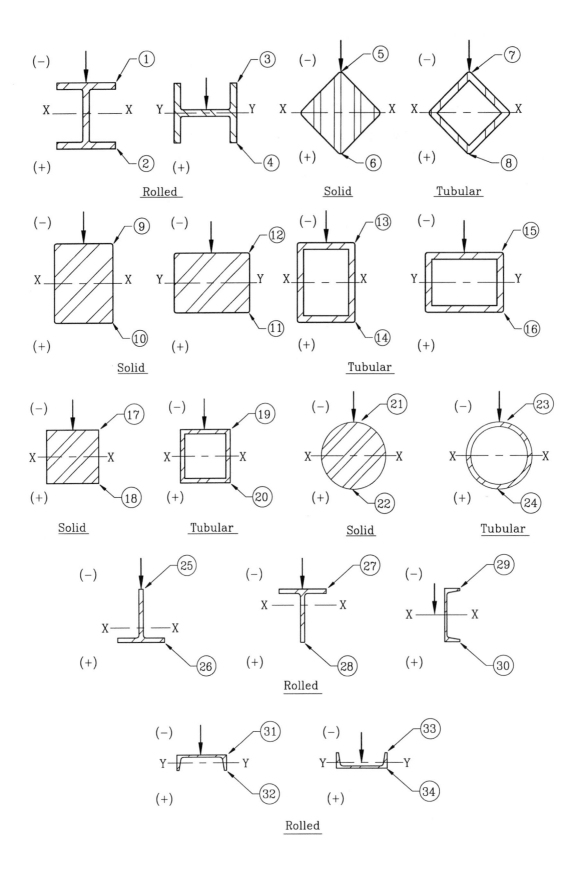

Figure 5.9 Bending of Various Sections about Axis Indicated

Table 5.2 Maximum Allowable Stresses

(Ref: *Structural Design Guide to AISC Specifications for Buildings*, pages 86-87, Rice and Hoffman.)

Fig No.	COMPACT			SEMI-COMPACT			NON-COMPACT		
	F_b	AISC Section Reference	Rice-Hoffman Reference	F_b	AISC Section Reference	Rice-Hoffman Reference	F_b	AISC Section Reference	Rice-Hoffman Reference
1	0.66 F_y	1.5.1.4.1	Table 3-1,-2 Col. (1)	1.5-5a	1.5.1.4.2	Table 3-1,-2 Col. (2)	1.5-6a 1.5-6b 1.5-7	1.5.1.4.6a	Table 3-1,-2 Cols.(4)(5)(5)
2	0.66 F_y	1.5.1.4.1	Table 3-1,-2 Col. (1)	1.5-5a	1.5.1.4.2	Table 3-1,-2 Col. (2)	0.60 F_y	1.5.1.4.5	-
3	0.75 F_y	1.5.1.4.3	Table 3-1,-2 Col. (7)	1.5-5b	1.5.1.4.3	Table 3-1,-2 Col. (8)	0.60 F_y	1.5.1.4.6b	Table 3-1,-2 Col. (9)
4	0.75 F_y	1.5.1.4.3	Table 3-1,-2 Col. (7)	1.5-5b	1.5.1.4.3	Table 3-1,-2 Col. (8)	0.60 F_y	1.5.1.4.5	-
5	-	-	-	-	-	-	0.75 F_y	1.5.1.4.3	-
6	-	-	-	-	-	-	0.75 F_y	1.5.1.4.3	-
7	*	-	*	**	-	*	0.60 F_y	1.5.1.4.4	-
8	**	-	*	**	-	*	0.60 F_y	1.5.1.4.4	-
9	0.66 F_y	1.5.1.4.1	Fig. 3-6	1.5-5a	1.5.1.4.2	Fig. 3-6 Table 3-3	Fig. 3-6	1.5.1.4.4	Fig. 3-6
10	0.66 F_y	1.5.1.4.1	-	1.5-5a	1.5.1.4.2	Table 3-3	0.60 F_y	1.5.1.4.5	-
11	-	-	-	-	-	-	0.75 F_y	1.5.1.4.3	-
12	-	-	-	-	-	-	0.75 F_y	1.5.1.4.3	-
13	0.66 F_y	1.5.1.4.1	Fig. 3-7	1.5-5a	1.5.1.4.2	Fig. 3-7 Table 3-3	Fig. 3-7	1.5.1.4.4	Fig. 3-7
14	0.66 F_y	1.5.1.4.1	-	1.5-5a	1.5.1.4.2	Table 3-3	0.60 F_y	1.5.1.4.5	-
15	-	-	-	-	-	-	0.60 F_y	1.5.1.4.4	-
16	-	-	-	-	-	-	0.60 F_y	1.5.1.4.4	-
17	-	-	-	-	-	-	0.75 F_y	1.5.1.4.3	-
18	-	-	-	-	-	-	0.75 F_y	1.5.1.4.3	-
19	0.66 F_y	1.5.1.4.1	Fig. 3-7	1.5-5a	1.5.1.4.2	Fig. 3-7 Table 3-3	Fig. 3-7	1.5.1.4.4	
20	0.66 F_y	1.5.1.4.1	-	1.5-5a	1.5.1.4.2	Table 3-3	0.60 F_y	1.5.1.4.4	-
21	-	-	-	-	-	-	0.75 F_y	1.5.1.4.3	-
22	-	-	-	-	-	-	0.75 F_y	1.5.1.4.3	-
23	-	-	-	-	-	-	0.60 F_y	1.5.1.4.6b	-
24	-	-	-	-	-	-	0.60 F_y	1.5.1.4.5	-
25	0.66 F_y	1.5.1.4.1	-	1.5-5a	1.5.1.4.2	Table 3-9	1.5-6a 1.5-6b 1.5-7	1.5.1.4.5	-
26	0.66 F_y	1.5.1.4.1	-	1.5-5a	1.5.1.4.2	-	0.60 F_y	1.5.1.4.5	-
27	0.66 F_y	1.5.1.4.1	-	1.5-5a	1.5.1.4.2	Table 3-8	1.5-6a 1.5-6b 1.5-7	1.5.1.4.5	-
28	0.66 F_y	1.5.1.4.1	-	1.5-5a	1.5.1.4.2	-	0.60 F_y	1.5.1.4.5	-
29	-	-	-	-	-	-	1.5-7	1.5.1.4.6a	-
30	-	-	-	-	-	-	0.60 F_y	1.5.1.4.5	-
31	-	-	-	-	-	-	0.60 F_y	1.5.1.4.6b	-
32	-	-	-	-	-	-	0.60 F_y	1.5.1.4.5	-
33	-	-	-	-	-	-	0.60 F_y	1.5.1.4.6b	-
34	-	-	-	-	-	-	0.60 F_y	1.5.1.4.5	-

* Reference equations cited for F_b give variable functions of F_y.

** As the hollow box walls become thicker, these allowable stresses approach 0.75 F_y as for solid sections.

6

ANALYSES AND DESIGN OF BEAM-COLUMNS

6.1   AXIAL COMPRESSION STRESSES

Members that are subjected to combined axial compression stresses and bending stresses as shown in Figure 6.1 are called beam-columns. All aspects that affect the design of pure beams and the design of pure columns are considered in the analysis and design of beam-columns. Exact solution to members of this kind are not easy to compute. However, AISC specifications provided in Section H (M5-54) show interaction formulas that have been developed from both the experimental and theoretical work and give approximate but conservative procedures to design and analyze these members. These safe and conservative interaction Formulas are H1-1, H1-2 and H1-3.

AISC Formula H1-1 checks the overall lateral stability of the member. It contains an amplification factor which considers the PΔ affect due to lateral deflection or buckling shape of the member.

$$\frac{f_a}{F_a} + \frac{C_{mx}\,f_{bx}}{\left(1 - \frac{f_a}{F'_{ex}}\right)F_{bx}} + \frac{C_{my}\,f_{by}}{\left(1 - \frac{f_a}{F'_{ey}}\right)F_{by}} \leq 1.0$$

AISC Formula H1-2 checks the overall stress of the member due to yielding at the connections. This formula usually governs the design if the member is not allowed to sway or is bent in reverse curvature.

$$\frac{f_a}{0.60\,F_y} + \frac{f_{bx}}{F_{bx}} + \frac{f_{by}}{F_{by}} \leq 1.0$$

Both Formulas H1-1 and H1-2 must be used if the ratio of the computed axial stress to the allowable axial stress is greater than 15%.

That is, $\frac{f_a}{F_a} \geq 0.15$.

Formula H1-3 is used when the ratio of the computed axial stress to the allowable axial stress is not greater than 15%.

$$\frac{f_a}{F_a} + \frac{f_{bx}}{F_{bx}} + \frac{f_{by}}{F_{by}} \leq 1.00 \qquad \text{AISC Eq. (H1-3)}$$

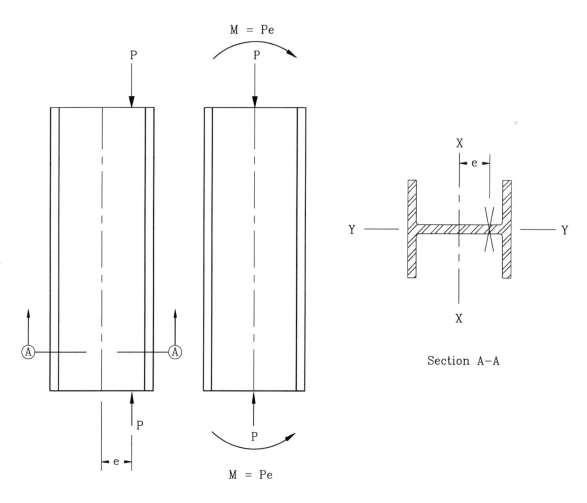

Figure 6.1 Eccentric Force on Beam-Column

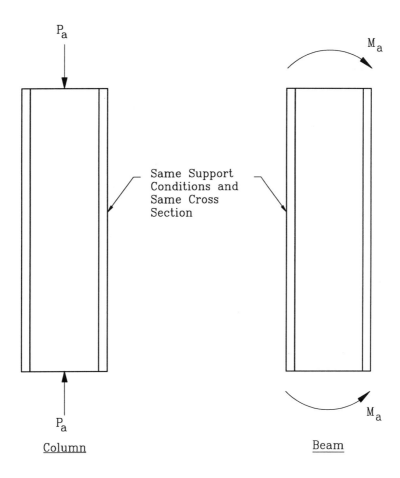

Figure 6.2 Pure Column and Pure Beam

6.2   DEFINITION OF TERMS FOR FORMULA H1-1

f_a = computed actual axial stress, P/A, where P is the applied axial compression load and A is the gross sectional area of member

F_a = allowable axial stress for maximum slenderness ratio of the column

F'_{ex} = Euler stress divided by a safety factor of 23/12

$$\frac{12 \, \pi^2 \, E}{23 \left(\frac{KL_x}{r_x}\right)^2}$$

The value of F'_{ex} is listed in Table 8 of AISC Manual M5-122 for various slenderness ratios for all grades of steel

f_b = actual bending stress, M_x/S_x, where S_x is the section modules of column about the x-x axis and M_x is the moment about the x-x axis at the point of consideration. For moment sign convention, refer to Figure 6.3 and Figure 6.4.

M_x = M_{x2}, which is the larger bending moment at the end of column when the column has no transverse load.

M_x = M_{x3}, which is the bending moment between the ends of a column when the column has transverse load.

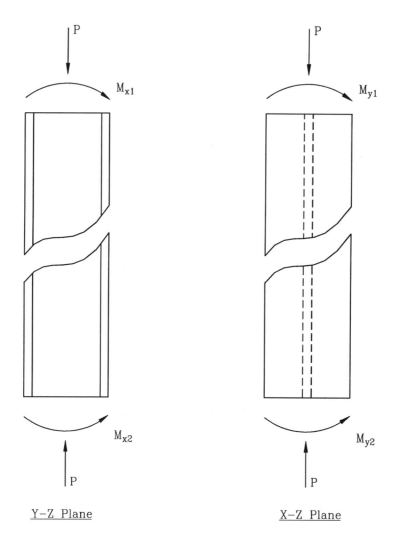

Figure 6.3 Axial and Moment About Both Axes of Beam-Column

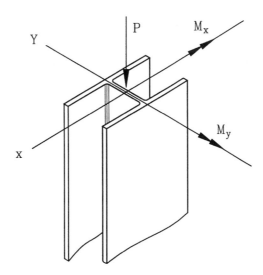

Figure 6.4 Sign Convention for Bending Moments

F_{bx} = allowable compressive bending stress about the strong axis of the member

F_{bx} = 0.66 F_y when $L_b \leq L_c$ Compact

F_{bx} = 0.60 F_y when $L_u \geq L_b > L_c$ Subcompact

$F_{bx} \leq$ 0.60 F_y when $L_b > L_u$ Noncompact

Note:

When computing the allowable bending stresses for noncompact sections in Formula H1-1, the value of C_b may be computed as follows:

C_b = 1.0 for frame members braced against joint translation

C_b = 1.75 + 1.05 (δ) M_1/M_2 + 0.3 $(M_1/M_2)^2 \leq$ 2.3 for frames subject to joint translation

C_{mx} = is a reduction factor or coefficient that reduces the maximum moment between the ends of the column to an equivalent uniform moment. AISC provides three different categories for computing this coefficient.

Category 1:

C_{mx} = 0.85 for members in frames subject to joint translation with or without transverse load between their supports.

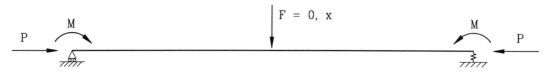

Figure 6.5 Beam-Column Allowed to Sway

Category 2:

C_{mx} = $0.6 - 0.4\,(\delta)\,(M_1/M_2) \geq 0.4$ for members in frames braced against joint translation and not subject to transverse load between their supports. The terms M_1, M_2 and δ are all defined in Chapter 4.

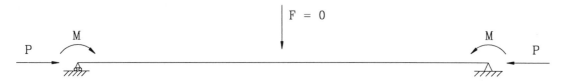

Figure 6.6 Beam-Column Braced with No Lateral Load

Category 3:

$C_m = 1 + \psi \dfrac{f_a}{F'_{ex}}$ for members in frames braced against joint translation and are subject to transverse load between the supports. Values of ψ are listed in Table C-H1.1 (M5-154).

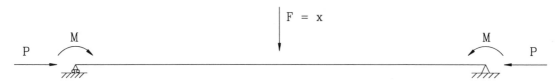

Figure 6.7 Beam-Column Braced with Lateral Load

Table 6.1 Values of M_1 and M_2 for Various Loading Conditions

Category	Loading Conditions ($f_a > 0.15 F_a$)	f_a	C_m	Remarks
①	Computed moments maximum at end; joint translation not prevented	$\dfrac{M_2}{S}$	0.85	M_1 ... $-M_2$ ... l_b $M_1 = M_2 \dfrac{M_1}{M_2}$ negative as shown; Check both formulas (H1−1 & H1−2)
②	Computed moments maximum at end; no transverse loading; joint translation prevented	$\dfrac{M_2}{S}$	$(0.6 \pm 0.4 \dfrac{M_1}{M_2})$ but not less than 0.4	M_1 ... $-M_2$ ... l_b Check both formulas (H1−1 & H1−2)
③	Transverse loading; joint translation prevented	$\dfrac{M_2}{S}$ Using Formula H1−2 $\dfrac{M_3}{S}$ Using Formula H1−1	$1 + \psi \dfrac{f_a}{F'_e}$	$-M_1$ ... M_2 ... M_3 ... l_b Check both formulas (H1−1 & H1−2)

F_{by} = allowable bending stress about weak axis of the member.

The definitions of the terms f_{by} and C_{my} are the same as the definitions of f_{bx} and C_{mx}, except that these terms are taken about the weak axis of the member.

6.3   DEFINITION OF TERMS FOR FORMULA H1-2 AND H1-3

The definitions of all the terms in Formula H1-2 and H1-3 are the same as the definitions for the terms in Formula H1-1 except as follows. The actual bending stresses, f_{bx} and f_{by}, are equal to the maximum bending moment at the end of the column divided by their respective section modulus.

$$f_{bx} = \frac{M_{x2}}{S_x}$$

$$f_{by} = \frac{M_{y2}}{S_y}$$

6.4   EXAMPLE PROBLEMS

6.4.1   EXAMPLE PROBLEM 1 — BEAM-COLUMN ANALYSIS

Check if the beam-column loaded as shown in Fig. P6.4.1 (a), satisfies the AISC requirements. A36 steel, $K_x = 0.8$ and $K_y = 0.9$. Bending is about the strong axis. The ends of the beam-column are prevented from possible movement. Lateral supports for the compression flange are provided at the ends of the column.

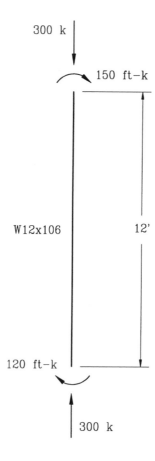

300 k

150 ft-k

W12x106   12'

120 ft-k

300 k

Fig. P6.4.1 (a)

Solution

1. Compute actual axial stress, f_a

    $$f_a = \frac{P}{A} = \frac{300}{31.2} = 9.6 \text{ ksi}$$

2. Determine allowable axial stress, F_a

    a. Compute slenderness ratio about x-x axis

    $$K_x L_x / r_x = 0.8 \times 12 \times \frac{12}{5.47} = 21.1$$

b. Compute slenderness ratio about y-y axis

$$K_y L_y / r_y = 0.9 \times 12 \times \frac{12}{3.11} = 41.7 \ldots \text{governs}$$

c. From M3-16, $F_a = 19.05$ ksi for $K_y L_y / r_y = 41.7$

3. Ratio of $f_a / F_a = \dfrac{9.6}{19.05} = 0.504 > 0.15$

Therefore, check both formulas H1-1 and H1-2.

4. Formula H1-1

$$\frac{f_a}{F_a} + \frac{C_{mx}\ f_{bx}}{\left(1 - \frac{f_a}{F'_{ex}}\right) F_{bx}} + \frac{C_{my}\ f_{by}}{\left(1 - \frac{f_a}{F'_{ey}}\right) F_{by}} \le 1.00$$

$f_a\ = 9.6$ ksi

$F_a\ = 19.05$ ksi

$C_{mx} = 0.6 - 0.4\ (\delta)\ (M_1 / M_2) \ge 0.4 \quad \ldots \text{Category 2}$

$0.6 - 0.4\ (+1)\ (120/150) = 0.28$, use 0.4 as minimum value.

$$f_{bx} = \frac{M_{x2}}{S_x} = \frac{(150 \times 12)}{145} = 12.4 \text{ ksi}$$

because $L_b = 12$ ft $< L_c = 12.9$ ft $\hfill$ (M3-27)

and $F_y = 36 < F'_y \ge 65$ $\hfill$ (M1-25)

Therefore, $F_{bx} = 0.66 \times 36 = 24$ ksi

$F'_{ex} = 336$ ksi for $K_x L_x / r_x = 21.1$ $\hfill$ (M5-122)

Check the formula H1-1

$$\frac{9.6}{19.05} + \frac{0.4\ (12.4)}{\left(1 - \frac{9.6}{336}\right) 24} + 0$$

$$= 0.504 + 0.213 = 0.717 < 1.0 \ldots \text{OK}$$

Check the formula H1-2

$$\frac{9.6}{0.6 \times 36} + \frac{12.4}{24} = 0.961 < 1.0 \ldots \text{OK}$$

Conclusion:

Since both formulas H1-1 and H1-2 are satisfied, the beam-column as loaded is adequate per AISC requirements.

6.4.2   EXAMPLE PROBLEM 2 — BEAM-COLUMN ANALYSIS

Given:

Use A36 steel. For the beam-column loaded as in Fig. P6.4.2 (a), check the adequacy of the section. The top of the column is prevented from movement within the plane of paper only.

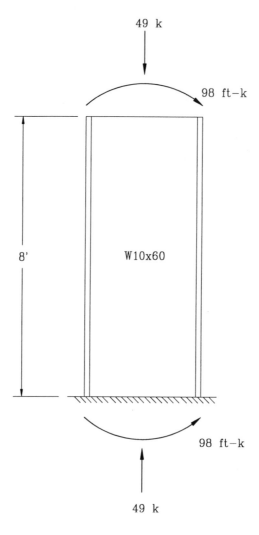

Fig. P6.4.2 (a)

Solution

A. Compute actual axial stress, f_a.

$$f_a = \frac{P}{A} = \frac{49}{17.7} = 2.76 \text{ ksi}$$

B. Determine the allowable axial stress, F_a.

$$\frac{K_x L_x}{r_x} = \frac{0.8 \times 8 \times 12}{4.41} = 17.4$$

$$\frac{K_y L_y}{r_y} = \frac{2.1 \times 8 \times 12}{2.57} = 78.4 \qquad \ldots \text{Governs}$$

From M3-16, $F_a = 13.55$ ksi

C. Check ratio of $\dfrac{f_a}{F_a}$

$$\frac{2.76}{15.55} = 0.17 > 0.15$$

Therefore, must check formulas H1-1 and H1-2

D. Formula H1-1

$$\frac{f_a}{F_a} + \frac{C_{mx} f_{bx}}{\left(1 - \frac{f_a}{F_{ex}'}\right) F_{bx}} + \frac{C_{my} f_{by}}{\left(1 - \frac{f_a}{F_{ey}'}\right) F_{by}} \le 1.0$$

$f_a = 2.76$ ksi

$F_a = 15.55$ ksi

$$C_{mx} = 0.6 - 0.4 \, (\delta) \left(\frac{M_1}{M_2}\right) \ge 0.4$$

$$C_{mx} = 0.6 - 0.4 \, (-1) \left(\frac{98}{98}\right) = 1.0$$

$$f_{bx} = \frac{M_x}{S_x} = \frac{98 \times 12}{67.1} = 17.52$$

$F_{bx} = 24$ ksi; therefore, $L_b < L_c = 8 \le 10.6$

$$F_{ex}' = \frac{12 \, \pi^2 \, E}{23 \left(\frac{k_x L_x}{r_x}\right)^2}$$

$$F_{ex}' = \frac{12 \times \pi^2 \times 29 \times 10^3}{23 \times 17.4^2}$$

$$F_{ex}' = 493$$

Substituting in formula H1-1

$$\frac{2.76}{15.55} + \frac{1.0 \times 17.52}{\left(1 - \frac{2.76}{493}\right) 24} = 0.912 \leq 1.0 \quad \text{OK}$$

Check Formula (H1-2)

$$\frac{2.76}{0.6 \times 36} + \frac{17.5}{23.6} = 0.128 + 0.74 = 0.868 < 1 \quad \text{OK}$$

Conclusion: This beam column is satisfactory.

6.5   DESIGN OF BEAM-COLUMNS

The method used to design beam-columns is accomplished by trial-and-error procedure. AISC provides an Equivalent Axial Load Formula in M3-10 by which it gives an effective axial load, P_{eff}, for the loads and moments being applied on the beam-columns.

$$P_{eff} = P + mM_x + mUM_y$$

Where

   P = Actual axial load kip

   m = A factor by which it converts the bending moment to an approximate equivalent axial compressive load. The value of m is listed in Table B, (M3-10) for $C_m = 0.85$.

   M_x = Bending moment about strong axis ft-kip.

   M_y = Bending moment about weak axis ft-kip.

   U = A factor which converts the bending moment in the weak axis to an equivalent moment in the strong axis. The value of U is listed in the Column Tables in Part 3 of AISC Manual.

   $$U = \frac{(F_{bx} \, S_x)}{(F_{by} \, S_y)} \text{ as defined under symbols in the AISC Manual.}$$

When the equivalent axial load is computed, then the Column Tables in Part 3 of AISC Manual are used to design for the most economical shape. The Equivalent Axial Load Formula is formulated as a result of manipulating the interaction Formula H1-1 from its stress form to an equivalent axial load form.

6.6   DESIGN PROCEDURE FOR BEAM-COLUMNS

First Trial:

1. Determine the effective length of KL; K is the effective length factor, and L is the actual unbraced length in the plane of bending.

2. Select the appropriate value of m from Table 6.2, first approximations line values.

3. Let the value of U equal 3.0.

4. Solve for $P'_{eff} = P + mM_x + mUM_y$.

5. From the Column Tables in Part 3 of AISC Manual, select a section whose $P_{all} \geq P'_{eff}$

Second Trial:

1. Select the appropriate value of m from Table B, subsequent approximations values for the depth of the shape selected in the preceding trial.

2. Use the value of U equal to the U value for the shape selected in the proceeding trial as shown in the column load table.

3. Solve for $P''_{eff} = P + mM_x + mUM_y$

4. From the Column Tables in Part 3 of AISC Manual, select a section whose $P_{all} \geq P''_{eff}$

If the selected section in the second trial is the same as the section selected in first trial, that means the value of m and U are stabilized, and no more trials are needed. If the sections are different, then perform more trials until the section repeats itself. The final selected section must be checked by the modified interaction Formulas H1-1 and H1-2 as shown in (M3-9).

Table 6.2 Values of m Used in Beam-Column Design
(AISC Table B, M3-10)

Values of m*													
F_y	36 ksi							50 ksi					
KL. (ft)	10	12	14	16	18	20	22 & over	10	12	14	16	18	20	22 & over
1st Approximation													
All shapes	2.4	2.3	2.2	2.2	2.1	2.0	1.9	2.4	2.3	2.2	2.0	1.9	1.8	1.7
Subsequent Approximations													
W,M,S4	3.6	2.6	1.9	1.6	---	---	---	2.7	1.9	1.6	1.6	---	---	---
W,M,S5	3.9	3.2	2.4	1.9	1.5	1.4	---	3.3	2.4	1.8	1.6	1.4	1.4	---
W,M,S6	3.2	2.7	2.3	2.0	1.9	1.6	1.5	3.0	2.5	2.2	1.9	1.8	1.6	1.5
W8	3.0	2.9	2.8	2.6	2.3	2.0	2.0	3.0	2.8	2.5	2.2	1.9	1.6	1.6
W10	2.6	2.5	2.5	2.4	2.3	2.1	2.0	2.5	2.5	2.4	2.3	2.1	1.9	1.7
W12	2.1	2.1	2.0	2.0	2.0	2.0	2.0	2.0	2.0	2.0	1.9	1.9	1.8	1.7
W14	1.8	1.7	1.7	1.7	1.7	1.7	1.7	1.8	1.7	1.7	1.7	1.7	1.7	1.7

*Values of m are for $C_m = 0.85$. When C_m is other than 0.85, multiply the tabular value of m by $C_m/0.85$.

6.7   P. E. PROBLEMS

6.7.1   P. E. PROBLEM 1 — BEAM-COLUMN DESIGN

Design for the most economical W14 section for the beam-column shown below. Joint translation is allowed. Bending about the strong axis. Use A242 steel and 8th edition of AISC Manual.

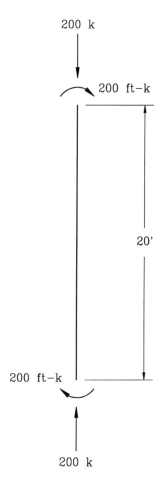

200 k

200 ft-k

20'

200 ft-k

200 k

Fig. P6.7.1 (a)

Solution

Note that A242 steel is being used. Its yield stress is not equal to 36 ksi, but it could be equal to 50-ksi material. Therefore, in using AISC Tables, refer to the values related to 50-ksi material.

The effective length factors, K, cannot be derived from the wording of this problem. Since joint translation is allowed, then the K value is greater than 1.0, but less than 2.1. Hence, choose $K_x = K_y = 1.60$.

First trial:

1. Effective length (KL) = $1.6 \times 20 = 32$ ft

2. Value of m = 1.7, from Table 6.2 (Same as Table B on M3-10) under first approximations. For 50-ksi material.

    Note: Value of m does not have to be corrected because joint translation is allowed, therefore the value of $C_{mx} = 0.85$.

3. Solve for $P'_{eff} = P + mM_x + mUM_y$

    $$= 200 + 1.7 \times 200 + 0 = 540 \text{ kip}$$

4. Select from M3-23, W14 × 132, 50-ksi material whose

    P_{all} = 551 kip > P'_{eff} = 540 kip.

Second trial:

1. Value of m from subsequent approximations 50 ksi, W14 and KL = 32 is equal to 1.7

2. Solve for $P''_{eff} = P + mM_x + mUM_y$

    $$= 200 + 1.7 \times 200 + 0 = 540 \text{ kip}$$

3. Select from M3-23, W14 × 132, 50 ksi material whose

    P_{all} = 551 kip > P''_{eff} = 540 kip.

Because the section in second trial is the same as the section selected in the first trial, no more trials are to be made.

Check Formula H1-1 modified (M3-9)

$$P_{eq} = P + \left\{ B_x\, M_x\, C_{mx} \left(\frac{F_a}{F_{bx}} \right) \right\} \frac{a_x}{\left[a_x - P\, (K_x\, L_x)^2 \right]}$$

$$+ \left\{ B_y\, M_y\, C_{my} \left(\frac{F_a}{F_{by}} \right) \right\} \frac{a_y}{\left[a_y - P\, (K_y\, L_y)^2 \right]}$$

$$P_{eq} = 200 + \frac{0.186 \times 200 \times 12 \times 0.85}{30} \left(\frac{551}{38.8}\right) \frac{228 \times 10^6}{\left[228 \times 10^6 - 200 \left(1.6 \times 20 \times 12\right)^2\right]} + 0$$

$P_{eq} = 481.32 \text{ kip} < P_{all} = 551 \text{ kip} \quad \ldots \text{OK}$

Check Formula H1-2 modified.

$$P_{eq} = P \left(\frac{F_a}{0.6 \ F_y}\right) + \frac{B_x \ M_x \ F_a}{F_{bx}} + \frac{B_y \ M_y \ F_a}{F_{by}}$$

$$P_{eq} = 200 \left[\frac{551}{38.8 \times 0.6 \times 50}\right] + \frac{0.186 \times 200 \times 12 \times 551}{(38.8 \times 30)} + 0$$

$$P_{eq} = 419 \text{ kip} < 551 \text{ kip} \qquad \text{OK}$$

Note that $F_{bx} = 30$ ksi because $L_c = 15.5 < L_b = 20 < L_u = 47.7$ and section W14 $\times$ 132, 50-ksi material is available per Group 2 in M1-7 and M1-8.

6.7.2   P. E. PROBLEM 2 — BEAM-COLUMN — STORE-FRONT

Design a column in a store-front building structure as shown in Fig. P6.7.2 (a). The column is braced laterally at 10-ft and 21-ft levels in both x and y directions. A 1,500-lb sign is hung at the end of a 6-ft cantilever, which is 8 ft-6 in. above the ground. The cantilever also supports a uniform load of 300 plf. Use A36 material.

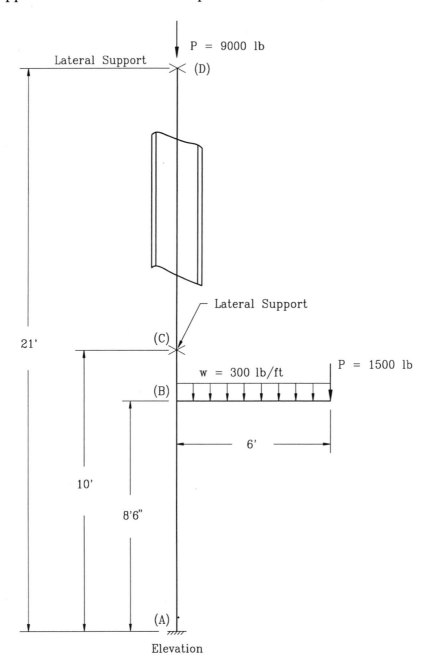

Fig. P6.7.2 (a)

Solution

1. Compute the reactions, shear forces and moments for the given loads. See Structure Analysis, Volume 1, Section 1 of the S.E. License Review Manual for Moment Distribution Method.

2. Draw the moment diagram for column AD .

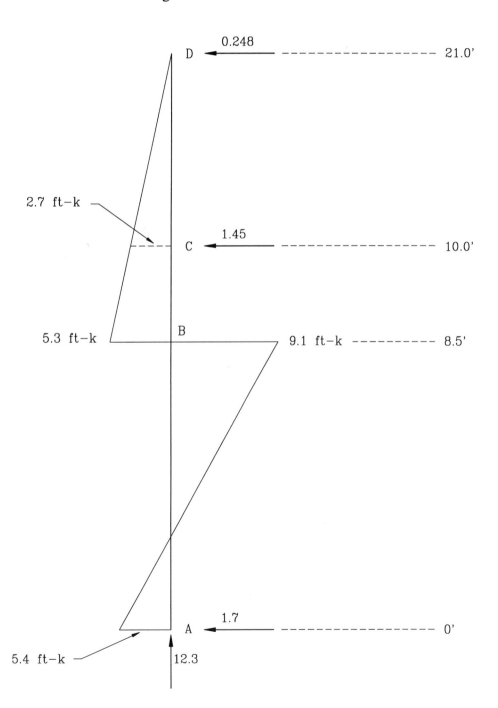

Fig. P6.7.2 (b)

3. Design of Column AC: $K = 0.8$ for a column with fixed and pinned end condition.

First trial:

1. Effective length (KL) = $0.8 \times 10 = 8.0$ ft

2. Value of m = 2.4 from Table B M3-10 under first approximation.

    $C_{mx} = 1.0$ for restrained end.

    $M_x = M_{3x} = 9.1$ ft-kip

    $P = 9{,}000 + 1{,}500 + 300 \times 6 = 12{,}300$ lb = 12.3 kip

3. Solve for $P'_{eff} = P + mM_x + mUM_y$

    $$= 12.3 + 2.4 \left(\frac{1.0}{0.85}\right) 9.1 + 0 = 38 \text{ kip}$$

4. Select from M3-33 W6 × 12, 36-ksi material whose

    $P_{all} = 44$ kip > $P'_{eff} = 38$ kip.

Second trial:

1. Value of m = 3.2 from subsequent approximations for W6.

2. Solve for $P''_{eff} = P + mM_x + mUM_y$

    $$= 12.3 + 3.2 \left(\frac{1.0}{0.85}\right) 9.1 + 0 = 47 \text{ kip}$$

3. Select from M3-33, W6 × 16, 36-ksi material whose

    $P_{all} = 62$ kip > $P''_{eff} = 47$ kip.

Third trial:

1. Value of m = 3.2 from subsequent approximations for W6.

2. Solve for $P_{eff}''' = P + mM_x + mUM_y$

    $$= 12.3 + 3.2 \left(\frac{1.0}{0.85}\right) 9.1 + 0 = 47 \text{ kip}$$

3. Select from M3-33, W6 × 16, 36-ksi material whose

    $P_{all} = 62$ kip > $P''_{eff} = 47$ kip.

Because the section in third trial is the same as the section selected in second trial, no more trials are needed.

Check Formula H1-1 modified:

$$F_a = \frac{P_{all}}{A} = \frac{62}{4.74} = 13.1 \text{ ksi}$$

$M_{2x} = 5.4$ ft-kip $M_{3x} = 9.1$ ft-kip $M_{1x} = 2.8$ ft-kip

$F_{bx} = 22$ ksi, because $L_c = 4.3 > L_b = 10 < L_u = 12$

$$P_{eq} = P + \left\{ B_x \, M_x \, C_{mx} \left(\frac{F_a}{F_{bx}} \right) \right\} \left[\frac{a_x}{a_x - P \, (K_x \, L_x)^2} \right]$$

$$+ \left\{ B_y \, M_y \, C_{my} \left(\frac{F_a}{F_{by}} \right) \right\} \left[\frac{a_y}{a_y - P \, (K_y \, L_y)^2} \right]$$

$$12.3 + \frac{0.465 \times 9.1 \times 12 \times 1.0 \times 13.1}{22} \left[\frac{4.77 \times 10^6}{4.77 \times 10^6 - 12.3 \, (0.8 \times 10 \times 12)^2} \right] + 0$$

$$= \; 43.3 \; \text{kip} \; < \; 62 \; \text{kip} \; \text{OK}$$

Check Formula H1-2 modified:

$$P \left(\frac{F_a}{0.6 \, F_y} \right) \; + \; \frac{(B_x) \, (M_x) \, (F_a)}{F_{bx}} \; + \; \frac{(B_y) \, (M_y) \, (F_a)}{F_{by}}$$

$$= \; 12.3 \left(\frac{13.1}{0.6 \times 36} \right) + \frac{(0.465) \, (5.4) \, (12) \, (13.1)}{22} + 0$$

$$= \; 25.4 \; \text{kip} \; < \; 62 \; \text{kip} \; \text{OK}$$

Note: M_{3x} is used in Formula H1-1 and M_{2x} is used in Formula H1-2.

7

BOLTED CONNECTIONS

7.1   MATERIAL

The ASTM materials for most bolts used in structural steel connections are as follows:

- A307
- A325
- A490

A307 bolts are called common, ordinary or machine bolts. They are made from low-carbon steel. A307 bolts are used to connect miscellaneous steel members that are subjected to static loads. The minimum tensile strength, F_u, is equal to 60 ksi.

A325 bolts are called high-strength bolts. They are made from medium heat-treated carbon steel. A325 bolts are used to connect structural steel members in buildings and bridges that are subjected to static or dynamic loads. The minimum tensile strength, F_u, is equal to 105 ksi.

A490 bolts are also called high-strength bolts. They are made from heat-treated alloy steel. A490 bolts are used to connect structural steel members in buildings and bridges that are subjected to static or dynamic loads. The minimum tensile strength, F_u, is equal to 150 ksi.

A bolt assembly consists of a bolt, nut and a washer all of the same type of material. One washer is required to be installed under the turned part of the bolt assembly. For A490 bolts used to connect material of yield stress less than 40 ksi, they will require two washers, one under the head and one under the nut.

7.2 BOLTS AND NUTS IDENTIFICATION

In accordance with the AISC M5-293, high-strength bolts are identified as follows:

- A325 Type 1 bolts are identified on the head by the following marks:
    1. Manufacturer's symbol
    2. Legend "A325"
- A490 Type 1 bolts are identified on the head by the following marks:
    1. Manufacturer's symbol
    2. Legend "A490"
- High-strength nuts are identified by three equally spaced circumferential lines.
- A307 bolts or nuts have no markings.

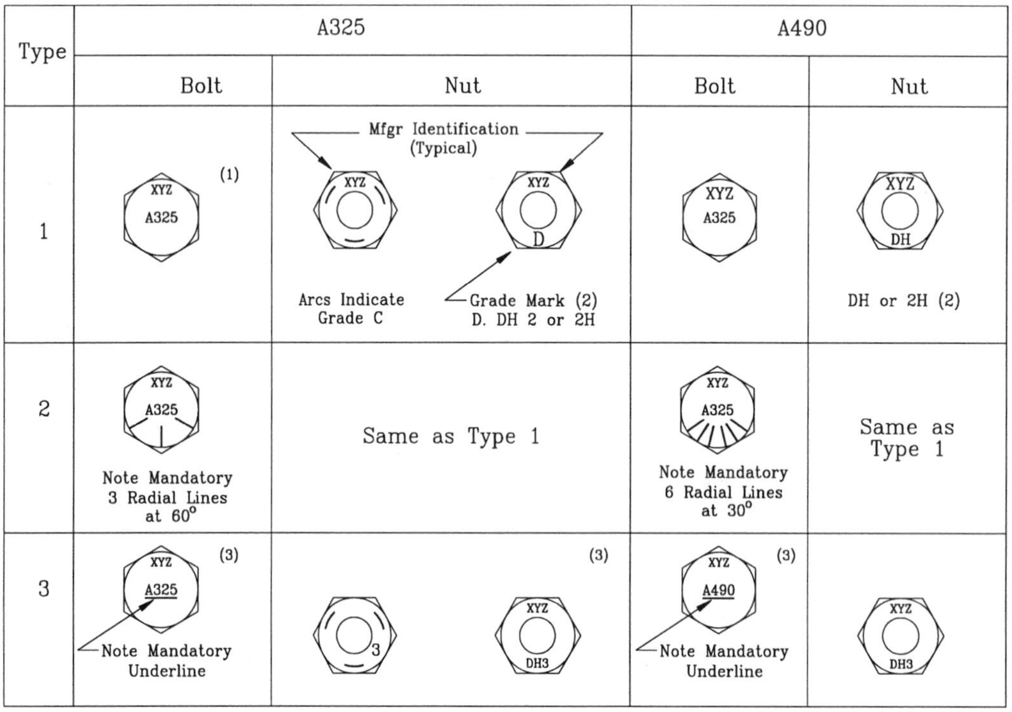

(1) Additional Optional 3 Radial Lines at 120° May be Added
(2) Type 3 Also Acceptable
(3) Additional Optional Mark Indicating Weather Grade May be Added

Figure 7.1 High-Strength Bolts Identification
(AISC Fig. C2 M5-293)

7.3   INSTALLATION OF HIGH-STRENGTH BOLTS

In accordance with the AISC Specifications, high-strength bolts are initially tightened at the time of installation. The initial tension load is equal to 70% of the minimum tensile strength of the bolt. The values of initial tension for bolts are listed in the AISC Manual Table 4 (M5-274). Initial tensioning is accomplished by one of the following methods:

a. Turn of the nut method, a method that is commonly used

b. Calibrated wrench tightening

c. Use of direct load indicator washers

d   Use of direct load indicator bolts

Table 7.1 Initial Tension Forces in Bolts
(AISC Table 4, M5-274)

Nominal Bolts Size, in.	Minimum Fastener Tension*, kip	
	A325 Bolts	A490 Bolts
1/2	12	15
5/8	19	24
3/4	28	35
7/8	39	49
1	51	64
1 1/8	56	80
1 1/4	71	102
1 3/8	85	121
1 1/2	103	148

*Equal to 70% of specified minimum tensile strengths of bolts, rounded off to the nearest kip.

7.4   INITIAL TIGHTENING OF HIGH-STRENGTH BOLTS

Slip-critical connections and connections subject to direct tension must be initially tensioned in accordance with AISC Table 4, M5-274 (Table 7.2).

Table 7.2
Fastener Tension Required for Slip-Critical Connections and
Connections Subject to Direct Tension.

Nominal Bolts Size, in.	Minimum Tension* in 1,000's of Pounds, kip	
	A325 Bolts	A490 Bolts
$1/2$	12	15
$5/8$	19	24
$3/4$	28	35
$7/8$	39	49
1	51	64
$1^1/8$	56	80
$1^1/4$	71	102
$1^3/8$	85	121
$1^1/2$	103	148

* *Equal to 70% of specified minimum tensile strengths of bolts (as specified in ASTM Specifications for tests of full size A325 and A490 bolts with UNC threads loaded in axial tension) rounded to the nearest kip.*

In accordance with AISC,M5-270, slip-critical joints are defined as joints in which slip would be detrimental to the serviceability of the structure. They include:

1. Joints subject to fatigue

2. Joints with bolts installed in oversize holes

3. Certain joints with bolts installed in slotted holes

4. Joints subject to significant load reversal

5. Joints in which welds and bolts share in transmitting load at a common fraying surface

In accordance with AISC, M5-64, fully-tensioned high-strength or welds shall be used for the following connections:

1. Column splices in all tier structures 200 ft or more in height

2. Column splices in all tier structures 100 to 200 ft in height, if least horizontal dimension is less than 40% of the height

3. Column splices in tier structures less than 100 ft in height, if least dimension is less than 25% of the height

4. Connections of all beams and girders to columns and of any other beams and girders on which bracing of columns is dependent in structures over 125 ft in height

5. In all structures carrying cranes of over 5-ton capacity

6. Connection for supports of running machinery or other live loads which produce impact or reversal of stress

7.5   BOLT SPACINGS

In accordance with Section J3 of AISC Specifications, bolt spacings are functions of bolt diameters and applied loads. In general, bolt spacings are as follows:

a. Minimum edge distance shall be in accordance with Section J3.9 and Table J3.5, M5-76.

b. Minimum spacings between bolts shall be in accordance with Section J3.8 of AISC Specifications. It is preferred to space the bolts at a distance equal to 3 times the diameter of the bolt.

c. Maximum edge distance shall be in accordance with Section J3.10, M5-77 which is 12 times the thickness of the material being connected but shall not exceed 6 inches.

Table 7.3 Minimum Edge Distance for Bolt Spacing
(AISC Table J3.5, M5-76)

Minimum Edges Distance, in. (Center of Standard Hole* to Edges of Connected Part)		
Nominal Rivet or Bolt Diameter (inch)	At Sheared Edges (inch)	At Rolled Edges of Plates, Shapes or Bars or Gas Cut Edges†
1/2	7/8	3/4
5/8	1-1/8	7/8
3/4	1-1/4	1
7/8	1-1/2‡	1-1/8
1	1-3/4‡	1-1/4
1-1/8	2	1-1/2
1-1/4	2-1/4	1-5/8
Over 1-1/4	1-3/4 × Diameter	1-1/4 × Diameter

* *For oversized or slotted holes, see AISC Table J3.6, M5-76*
† *All edge distances in this column may be reduced 1/8 in. when the hole is at a point where stress does not exceed 25% of the maximum allowed stress in the element.*
‡ *These may be 1-1/4 in. at the ends of beam connection angles.*

7.6   DEFINITIONS RELATED TO BOLTS

Single shear (S) connection: A connection when the bolts are subjected to a shear load that tends to shear off the bolts in one single plane between the connecting plates.

Double shear (D) connection: A connection when the bolts are subjected to a shear load that tends to shear off the bolts in two planes between the connecting plates.

N-Type connection is a bearing-type connection with threads of bolts included in the shear plane.

X-Type connection is a bearing-type connection with threads of bolts are excluded from the shear plane.

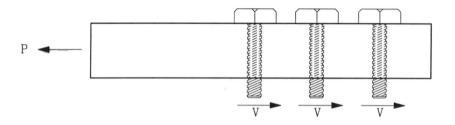

Figure 7.2 Bolts in Single Shear

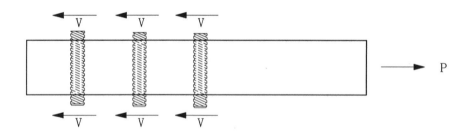

Figure 7.3 Bolts in Double Shear

7.7   TYPE OF CONNECTIONS

Type of connections that are frequently used in structural steel members are as follows:

1.   Tension-type connections

2.   Shear in slip critical-type connections

3.   Shear in bearing-type connections

4.   Eccentric-type connections

5.   Combination of shear- and tension-type connections

7.8   ALLOWABLE STRESSES

Table 7.4 Allowable Stresses in Bolts
(AISC Table J3.2, M5-73)

Description of Fasteners	Allowable Tension (F_t)	Allowable Shear (F_v)			
		Slip-Critical Connections			Bearing type Connec-tions
		Standard Size Holes	Oversized and Short-slotted Holes	Long-slotted Holes	
A502, Grade 1, hot-driven rivets	23.0				17.5
A502, Grades 2 and 3, hot-driven rivets	29.0				22.0
A307 bolts	20.0				10.0
Threaded parts meeting the requirements of Secs. A3.1 and A3.4, and A449 bolts meeting the requirements of Sec. A3.4, when threads are not excluded from shear planes	$0.33F_u$				$0.17\ F_u$
Threaded parts meeting the requirements of Secs. A3.1 and A3.4, and A449 bolts meeting the requirements of Sec. A3.4, when threads are excluded from shear planes	$0.33F_u$				$0.22\ F_u$
A325 bolts, when threads are not excluded from shear planes	44.0	17.0	15.0	12.0	21.0
A325 bolts, when threads are excluded from shear planes	44.0	17.0	15.0	12.0	30.0
A490 bolts, when threads are not excluded from shear planes	54.0	21.0	18.0	15.0	28.0
A490 bolts, when threads are excluded from shear planes	54.0	21.0	18.0	15.0	40.0

Refer to AISC M5-73, Table J3.2 for notes, remarks and exceptions related to this table.

7.9   TENSION-TYPE CONNECTION

$$f_t = \frac{P}{n\,A_b} \le F_t$$

or

$$\frac{P}{n} \le r_t$$

Where

f_t = Actual tensile stress

P = Tensile load

n = Number of bolts in the connection

A_b = Nominal area of bolt

F_t = Allowable tensile stress per AISC (M5-73)

r_t = Allowable tensile load per bolt AISC Table 1-A (M4-3)

Table 7.5 Allowable Tensile Loads in Bolts
(AISC Table 1-A, M4-3)

		Tension Allowable loads, kip							
		Bolts and Rivets Tension on Gross (Nominal) Area							
ASTM Designation	F_t ksi	Nominal Diameter, d, in.							
		5/8	3/4	7/8	1	1 1/8	1 1/4	1 3/8	1 1/2
		Area (based on Nominal Diameter), in.^{2}							
		0.3068	0.4418	0.6013	0.7854	0.9940	1.227	1.485	1.767
A307 bolts	20.0	6.1	8.8	12.0	15.7	19.9	24.5	29.7	35.3
A325 bolts	44.0	13.5	19.4	26.5	34.6	43.7	54.0	65.3	77.7
A490 bolts	54.0	16.6	23.9	32.5	42.4	53.7	66.3	80.2	95.4
A502-1 rivets	23.0	7.1	10.2	13.8	18.1	22.9	28.2	34.2	40.6
A502-2 ,3 rivets	29.0	8.9	12.8	17.4	22.8	28.8	35.6	43.1	51.2

The above table lists ASTM specified materials that are generally intended for use as structural fasteners. For dynamic and fatigue loading, only A325 or A490 high-strength bolts should be specified. See AISC Specification. Appendix B, K4. For allowable combined shear and tension loads, see AISC Specification Sect. J3.5 and J3.6.

7.10   EXAMPLE PROBLEM

7.10.1   EXAMPLE PROBLEM 1 — TENSILE CAPACITY OF BOLT CONNECTION

Determine the allowable tensile load that can be applied on the connection shown in Fig. P7.10.1 (a). The bolts in the connection are 7/8-in. diameter A325.

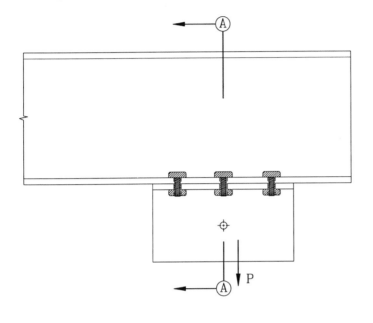

Section: A–A

Fig. P7.10.1 (a)

Solution

$n = 6$ bolts, A325, 7/8-in. diameter

$r_t = 26.5$ kip/bolt . . . (M4-3)

$P/n \le r_t$

$P_{all} = n \times r_t = 6 \times 26.5 = 159$ kip

7.11   SLIP-CRITICAL CONNECTION

When a bolt is initially tightened, the resulting tensile force in the bolt produces a sufficient clamping force to prevent slippage within the connection. Safety factor against slippage is about 1.5. The barrel of the bolt does *not* come into contact with the connection plates, hence no bearing stresses are produced.

7.11.1   MECHANICS OF SLIP-CRITICAL CONNECTION

The connection shown below is to be designed against slippage with a safety factor of 1.5. Use A325 bolts having a 7/8-in. diameter. Using statics, find the largest allowable load, P, that may be applied. Neglect analysis of plates.

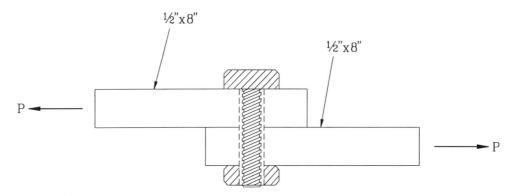

Figure 7.4 Slip-Critical Bolted Connection

A free-body diagram of plate and part of the bolt is shown below.

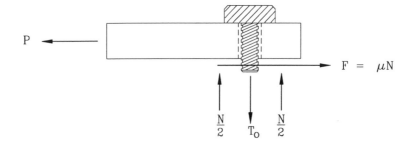

Figure 7.5 Free-Body Diagram of a Slip-Critical Connection

$$\Sigma F_y = 0 \qquad T_o = \left(\frac{N}{2}\right) + \left(\frac{N}{2}\right)$$

$$N = T_o = 39 \text{ kip}$$

$$\Sigma F_x = 0 \qquad P = F = \mu N = 0.40\,(39) = 15.6 \text{ kip}$$

Where

N = Normal force on top plate

u = Coefficient of friction between two plates, 0.40 for structural connections

F = Friction force between two plates

T_o = initial tension in bolt (AISC Table 4, M5-274). For a 7/8 in. diameter bolt $T_o = 39$ kip.

Consequently, for $P = 15.6$ kip, the plates are on the verge of slipping. Using a safety factor of 1.5, then the allowable load is as follows:

$$P_{all} = \left(\frac{15.6}{1.5}\right) = 10.4 \text{ kip which is about the same value as listed in AISC Table}$$

1-D, M4-5.

7.11.2 SLIP-CRITICAL CONNECTION STRESSES

The symbol for slip-critical connections is SC. Example: A325-SC means a high-strength bolt A325 in slip-critical connection. In the 8th Edition of the AISC Manual, a slip-critical connection is described as friction-type connection with symbol of F.

$$f_v = \frac{P}{n\,A_b} \leq F_v$$

or

$$\frac{P}{n} \leq r_{SC}$$

Where

f_v = Actual shear stress

P = Shear load

n = Number of bolts in the connection

A_b = Nominal area of bolt

F_v = Allowable shear stress from AISC (M5-73)

r_{SC} = Allowable shear load per bolt from AISC Table 1-D (M4-5)

Table 7.6 Allowable Shear Load of Bolts
(AISC Table 1-D, M4-5)

BOLTS, THREADED PARTS AND RIVETS
Shear
Allowable load in kips

TABLE I-D. SHEAR

	ASTM Designation	Connection Type[a]	Hole Type[b]	F_u ksi	Loading[c]	Nominal Diameter d, in.							
						5/8	3/4	7/8	1	1 1/8	1 1/4	1 3/8	1 1/2
						Area (Based on Nominal Diameter) in.²							
						.3068	.4418	.6013	.7854	.9940	1.227	1.485	1.767
Bolts	A307	—	STD NSL	10.0	S D	3.1 6.1	4.4 8.8	6.0 12.0	7.9 15.7	9.9 19.9	12.3 24.5	14.8 29.7	17.7 35.3
	A325	SC[a] Class A	STD	17.0	S D	5.22 10.4	7.51 15.0	10.2 20.4	13.4 26.7	16.9 33.8	20.9 41.7	25.2 50.5	30.0 60.1
			OVS, SSL	15.0	S D	4.60 9.20	6.63 13.3	9.02 18.0	11.8 23.6	14.9 29.8	18.4 36.8	22.3 44.6	26.5 53.0
			LSL	12.0	S D	3.68 7.36	5.30 10.6	7.22 14.4	9.42 18.8	11.9 23.9	14.7 29.4	17.8 35.6	21.2 42.4
		N	STD, NSL	21.0	S D	6.4 12.9	9.3 18.6	12.6 25.3	16.5 33.0	20.9 41.7	25.8 51.5	31.2 62.4	37.1 74.2
		X	STD, NSL	30.0	S D	9.2 18.4	13.3 26.5	18.0 36.1	23.6 47.1	29.8 59.6	36.8 73.6	44.5 89.1	53.0 106.0
	A490	SC[a] Class A	STD	21.0	S D	6.44 12.9	9.28 18.6	12.6 25.3	16.5 33.0	20.9 41.7	25.8 51.5	31.2 62.4	37.1 74.2
			OVS, SSL	18.0	S D	5.52 11.0	7.95 15.9	10.8 21.6	14.1 28.3	17.9 35.8	22.1 44.2	26.7 53.5	31.8 63.6
			LSL	15.0	S D	4.60 9.20	6.63 13.3	9.02 18.0	11.8 23.6	14.9 29.8	18.4 36.8	22.3 44.6	26.5 53.0
		N	STD, NSL	28.0	S D	8.6 17.2	12.4 24.7	16.8 33.7	22.0 44.0	27.8 55.7	34.4 68.7	41.6 83.2	49.5 99.0
		X	STD, NSL	40.0	S D	12.3 24.5	17.7 35.3	24.1 48.1	31.4 62.8	39.8 79.5	49.1 98.2	59.4 119.0	70.7 141.0
Rivets	A502-1	—	STD	17.5	S D	5.4 10.7	7.7 15.5	10.5 21.0	13.7 27.5	17.4 34.8	21.5 42.9	26.0 52.0	30.9 61.8
	A502-2 A502-3	—	STD	22.0	S D	6.7 13.5	9.7 19.4	13.2 26.5	17.3 34.6	21.9 43.7	27.0 54.0	32.7 65.3	38.9 77.7
Threaded Parts	A36 (F_u=58 ksi)	N	STD	9.9	S D	3.0 6.1	4.4 8.7	6.0 11.9	7.8 15.6	9.8 19.7	12.1 24.3	14.7 29.4	17.5 35.0
		X	STD	12.8	S D	3.9 7.9	5.7 11.3	7.7 15.4	10.1 20.1	12.7 25.4	15.7 31.4	19.0 38.0	22.6 45.2
	A572, Gr. 50 (F_u=65 ksi)	N	STD	11.1	S D	3.4 6.8	4.9 9.8	6.7 13.3	8.7 17.4	11.0 22.1	13.6 27.2	16.5 33.0	19.6 39.2
		X	STD	14.3	S D	4.4 8.8	6.3 12.6	8.6 17.2	11.2 22.5	14.2 28.4	17.5 35.1	21.2 42.5	25.3 50.5
	A588 (F_u=70 ksi)	N	STD	11.9	S D	3.7 7.3	5.3 10.5	7.2 14.3	9.3 18.7	11.8 23.7	14.6 29.2	17.7 35.3	21.0 42.1
		X	STD	15.4	S D	4.7 9.4	6.8 13.6	9.3 18.5	12.1 24.2	15.3 30.6	18.9 37.8	22.9 45.7	27.2 54.4

[a]SC = Slip critical connection.
　N: Bearing-type connection with threads *included* in shear plane.
　X: Bearing-type connection with threads *excluded* from shear plane.
[b]STD: Standard round holes (d + 1/16 in.)　　　　OVS: Oversize round holes
　LSL: Long-slotted holes　　　　　　　　　　　SSL: Short-slotted holes
　NSL: Long- or short-slotted hole normal to load direction
　　　　(required in bearing-type connection).
[c]S: Single shear　　　　D: Double shear.
For threaded parts of materials not listed, use $F_v = 0.17F_u$ when threads are included in a shear plane, and $F_v = 0.22F_u$ when threads are excluded from a shear plane.
To fully pretension bolts 1 1/8-in. dia. and greater, special impact wrenches may be required.
When bearing-type connections used to splice tension members have a fastener pattern whose length, measured parallel to the line of force, exceeds 50 in., tabulated values shall be reduced by 20%. See AISC ASD Commentary Sect. J3.4.

7.12   EXAMPLE PROBLEM

7.12.1   EXAMPLE PROBLEM 1 — CAPACITY OF BOLTS IN SINGLE SHEAR

Determine the number of 7/8-in.-diameter A325-SC bolts required to support the beam reaction of 60 kip in single shear as shown in Fig. P7.12.1 (a)

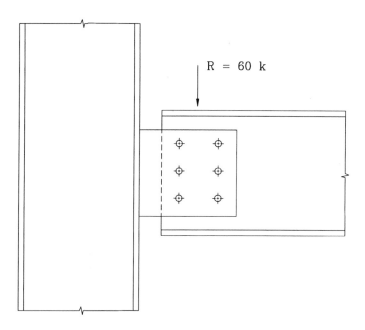

Fig. P7.12.1 (a)

Solution

P $= 60$ kip

$r_{SC} = 10.2$ kip/bolt . . . (M4-5)

$\dfrac{P}{n} \leq r_{SC}$

$n = \dfrac{P}{r_{SC}} = \dfrac{60}{10.2} = 5.9$ bolts   Use 6 bolts.

7.13   BEARING-TYPE CONNECTIONS

Same as slip-critical connections except that the initial tensioning force may not be sufficient to prevent slippage under the designed load conditions. Therefore, the connecting plates may slip and come into contact with the bolt barrel, resulting in bearing stresses. The safety factor against slippage in this case is about 1.0.

The symbol for bolts in a bearing-type connection is N or X. Example: A325-N or A325-X.

$$f_{br} = \frac{P}{n \, d_b \, t} \leq F_{br}$$

$$\frac{P}{n} \leq r_{N,X} \quad \text{due to shear in bolts}$$

$$\frac{P}{n} \leq r_s \quad \text{due to spacing of bolts}$$

$$\frac{P}{n \, t} \leq r_{lv} \quad \text{due to edge distance of bolts}$$

Where

f_{br}	=	Actual bearing stress
P	=	Shear load
n	=	Number of bolts in the connection
d_b	=	Diameter of bolt
F_{br}	=	Allowable bearing stress from AISC (M5-73)
$r_{N,X}$	=	Allowable shear load per bolt from AISC Table 1-D (M4-5)
r_s	=	Allowable bearing load per bolt due to spacing of bolts, AISC Table 1-E (M4-6)
r_{lv}	=	Allowable bearing load per bolt due to edge distance of bolts, AISC Table 1-F (M4-7)
t	=	Thickness of material

Table 7.7 Allowable Bearing Load for Bolts
(AISC Table 1-E, M4-6)

BOLTS AND THREADED PARTS
Bearing
Allowable loads in kips

TABLE I-E. BEARING
Slip-critical and Bearing-type Connections

Material Thickness	F_u = 58 ksi Bolt dia.			F_u = 65 ksi Bolt dia.			F_u = 70 ksi Bolt dia.			F_u = 100 ksi Bolt dia.		
	3/4	7/8	1	3/4	7/8	1	3/4	7/8	1	3/4	7/8	1
1/8	6.5	7.6	8.7	7.3	8.5	9.8	7.9	9.2	10.5	11.3	13.1	15.0
3/16	9.8	11.4	13.1	11.0	12.8	14.6	11.8	13.8	15.8	16.9	19.7	22.5
1/4	13.1	15.2	17.4	14.6	17.1	19.5	15.8	18.4	21.0	22.5	26.3	30.0
5/16	16.3	19.0	21.8	18.3	21.3	24.4	19.7	23.0	26.3	28.1	32.8	37.5
3/8	19.6	22.8	26.1	21.9	25.6	29.3	23.6	27.6	31.5	33.8	39.4	45.0
7/16	22.8	26.6	30.5	25.6	29.9	34.1	27.6	32.2	36.8		45.9	52.5
1/2	26.1	30.5	34.8	29.3	34.1	39.0	31.5	36.8	42.0			60.0
9/16	29.4	34.3	39.2	32.9	38.4	43.9		41.3	47.3			
5/8	32.6	38.1	43.5		42.7	48.8		45.9	52.5			
11/16		41.9	47.9		46.9	53.6			57.8			
3/4		45.7	52.2			58.5						
13/16			56.6									
7/8			60.9									
15/16												
1	52.2	60.9	69.6	58.5	68.3	78.0	63.0	73.5	84.0	90.0	105.0	120.0

Notes:
This table is applicable to all mechanical fasteners in both slip-critical and bearing-type connections utilizing standard holes. Standard holes shall have a diameter nominally 1/16-in. larger than the nominal bolt diameter (d + 1/16 in.).
Tabulated bearing values are based on F_p = 1.2 F_u.
F_u = specified minimum tensile strength of the connected part.
In connections transmitting axial force whose length between extreme fasteners measured parallel to the line of force exceeds 50 in., tabulated values shall be reduced 20%.
Connections using high-strength bolts in slotted holes with the load applied in a direction other than approximately normal (between 80 and 100 degrees) to the axis of the hole and connections with bolts in oversize holes shall be designed for resistance against slip at working load in accordance with AISC ASD Specification Sect. J3.8.
Tabulated values apply when the distance l parallel to the line of force from the center of the bolt to the edge of the connected part is not less than 1½ d and the distance from the center of a bolt to the center of an adjacent bolt is not less than 3d. See AISC ASD Commentary J3.8.
Under certain conditions, values greater than the tabulated values may be justified under Specification Sect. J3.7.
Values are limited to the double-shear bearing capacity of A490-X bolts.
Values for decimal thicknesses may be obtained by multiplying the decimal value of the unlisted thickness by the value given for a 1-in. thickness.

Table 7.7 (Continued) Allowable Bearing Load for Bolts
(AISC Table 1-F, M4-7)

BOLTS AND RIVETS
Bearing
Allowable loads in kips

TABLE I-F. EDGE DISTANCE

Edge Distance[b] l_v In.	Design Loads, Kips[a] (for one fastener, 1-in. thick material)			
	$F_u = 58$	$F_u = 65$	$F_u = 70$	$F_u = 100$
1	29.0	32.5	35.0	50.0
1⅛	32.6	36.6	39.4	56.3
1¼	36.3	40.6	43.8	62.5
<1½	43.5	48.8	52.5	75.0

spacing = 3
n = no. of bolts

COPED

Bolt Dia.	1½ d In.	Values when edge distance is 1½ d or greater [c]			
1	1½	69.6	78.0	84.0	120
⅞	1⁵⁄₁₆	60.9	68.3	73.5	105
¾	1⅛	52.2	58.5	63.0	90.0

[a]Total design load = Σ(tabular value) × t × n, kips
where
　t = thickness of critical connected part, in.
　n = number of fasteners.

[b]$l_v \geq 2P/F_u t$ (AISC ASD Spec. J3.9) distance center of hole to free edge of connected part in direction of force, in.

where
　F_u = specified minimum tensile strength of material, ksi
　P = force transmitted by one fastener to the critical connected part, kips
[c]$P = 1.2 F_u d$ (AISC ASD Spec. Sect. J3.7).

7.14   EXAMPLE PROBLEM

7.14.1   EXAMPLE PROBLEM 1 — CONNECTION PLATES

Determine the allowable load, P, that can be applied on the connection shown in Fig. P7.14.1 (a). The bolts are 7/8-in. diameter and A325-N type. The plates are made of A36 steel.

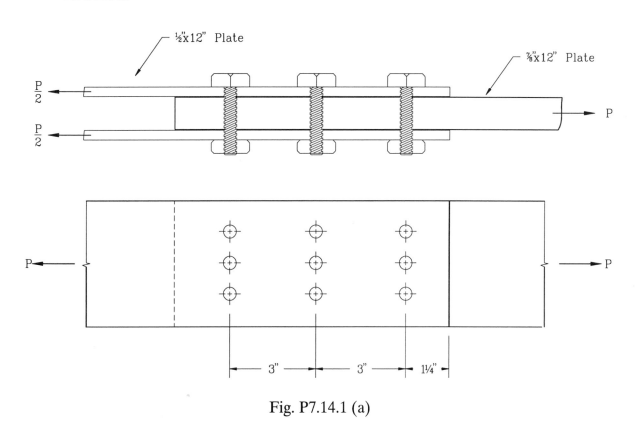

Fig. P7.14.1 (a)

Solution

Note that the bolts in the top and bottom plates are in single shear and the bolts in the middle plate are in double shear. The allowable load is the least value computed from the calculations to be made for shear, bearing and tension.

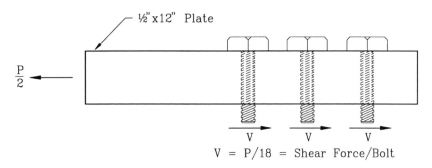

Fig. P7.14.1 (b) Free-Body Diagram-Top Plate

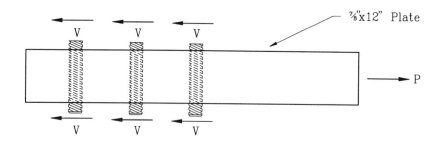

Fig. P7.14.1 (c) Free-Body Diagram-Middle Plate

A. Check middle plate for shear (AISC Table 1-D, M4-5):

$\frac{P}{n} \le r_N$ due to double shear in bolts

$P = n \times r_N = 9 \times 25.3 = 227.7$ kip

B. Check middle plate for bearing due to bolt spacings. (AISC Table 1-E, M4-6):

$\frac{P}{n} \le r_s$ due to 3-in. spacing of bolts and plate thickness of 1.0 inch.

$P = n \times r_s = 9 \times 45.7 = 411.3$ kip

Note that the maximum value of r_s is equal to 45.7 kip per bolt. The value of 60.9 kip per bolt shown in the bottom of the AISC Table 1-E for material thickness of 1 inch, is the value to be used for obtaining the allowable load per bolt for plates in decimal thickness that are not listed in this table.

C. Check middle plate for bearing due to edge distance (AISC Table 1-F, M4-7):

$\frac{P}{n\,t} \le r_{lv}$ due to bolts edge distance   (For $l_v = 1\text{-}^1/_4$ in., $F_u = 58$ ksi)

$P = r_{lv} \times t \times n = 36.3 \times \frac{7}{8} \times 9 = 285.9$ kip

D. Check middle plate for tension:

$P = 0.6\,F_y\,A_g = 0.6 \times 36 \times \frac{7}{8} \times 12 = 226.8$ kip

$P = 0.5\,F_u\,A_e = 0.5\,F_u\,U\,A_n$

$U = 1.0$

$A_n = (\frac{7}{8} \times 12) - 3[(\frac{7}{8} + \frac{1}{8})]\frac{7}{8} = 7.9$ in.^{2}

$P = 0.5 \times 58 \times 1.0 \times 7.9 = 229.1$ kip

The allowable load, P, is equal to the least value computed from the above calculations, which is equal to 226.8 kip due to tension in the middle plate.

7.15   ECCENTRIC-TYPE CONNECTIONS

A connection that is subjected to a load which does not pass through the center of its bolt pattern is called an eccentric-type connection. The solution for such a connection is accomplished by an elastic method or by an ultimate strength method. The elastic method is described below. The ultimate strength method is described in the AISC Manual. AISC provides tables shown in M4-62 through M4-69 for some bolt patterns that are subjected to eccentric loads. These tables are based on the ultimate strength method.

7.15.1   ELASTIC METHOD

Figure 7.6 shows a typical eccentric-type connection which is subjected to a load that does not pass through the center of bolt pattern. The bolts for such type loadings are subjected to a combination of direct shear plus bending moments. Assumptions for load distribution among the bolts in eccentric-type connections are as follows:

1.   Plates are perfectly rigid.

2.   Bolts are perfectly elastic.

3.   Rotation of the plates produces shear forces in bolts which are proportional to and normal to radius from center of bolt pattern, CBP, to the bolt in question.

4.   Stresses in bolts are assumed to be uniform.

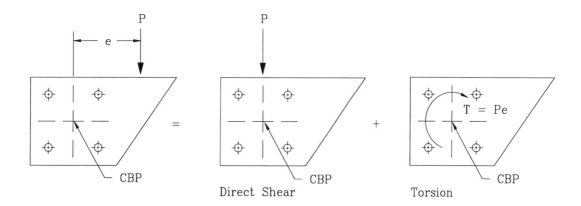

Figure 7.6 Eccentric Connection

7.15.2 PROCEDURES FOR ELASTIC METHOD — ECCENTRIC CONNECTION

Step 1:

Determine the location of the center of the bolt pattern, CBP, and the eccentricity distance, e.

Step 2:

Compute the value of α

$$\alpha = \frac{Pe}{\Sigma\left(d_i^2\right)} = \frac{Pe}{\Sigma\left(x^2 + y^2\right)_i}$$

Step 3:

Calculate the direct shear forces in each bolt.

$$f_{iy} = \frac{P_y}{n} \qquad \text{and} \qquad f_{ix} = \frac{P_x}{n}$$

where

P_y = Load along the y-axis

P_x = Load along the x-axis

n = Number of bolts in the connection

Step 4:

Calculate the vertical and horizontal components, R_{yi} and R_{xi}, in each bolt resulting from the eccentricity of load, P.

$$R_{yi} = \alpha\, x_i \quad \text{and} \quad R_{xi} = \alpha\, y_i$$

Note: The direction of these components is in the opposite direction of the moment.

Step 5:

Calculate the resultant force, R_i, in each bolt.

$$R_i = \sqrt{(f_{iy} + R_{yi})^2 + (f_{ix} + R_{xi})^2}$$

Step 6:

Analyze or design the connection for the largest resultant force in Step 5.

7.16   EXAMPLE PROBLEM

7.16.1   EXAMPLE PROBLEM 1 — BOLTED ECCENTRIC-TYPE CONNECTION

Determine the minimum diameter of high-strength bolts, A325-SC required to support an eccentric load as shown in Fig. P7.16.1 (a) . The bolts are in single shear.

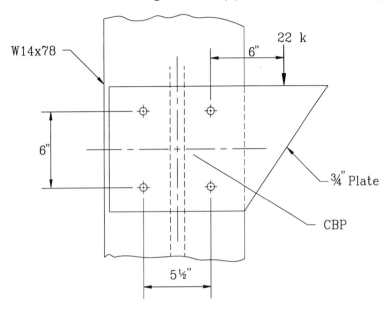

Fig. P7.16.1 (a)

Solution

Step 1:

Locate the center of the bolt pattern, CBP. It is centrally located between the bolts.

The eccentricity distance, $e = 6 + \dfrac{5.5}{2} = 8.75$ in.

Step 2:

Compute the value of α.

$$\alpha = \frac{Pe}{\Sigma \left(d_i^2 \right)} = \frac{Pe}{\Sigma \left(x^2 + y^2 \right)_i}$$

$$\alpha = \frac{22 \times 8.75}{4 \left(2.75^2 + 3.00^2 \right)} = 2.91 \text{ kip/in.}$$

Step 3:

Calculate the direct shear force in each bolt.

$$f_{iy} = \frac{P_y}{n} \text{ in y-axis.}$$

$$= \frac{22}{4} = 5.5 \text{ kip}$$

$$f_{ix} = \frac{0}{4} = 0 \text{ in. x-axis}$$

Step 4:

Calculate the vertical and horizontal components, R_{yi} and R_{xi}, in each bolt resulting from the eccentricity of load, P.

$$\alpha \times R_{yi} = 2.91 \times 2.75 = 8.00 \text{ kip}$$

$$\alpha \times R_{xi} = 2.91 \times 3.00 = 8.73 \text{ kip}$$

Step 5:

Calculate the resultant force, R_i, in each bolt.

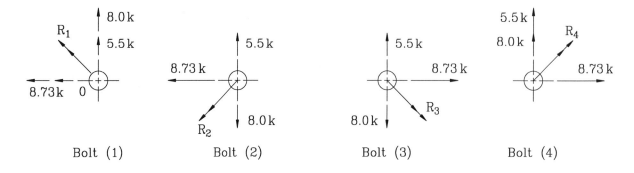

Fig. P7.16.1 (b)

$$R_i = \sqrt{(f_{iy} + R_{yi})^2 + (f_{ix} + R_{xi})^2}$$

$$R_1 = \sqrt{(5.5 + 8.00)^2 + (0.0 + 8.73)^2} = 16.1 \text{ kip}$$

$$R_2 = \sqrt{(5.5 - 8.00)^2 + (0.0 - 8.73)^2} = 9.1 \text{ kip}$$

$$R_3 = \sqrt{(5.5 - 8.00)^2 + (0.0 + 8.73)^2} = 9.1 \text{ kip}$$

$$R_4 = \sqrt{(5.5 + 8.00)^2 + (0.0 + 8.73)^2} = 16.1 \text{ kip}$$

Step 6:

The largest resultant force in Step 5 is 16.1 kip.

From M4-5 for A325-SC bolts in single shear, select diameter 1-1/8 in. whose r_{SC} = 16.9 kip which is greater than the largest resultant force of 16.1 kip.

7.17   P. E. PROBLEM

7.17.1   P. E. PROBLEM 1 — BOLTED ECCENTRIC-TYPE CONNECTION

Determine the allowable load P that can be applied on the connection shown in Fig. P7.17.1 (a). Bolts are 3/4-in. diameter and A325-X type. Plate thickness is 1.0 in. Material of plate is A36 steel.

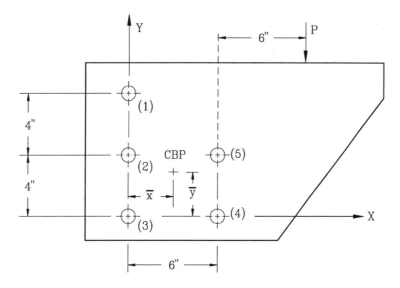

Fig. P7.17.1 (a)

Solution

Step 1:

Determine the location of the center of bolt pattern, CBP. Use bolt No. 3 as the origin.

$$\bar{x} = \frac{\Sigma\ x_i\ A_i}{\Sigma\ A_i} = \frac{(0 + 0 + 0 + 6A + 6A)}{5A} = 2.4\ \text{in.}$$

$$\bar{y} = \frac{\Sigma\ y_i\ A_i}{\Sigma\ A_i} = \frac{(8A + 4A + 0 + 0 + 4A)}{5A} = 3.2\ \text{in.}$$

Eccentricity distance, $e = 6 + 6 - 2.4 = 9.6$ inches

Step 2:

Compute the value of α.

$$\alpha = \frac{Pe}{\Sigma\ \left(d_i^2\right)} = \frac{Pe}{\Sigma\ \left(x^2 + y^2\right)_i}$$

$$\alpha = \frac{P \times 9.6}{\left(2.4^2 + 4.8^2\right)_1 + \left(2.4^2 + 0.8^2\right)_2 + \left(2.4^2 + 3.2^2\right)_3 + \left(3.6^2 + 3.2^2\right)_4 + \left(3.6^2 + 0.8^2\right)_5}$$

$$\alpha = 0.109\ P\ \text{kip/in.}$$

Step 3:

Calculate the direct shear forces in each bolt.

$$f_{iy} = \frac{P_y}{n} = \frac{P}{5} = 0.2\,P \text{ in the y-direction}$$

$$f_{ix} = \frac{P_x}{n} = \frac{0}{5} = 0.0 \text{ in the x-direction}$$

Step 4:

Calculate the vertical and horizontal components, R_{yi} and R_{xi}, in each bolt resulting from the eccentricity of load, P.

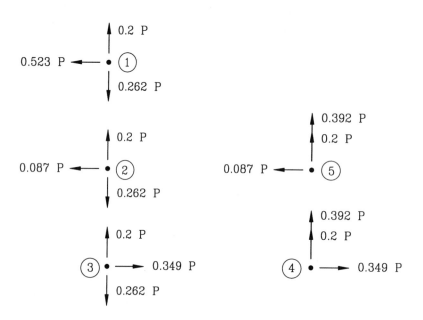

Fig. P7.17.1 (b)

$R_{yi} = \alpha \times x_i \quad \text{and} \quad R_{xi} = \alpha \times y_i$

Bolt No. 1: $R_y = 0.109\,P\,(2.4) = 0.262\,P$

 $R_x = 0.109\,P\,(4.8) = 0.523\,P$

Bolt No. 2: $R_y = 0.109\,P\,(2.4) = 0.262\,P$

 $R_x = 0.109\,P\,(0.8) = 0.087\,P$

Bolt No. 3: $R_y = 0.109\,P\,(2.4) = 0.262\,P$

 $R_x = 0.109\,P\,(3.2) = 0.349\,P$

Bolt No. 4: $R_y = 0.109\,P\,(3.6) = 0.392\,P$

 $R_x = 0.109\,P\,(3.2) = 0.349\,P$

Bolt No. 5: $R_y = 0.109\,P\,(3.6) = 0.392\,P$

 $R_x = 0.109\,P\,(0.8) = 0.087\,P$

Step 5:

Calculate the resultant force, R_i, in each bolt.

$$R_i = \sqrt{\left(f_{iy} + R_{yi}\right)^2 + \left(f_{ix} + R_{xi}\right)^2}$$

$$R_1 = \sqrt{(0.2\ P - 0.26\ P)^2 + (0.0 - 0.523\ P)^2} = 0.527\ P$$

$$R_2 = \sqrt{(0.2\ P - 0.26\ P)^2 + (0.0 - 0.087\ P)^2} = 0.107\ P$$

$$R_3 = \sqrt{(0.2\ P - 0.26\ P)^2 + (0.0 + 0.349\ P)^2} = 0.354\ P$$

$$R_4 = \sqrt{(0.2\ P + 0.392\ P)^2 + (0.0 + 0.349\ P)^2} = 0.687\ P$$

$$R_5 = \sqrt{(0.2\ P + 0.392\ P)^2 + (0.0 - 0.087\ P)^2} = 0.598\ P$$

Largest $R_i = 0.687P$ in bolt No. 4

Step 6:

Analyze or design the connection for the largest resultant force in Step 5.

From M4-5 the allowable load per bolt for A325-X bolts in single shear whose diameter 3/4 in. is equal to $r_X = 13.3$ kip.

Let the resultant $R_4 = r_X$ and solve for P.

$$P = \frac{13.3}{0.687} = 19.36 \text{ kip}$$

Check bearing stresses on the plate

$$f_{br} = \frac{P}{dt} \le F_{br}$$

where

$F_{br} = 1.5\ F_u.$ ... AISC Eq. J3-4 (M5-75)

d   = Diameter of bolt.

t   = Thickness of material

$$f_{br} = \frac{19.36}{0.75 \times 1} = 25.83 \le 1.5 \times 58 = 87 \text{ ksi} \dots \text{OK}$$

7.18   EXAMPLE PROBLEMS

7.18.1   EXAMPLE PROBLEM 1 — USING AISC ULTIMATE STRENGTH TABLES

Determine the minimum diameter of the high-strength bolts, A325-SC, required to support the eccentric load as shown in Fig. P7.18.1 (a). The bolts are in single shear.

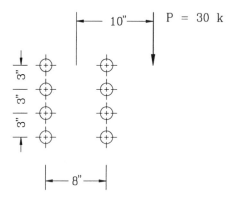

Fig. P7.18.1 (a) Eccentric Bolted Connection

Solution

P   = 30 kip

n   = 4 bolts in one vertical row

l   = 10 in. which is the eccentricity distance, e

Refer to AISC Table XIV (M4-65), which has a bolt pattern matching the bolt pattern given and determine the coefficient, C.

For b = 3 in., l = 10 in. and n = 4 in. the value of C = 3.13

Resultant force = $\dfrac{P}{C}$ = $\dfrac{30}{3.13}$ = 9.59 kip

From M4-5 for A325-SC bolts in single shear, select 7/8-in. diameter whose r_{SC} = 10.2 kip which is greater than the largest resultant force of 9.59 kip.

Table 7.8 Eccentric Loads on Fastener Groups
(AISC Table XIV, M4-65)

ECCENTRIC LOADS ON FASTENER GROUPS
TABLE XIV Coefficients *C*

Required minimum $C = \dfrac{P}{r_v}$

$P = C \times r_v$

n = Total number of fasteners in one vertical row
P = Allowable load acting with lever arm l, in.
r_v = Allowable load on one fastener by Specification
C = Coefficients tabulated below.

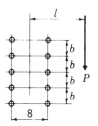

	l In.	n											
		1	2	3	4	5	6	7	8	9	10	11	12
b = 3 In.	2	1.31	2.91	4.74	6.85	8.85	10.88	12.91	14.94	16.97	18.99	21.00	23.00
	3	1.16	2.54	4.15	5.99	8.02	10.06	12.12	14.19	16.26	18.32	20.37	22.42
	4	.98	2.24	3.66	5.33	7.20	9.18	11.23	13.32	15.41	17.50	19.59	21.67
	5	.92	2.20	3.27	4.80	6.50	8.37	10.35	12.40	14.49	16.60	18.71	20.81
	6	.79	1.80	2.96	4.35	5.91	7.65	9.53	11.51	13.57	15.66	17.77	19.89
	7	.71	1.63	2.70	3.97	5.40	7.02	8.79	10.69	12.68	14.73	16.82	18.93
	8	.65	1.50	2.46	3.65	4.97	6.48	8.13	9.93	11.84	13.83	15.89	17.98
	9	.60	1.38	2.27	3.37	4.59	6.01	7.56	9.26	11.08	13.00	14.99	17.05
	10	.56	1.28	2.11	3.13	4.27	5.59	7.05	8.65	10.38	12.22	14.15	16.15
	12	.49	1.11	1.84	2.73	3.73	4.90	6.19	7.63	9.18	10.86	12.65	14.52
	14	.44	.99	1.64	2.42	3.32	4.36	5.51	6.80	8.20	9.73	11.37	13.11
	16	.39	.89	1.47	2.17	2.98	3.91	4.95	6.13	7.40	8.80	10.30	11.90
	18	.36	.81	1.33	1.97	2.70	3.55	4.50	5.57	6.73	8.01	9.39	10.87
	20	.33	.74	1.22	1.80	2.47	3.25	4.12	5.10	6.17	7.35	8.62	10.00
	24	.28	.63	1.04	1.54	2.11	2.77	3.51	4.35	5.28	6.30	7.39	8.59
	28	.25	.55	.91	1.34	1.83	2.41	3.06	3.79	4.60	5.50	6.46	7.51
	32	.22	.49	.81	1.18	1.62	2.13	2.71	3.36	4.08	4.87	5.73	6.67
	36	.20	.44	.73	1.06	1.46	1.91	2.43	3.01	3.66	4.37	5.15	5.99
b = 6 In.	2	1.31	3.37	5.42	7.46	9.49	11.50	13.50	15.49	17.47	19.46	21.43	23.41
	3	1.16	2.94	4.99	7.08	9.15	11.21	13.24	15.26	17.27	19.27	21.26	23.25
	4	.98	2.63	4.55	6.64	8.74	10.83	12.90	14.95	16.99	19.01	21.03	23.03
	5	.92	2.37	4.15	6.18	8.29	10.41	12.51	14.59	16.66	18.70	20.74	22.77
	6	.79	2.15	3.78	5.74	7.82	9.95	12.07	14.18	16.27	18.35	20.41	22.45
	7	.71	1.97	3.47	5.33	7.36	9.47	11.60	13.73	15.84	17.94	20.03	22.10
	8	.65	1.81	3.19	4.96	6.92	8.99	11.12	13.26	15.39	17.51	19.61	21.71
	9	.60	1.67	2.95	4.63	6.50	8.53	10.64	12.77	14.91	17.05	19.17	21.28
	10	.56	1.55	2.75	4.33	6.11	8.09	10.16	12.28	14.43	16.57	18.71	20.84
	12	.49	1.35	2.41	3.82	5.43	7.27	9.25	11.33	13.44	15.59	17.74	19.89
	14	.44	1.20	2.14	3.41	4.87	6.57	8.44	10.42	12.49	14.60	16.74	18.90
	16	.39	1.08	1.92	3.07	4.40	5.97	7.71	9.60	11.59	13.65	15.76	17.90
	18	.36	1.01	1.75	2.79	4.00	5.46	7.08	8.86	10.77	12.76	14.82	16.93
	20	.33	.89	1.60	2.56	3.67	5.02	6.53	8.21	10.02	11.93	13.93	15.99
	24	.28	.76	1.37	2.19	3.14	4.32	5.63	7.11	8.72	10.45	12.29	14.27
	28	.25	.66	1.19	1.90	2.75	3.78	4.93	6.26	7.70	9.27	10.96	12.74
	32	.22	.59	1.06	1.69	2.44	3.35	4.38	5.58	6.88	8.31	9.85	11.49
	36	.20	.52	.95	1.51	2.19	3.01	3.94	5.02	6.21	7.52	8.93	10.44

7.18.2   EXAMPLE PROBLEM 2 — DESIGN OF AN ECCENTRIC BOLTED CONNECTION

Determine size of bolt, A325-SC for eccentric connection shown in Fig. P7.18.2 (a).

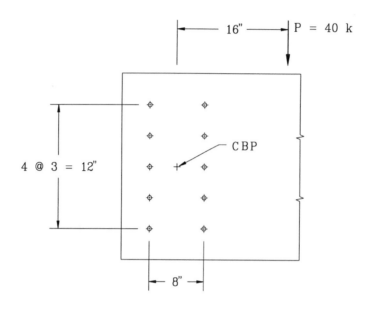

Fig. P7.18.2 (a) Eccentric Bolted Connection

Solution

Elastic Method:

$$\alpha = \frac{P\ e}{\Sigma\ (x^2\ +\ y^2)_i}$$

$$\alpha = \frac{40 \times 16}{2 \times (4^2\ +\ 0)\ +\ 4 \times (4^2\ +\ 3^2)\ +\ 4 \times (4^2\ +\ 6^2)} = 1.88$$

$$R = \sqrt{\left(\frac{40}{10}\ +\ 1.88 \times 4\right)^2\ +\ (0\ +\ 1.88 \times 6)^2} = 16.12$$

Use: $d_b = 1\frac{1}{8}$ whose $r_v = 16.9 > 16.12$ . . . OK

Ultimate Method:

From M4-65:   P = 40 kip;   n = 5; L = 16; b = 3

Find, C = 2.98

$$r_v = \frac{P}{C} = \frac{40}{2.98} = 13.42$$

Use: 1-in.-diameter bolts.

7.19 P. E. PROBLEMS

7.19.1 P. E. PROBLEM 1 — BOLTED CONNECTION — SHEAR AND TENSION

Given:

A tension member is connected to a column, W10 × 77, as shown in Fig. P7.19.1 (a).

Criteria:

- Material: Steel A36, bolts A325X.

- Assume connection between double angle 5 × 3 and Plate B is adequate.

- No stress increases allowed.

- Plate A has a width equal to the flange width of W10 × 77.

- Assume column cannot rotate to reduce eccentricity.

- Assume elastic distribution of bolt stresses.

- Assume connection between Plates A and B is adequate.

Required:

A. Are indicated bolts adequate? (Show calculations.)

B. List three possible modifications to the connection, assuming W10 × 77 flange is inadequate. (No calculations are required.)

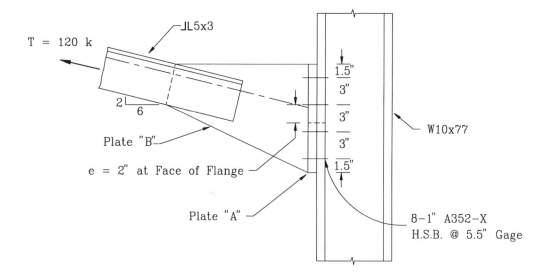

Fig. P7.19.1 (a)

Solution

A.

    1.   Calculate the x and y components of the 120-kip tensile load.

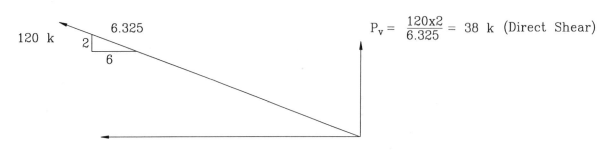

$$P_v = \frac{120 \times 2}{6.325} = 38 \text{ k (Direct Shear)}$$

$$P_T = \frac{120 \times 6}{6.325} = 114 \text{ k (Direct Tension)}$$

Fig. P7.19.1 (b)

    2.   The direct shear load, $P_v = 38$ kip, is equally distributed among the 8 bolts. Therefore, each bolt has $\frac{38}{8} = 4.75$ kip in shear.

    3. P_T is an eccentric-type load on the bolt pattern. Therefore, it needs to be resolved into a direct tension load plus bending.

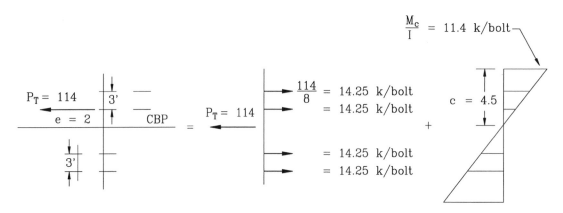

Eccentric Load = Direct Tension + Bending

Fig. P7.19.1 (c)

$$\frac{Mc}{I} = \frac{114 \times 2 \times 4.5}{\left(4.5^2 + 1.5^2\right) 2 \times 2} = 11.4 \text{ kip/bolt}$$

4. Maximum combined shear and tension load is in top row:

Fig. P7.19.1 (d)

5. Check stress in top row bolt:

a. $f_v = \dfrac{P_v}{A_b} = \dfrac{4.75}{0.785} = 6.05$ ksi $< F_v = 30$ ksi $\ldots$ (M5-73)

b. $f_t = \dfrac{P_T}{A_b} = \dfrac{25.65}{0.785} = 32.68$ ksi $< F'_t$

Where

$$F'_t = \sqrt{44^2 - 2.15\,f_v^2} \qquad \ldots \text{(M5-74)}$$

$$F'_t = 43.096 \text{ ksi}$$

B   Modification:

1. 120-k tensile load should pass through the center of bolt pattern, CBP.

2. Weld stiffeners between flanges of W10 × 77 at top and bottom of the connection.

3. Add a fifth row of 1.0-in.-diameter bolts on top of Plate A to eliminate the eccentricity in the connection and to reduce the actual tensile stress.

Remarks:

For shear tension connections the allowable stresses are as follows:

A. Slip Critical-Type Connections:

$$f_t = \frac{P_T}{nA_b} \le F_t \qquad\qquad \text{M5-73 and M5-74}$$

$$f_v = \frac{P_v}{nA_b} \le \overline{F_v} \qquad\qquad \text{M5-74, } \overline{F_v} = \left(1 - \frac{f_t\,A_b}{T_b}\right) F_v$$

B. Bearing-Type Connections:

$$f_t = \frac{P_T}{nA_b} \le \overline{F_t} \qquad\qquad \text{M5-74, Table J8.3}$$

$$f_v = \frac{P_v}{nA_b} \le F_v \qquad\qquad \text{M5-73}$$

7.19.2   P. E. PROBLEM 2 — ECCENTRIC BOLT CONNECTION

Given:

A W21 × 50 beam is to be connected rigidly to a W10 × 49 column as shown. The applied moment and reaction are due to LL, DL and wind.

Determine the size of tees for connecting the flanges and the double angles for connecting the beam web. Also, determine the number of 7/8-in.-diameter A325-SC bolts required for each connection.

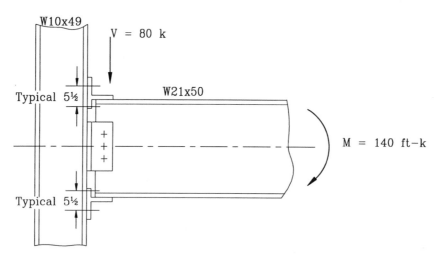

Fig. P7.19.2 (a)

Solution

1. Since wind is included, then the allowable working stress may be increased by 33% or the design loads may be reduced by 25%.

    M = Applied Moment = 140 ft-kip × 75% = 105 ft-kip

    V = End Reaction = 80 kip × 75% = 60 kip

2. Design of connection between the beam web and the framing double angles.

    a. For A325-SC bolts, the allowable load per bolt, r_{SC}, in double shear from (M4-5) is equal to 20.4 kip.

    $$n = \frac{P_v}{r_{SC}} = \frac{V}{r_{SC}} = \frac{60}{20.4} = 2.94 \quad \text{Use 3 bolts}$$

    b. Framing angles, A36 material

    For 7/8-in.-diameter A325-SC bolts and V = 60 kip

    Select a double angle 3 × 3 × 5/16 by 10 in. long (M4-19).

    Check AISC Table II-C (M4-22).

    For t = 5/16 in., d = 7/8-in. diameter,

    Length of angles = 10 in. and n = 3

    Capacity of framing angles = 78.2 kip > 60 kip . . . OK

3. Design the connection between the framing angles at the beam's web and the column flange. Neglect the effect of eccentricity.

   For 7/8-in.-diameter A325-SC bolts in single shear, the allowable load per bolt $r_{SC} = 10.2$ kip (M4-5).

   $$n = \frac{P_v}{r_{SC}} = \frac{V}{r_{SC}} = \frac{60}{10.2} = 5.88 \qquad \text{Use 6 bolts.}$$

   Use three bolts in each row for each framing angle.

4. The tension and compression forces transmitted by the tees due to the applied moment:

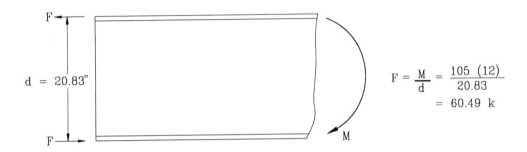

$$F = \frac{M}{d} = \frac{105\ (12)}{20.83}$$
$$= 60.49 \text{ k}$$

$$d = 20.83"$$

Fig. P7.19.2 (b)

$$F = \frac{M}{d} = \frac{105 \times 12}{20.83} = 60.49 \text{ kip}$$

5. Determine size of tee:

   a. Length of tee = gage + 2e < b_f of column (W10 × 49)
   $$= 5.5 + 2 \times 1.5$$
   $$= 8.5 \text{ in.} < 10 \text{ in.} \qquad \text{OK}$$

   b. Stem of tee = 7.5 in. minimum to allow enough space for two bolts per line.

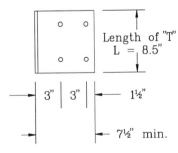

Fig. P7.19.2 (c)

c.   Width of tee flange should be ≤ 11.5 in. so the tee will not interfere with the double angles connected to beam's web.

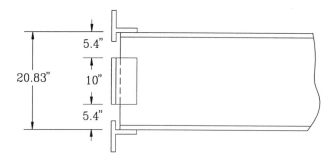

Fig. P7.19.2 (d)

d.   Neglect the prying action on the bolts and select the flange thickness of the tee based on the flange being fixed at the bolt line.

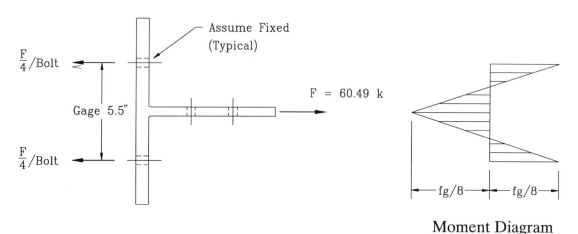

Moment Diagram

Fig. P7.19.2 (e)

$$\text{Maximum moment} = \frac{F(g)}{8} = \frac{60.49 \times 5.5}{8} = 41.58 \text{ in.-kip}$$

$$t_f = \sqrt{\frac{6M}{bF_b}} = \sqrt{\frac{6 \times 41.58}{8.5 \times 0.75 \times 36}} = 1.04 \text{ in.}$$

Based on the above criteria, select WT9 $\times$ 59.5 $\times$ 8.5 in. long

$$b_f = 11\frac{1}{4} < 11.5 \quad \text{OK}$$

$$t_f = 1\frac{1}{16} \quad\quad\quad\quad \text{OK}$$

$$d = 9\frac{1}{2} > 7.5 \quad \text{OK}$$

$$t_w = 5/8$$

6. Determine the number of bolts required to connect the tee stem to the beam flange using 7/8-in.-diameter A325-SC bolts.

The allowable load per bolt, r_{SC}, in single shear from (M4-5) is equal to 10.2 kip.

$$n = \frac{P_v}{r_{SC}} = \frac{F}{r_{SC}} = \frac{60.49}{10.2} = 5.93 \text{ Use 6 bolts.}$$

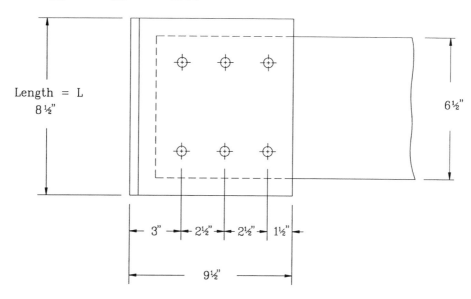

Fig. P7.19.2 (f)

7. Check tensile stress in tee stem.

$$f_t = \frac{P}{A_g} \leq 0.6 \, F_y$$

$$f_t = \frac{60.49}{\left(\frac{5}{8}\right) \times 8.5} = 11.38 \text{ ksi} < 0.6 \, F_y = 22 \text{ ksi} \qquad \text{OK}$$

$$f_t = \frac{P}{A_e} \leq .5 \, F_u$$

$$f_t = \frac{60.49}{4.06} = 14.89 \text{ ksi} < 0.5 \, F_u = 29 \text{ ksi} \qquad \text{OK}$$

$$A_e = U \times A_n \qquad U = 1.0$$

$$A_n = (5/8 \times 8.5) - 2(7/8 + 1/8) \, 5/8 = 4.06 \text{ in.}^2$$

8.   Check prying action on bolts between the tee flange and the column (M4-90).

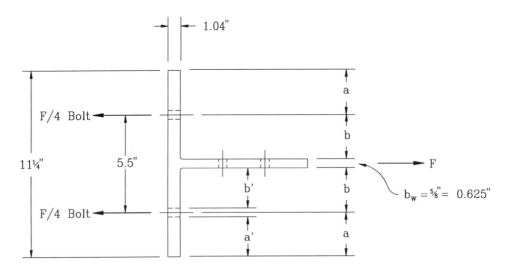

Fig. P7.19.2 (g)

$$b = \frac{(5.5 - .625)}{2} = 2.44 > 1.25 \qquad \text{OK}$$

to provide clearance for wrenches and tools.

$$a = \frac{(11.25 - 5.5)}{2} = 2.88 < 1.25 \times b = 1.25 \times 2.44 = 3.05$$

Therefore, fully effective.

$$b' = b - \frac{d}{2} = 2.44 - 0.44 = 2.00$$

$$a' = a + \frac{d}{2} = 2.88 + 0.44 = 3.32$$

$$a' + b' = 2.00 + 3.32 = 5.32$$

p = length of flange distributed to each bolt

$$p = \frac{8.5}{2} = 4.25$$

d' = 15/16 = 0.938 = diameter of hole.

$$\delta = 1 - \frac{d'}{p} = \left(1 - \frac{0.938}{4.25}\right) = 0.779$$

$$\varrho = \frac{b'}{a'} = \frac{2.00}{3.32} = 0.602$$

$$\alpha' = \frac{1}{\delta(1 + \varrho)}\left[\left(\frac{t_c}{t}\right)^2 - 1\right]$$

$$\alpha' = \frac{1}{0.779(1 + 0.602)}\left[\left(\frac{1.665}{1.04}\right)^2 - 1\right] = 0.481$$

$$t_c = \sqrt{\frac{8\ B\ b'}{p\ F_y}} = \sqrt{\frac{8 \times 26.5 \times 2.00}{4.25 \times 36}} = 1.665$$

$$T_{all} = B\left(\frac{t}{t_c}\right)^2 (1 + \delta\ \alpha')$$

$$T_{all} = 26.5\left(\frac{1.04}{1.665}\right)^2 (1 + 0.779 \times 0.481)$$

$$= 14.225 < \frac{F}{4} = \frac{60.49}{4} = 15.123$$

Since T_{all} is less than T_{actual}, select a section with thicker plate and repeat the above steps.

7.19.3 P. E. PROBLEM 3 — DESIGN OF BOLT SIZE IN A BRACKET

A bracket supports a 25-kip load with bolt pattern as shown with A325 × bolts in single shear.

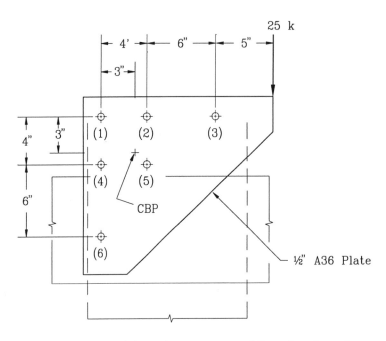

Fig. P7.19.3 (a) Bolt Pattern and Bracket Load

Find:

Smallest bolt size acceptable.

Solution

1. Find center of bolt pattern:

$$\bar{x} = \frac{\sum x_i A_i}{\sum A_i}$$

$$= \frac{0 + 0 + 0 + 4A + 10A + 4A}{6A} = 3 \text{ in.}$$

$$\bar{y} = \frac{0 + 0 + 0 + 4A + 10A + 4A}{6A} = 3 \text{ in.}$$

2. Calculate $\propto \ = \ \dfrac{T}{\sum d_i^2}$

$$T \ = \ Pe \ = \ 25 \ (15 \ - \ 3) \ = \ 300 \ \text{kip-in.}$$

$$\propto \ = \ \frac{300}{\left[\begin{array}{c}(3^2 \ + \ 3^2) \ + \ (1^2 \ + \ 3^2) \ + \ (7^2 \ + \ 3^2) \\ + \ (3^2 \ + \ 1^2) \ + \ (1^2 \ + \ 1^2) \ + \ (3^2 \ + \ 7^2)\end{array}\right]}$$

$$= \ 1.94 \ \text{kip-in.}$$

3. Direct shear force per bolt, F_s:

$$F_s \ = \ \frac{P}{6} \ = \ \frac{25}{6} \ = \ 4.2 \ \text{kip} \qquad \downarrow$$

4. Find force for bolt due to torsion, T:

$$R_{x1} \ = \ \propto y_i \ = \ (1.94)(3 \qquad = \ 5.82 \ \text{kip} \quad \leftarrow$$
$$R_{y1} \ = \ \propto x_i \ = \ (1.94)(3) \qquad = \ 5.82 \ \text{kip} \downarrow$$
$$R_{x2} \ = \ (1.94)(3) \ = \ 5.82 \ \text{kip} \qquad \leftarrow$$
$$R_{y2} \ = \ (1.94)(1) \ = \ 1.94 \ \text{kip} \qquad \uparrow$$
$$R_{x3} \ = \ (1.94)(3) \ = \ 5.82 \ \text{kip} \qquad \leftarrow$$
$$R_{y3} \ = \ (1.94)(7) \ = \ 13.58 \ \text{kip} \qquad \uparrow$$
$$R_{x4} \ = \ (1.94)(1) \ = \ 1.94 \ \text{kip} \qquad \rightarrow$$
$$R_{y4} \ = \ (1.94)(3) \ = \ 5.82 \ \text{kip} \qquad \downarrow$$
$$R_{x5} \ = \ (1.94)(1) \ = \ 1.94 \ \text{kip} \qquad \rightarrow$$
$$R_{y5} \ = \ (1.94)(1) \ = \ 1.94 \ \text{kip} \qquad \uparrow$$
$$R_{x6} \ = \ (1.94)(7) \ = \ 13.58 \ \text{kip} \qquad \rightarrow$$
$$R_{y6} \ = \ (1.94)(3) \ = \ 5.82 \ \text{kip} \qquad \downarrow$$

5.   Find combined forces on bolts:

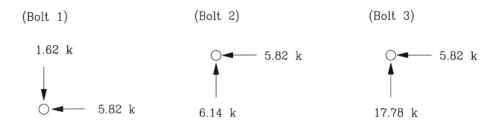

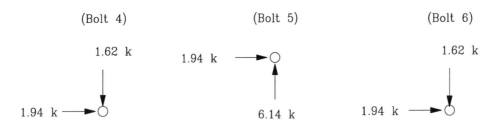

Fig. P7.19.3 (b)

6.   Find bolt with maximum shear force:

Bolt

1. $\sqrt{1.62^2 + 5.82^2}$ = 6.04 kip

2. $\sqrt{5.82^2 + 6.14^2}$ = 8.46 kip

3. $\sqrt{5.82^2 + 17.78^2}$ = 18.71 kip   ←   LARGEST

4. $\sqrt{1.94^2 + 1.62^2}$ = 2.53 kip

5. $\sqrt{1.94^2 + 6.14^2}$ = 6.44 kip

6. $\sqrt{13.58^2 + 1.62^2}$ = 13.68 kip

7.   Calculate required bolt size:

F_v = 30 ksi (Threads excluded from shear plane, A325 X)

Therefore,

$$\text{Area Required} = \frac{18.71 \text{ kip}}{30 \text{ ksi}} = 0.62 \text{ in.}^2$$

Use 3/4-in.-diameter A325 bolt, whose area is equal 0.785 in.^{2}

8. Assume bearing connection; check bearing stresses for bolt hole No. 3.

$$\sigma_{Bearing} = \frac{\text{Shear Force}}{(\text{Plate Thick})\,(\text{Bolt Dia.})}$$

$$= \frac{18.71 \text{ kip}}{(0.5 \text{ in.}) \times (3/4 \text{ in.})} = 50 \text{ ksi}$$

$$\sigma_{Bear/Allow} = 1.5 \text{ F}_u$$

$$= 1.5 \times 58 = 87 \text{ ksi}$$

Therefore,

$$\sigma_{Bear} = 50 \text{ ksi} \leq \sigma_{Allow} = 87 \text{ ksi} \qquad \text{OK}$$

7.20   S.E. EXAMINATION PROBLEM

7.20.1   1972 S.E. PROBLEM B1 — CRANE RUNWAY BRACKET DESIGN — WT. 3.0

A supporting bracket for a traveling crane runway has been designed as shown using friction-type high-strength bolts (ASTM A325). Gravity and lateral forces are carried by the bracket. Longitudinal forces are carried elsewhere. Loads are as follows (acting on the bracket):

Lifted load   = 50 kip

Crane trolley = 4 kip

All other DL = 2 kip

Consider impact and lateral loads in your analysis.

Assumptions

*   A36 steel

Required

Find the resultant load on the critical bolt.

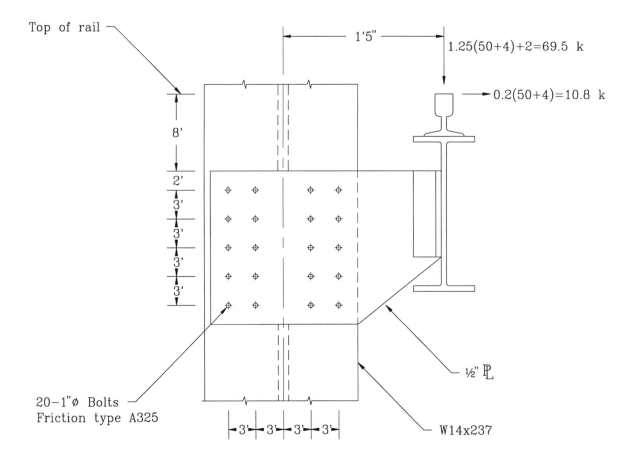

Fig. P7.20.1 (a) Bracket Connection

Solution

See above for loads and dimensions.

Assume given loads are given for this bracket alone.

Top right bolt is most critical.

Fig. P7.20.1 (b) Joint Bolt — Load Pattern

Use statics to transfer loads to CBP:

$P_v = 69.5$ kip

$P_h = 10.8$ kip

$T = (69.5 \times 17 \text{ in.}) + 10.8 (8 + 8) = 1{,}354$ in.-kip

Shear forces due to direct shear:

$$F_{sx} = \frac{10.8}{20} = 0.54 \text{ kip} \rightarrow$$

$$F_{sy} = \frac{69.5}{20} = 3.48 \text{ kip} \downarrow$$

Shear forces due to torsion:

$$\alpha = \frac{T}{\sum Ad_i^2} = \frac{1{,}345}{(10 \times 3^2) + (10 \times 6^2) = (8 \times 3^2) + (8 \times 6^2)}$$

$$= 1.67 \text{ kip/in.} \quad \text{(maximum bolt force in top, right bolt)}$$

$F_{rx} = \alpha Y = 1.67 \times 6 = 10.0$ kip $\rightarrow$

$F_{rx} = \alpha Y = 1.67 \times 6 = 10.0$ kip $\rightarrow$

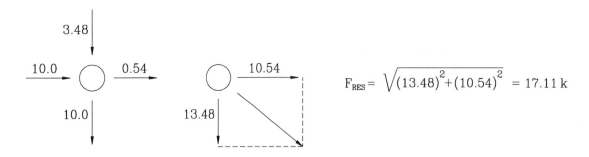

Fig. P7.20.1 (c) Resultant Forces on Top, Right Bolt

For slip-critical type connections, use M4-5, where for A325-SC

Allowable single shear force = 13.4 kip < 17.11 kip . . . NG

8

WELDED CONNECTIONS

8.1   ARC WELDING

Arc welding is a process by which two pieces of metal are joined together by fusion or, in other words, by melting. The joint to be welded is intensely heated by an electric arc to about 6,500°F. At this high temperature, the joint between the two parts, plus a filler called welding electrode, melt and intermix together. Upon cooling, the molten joint will solidify, thus producing one bonded metallurgical piece.

During arc welding, the molten pool of the joint must be shielded from the air. When air is entrapped in the molten pool, it will produce a porous and defective joint. Shielding is accomplished by use of one of the following methods:

1. Chemical coating on the electrodes
2. Inert gas
3. Granular flux
4. Chemical material placed inside the core of electrodes

In structural steel work, arc welding is accomplished by one of the following methods:

1. Manual arc welding
2. Automatic arc welding

It is highly recommended to design the joints for the automatic arc welding process because the rate of deposit is much higher than the manual arc welding process.

Source of electric power is either AC or DC. Typical arc welding electric circuit is illustrated in Figure 8.1. Typical shielded molten pool at a joint is illustrated in Figure 8.2.

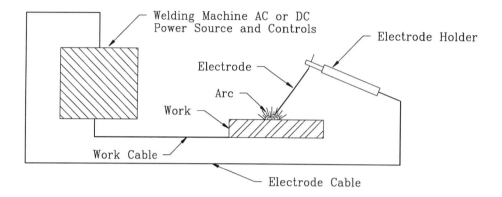

Figure 8.1 Arc Welding Circuit
(Ref. Lincoln Electric Procedure Handbook)

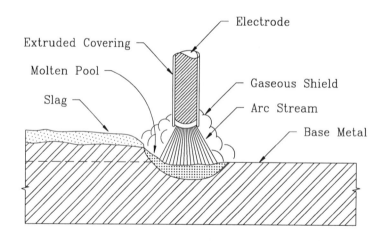

Figure 8.2 Elements of Shielded Metal Arc Welding Process
(Ref. Lincoln Electric Procedure Handbook)

8.2   WELDED JOINTS

Types of welded joints are determined by the design application. Typical welded joints are shown in Figure 8.3. Welded joints must be qualified prior to use. The AISC Manual M4-155 to M1-173 shows several pre-qualified welded joints.

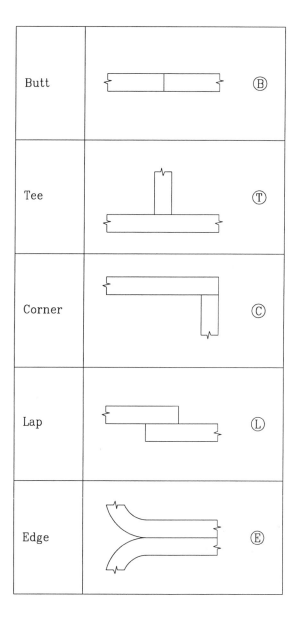

Figure 8.3 Types of Welded Joints
(Ref. Lincoln Electric Procedure Handbook)

8.3 TYPES OF WELDS

There are basically two types of welds. One is called fillet weld and the other is called groove weld. These two type of welds are shown in Figure 8.4.

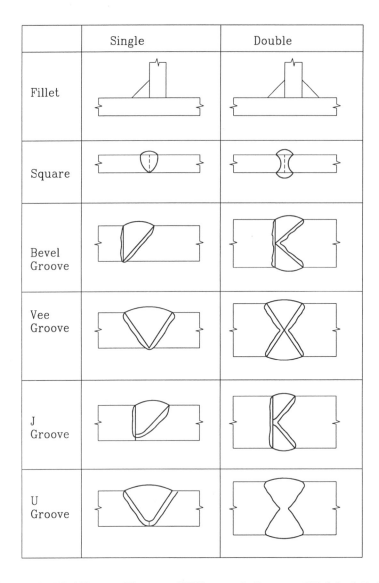

	Single	Double
Fillet		
Square		
Bevel Groove		
Vee Groove		
J Groove		
U Groove		

Figure 8.4 Different Types of Fillet and Groove Welded Joints
(Ref. Lincoln Electric Procedure Handbook)

8.4   BASIC WELD SYMBOLS

American Welding Society (AWS) has adopted symbols to describe the joint configurations, the type of weld, whether the weld is to be accomplished in the shop or in the field, and some other instructions. Figures 8.5 and 8.6 show the basic weld symbols as shown in M4-155 of the AISC Manual.

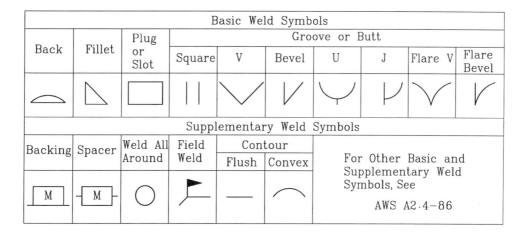

Figure 8.5 Standard Symbols Used in Welding
(Standard Symbols As Shown In AISC Manual, M4-155)

8.4.1 STANDARD LOCATION OF ELEMENTS OF A WELDING SYMBOL

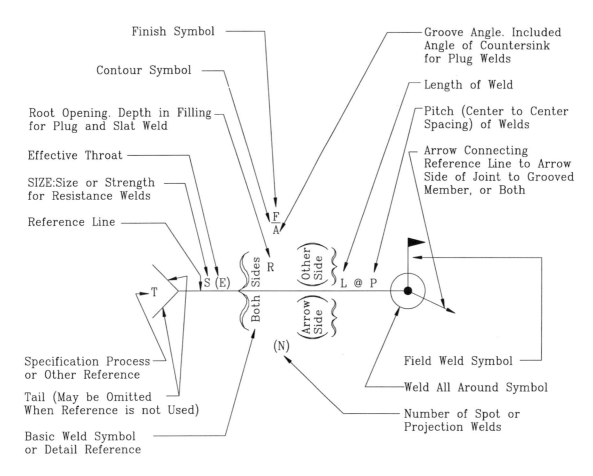

Figure 8.6 Standard Location of Elements of a Welding Symbol
(Ref. AISC Manual M4-155)

8.5 POSITIONS OF WELD

Various weld positions are listed in Figure 8.7. Certain weld electrodes and welding processes are limited by the position of the weld. The most economical weld positions are flat positions and horizontal positions.

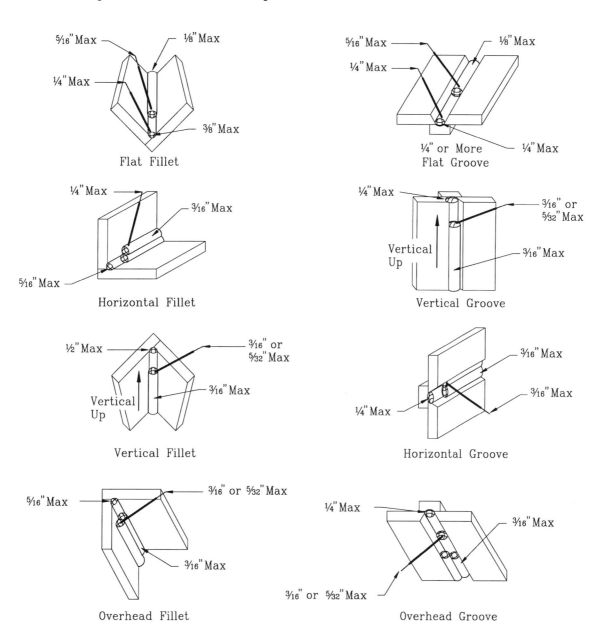

Figure 8.7 Various Weld Positions
(Ref. Lincoln Electric Procedure Handbook)

8.6   WELD INSPECTIONS AND CERTIFICATIONS

The following is a list of methods used for welding inspection:

1. Ultrasonic — This type of inspection is commonly used on structural steel buildings

2. Radiographic — This type of inspection is commonly used on plate work.

3. Magnetic particles

4. Liquid penetrates

5. Visual inspections

Continuous welding inspection is required by governing building authorities and building codes for structural members used in moment-resisting frames.

Welders must be certified and qualified to weld.

Welding procedures must be approved and certified by the governing building authorities.

8.7   ALLOWABLE STRESSES ON WELDS

In accordance with the AISC Specifications, allowable stresses for welds shall be in accordance with Table J2.5 (M5-70) except as modified by AISC provisions of Section K4 for members subject to fatigue and in accordance with Appendix K4, M5-106.

Table 8.1 Allowable Stress on Welds
(AISC Table J2.5, M5-70)

TABLE J2.5
Allowable Stress on Welds[f]

Type of Weld and Stress[a]	Allowable Stress	Required Weld Strength Level[b,c]
Complete-penetration Groove Welds		
Tension normal to effective area	Same as base metal	"Matching" weld metal shall be used.
Compression normal to effective area	Same as base metal	Weld metal with a strength level equal to or less than "matching" weld metal is permitted.
Tension or compression parallel to axis of weld	Same as base metal	
Shear on effective area	0.30 × nominal tensile strength of weld metal (ksi)	
Partial-penetration Groove Welds[d]		
Compression normal to effective area	Same as base metal	Weld metal with a strength level equal to or less than "matching" weld metal is permitted.
Tension or compression parallel to axis of weld[e]	Same as base metal	
Shear parallel to axis of weld	0.30 × nominal tensile strength of weld metal (ksi)	
Tension normal to effective area	0.30 × nominal tensile strength of weld metal (ksi), except tensile stress on base metal shall not exceed 0.60 × yield stress of base metal	
Fillet Welds		
Shear on effective area	0.30 × nominal tensile strength of weld metal (ksi)	Weld metal with a strength level equal to or less than "matching" weld metal is permitted.
Tension or compression Parallel to axis of weld[e]	Same as base metal	
Plug and Slot Welds		
Shear parallel to faying surfaces (on effective area)	0.30 × nominal tensile strength of weld metal (ksi)	Weld metal with a strength level equal to or less than "matching" weld metal is permitted.

[a]For definition of effective area, see Sect. J2.
[b]For "matching" weld metal, see Table 4.1.1, AWS D1.1.
[c]Weld metal one strength level stronger than "matching" weld metal will be permitted.
[d]See Sect. J2.1b for a limitation on use of partial-penetration groove welded joints.
[e]Fillet welds and partial-penetration groove welds joining the component elements of built-up members, such as flange-to-web connections, may be designed without regard to the tensile or compressive stress in these elements parallel to the axis of the welds.
[f]The design of connected material is governed by Chapters D through G. Also see Commentary Sect. J2.4.

8.8   DISTRIBUTION OF STRESSES IN FILLET WELDS

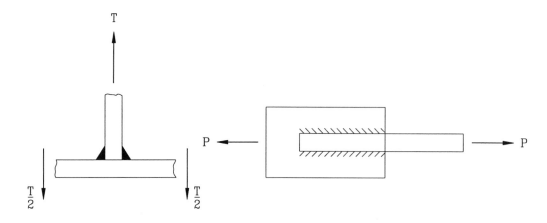

Figure 8.8 Stresses in a Fillet Weld

The distribution of stresses within the fillet welds is completely different for each of the two cases shown above. However, the allowable shear stress on the effective throat width for each case is the same. Effective throat width, t_e, is defined as the shortest distance between the root of weld and the surface of the weld as shown in Figure 8.9.

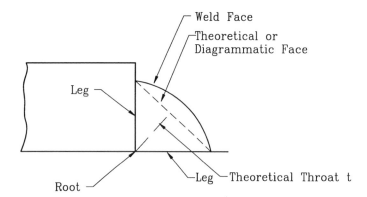

Figure 8.9 Components of Fillet Weld

8.9   PROCEDURE FOR FILLET WELDS — SHEAR LOADS

Case:

Shear forces passing through the center of weld pattern, CWP

Step 1:

Solve for the unknown in the following equation:

$$f_v = \frac{P}{A_w} = \frac{P}{l_w \, t_e} \leq F_v = 0.3 \times F_u$$

where

f_v = Actual shear stress in the weld

P = Applied shear load

A_w = Area of weld

l_w = Total length of weld

t_e = Throat width of weld, ($t_e = 0.707 \times w$)

F_v = Allowable shear stress of weld.

F_u = Tensile strength of weld electrodes

w = Size of fillet weld

Step 2:

Check stresses in base metal.

Step 3:

Check AISC restrictions on minimum and maximum size of weld per section J2.2b, (M5-67).

Table 8.2 Minimum Size of Fillet Welds
(AISC Table J2.4, M5-67)

Material Thickness of Thicker Part Joined (in.)	Minimum Size of Fillet Weld[a] (in.)
To $1/4$ inclusive	$1/8$
Over $1/4$ to $1/2$	$3/16$
Over $1/2$ to $3/4$	$1/4$
Over $3/4$	$5/16$
[a]Leg dimension of fillet welds. Single-pass welds must be used.	

Table 8.3 Minimum Effective Throat Thickness of Partial-Penetration Groove Welds
(AISC Table J2.3, M5-66)

Material Thickness of Thicker Part Joined (in.)	Minimum Effective Throat Thickness[a] (in.)
To $1/4$ inclusive	$1/8$
Over $1/4$ to $1/2$	$3/16$
Over $1/2$ to $3/4$	$1/4$
Over $3/4$ to $1 1/2$	$5/16$
Over $1 1/2$ to $2 1/4$	$3/8$
Over $2 1/4$ to 6	$1/2$
Over 6	$5/8$
[a]See Section J2.	

8.10   EXAMPLE PROBLEM

8.10.1   EXAMPLE PROBLEM 1 — CAPACITY OF FILLET WELDS

Determine the allowable load that can be applied on the connection shown in Fig. P8.10.1 (a) below. A36 steel for plates. E70 electrodes. Use 7/16-in. fillet welds.

Solution

Step 1:

Solve for the unknown load, P, in the following equation:

$$f_v = \frac{P}{A_w} = \frac{P}{l_w\,t_e} \le F_v = 0.3 \times F_u$$

$$P = l_w t_e \times 0.3 \times F_u$$

$$P = (16 + 8 + 16)\left(0.707 \times \frac{7}{16}\right) \times 0.3 \times 70 = 259.8 \text{ kip}$$

Step 2:

Check the tensile stresses in the plates.

$$f_t = \frac{P}{A_g} \le 0.6\,F_y$$

$$P = A_g \times 0.6\,F_y = \left(8 \times \frac{3}{4}\right) 0.6 \times 36 = 129.6 \text{ kip} \ldots \text{governs}$$

$$P = A_e \times 0.5\,F_u = U \times A_n \times 0.5\,F_u$$

$$= 1.0\left(8 \times \frac{3}{4}\right) 0.5 \times 58 = 174 \text{ kip} 1.0\,(8 \times 3/4)\,0.5 \times 58 = 174 \text{ kip}$$

Therefore, the allowable load, P, is equal to the least value computed from the above P = 129.6 kip.

Step 3:

Check size of weld for 3/4-in. plate thickness.

$$w_{max} = 3/4 - 1/16 = 11/16 > w = 7/16 > w_{min} = 5/16 \quad \ldots \text{OK}$$

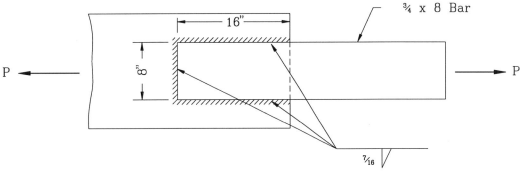

Fig. P8.10.1 (a)

8.11   BALANCE DESIGN FOR WELDED MEMBERS

In accordance with Sections K4 and J1.9 of AISC Specifications, when a welded member transmitting axial stress is subjected to repeated variation of stress or stress reversal, the load should be designed to pass through the center of the weld pattern. This requirement is in order to avoid eccentric loading and fatigue, unless provisions are made for the effect of the resulting eccentricity. Special considerations must be taken when welding angles in trusses or in bracing systems to make sure that the center of gravity of the weld pattern, CWP, coincides with the line of action of the forces in angles. The following is a procedure to balance the weld design for an angle.

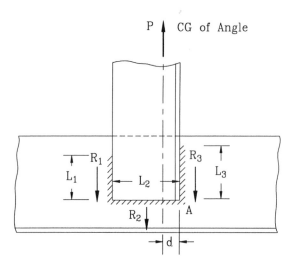

Figure 8.10 Force Components of a Fillet Weld

Procedure to balance the weld at an angle:

Step 1:.

End of angle

　Length, L_2 = width of angle

　Force, $R_2 = F_v \times L_2 t_e$

Step 2:

Along edge of angle, $\Sigma\, M_A = 0$

$$P \times d = \frac{R_2 \times L_2}{2} + R_1 \times L_2$$

　Force, $R_1 = \left(P\, d - \frac{R_2\, L_2}{2}\right) \frac{1}{L_2}$

　Length, $L_1 = \frac{R_1}{F_v \times t_e}$

Step 3:

Along heel of angle, $\Sigma F_v = 0$

Force, $R_3 = P - R_1 - R_2$

Length, $L_3 = \dfrac{R_3}{F_v \times t_e}$

8.12   EXAMPLE PROBLEM

8.12.1   EXAMPLE PROBLEM 1 — DESIGN OF FILLET WELD

Design the weld lengths at the end of the angle shown in Fig. P8.12.1 (a) for the allowable tension load that can be applied on the angle. Use E70 electrodes. The angle is made from A36 steel. Consider the axial load on the angle may fluctuate in its magnitude.

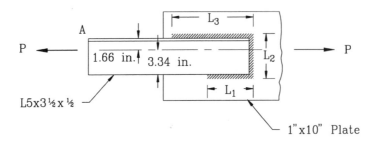

Fig. P8.12.1 (a)

Solution

Maximum size of fillet weld

$$w = 1/2 - 1/16 = 7/16 \text{ in.}$$

$$t_e = 0.707 (7/16) = 0.31 \text{ in.}$$

$$A_g = 4.0 \text{ in.}^2 \qquad \text{For angle } 5 \times 3\text{-}1/2 \times 1/2$$

$$P_{all} = 0.6 \times F_y \times A_g = 0.6 \times 36 \times 4.0 = 86.4 \text{ kip}$$

Balancing the weld:

Step 1:

Length, L_2, is equal to width of angle = 5.0 in.

Step 2:

$$\text{Force} \quad R_2 = F_v \times L_2 \times t_e$$

$$R_2 = 0.3 \times 70 \times 5 \times 0.31 = 32.6 \text{ kip}$$

Step 3:

Sum the moments about line, A.

$$\Sigma M_A = 0$$

$$P \times d = \frac{R_2 \times L_2}{2} + R_1 \times L_2$$

$$R_1 = \frac{\left(P \times d - \frac{R_2 \times L_2}{2} \right)}{L_2}$$

$$R_1 = \frac{\left(86.4 \times 1.66 - \frac{32.6 \times 5.0}{2}\right)}{5} = 12.4 \text{ kip}$$

$$L_1 = \frac{R_1}{F_v \times t_e}$$

$$= \frac{12.4}{21 \times 0.31} = 1.9 \text{ in. Use 2 inches.}$$

Step 4:

$$\Sigma F_v = 0$$

$$R_3 = P - R_1 - R_2$$

$$= 86.4 - 12.3 - 32.6 = 41.5 \text{ kip}$$

$$L_3 = \frac{R_3}{F_v \times t_e}$$

$$= \frac{41.5}{21 \times 0.31} = 6.4 \text{ in.} \qquad \text{Use 6.5 inches.}$$

8.13   ECCENTRIC-TYPE CONNECTIONS

A connection that is subjected to loads that do not pass through the center of its weld pattern as shown in Figure 8.11 is called an eccentric-type connection. The solution for such a connection is accomplished by an elastic method or by an ultimate strength method. The elastic method is described in Section 8.13.1 The ultimate strength method is described in AISC Manual. The AISC provides tables shown in M4-75 through M4-82 for some weld patterns that are subjected to eccentric loads. These tables are based on ultimate strength method.

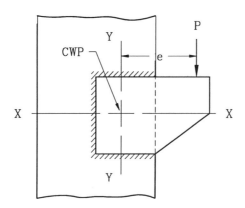

Figure 8.11 Eccentric-Type Weld Connection

8.13.1   ELASTIC METHOD OF ANALYSIS

Figure 8.12 shows a typical eccentric-type connection which is subjected to a load that does not pass through the center of weld pattern. The welds, for such type loadings, are subjected to a combination of direct shears plus bending moments. Assumptions for load distribution in an eccentric-type connection are as follows:

1.   An equal share of the vertical component of the load

2.   An equal share of the horizontal component of the load

3.   A proportional share of the eccentric moment portion of the load

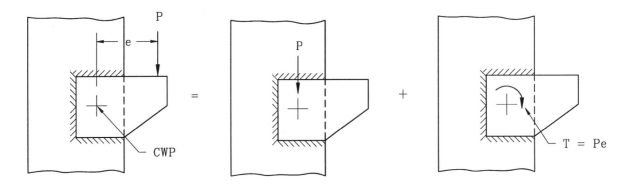

Figure 8.12 Force Components of an Eccentric Weld Joint

8.13.2   PROCEDURE FOR ECCENTRIC-TYPE CONNECTION BY ELASTIC METHOD

Step 1:

Determine the location of center of weld pattern, CWP, and eccentricity distance, e.

Step 2:

Compute the value of α.

$$\alpha = \frac{Pe}{J} = \frac{Pe}{\Sigma \left(I_x + I_y\right)_w}$$

where

$\quad$ Pe $\;=\;$ Net moment acting about the CWP
$\quad$ J $\quad=\;$ Polar moment of inertia
$\quad$ J $\quad=\;$ $\Sigma (I_x+I_y)_w$
$\quad$ I_x and I_y are moment of inertias of the welds.

Step 3:

Calculate the direct shear forces in the weld.

$$f_{iy} = \frac{P_y}{A_w} \quad \text{and} \quad f_{ix} = \frac{P_x}{A_w}$$

where

$\quad$ P_y $\;=\;$ load along the y-axis
$\quad$ P_x $\;=\;$ load along the x-axis
$\quad$ A_w $=\;$ area of the weld in connection
$\quad$ A_w $=\; l_w \times t_e$

Step 4:

Calculate the vertical and horizontal stress components, R_{yi} and R_{xi}, in the most re-mote element of the weld from the center of the weld pattern.

$$R_{yi} = \alpha\,(x_i) \quad \text{and} \quad R_{xi} = \alpha\,(y_i)$$

Note that the direction of stress components are in opposite direction of the net moments.

Step 5:

Calculate the resultant shear stress, R_i.

$$R_i = \sqrt{(f_{iy} + R_{yi})^2 + (f_{ix} + R_{xi})^2},$$

This value is to be analyzed or designed per AISC Code.

8.14   EXAMPLE PROBLEMS

8.14.1   EXAMPLE PROBLEM 1 — ECCENTRIC FILLET WELD CONNECTION

Determine the allowable load, P, that can be applied on the connection shown in Fig.
P8.14.1 (a). The weld is made of E70 electrodes. The material is A36 steel.

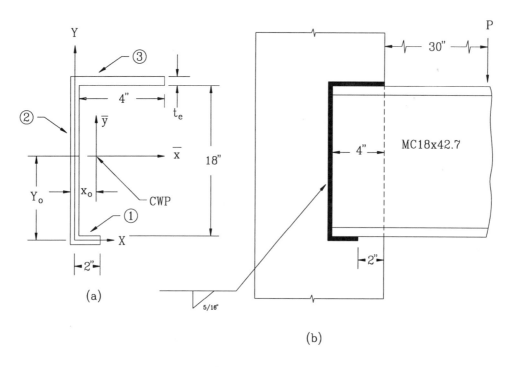

Fig. P8.14.1 (a)

Solution

Step 1:

Determine the location of the center of the weld pattern, CWP, from the origin located
at the lower left-hand corner.

$$\overline{X}_o = \frac{\Sigma \ X_i \ A_i}{\Sigma A_i}$$

$$= \frac{1 \ (2t_e) \ + \ 0 \ (18t_e) \ + \ 2 \ (4t_e)}{2t_e \ + \ 18t_e \ + \ 4t_e}$$

$$= 0.42 \text{ in.}$$

$$\overline{Y}_o = \frac{\Sigma \ Y_i \ A_i}{\Sigma A_i}$$

$$= \frac{0 \ (2t_e) \ + \ 9 \ (18t_e) \ + \ 18 \ (4t_e)}{2t_e \ + \ 18t_e \ + \ 4t_e}$$

$$= 9.8 \ \text{in.}$$

$$e \ = 30 + 4 - 0.42 = 33.58 \ \text{inches.}$$

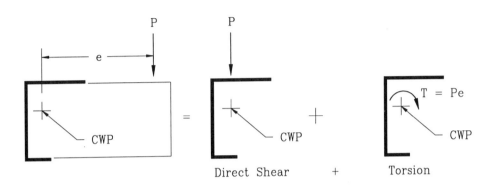

Fig. P8.14.1 (b) Equivalent Loading System

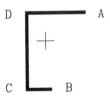

Fig. P8.14.1 (c) Remote Elements of Weld

Step 2:

Compute the value of α.

$$\alpha \ = \frac{Pe}{\Sigma \left(I_x \ + \ I_y\right)_w}$$

$$\alpha \ = \frac{P \ (33.58)}{\Sigma \left(I_x \ + \ I_y\right)_w}$$

$$I_x = \frac{2t_e^3}{12} + 2t_e \times 9.8^2 + \frac{t_e \ 18^3}{12} + 18 \ t_e \left(9.8 \ - \ \frac{18}{2}\right)^2 + \frac{4t_e^3}{12} + 4 \ t_e(18 \ - \ 9.8)^2$$

Because the value of t_e is very small, let the computations of $t_e^3 = 0$.

$$I_x = 0 + 2t_e (9.8)^2 + \left(\frac{t_e (18)^3}{12}\right) + 18 \, t_e \left(9.8 - \frac{18}{2}\right)^2$$

$$+ 0 + 4 \, t_e (18 - 9.8)^2$$

$$= 958.56 \, t_e$$

$$I_y = \frac{t_e \times 2^3}{12} + 2t_e (1 - 0.42)^2 + \left(18 \frac{t_e^3}{12}\right)$$

$$\overset{\longleftarrow}{} \text{Neglect}$$

$$+ 18t_e (0.42)^2 + \frac{t_e (4)^3}{12} + 4t_e (2 - 0.42)^2$$

$$= 19.83 \, t_e$$

$$\alpha = \frac{P \, (33.58)}{\Sigma \, (959 \, t_e + 19.83 \, t_e)}$$

$$= \frac{P \, (33.58)}{\Sigma \, (959 + 19.83) \, (0.707) \left(\frac{5}{16}\right)}$$

$$= 0.155 \, P$$

Step 3:

Calculate the direct shear forces in the weld.

$$f_{iy} = \frac{P_y}{A_w}$$

$$f_{iy} = \frac{P_y}{L_w t_e} = \frac{P}{(4 + 18 + 2) \times 0.707 \times \left(\frac{5}{16}\right)} = 0.19 \, P$$

$$f_{ix} = \frac{P_x}{A_w}$$

$$f_{ix} = \frac{P_x}{L_w t_e} = \frac{0}{(4 + 18 + 2) \times 0.707 \times \left(\frac{5}{16}\right)} = 0$$

Step 4:

Calculate the vertical and horizontal components, R_{yi} and R_{xi}, in the most remote element of the weld from the center of the weld pattern that is at point B.

$$R_{yi} = \alpha \, x_i \quad \text{and} \quad R_{xi} = \alpha \, y_i$$

$$R_{yi} = 0.155 \, P \, (2 - 0.42)$$

$$= 0.155 \, P \times 1.58 = 0.245 \, P$$

$$R_{xi} = 0.155 \, P \, (9.8) = 1.52 \, P$$

Step 5:

Calculate the resultant shear stress, R_i.

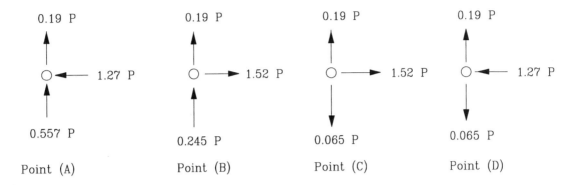

Fig. P8.14.1 (d) Resultant Forces on Weld Corners

$$R_i = \sqrt{\left(f_{iy} + R_{yi}\right)^2 + \left(f_{ix} + R_{xi}\right)^2}$$

$$R_i = \sqrt{(0.19\ P + 0.245\ P)^2 + (0 + 1.52\ P)^2} = 1.58\ P$$

Step 6:

$R_i = 1.58\ P \leq 0.3 \times 70 = 21\ \text{ksi}$

$P_{all} = \dfrac{21}{1.58} = 13.3\ \text{kip}$

8.14.2   EXAMPLE PROBLEM 2 — SIZING OF FILLET WELD

Determine the size of fillet weld required for the connection shown in Fig. P8.14.2 (a) by ultimate strength method. A36 material and E70 electrodes. Load P = 15 kip.

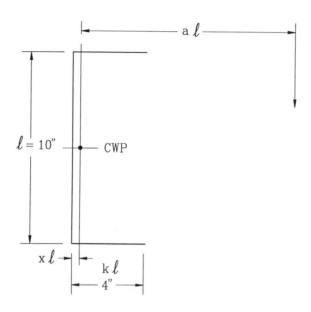

Fig. P8.14.2 (a) Eccentric Welded Connection

Solution

Refer to Fig. P8.14.2 (a) and AISC Table XXIII in M4-79.

$l = 10$ in., $k\ell = 4$ in.

Therefore, $k = \dfrac{k\ell}{\ell} = \dfrac{4}{10} = 0.4$

$x = 0.088$ for $k = 0.4$

Therefore, $X_o = x \times \ell = 0.088 \times 10 = 0.89$

$a\ell = (8 + 4 - 0.89) = 11.1$ in.

Therefore, $a = \dfrac{a\ell}{\ell} = \dfrac{11.1}{10} = 1.11$

$C = 0.463$ for $k = 0.4$ and $a = 1.11$

$C_1 = 1.0$ for E70 from AISC Table in M4-72

$D = \dfrac{P}{CC_1\ell} = \dfrac{15}{0.463 \times 1.0 \times 10} = 3.24$

Size of weld = $w = \dfrac{3.24}{16}$,   Use 1/4 inch.

Check weld size per AISC requirements:

$w_{max} = 1/2 - 1/16 = 7/16$ in. $\geq w = 1/4$ in. $\geq w_{min} = 3/16$ inch

Table 8.4 Coefficients, C
(AISC Table XXIII, M4-79)

ECCENTRIC LOADS ON WELD GROUPS
TABLE XXIII Coefficients *C*

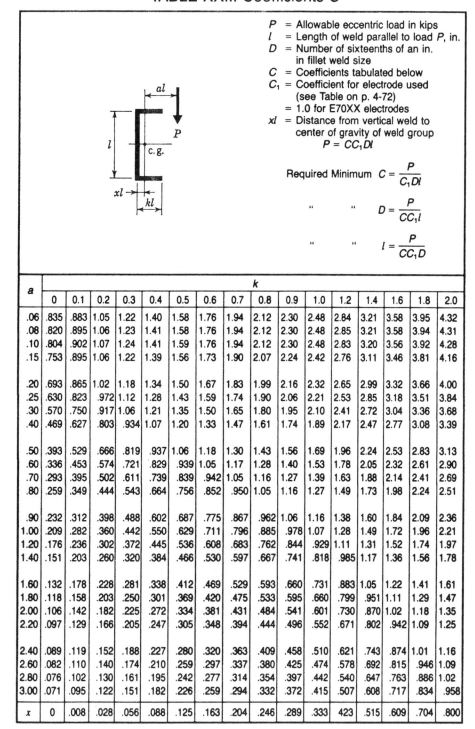

P = Allowable eccentric load in kips
l = Length of weld parallel to load P, in.
D = Number of sixteenths of an in. in fillet weld size
C = Coefficients tabulated below
C_1 = Coefficient for electrode used (see Table on p. 4-72)
= 1.0 for E70XX electrodes
xl = Distance from vertical weld to center of gravity of weld group

$$P = CC_1Dl$$

Required Minimum $\quad C = \dfrac{P}{C_1Dl}$

"   " $\quad D = \dfrac{P}{CC_1l}$

"   " $\quad l = \dfrac{P}{CC_1D}$

a								*k*								
	0	0.1	0.2	0.3	0.4	0.5	0.6	0.7	0.8	0.9	1.0	1.2	1.4	1.6	1.8	2.0
.06	.835	.883	1.05	1.22	1.40	1.58	1.76	1.94	2.12	2.30	2.48	2.84	3.21	3.58	3.95	4.32
.08	.820	.895	1.06	1.23	1.41	1.58	1.76	1.94	2.12	2.30	2.48	2.85	3.21	3.58	3.94	4.31
.10	.804	.902	1.07	1.24	1.41	1.59	1.76	1.94	2.12	2.30	2.48	2.83	3.20	3.56	3.92	4.28
.15	.753	.895	1.06	1.22	1.39	1.56	1.73	1.90	2.07	2.24	2.42	2.76	3.11	3.46	3.81	4.16
.20	.693	.865	1.02	1.18	1.34	1.50	1.67	1.83	1.99	2.16	2.32	2.65	2.99	3.32	3.66	4.00
.25	.630	.823	.972	1.12	1.28	1.43	1.59	1.74	1.90	2.06	2.21	2.53	2.85	3.18	3.51	3.84
.30	.570	.750	.917	1.06	1.21	1.35	1.50	1.65	1.80	1.95	2.10	2.41	2.72	3.04	3.36	3.68
.40	.469	.627	.803	.934	1.07	1.20	1.33	1.47	1.61	1.74	1.89	2.17	2.47	2.77	3.08	3.39
.50	.393	.529	.666	.819	.937	1.06	1.18	1.30	1.43	1.56	1.69	1.96	2.24	2.53	2.83	3.13
.60	.336	.453	.574	.721	.829	.939	1.05	1.17	1.28	1.40	1.53	1.78	2.05	2.32	2.61	2.90
.70	.293	.395	.502	.611	.739	.839	.942	1.05	1.16	1.27	1.39	1.63	1.88	2.14	2.41	2.69
.80	.259	.349	.444	.543	.664	.756	.852	.950	1.05	1.16	1.27	1.49	1.73	1.98	2.24	2.51
.90	.232	.312	.398	.488	.602	.687	.775	.867	.962	1.06	1.16	1.38	1.60	1.84	2.09	2.36
1.00	.209	.282	.360	.442	.550	.629	.711	.796	.885	.978	1.07	1.28	1.49	1.72	1.96	2.21
1.20	.176	.236	.302	.372	.445	.536	.608	.683	.762	.844	.929	1.11	1.31	1.52	1.74	1.97
1.40	.151	.203	.260	.320	.384	.466	.530	.597	.667	.741	.818	.985	1.17	1.36	1.56	1.78
1.60	.132	.178	.228	.281	.338	.412	.469	.529	.593	.660	.731	.883	1.05	1.22	1.41	1.61
1.80	.118	.158	.203	.250	.301	.369	.420	.475	.533	.595	.660	.799	.951	1.11	1.29	1.47
2.00	.106	.142	.182	.225	.272	.334	.381	.431	.484	.541	.601	.730	.870	1.02	1.18	1.35
2.20	.097	.129	.166	.205	.247	.305	.348	.394	.444	.496	.552	.671	.802	.942	1.09	1.25
2.40	.089	.119	.152	.188	.227	.280	.320	.363	.409	.458	.510	.621	.743	.874	1.01	1.16
2.60	.082	.110	.140	.174	.210	.259	.297	.337	.380	.425	.474	.578	.692	.815	.946	1.09
2.80	.076	.102	.130	.161	.195	.242	.277	.314	.354	.397	.442	.540	.647	.763	.886	1.02
3.00	.071	.095	.122	.151	.182	.226	.259	.294	.332	.372	.415	.507	.608	.717	.834	.958
x	0	.008	.028	.056	.088	.125	.163	.204	.246	.289	.333	423	.515	.609	.704	.800

8.14.3   EXAMPLE PROBLEM 3 — DESIGN OF ECCENTRIC WELDED CONNECTION

Determine the size of fillet welds required for the eccentric connection shown in Fig. 8.14.3 (a)

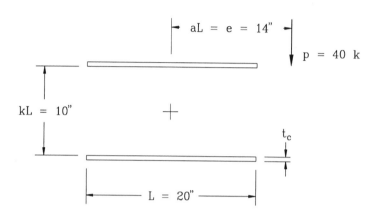

Fig. P8.14.3 (a)

Solution

Elastic Method

$$I_x = 2 \left(20 \times t_c \times 5^2 \right)$$

$$I_x = 1000 \ t_c$$

$$I_y = 2 \left(\frac{20^3 \times t_c}{12} \right) = 1333 \ t_c$$

$$\alpha = \frac{40 \times 14}{(1000 + 1333) \ t_c} = \frac{560}{2333 \ t_c}$$

$$\alpha = \frac{0.24}{t_c}$$

$$\tau = \sqrt{ \left(\frac{40}{20 \times 2 \times t_c} + \frac{0.24 \times 10}{t_c} \right)^2 + \left(0 + \frac{0.24 \times 5}{t_c} \right)^2 }$$

$$\tau = \frac{3.1}{t_c}$$

$$\frac{3.1}{t_c} \leq 21 \qquad t_c = \frac{3.1}{21} = 0.148$$

$$w = \frac{0.148}{0.707} = 0.209 \qquad \text{Use } 1/4\text{-in. weld}$$

Ultimate Method

Ref: M4-76: $aL = 14$; $L = 20$ in.

Therefore, $a = 0.70$

$kL = 10$;

Therefore, $k = 0.50$

and therefore, $C = 0.731$

Required minimum $D = \dfrac{P}{C\ C_1\ L} = \dfrac{40}{0.731 \times 1 \times 20} = 2.74$

Use $^3/_{16}$-in. weld.

8.15 SHEAR STRESSES AND BENDING STRESSES IN WELDED CONNECTIONS

Many welded connections are designed so that the weld is subjected to direct shear stress plus bending moment as illustrated by Figure 8.13. Using simple statics, one can see that the eccentric load can be substituted by load, P, and a moment equal to Pe acting at the interface.

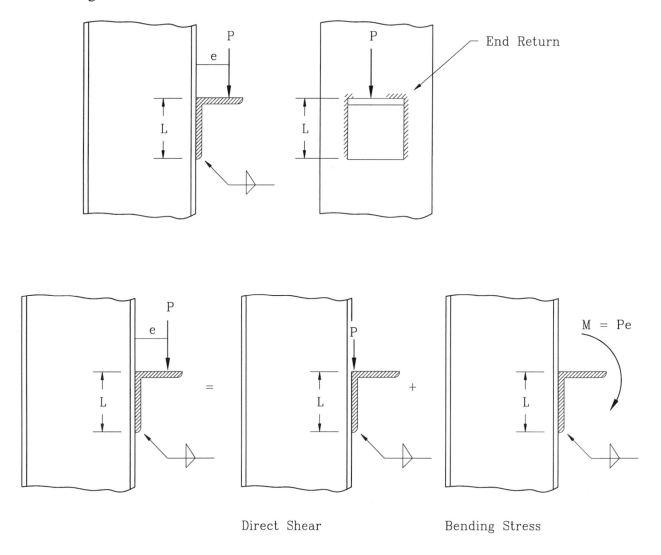

Figure 8.13 Combined Bending and Shear Stresses in Welded Joints

8.15.1 PROCEDURE FOR ANALYSIS AND DESIGN OF WELDED CONNECTIONS SUBJECTED TO SHEAR AND BENDING STRESSES

Step 1:

Calculate shear stress due to load, P.

$$f_v = \frac{P}{A_w} = \frac{P}{l_w \times t_c}$$

Step 2:

Calculate the bending stress.

$$f_b = \frac{Mc}{I} = \frac{P(e)y}{I}$$

The neutral axis is based on the effective area of the weld.

y = distance from the neutral axis to any point where the stress is desired.

I = moment of inertia about the neutral axis for the effective weld area.

Step 3:

Since Step 1 gives shear stress and Step 2 gives bending stress, one must be careful in combining these two stresses. Pleas note that the maximum bending stress occurs at the farthest point from the neutral axis while the maximum shear stress occurs at the neutral axis. A conservative procedure is to do as follows:

$$f_R = \sqrt{(f_v)^2 + (f_b)^2} \le f_{all}$$

9

DESIGN AND ANALYSIS OF CONNECTIONS

9.1 INTRODUCTION

The AISC Manual gives a variety of connections and their corresponding strength capabilities. Some of these tables were introduced in the chapters dealing with bolts and welds. The following presentation will present a rational method which may be found in any of the references listed.

9.2 TYPES OF CONNECTIONS

According to AISC Manual there are three types of connections (see M5-24):

Type 1 = Rigid connection; the angles between various members within the connection do not change.

Type 2 = Non-rigid connection; relative rotation of members in the connection is allowed.

Type 3 = Semi-rigid connection; partial restraint against rotation is provided.

Most connections are assumed to be of either Type 1 or 2. Extensive calculations must be performed to designate a connection as Type 3.

Some examples of various types of connections are shown in Figures 9.1, 9.2, and 9.3.
Type 1 — Rigid Connections:

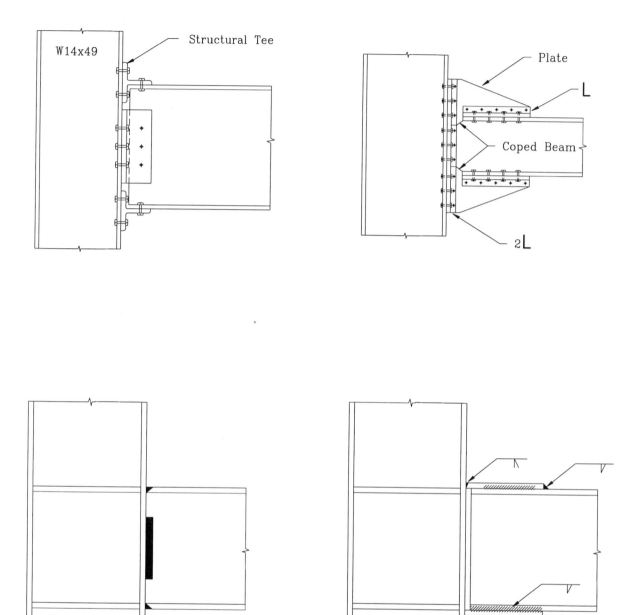

Figure 9.1 Rigid Connection

Type 2 — Non-Rigid Connections:

Please note that for non-rigid connections the web alone is connected to the column so that rotation is allowed. In Figure 9.2b, the top angle and the seat angle should be flexible enough to allow for rotation of the flanges. Connections Figure 9.2a and c are preferred for non-rigid type.

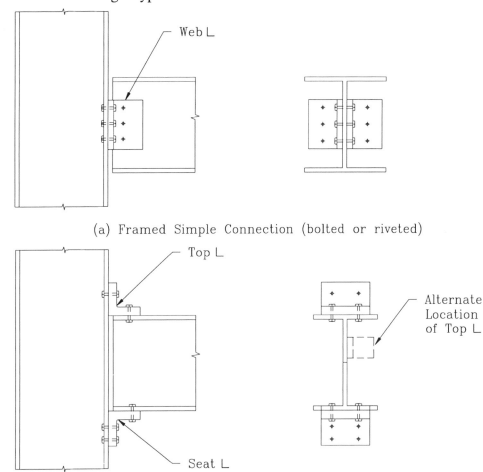

(a) Framed Simple Connection (bolted or riveted)

(b) Seated Simple Connection (bolted or Riveted)

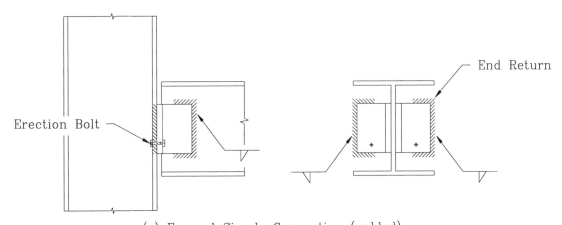

(c) Framed Simple Connection (welded)

Figure 9.2 Non-Rigid Connections

Type 3 — Semi-Rigid Connections:

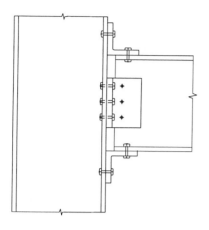

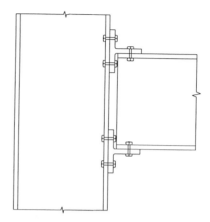

(a)   Web L with Seat L and Top L   (b)   Structural Tee Connection

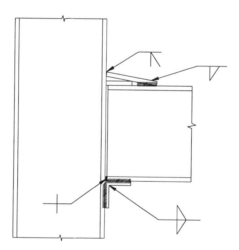

(c)   Welded Semi-Rigid Connection

Figure 9.3 Semi-Rigid Connections

Since the flanges of W and S beams have the largest bending stresses and most of the cross-sectional area, the connections are generally designed on the assumption that the entire bending moment is transferred through the flanges. Likewise, the formula

$$\tau = \frac{VQ}{Ib}$$

tells us that the maximum shear stress is at the neutral axis. Hence, most connections are designed on the assumption that the entire shear force is transferred entirely through the web or webs.

9.3   EXAMPLE PROBLEMS

9.3.1   EXAMPLE PROBLEM 1 — FILLET WELD DESIGN

Design the welds for the connection shown in Fig. P9.3.1 (a). Use E70 electrodes, A36 steel and fillet welds. The shear and bending moment in the beam at the connection are shown in Fig. P9.3.1 (a). The webs of the beam are welded on both sides.

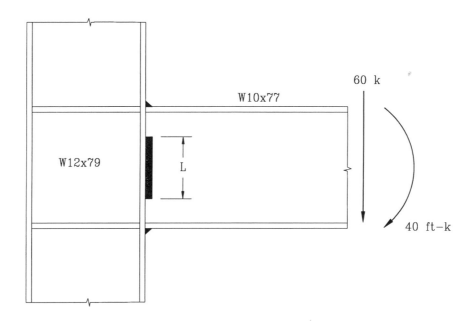

Fig. P9.3.1 (a). Fillet Weld Design

Solution

A.   Design of welds to flanges:

   M = 40 ft-kip

   b_f = 10.195 for W10 × 77

and b_f = 12.08 for W12 × 79

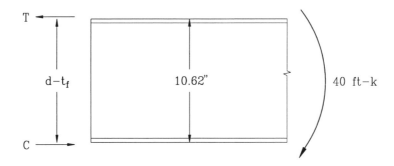

Fig. P9.3.1 (b). Internal Forces in W Section

$$T = C,$$

$$T(d - t_f) = 40 \times 12$$

$$T = \frac{40 \times 12}{10.62 - 0.87} = 49 \text{ kip}$$

$$\tau_{allow} = 21 \text{ ksi}$$

Hence, let the length of the weld on the flanges of the beam be 10 inches.

Therefore,

$$\frac{T}{A_e} = \frac{49}{10 \, t_e} \leq 21$$

$$t_e \leq \frac{49}{10 \times 21} \leq 0.234$$

$$W \leq \frac{0.234}{0.707} = 0.33 \text{ in.} \qquad \text{Use } ^3/_8\text{-in. weld}$$

Note:

$t_f = 0.736$ for W12 $\times$ 79

$t_f = 0.868$ for W10 $\times$ 77

Checking the maximum and minimum size welds required by the AISC, we find that the $^3/_8$-in. weld is acceptable for the flanges.

B.   Design of welds for the webs:

Let the length of the weld along the web be 7 inches.

Hence,

$$\frac{V}{A_e} = \frac{V}{2(7 \, t_e)} \leq \tau_{allow} = 21 \text{ ksi}$$

$$\frac{60}{14 \times 21} \leq t_e$$

Hence,

$$t_e \geq 0.204 \text{ in.}$$

$$W \geq \frac{0.204}{0.707} = 0.29 \text{ in.}$$

Use a $^5/_{16}$-in. weld which satisfies AISC requirements for maximum and minimum weld sizes allowed for the connecting members.

The above design is rather simple; however, most other connections can be designed along the same general procedure.

9.3.2   EXAMPLE PROBLEM 2 — DESIGN OF SINGLE SHEAR PLATE

Design the single shear plate for the connection shown in Fig. P9.3.1 (a). Use A36 steel.

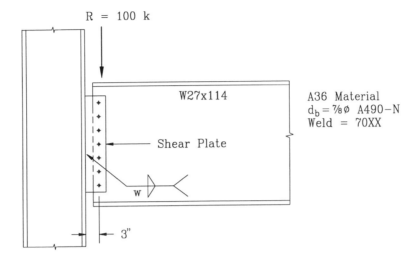

Fig. P9.3.2 (a) Shear Plate Design

Solution

A.   Shear plate thickness $= t_p \leq \dfrac{d_b}{2} + \dfrac{1}{16} = \left(\dfrac{7}{8}\right)\left(\dfrac{1}{2}\right) + \dfrac{1}{16} = \dfrac{1}{2}$

Use $t_p = \dfrac{7}{16}$ in.

B.   Number of bolts required:

$$\frac{P}{r_N} = C \qquad r_N = 16.8 \ldots \text{M4-5}$$

$$\frac{100}{16.8} = 5.95$$

$$n = 7 \qquad \text{from Table XI} \ldots \text{M4-62}$$

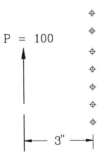

P = 100

3"

Fig. P9.3.2 (b) Load Diagrams

C. Length of Shear Plate:

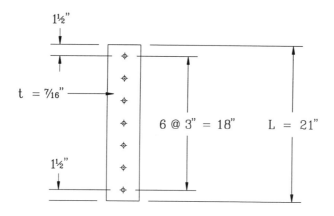

Fig. P9.3.2 (c) Shear Plate

$$L = (n - 1) s + 2e \geq \frac{T}{2}$$

Where $T = 24$; $e = 1.5$; $s = 3$; $n = 7$

$$(7 - 1) 3 + 2 \times 1.5 \geq \frac{24}{2}$$

$$21 > 12 \qquad \text{OK}$$

D. Check Shear Plate for Shear Capacity:

$$\frac{P}{A} = \frac{P}{L \, t_p} = \frac{100}{21 \times 7/16}$$

$$= 10.88 < 0.4 \times 36 = 14.4 \text{ ksi } \ldots \text{ OK}$$

E. Determine Weld Size of Shear Plate of Column:

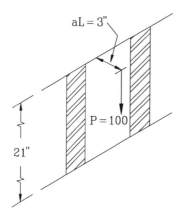

Fig. P9.3.2 (d) Weld Pattern in Isometric View

$$aL \;=\; 3$$

$$L \;=\; 21$$

$$\therefore a \;=\; \frac{3}{21} \;=\; 0.167$$

From M4-75, k = 0, a = 0.167, find C = 1.4

$$\text{Size of weld in sixteenth} \;=\; D \;=\; \frac{P}{C\,C_1\,L}$$

$$=\; \frac{100}{1.4 \times 1.0 \times 21}$$

$$=\; 3.41 \;\cong\; \frac{1}{4}$$

Note:

$$w \;\le\; 0.75 t_p$$

$$\frac{1}{4} \;\le\; 0.75 \times \frac{7}{16} \;=\; 0.328 \;\ldots\; \text{OK}$$

F.   Check Net Shear Fracture:

$$R \;=\; 0.3\,F_u \left[L - n\!\left(d_s + \frac{1}{16}\right) \right] t$$

$$=\; 0.3 \times 58 \times \left[21 - 7 \times \left(\frac{7}{8} + \frac{1}{16}\right) \right] \times \frac{7}{16}$$

$$=\; 110 \text{ k} \;>\; 100 \;\ldots\; \text{OK}$$

G.   Check Bolt Bearing:

$$\frac{P}{n\,d_b\,t_p} \;\le\; 1.2\,F_u$$

$$\frac{100}{7 \times 7/8 \times 7/16} \;=\; 37.3 \;<\; 1.2 \times 58 \;=\; 69.6 \;\ldots\; \text{OK}$$

If beam flange is coped, check block shears as stated in Step H as follows.

H. Check block shear, *if top flange of beam is coped*.

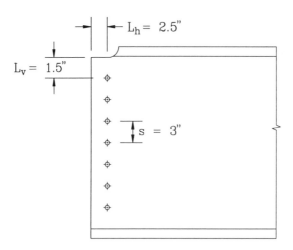

Fig. P9.3.2 (e) Notched Beam End

R_{BS} = Resistance to block shear, kip

= $0.3\ A_v\ F_u\ +\ 0.5\ A_t\ F_u$

= $\left\{ (0.3\ L_v\ +\ 0.5\ L_h)\ +\ 0.3\left[(n\ -\ 1)(s\ -\ d_h)\ -\ \dfrac{d_h}{2} \right]\ -\ \dfrac{d_h}{4} \right\}\ F_u\ t$

d_h = $d_b\ +\ \dfrac{1}{16}$ = Diameter of hole

n = Number of bolts = 7

= $\left\{ (0.3 \times 1.5\ +\ 0.5 \times 2.5)\ +\ 0.3\left[(7\ -\ 1)\left(3\ -\ \left(\dfrac{7}{8}\ +\ \dfrac{1}{16} \right) \right) \right. \right.$

$\left. \left. -\ \left(\dfrac{7}{8}\ +\ \dfrac{1}{16} \right) \times \dfrac{1}{2} \right]\ -\ \left(\dfrac{7}{8}\ +\ \dfrac{1}{16} \right) \times \dfrac{1}{4} \right\} \times 58 \times \dfrac{7}{16}$

= 127.8 kip > 100 ... OK

9.3.3   EXAMPLE PROBLEM 3 — DESIGN OF A COLUMN SPLICE

Design a gravity column splice so as the connection is capable to support 50% of the moment capacity and 50% of the shear capacity of the column, W24 × 132.

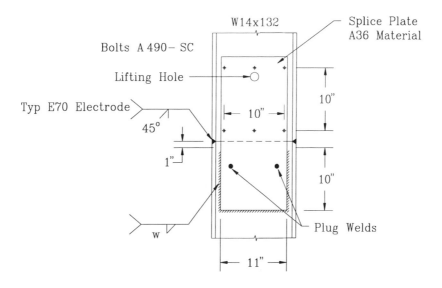

Fig. P9.3.3 (a) Column Splice Connection

Solution

A. Moment Capacity of Column Splice = $F_b S$ = 24 ksi × 209 in.³ = 5016 in.-kip

$$50\% \text{ Moment Capacity} = \frac{5016}{2} = 2508 \text{ in.-kip}$$

$$T = C = \frac{M}{d - t} = \frac{2508}{14.66 - 1} = 183.6 \text{ kip}$$

Partial pen weld at the flanges:

$$183.6 \text{ kip} = 0.6 \ F_y \ b_f \ t_e$$

$$183.6 = 0.6 \times 36 \times 14.725 \times t_c$$

$$t_c = 0.577 \text{ in.} = \text{ Effective weld size}$$

Use $\left(\frac{2}{3}t + \frac{1}{8}\right)$

B. Shear Capacity of Column $= 0.4\ F_y\ d\ t_w$

$$= 0.4 \times 36 \times 14.66 \times 0.645$$

$$= 136\ \text{kip}$$

50% Shear Capacity $= \dfrac{136}{2} = 68\ \text{kip}$

Thickness of Splice Plate:

$$\frac{V}{11\ t} \le 14.4$$

$$\frac{68}{11 \times 14.4} = t = 0.43\ \text{in.} \qquad \text{Use } \tfrac{1}{2} \text{ in.}$$

C. Check Size of Bolts at Splice Plate

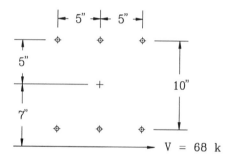

Fig. P9.3.3 (b) Bolt Group Free-Body

$$\alpha = \frac{68 \times 7}{2(5^2 + 0) + 4(5^2 + 5^2)} = \frac{476}{250} = 1.9$$

$$R = \sqrt{\left(\frac{68}{6} + 1.9 \times 5\right)^2 + (0 + 1.9 \times 5)^2} = 22.89$$

Use $1^{1}/_{4}$-in.-diameter bolts.

D. Check Weld Size at Splice Plate:

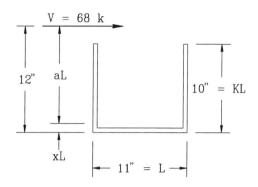

Fig. P9.3.3 (c) Weld Pattern

$$KL = 10$$
$$L = 11$$

Therefore, $k = \dfrac{10}{11} = 0.91$

Therefore, $x = 0.289$

$$xL = 0.289 \times 11 = 3.2 \text{ in.}$$

$$aL = 12 - 3.2 = 8.8 \text{ in.}$$

$$a = \dfrac{8.8}{11} = 0.8$$

$$C = 1.16$$

$$D = \dfrac{P}{C\,C_1\,L} = \dfrac{68}{1.16 \times 1 \times 11} = 5.32$$

Note: Check weld size for allowable minimum and maximum weld size.

9.3.4   EXAMPLE PROBLEM 4 — DESIGN OF A MOMENT CONNECTION

Design a moment connection for W24 × 55 beam framed to both flanges of a W114 × 74 column. Applied loads are as shown in the figure below.

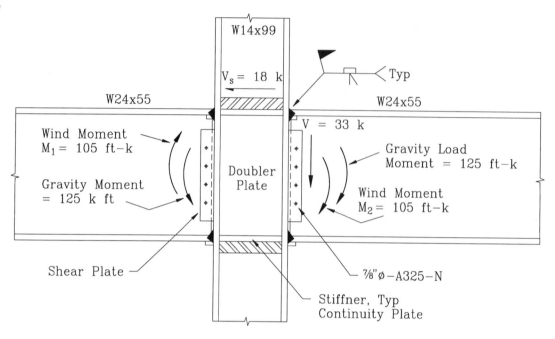

Fig. P9.3.4 (a) Moment Connection

Solution

A. To develop the full plastic moment capacity of the girder, weld the flanges with full penetrating weld.

B. Design Web Connection:

$$\frac{V}{r_v} = \frac{33}{12.6} = 2.6 \qquad \text{from M4-5}$$

Use 4 bolts.

C. Check Bearing on Beam Web:

$$F_u = 58 \text{ ksi}; \quad t_{w_b} = 0.395; \quad r_s = 60.9 \quad \leftarrow \text{M4-6}$$

$$R = n\,r_s\,t_{wb} = 4 \times 60.9 \times 0.395 = 96 \text{ kip} > 33 \ldots \text{OK}$$

D. Design Shear Plate:

$$t_p \leq \frac{d_b}{2} + \frac{1}{16} = \frac{1}{2} \qquad \text{Use } \frac{3}{8} \text{ in.}$$

$$L_p = (n - 1)\, s + 2e \geq \frac{T}{2} \qquad \text{Where } T = 21 \text{ in.}$$

$$= (4 - 1)\, 3 + 2 \times 1.5 = 12 > \frac{21}{2} = 10.5 \ldots \text{OK}$$

Use plate of 12 in. $\times \frac{3}{8}$ inch.

E. $\qquad A_{net} = t_p \left(L - n \left(d_b + \frac{1}{16} \right) \right)$

$$= \frac{3}{8} \left(12 - 4 \left(\frac{7}{8} + \frac{1}{16} \right) \right) = 3.09 \text{ in.}^2$$

F. Check Net Shear Fracture Capacity:

$$R = 0.3\, F_u\, A_n = 0.3 \times 58 \times 3.09 = 54 > 33 \ldots \text{OK}$$

G. Check Bearing on Shear Plate:

$$4 \times 22.8 = 91.2 \text{ kip} > 33 \ldots \text{OK}$$

(22.8 is from Table 1E (M4-6) for $t_p = 3/8$)

H. Weld to Column Flanges:

$$D_{min.} = \frac{V}{Aw} = \frac{33}{2 \times 0.928 \times 12} = 1.5$$

Use minimum weld size $= \frac{3}{16}$ in. per AISC Table J2.4.

I. Web Panel Shear in the Column:

$$\sum F = \frac{M_1}{0.95\, d_1} + \frac{M_2}{0.95\, d_2} - V_s$$

$$= \frac{(105 + 125)\, 12}{0.95 \times 23.57} + \frac{(105 - 125)\, 12}{0.95 \times 23.56} - 18 = 94.54 \text{ kip}$$

Web Resisting Force $= 0.4\, F_y\, t_w\, d_c$

$$= (0.4 \times 36 \times 0.485 \times 14.16) \times 1.33$$

$$= 132 > 94.54$$

Doubler plate is not required.

Note: If doubler plate is required, find plate thickness and length,
$L = d_b + 10\, k_b$

J.   Column-Web Stiffeners:

$$F = \text{Horizontal Force at Stiffener}$$

$$= \frac{M \times 12}{d - t_f} = \frac{(105 + 125) \times 12}{23.57 - 0.505} = 120 \text{ kip}$$

$$P_{bf} = 120 \times \frac{4}{3} = 160 \quad \dots \text{ M5-80}$$

1.   Stiffener plate is required at compression flange if:

$$d_c > \frac{4100 \ t_{wc}^3 \ \sqrt{F_{yc}}}{P_{bf}} \qquad \dots\dots\dots\dots\text{M5}-82$$

$$\frac{4100 \times 0.485^3 \times \sqrt{36}}{160} = 17.54 \not< d_c = 11\frac{1}{4} \text{ in.}$$

Therefore, stiffener is not required.

2.   Stiffener plate is required at tension flange if :

$$t_{fc} < 0.4 \ \sqrt{\frac{P_{bf}}{F_{yc}}} \quad \dots \text{ M5-80}$$

$$0.4 \ \sqrt{\frac{160}{36}} = 0.843 > 0.78$$

Therefore, stiffener is required.

3.   Stiffener size

$$A_{sf} = \frac{P_{bf} - F_{yc} \ t_{wc} \left(t_{fb} + 5k_c\right)}{F_{yst}} \quad \dots \text{ M5-83}$$

$$= \frac{160 - 36 \times 0.485 \times \left(0.505 + 5 \times 1\frac{9}{16}\right)}{36}$$

$$= 0.41 \text{ in.}$$

$$w = \text{Stiffener Width} = w + \frac{t_{wc}}{2} \geq \frac{b_{fb}}{3}$$

$$t = \text{Stiffener Thickness} \geq \frac{t_{fb}}{2}$$

Welding, refer to example problem on M4-108.

9.4   P. E. PROBLEM

9.4.1   P. E. PROBLEM 1 — ANALYSIS OF BEAM AND WELD DESIGN

A beam is loaded as shown in Fig. P9.4.1 (a).

    A. Find maximum bending stress.

    B. Check web crippling at the end if the beam is supported on a 6-in. bearing plate.

    C. Design weld at the connection between channel W-section.

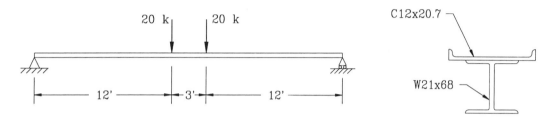

Fig. P9.4.1 (a)

Solution

    A. Locate centroid of the composite section:

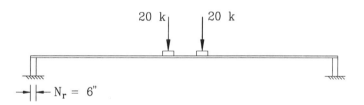

Fig. P9.4.1 (b)

$$\bar{y} = \frac{20 \times 10.56 + 6.09 \times 21.83}{6.09 + 20}$$

$$= 13.2 \text{ in.}$$

$$I_{NA} = \left(1480 + 20 \times 2.64^2\right) + \left(3.88 + 6.09 \times 8.64^2\right)$$

$$= 2077.7 \text{ in.}^4$$

$$M_{max} = 20 \text{ kip} \times 12 \text{ ft} = 240 \text{ ft-kip}$$

$$f_{bx} = \frac{Mc}{I} = \frac{(240 \times 12) \times 13.2}{2077.7} = 18.3 \text{ ksi} \leq 0.6 \, F_y = 22 \text{ ksi} \quad \text{OK}$$

$$f_v = \frac{V_{max}}{A} = \frac{20 \text{ k}}{21.13 \times 0.43} = 2.2 \text{ ksi} \leq 0.4 \, F_y \qquad\qquad \text{OK}$$

B.   k = 1.3125 in. t_w = 0.43 in. N_r = 6 in.

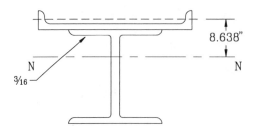

Fig. P9.4.1 (c)

For reaction = 20 k

$$\frac{R}{(N_r + k)\, t_w} \leq 0.66\, F_y = 24\ \text{ksi}$$

$$\frac{20}{(6 + 2.5 \times 1.3125) \times 0.43} = 5.01 < 24 \qquad\qquad \text{OK}$$

Web crippling is NOT a problem.

C. Shear flow at the connection = $\dfrac{VQ}{In}$ = v

   n = Number of weld lines

$$v = \frac{20 \times 6.09 \times 8.638}{2077.7 \times 2}$$

   = 253 in.-lb

$$\frac{253\ \text{lb}}{0.707\ w \times 1} = 21,000$$

$$253 = 14847\ w$$

$$w = 0.017$$

Use minimum weld size of 3/16 inch.

INDEX

P

R

S

T

U

W

NOTES

NOTES

NOTES

NOTES